INTERNATIONAL SERIES IN
EXPERIMENTAL PSYCHOLOGY
GENERAL EDITOR: H. J. EYSENCK

VOLUME 25

# The Biology of Human Conduct

EAST-WEST MODELS OF TEMPERAMENT AND PERSONALITY

## OTHER TITLES IN THE SERIES IN EXPERIMENTAL PSYCHOLOGY

## NOTICE TO READERS

Dear Reader,

If your library is not already a standing order customer or subscriber to this series, may we recommend that you place a standing or subscription order to receive immediately upon publication all new issues and volumes published in this valuable series. Should you find that these volumes no longer serve your needs your order can be cancelled at any time without notice.

The Editors and the Publisher will be glad to receive suggestions or outlines of suitable titles, reviews or symposia for consideration for rapid publication in this series.

ROBERT MAXWELL
Publisher at Pergamon Press

# The Biology of Human Conduct

## EAST-WEST MODELS OF
## TEMPERAMENT AND PERSONALITY

by

## G. L. MANGAN
*Department of Experimental Psychology,*
*University of Oxford*

## PERGAMON PRESS
OXFORD · NEW YORK · TORONTO · SYDNEY · PARIS · FRANKFURT

| U.K. | Pergamon Press Ltd., Headington Hill Hall, Oxford OX3 0BW, England |
|---|---|
| U.S.A. | Pergamon Press Inc., Maxwell House, Fairview Park, Elmsford, New York 10523, U.S.A. |
| CANADA | Pergamon Press Canada Ltd., Suite 104, 150 Consumers Road, Willowdale, Ontario M2J 1P9, Canada |
| AUSTRALIA | Pergamon Press (Aust.) Pty. Ltd., P.O. Box 544, Potts Point, N.S.W. 2011, Australia |
| FRANCE | Pergamon Press SARL, 24 rue des Ecoles, 75240 Paris, Cedex 05, France |
| FEDERAL REPUBLIC OF GERMANY | Pergamon Press GmbH, 6242 Kronberg/Taunus, Hammerweg 6, Federal Republic of Germany |

First edition 1982

**British Library Cataloguing in Publication Data**
Mangan, G. L.
The biology of human conduct — (International series in experimental psychology; v. 25)
1. Personality
I. Title    II. Series
155.2    BF698

ISBN 0-08-026781-5

**Library of Congress Catalog Card No:** 81-81642

Printed in Great Britain by A. Wheaton & Co. Ltd, Exeter

TO THE "TROIKA" OF WEST–EAST DIALOGUE —

GARDNER MURPHY, GREGORY RAZRAN, HANS EYSENCK

# PREFACE

THE PRESENT volume is the detritus of my interest in, and attempts to teach, the essentials of temperament and personality over the past 20 years. From early student days, I was aware of Pavlov's contributions to the study of higher nervous activity, mainly from the Anrep and Gantt translations of his books, but initially this occupied only a relatively small place in my thinking about personality. This had been nurtured in an avowedly analytic culture, and thus tended to be global and undifferentiated, although increasingly responsive to the empirical dicta imposed by a trait approach to personality, particularly as described by Eysenck, with its insistence on data, methods, particulars.

At some stage in the early 1960s, I discovered Gregory Razran's marvellously evocative account, in his *Psychological Review* article, of Soviet research in specific areas of higher nervous activity, descriptions of interoceptive and semantic conditioning, the second signal system, concepts which had eluded notice in my previous, more cursory examination of Pavlovian theory. This galvanised a search through the early and contemporary literature, a search which progressed through the pages of Sechenov's "Reflexes of the brain", Sokolov's *Perception and the Conditioned Reflex*, Bykov's *The Cerebral Cortex and the Internal Organs*, Vygotsky's *Thought and Language*, and many articles by Razran and Gantt. I became increasingly more interested in Pavlov's typological theorising, particularly in the later Teplov/Nebylitsyn version of his theory, an interest which was accelerated by publication of Gray's *Pavlov's Typology* and of Eysenck's post-1967 revision of his own typological theory.

At that time, I had with me, in the University of Queensland, a group of talented and enthusiastic graduate students. We became involved in the translation of Nebylitsyn's book *Fundamental Properties of the Human Nervous System,* and employed his model to direct a research programme aimed at relating Western personality dimensions to typological properties — still, I must admit, data-oriented, method-dominated.

In between times, I spent a period with Gardner Murphy at the Menninger Foundation, and it was he, with his strikingly inductionist inclinations, who led me towards a more biosocial approach to personality dynamics. Since then, I have become increasingly more venturesome in my thinking about typology and personality, while, I hope, still preserving most of the rigour of my earlier involvement in psychometrics, psychophysiology and general experimental psychology.

This book is an attempt to record what proved to be, at times, painful progress towards an integration of the conceptual frameworks represented in Soviet differential psychophysiology and Western personality theory — that blooming, buzzing confusion which besets us all. Such progress, of course, is never achieved, if at all, without penalty. It is seldom a smooth, confident advance towards an expanding conceptual horizon, more a series of lurches, which we grace with the description "inductive leaps", interspersed with long periods of uncertainty, hiatuses, gaps in understanding. These are clearly reflected in the following pages. The material at times lacks coherence, interpretations are sometimes debatable, conclusions hesitant. In self-extenuation, might I say that the purpose of the book is simply to assemble some relevant data not readily available from primary sources, to suggest hypotheses, to present a few ideas about personality and temperament, in the hope that this might enthuse some personality theorists to exploit, or at least recognise, the theoretical possibilities of both approaches.

Possibly, my efforts will produce little more than persisting and irritating zeigarniks. But then, at this point, perhaps that is enough. If so, my feelings and my apologia are best expressed in the lines of Gerard Manley Hopkins, to R.B.:

> Sweet fire the sire of muse, my soul needs this;
> I want the one rapture of an inspiration.
> O then if in my lagging lines you miss
> The roll, the rise, the carol, the creation,
> My winter world, that scarcely breathes that bliss
> Now, yields you, with some sighs, our explanation.

G. L. Mangan,
Department of Experimental Psychology,
University of Oxford,
February, 1981.

*The array of questions with which science must deal has expanded considerably... Hence the involvement of individual scientists must inevitably shrink to an increasingly limited domain within the totality of our knowledge. What is worse, this specialisation makes it increasingly difficult to keep pace with advances in scientific fields and thus to maintain a unified, general conception of science, without which the spirit of enquiry must necessarily suffer a loss in true profundity. A predicament emerges similar to that described symbolically in the biblical story of the tower of Babel.*

Albert Einstein (1965)

But then,

*As the scope of universal principles tends towards infinity, their psychological content, at the same time, tends towards zero.*

L. S. Vygotsky (1968)

# ACKNOWLEDGEMENTS

MANY have contributed to the ideas and views expressed in this book, in both formal and informal ways. I owe a particular debt of gratitude to the following: to many of my former graduate students — to Bob Morrish, David Siddle, George Wilson, Ken White, John O'Gorman, and Lister Bainbridge — who provided the initial impetus; to academic colleagues, especially Gardner Murphy and Gordon Claridge, who helped to identify the problems, and to structure the arguments; to John Golding, Timothy Paisey and David Robinson, who offered valuable comments and constructive suggestions about many of the contentious issues; thanks are also due to my research assistant, Marcus Richards, and to typist Valerie Mitchell.

# CONTENTS

# Models of Temperament

THERE are two major data sources in the analysis of temperament. The first, which is favoured by most personality theorists in the West, embraces naturalistic and empirical data from animal and human behaviour genetic studies, and data derived from cross-sectional and longitudinal studies which have attempted to dimensionalise human neonatal and adult behaviour. The second employs constructs derived from Pavlov's typological theory, and is most faithfully represented in the views of the Soviet psychophysiologists Teplov and Nebylitsyn and, more recently, by Strelau's Warsaw group. In the four chapters of this section, we shall attempt to review evidence from both these sources, and briefly consider the most important variables monitoring the genotype/environment interaction.

CHAPTER 1

# Behaviour Genetic Model

*Nature, to be commanded, must be obeyed.*
Francis Bacon

## Introduction

ALTHOUGH historically, personality has been regarded as an amalgam of affective, conative, constitutional, and, to a lesser extent, cognitive elements, there has been considerable debate about the relative contribution of each of these to the structure and dynamics of personality. As a result, over the past 50 years a variety of methodological and substantive bias has generated a broad spectrum of personality theories, ranging from the differential psychophysiology of the Soviet school of Teplov and Nebylitsyn, through the factor theories of Cattell and Eysenck, to the dynamic and ego theories of Kelly and Rogers, which find their antecedents in the speculations of William James about the nature of the self-concept.

While, generally speaking, all theories formally acknowledge the importance of both genotype and environment, "environmentalist" theories of personality continue to enjoy the widest acceptance. Until recently, little more than academic interest has been shown in the study of genotype, and consequently, in the nature and significance of the genotype/environment interaction. Mainstream personality theory is still in broad agreement with Allport's (1955) contention that

> The psychology of personality must be a psychology of post-instinctive behaviour ... whatever the drives or irritabilities of the infant are, they become completely transformed in the process of growth into contemporary systems of motives.

It has become increasingly apparent, however, that lack of information about the genetic components of personality has impeded progress in certain fields, in particular, social, developmental and clinical psychology. As a consequence, there has been some shift of emphasis towards broader bio-social

3

theories of personality, such as Eysenck's (1967) biological theory, which attempts to take into account genotypic differences along a number of basic drive dimensions, such as extraversion (arousability) and neuroticism (emotionality), and, less enthusiastically, the complexities of genotype/-environment interaction. A good deal of developmental data attest that since needs emerge and are experienced with different urgencies at different developmental times, and since "residues" (unresolved conflicts, for example) from previous developmental stages can effect subsequent personality development, the reciprocal interweaving (to use Gesell's term) of genotype and environment throughout the course of development is a critical personality variable.

Probably the most naive, and certainly the most fraught assumption underlying the "environmentalist" approach to personality is the uniformity hypothesis, the contention that genetically different individuals are equally affected by similar experiences, i.e. that the effect of environment is constant over all genotypes. In effect, this reduces the genotype/environment interaction term to zero. The logic underlying this rather loose inference is difficult to appreciate, since there is clear evidence of complex interactions between genes, and between genes and environment, which modulate and complicate genetic predispositions. Note that what is inherited is not behaviour but a predisposition, viz. a weighted probability that sets of predictors (genes), in certain combinations, separately and interactively with sets of environ-mental conditions, also in particular combinations and sequences, will lead to certain behavioural outcomes, and will bias behavioural development in certain ways. Minimal changes in combinations and/or sequences can profoundly affect outcomes (Hogarth, 1974). Certainly there need be no opposition between genotype and disposition to change (i.e. buffering) since the latter itself may be determined by genetic factors.

Genetic predisposition may take several forms, but two principles seem paramount. The first is differential susceptibility. This is most strikingly illustrated by the fact that some diseases of specific aetiology — TB, poliomyelitis, scarlet fever, rickets, diabetes, for example — show significantly higher concordance in identical twin pairs. In all cases, of course, some external agent is involved, but different genotypes are not equally susceptible.

The same applies at more complex behavioural levels. With animals, for example, traumatic noxious stimulation in early infancy may increase or decrease adult emotionality, or have no effect whatsoever, depending on genotype (Henderson, 1967). Similar results have been reported for aggressiveness. Early experience which significantly affects adult aggressive-ness in one strain of mice appears to have no effect on adult fighting in another (Ginsberg, 1967).

In human research, much the same findings have been reported. For example, Bowlby (1951), on the basis of his findings with a group of "affectionless psychopaths", maintained that long-term separation of the child from his mother at a critical period of development profoundly and irreversibly depreciates the child's capacity to form stable emotional bonds in later life. Subsequently, however, it became obvious that not all children were equally susceptible, that some children survived such experience relatively unscathed. In a later study, therefore, Bowlby (1973) introduced the concept of "resilience", to account for reduced vulnerability in some children, although precisely what resilience, or vulnerability implies is a matter of conjecture. It has been suggested (Langmeier and Matejcek, 1975) that resilience is inversely related to sentience need — the need for warm sensuous contact with the nurturing figure — which some authors claim to be genetically based (cf. pp. 17–19).

The second principle is selective exposure. This implies that the genotype will in part determine the nature of the experiences which the individual will undergo, in that, to some degree, these depend on the stimulus-cue value that the individual himself represents to others. The consequences of being intelligent, or athletic, for example, are obvious enough. Such consequences, however, are in part underlying variance which originates in the genes.

An example is the outcome of accelerated or retarded rate of progress through the maturational changes of puberty, which is under gene control, and which carries with it large differences in social and personal experiences. Late maturing adolescents are often dependent and socially anxious, due partly to the manner in which peers and adults respond to them. On the other hand, early maturing adolescents tend to be socially dominant, probably as a consequence of early conferment of social responsibility. The long-range effects of such differential patterns of social reinforcement are obvious enough.

These two principles seem to monitor genetic predisposition, the first, differential susceptibility, focusing on the genotype as reactive to experience, the second, selective exposure, focusing on the genotype as a stimulus to experience. Behavioural repertoires, therefore, are a product of genetic predisposition and experience, acting separately and interactively. In this interaction the organism plays a dynamic role. As Vale and Vale (1969) comment:

> We must recognise a more profound role of organismic variation than that of merely affecting rate or level of a process by which E elicits R; we must conceive of the organism as a co-determiner with, and not merely the agent of, the environment ....
> If organisms are meaningfully different, they may be expected to react differentially to the same treatment, and the search for general, invariant relations between environmental treatments and behaviour responses may be foredoomed.

## Temperament

Most agree with Allport's (1961) definition of temperament as

the characteristic phenomena of an individual's nature, including his susceptibility to
emotional stimulation, his customary strength and speed of response, the quality of his
prevailing mood, and all the peculiarities of fluctuation and intensity of mood, these being
phenomena regarded as being dependent on constitutional make-up, and therefore largely
hereditary in origin (p. 34).

In deciding whether a behavioural predisposition should be included under
the rubric "temperament", a number of criteria have been suggested. The first is
that the behaviour must have adaptive value, i.e. some evolutionary history, in
that it has survived natural selection. Secondly, it should be present in early life,
and show some stability during childhood. Finally, there must be some
evidence that it is inherited. Note, however, that trait stability over time does
not, of itself, imply heritability. Genes may be switched on or off at particular
ages, so that stability and heritability are not necessarily highly intercorrelated.

On the basis of these criteria, a considerable amount of data suggest that the
important sources of variance in temperament are

(a) basic drives such as " fear/emotionality", aggression, affiliation,
specifically the intensity of such drives, and, in the human case, whether drive
gratification requires the involvement of another person;

(b) general biological drives or tendencies such as basic arousal tonus,
activity level, for example, which influence a wide range of behaviours;

(c) less importantly, since arguably these variables should not be classed as
temperament variables, native capacities such as intellectual, visual, spatial
abilities.

These variables interact with life experiences, which provide the context in
which normal sensory and emotional development are likely to be achieved,
which extend the range of drive cues, and, at the same time, provide a variety of
outlets for the same drive.

Data relevant to temperament derive from both animal and human
behaviour genetics. These areas overlap to some degree, but each has its own
particular methodology and objectives. A critical issue is obviously that of
continuity between animal and human behaviour, on which final judgment
must be reserved. Despite this, comparisons are useful in indicating the main
dimensions of temperament.

### Animal Studies
*Methodology*

Although, as we shall see later (p. 20), many of the assumptions underlying
the concept of heritability, as it is commonly employed, are questionable, at this

stage we shall simply note that the term refers to that portion of variance due to hereditary differences. Where few or no genetic differences exist, as in the case of identical twins, or inbred strains of animals, all behavioural variance is assumed to be environmental in origin. Where large gene differences exist, as between pure strains, behavioural differences will be largely genetic in origin, providing environmental variation is adequately controlled. However, where large differences exist in both genes and trait-relevant experience, as in comparisons of measured IQ among different human races, heritability can only be crudely estimated.

Selective breeding, and the analysis of inbred and pure strains and hybrid crosses, are the most favoured methods in animal genetic studies. In selective breeding experiments, experimenters begin with individual differences in behaviour (the phenotype), and seek to establish that genetic differences underlie the observed behavioural variance. Selective mating, using phenotypic criteria, is practised over generations in an effort to establish distinct lines. Where such selection is possible, this suggests that gene differences in part underlie differences in behaviour which exist in the population.

Selective breeding usually involves inbreeding, i.e. the mating of progeny of consanguineous parents. Through inbreeding, the individual may receive two copies of a gene, the alleles, which are identical by descent. Thus inbreeding makes an individual homozygous for genes that are identical by descent.

The use of inbred strains is a powerful tool in behaviour genetic analysis. A large number of identical genotypes can be studied in a variety of environments, and sophisticated biometrical analysis can be applied to traits of interest. The mechanics of such procedures are complex, but the logic is simple. Differences between animals of the same strain must be environmental in origin, whereas behavioural differences between animals of different strains will be both genetic and environmental.

In the animal behaviour literature, often little distinction is made between selective breeding and inbreeding. While the former usually involves the latter, increasingly with later generations, they are not the same, and it is well to note that different effects may result from the different procedures. A case in point is Gray's (1971b) contention that inbreeding in rodents reverses the direction of sex differences in strains selectively bred for emotionality. In the selectively bred strain, males are more emotional than females, while in the inbred strains, females are more emotional than males. There is also evidence from a number of sources (Wilcox and Bush, 1972; Bruell, 1969) that outbreeding results in increased emotionality, measured by defecation and high passive avoidance (fearfulness?), particularly in males. While these issues have not yet been satisfactorily resolved, the data strike a cautionary note.

Continued inbreeding results in pure strains, i.e. strains homozygous for as many genes as possible. On repetition *ad infinitum*, even with a moderate degree of inbreeding, complete homozygosis may eventually be obtained, except for the small contribution of mutations to genetic variance. In experimental animals in which inbreeding can be carried out almost at will, however, it is clear that a large number of generations may be required for a population to become homozygous, even when close inbreeding, such as brother/sister matings, is practised at every generation.

A general point which might be made in all selective breeding experiments is that if we select for a particular phenotype, this may mean that individuals who are phenotypically identical on some particular trait may have been selected for different genes in the set controlling that particular phenotypic trait. For example, if we select for an animal deficient in some enzyme or hormone "X", then it is entirely possible that two pure-bred strains identical for the deficiency of "X" have different genotypes in the set of genes controlling "X". Thus, as polymorphism increases, so does uncertainty about what is happening at the gene level. A simple example from molecular genetics is the utilisation of lactose in the *E. coli bacterium*, which is dependent on five different genes. Three of these are structures genes , the other two controller genes. If we select for bacteria unable to grow on lactose, we find that mutations in any of these five genes may cause the same phenotype, i.e. lac⁻ (Levine, 1968).

*Control for environmental variance*

Behaviour-genetical analysis obviously requires careful control of all environmental factors which might influence the behaviour under study. For behaviours of interest to personality theorists, the most important of these are maternal influences. To illustrate the point, consider evidence that anxious mothers tend to have fearful offspring. This observation, of itself, however, does not support genetic transmission of anxiety, since anxious mothers may transmit anxiety to their offspring prenatally, i.e. via hormonal mechanisms activated by the anxiety state, or postnatally, e.g. via parental practice and social modelling.

There are standard methods for controlling for these effects. To control for prenatal maternal effects the technique of reciprocal crossing is employed. Here males of one strain are mated with females of the other strain, and conversely, males of the second strain are mated with females of the first. All offspring of pure-bred crosses, theoretically, will have inherited half their genes from each strain, and thus are genetically identical hybrids. If postnatal differences can be ruled out, or controlled by cross-fostering, any differences between the two groups of offspring are probably attributable to differences in prenatal environment. Therefore, any large differences which may be observed in behaviour among hybrid offspring of a reciprocal cross provide evidence of a prenatal maternal effect.[1]

Prenatal effects, which may profoundly affect both structure and function, can be produced by alterations in the intra-uterine environment. Relatively direct effects result from drugs, hormones and changes in maternal diet. Administration of pituitary growth hormone to pregnant rats, for example, significantly increases the number of brain cells, total brain weight and cortical cell density in their offspring. Conversely, protein deficiency in early foetal life decreases the number and size of brain cells (Zamenhof, Van Marthens and Margolis, 1968). Brains of offspring born to rats maintained on a protein insufficient diet during gestation contain significantly less DNA, and a deficiency in the number of cortical neurones may be irreversible. Effects from maternal malnutrition in man have long been known, and deficits in physical growth and biochemical maturation, together with retarded intellectual and emotional development, are well documented (Eichenwald and Fry, 1969).

Indirect effects can arise through social experience. For example, psychological stress will elicit in the pregnant mother a neuroendocrine response which alters the chemical composition of her blood, and affects the foetus through placental transfer. Because emotional reactivity is mediated by the endocrine system, studies of the effect of maternal emotion on subsequent behaviour of the offspring are of special interest. That such effects might occur in humans is indicated by studies with rodents. Thompson (1957) reports that pregnant rats exposed to a buzzer, which, prior to mating, was associated with shock, have significantly more emotional offspring. On the other hand, systematic handling of a rat during pregnancy will significantly decrease the emotional responsivity of her offspring when they are adult (Ader and Conklin, 1963). Parallel data from human mothers are difficult to obtain for obvious reasons. However, there are some correlational studies relating maternal stress to neonatal behaviour which suggest that anxious mothers have more anxious babies (Ottinger and Simmons, 1964).

To control for postnatal maternal effects, the usual procedure is to cross-foster litters as soon as possible after birth. Half of each litter is assigned to mothers of the other strain. The importance of this control is suggested by data from the so-called enrichment studies, in which rats, in the pre-weaning period, are simply taken out of the litter for a few minutes daily and placed in a separate container. These rats grow faster, live longer, and stand physical stress better than unhandled controls. The central nervous system matures earlier, and the

---

[1]Even in the purest strains, there is, of course, inevitably some variation due to crossing over, and, to a small extent, to mutation. Perhaps cloning is necessary to produce true pure strains, as has proved to be the case in horticulture.

animals are less fearful in unfamilar surroundings (Denenberg, 1967; Levine, 1962). An interesting finding is that a variety of physical stimuli — shock, shaking, temperature change and other sources of stimulation, some noxious — produces the same effect as gentle handling. Apparently stimulation, whatever its source, promotes activity of the adrenal glands, and the accelerated development of the endocrine system affects not only physiological maturation, but adult behaviour as well.

*Illustrative data from animal studies*

A good deal of the animal data have been derived from selective breeding experiments, concerned with aversive conditioning rates, preference for alcohol, response to drugs, seizure susceptibility, aggressiveness, dominance, activity level, maze learning. The best known of these are Rundquist's (1933) data on voluntary activity or activity level in rats, Hall's studies of emotionality and aggressiveness in rats and mice (Hall, 1934, 1941; reviewed in Stevens, 1951), studies of susceptibility to audiogenic seizure (Witt and Hall, 1949), Broadhurst's extensive studies of emotionality (1960, 1969, 1975) and the classic studies of maze learning (Tryon, 1942; Heron, 1941; Thompson, 1954) which, although not germane to the present discussion, throw up a number of issues which have relevance for the study of temperament.

From the considerable amount of published research with both animal and human Ss (cf. sections on behavioural genetics, "Annual Review of Psychology", 1971 and 1974, which cite over 700 references), there is evidence for at least four personality dimensions or temperament traits which have strong genetic components — emotionality, introversion–extraversion, aggression and affiliation. Arguably, we might also include activity level. Gottesman (1968), for example, notes

> ... the traits which should be singled out for research within a behaviour genetics framework are those with possible evolutionary significance, and those that existing research shows to have heritabilities greater than 33% per cent in some samples. Among the traits I would nominate are introversion, aggression, anxiety, attention to detail and social attachment.

A special problem in considering genotypic determination of social behaviour is that of behavioural classification. A number of classificatory systems have been suggested — those of Harlow and Tinbergen, for example, come readily to mind — but none seems entirely satisfactory. However, at the simplest descriptive level of analysis, we can distinguish two sets of traits, affectional and aggressive, which are basic to any diadic relationship, in that they subsume all orientations which strengthen or loosen ties between individuals. These traits are not necessarily antagonistic. In many behavioural acts — such as mutual grooming and allopreening, for example — we find affiliative and aggressive tendencies closely interwoven. Such behaviours may involve a displaced or suppressed form of aggression, as does reaction formation in humans — or so it is claimed. Interestingly enough, while most ethologists and animal behaviourists recognise the importance of these two tendencies in social animals, psychologists from Watson on have tended to ignore the study of human love, except for a few authors such as Fromm (1956) and Sorokin (1954), although Watson himself considered love, with fear and anger, to be an innate, basic emotion,

## A. EMOTIONALITY

A number of studies of emotionality, dating from Hall (1934) (Figure 1) have employed the open field test, with defecation rate (D) and ambulation (A), which are negatively correlated, the most commonly used measures. There is some consensus that emotionality is a unitary construct which is unaffected by strain differences (Gray, 1971a,b; Broadhurst, 1960, 1969; Royce et al., 1973) so that the emotionally reactive rodent should manifest both a high elimination rate and a tendency to freeze in a variety of situations. There has been some dissent from this view, however (e.g. Archer, 1973). Perhaps the most critical evidence on this point is the factor analysis reported by Poley and Royce (1976) of a battery of emotionality measures employed in mouse studies, which disclosed

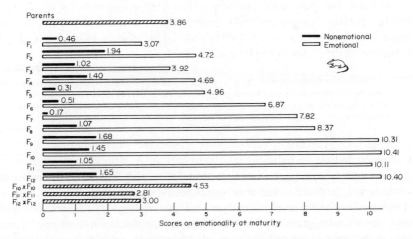

Figure 1. Evidence for inheritance of emotionality in rats. The black bars represent emotionality scores of the low strain; white, of the very reactive strain; cross-hatched bars, parent generation and crossbreedings of the two selected strains (Data from Hall, 1941, 1951).

that while D and A load separate first-order factors, which the authors described as autonomic balance and motor discharge, a higher-order analysis (Royce, 1977) yielded an emotionality factor, loading both elimination measures and freezing responses. On this basis, high emotionality gives rise to both high defecation and low exploratory behaviour, a finding in line with results reported earlier by Whimbey and Denenberg (1967) with rats.

The first significant study of emotionality is Hall's (cf. Figure 1) report that an emotionally reactive strain was stabilised at the tenth generation, the measures of emotionality being defecation and urination rates (Hall, 1941, 1951). The most impressive data, however, are reported by Broadhurst (1960, 1969, 1975). He initiated an extensive selective breeding programme which produced the Maudsley reactive (MR) and Maudsley non-reactive (MNR) strains of rats. High and low reactive lines diverged rapidly, with little overlap between strains after the first few generations of breeding. Neither cross-fostering litters nor crossing between the two lines revealed significant maternal effects (Broadhurst, 1975).

Additionally, there are some interesting data from analysis of pure strains. For example, Jones (1965) describes large differences in emotional reactivity, as well as in aggressiveness, activity levels and speed of learning between three different strains of mice.

D appears to have stronger heritability than A. Using reciprocal cross data from MR and MNR strains, Broadhurst (1969) reports that the heritability of D is greater than 90%, and of A lies between 45% and 75%.

Some evidence suggests indirectly that emotionality and fearfulness are dependent or equivalent measures. Savage (1964), Weldon (1967) and Ferraro and York (1968), for example, report that the MR strain, which is selectively bred for emotionality, shows significantly higher passive avoidance than the MNR strain. Gray (1971a) claims that passive avoidance is a measure of fearfulness.

B. AGGRESSION

There are two distinct points of view about the genetic components of aggression. Ethologists stress that aggression is an instinctive force, analogous to hunger or thirst, possessing internal energy which must find periodic relief. Lorenz (1966), for example, in assuming an energy model, views aggressive acts as evidence of an internal drive process, carthartic relief being assumed to follow discharge of surplus aggressive energy. A similar view is expressed by Feshbach (1964), who reports that aggressive responses alleviate stress, and by

Freud and personality theorists of dynamic persuasion. A number of experiments have been reported — Singer's (1968) demonstration of hostile humour reducing residual aggressive motivation and tension is a good case in point — which purport to demonstrate this.

On the other hand, the opposite point of view has been expressed by a number of authors (e.g., Zeigler, 1964; Scott, 1966; Berkowitz, 1969; Kaufman, 1970). They propose that, although there are internal mechanisms which, when appropriately stimulated, reliably lead to fighting, the eliciting stimulus is external. Thus aggression can be neither instinctive nor spontaneous. It is also clear that certain social experiences, or lack of them, can eliminate fighting. Thus, it is argued, aggression is a sociality learned behaviour, with the social context determining the initiation, form and intensity of the aggressive act. Aggressive responses can be both classically (Thompson and Sturm, 1965) and instrumentally conditioned, in animals (Azrin, Hutchinson and Hake, 1967) and humans (Bandura and Walters, 1963), the eliciting stimulus being punishment, and, additionally in the human case, threats to self-esteem (Feshbach, 1964).

The logic of the environmentalist argument, however, is unconvincing. Aggressivity, as such, appears to be largely under genetic control. This is suggested by the great variation among species (Lorenz, 1966; Scott, 1962; Lagerspitz, 1961), and among strains or breeds within species. Krushinskii (1962) has traced through pedigree the transmission of one form of aggressiveness, the "active defence reaction" or the "watch" reflex. This appears to be inherited independently of the passive defence reaction, expressed as fear of strange persons and places, although the two occasionally combine to produce an "aggressive-cowardly" animal, which alternates aggressive approach with strong avoidance.

It is clear, however, that beyond genetic and early experiential factors, individual differences in the expression of aggression are learned. There is, of course, the further point, that given the intrinsically interpersonal nature of aggression, in that aggressive thoughts and acts are both elicited by and expressed towards social objects, a considerable amount of imitative and modelling behaviour may steer the direction and intensity of aggressive responses, particularly in humans.

Behaviour genetical studies of aggression (fighting) report clearcut findings. Hall and Klein (1942) report that non-emotional rats (selectively bred) fight significantly more often and more fiercely than emotional (fearful) rats. Scott (1942) reports different degrees of pugnacity among three purebred strains of mice, as do Ginsberg and Allee (1942) among three inbred strains of mice controlled for postnatal effects (cross fostering).

Guhl, Craig and Mueller (1960) report evidence of selective breeding for success in fighting with chickens, maximal separation occurring by the fourth generation. Craig, Ortman and Guhl (1965) report maximal separation in five generations when selecting for social dominance, which is correlated with aggressiveness. Lagerspitz (1961) reports similar results with mice. Cross-fostering control techniques discount the possibility that the difference between strains is due to postnatal maternal effects (Lagerspitz and Wuorinen, 1965). Of interest is the fact that animals selected for aggressivity were more active, less emotional (fearful) and differed on several neurochemical variables. At the thirteenth and fourteenth generations of the study, aggressive animals had heavier forebrains, and their brains contained significantly greater concentrations of neurochemicals thought to be important in the expression of aggressiveness (Lagerspitz, Tirri and Lagerspitz, 1968).

A number of studies also reveal significant differences between inbred strains of rodents in the latency, amount and duration of fighting (Scott, 1966). A general conclusion is that cross-fostering does not markedly modify genotypic differences in aggressive behaviours. Strain differences are also evident in behaviour associated with aggressiveness, particularly social dominance (Lindzey, Winston and Manosevitz, 1961).

Mechanisms underlying aggressivity are unclear, although it is possible that the selective mechanism resides in the adrenaline/noradrenaline axis, i.e. in the control mechanism in the endocrine system. High level of adrenaline output seems to be associated with fear, and high level of noradrenaline with aggressiveness and anger. Aggressive species probably have a highly active noradrenaline system, and timid species an active adrenaline system. It is also possible that different forms of aggression in animals are under different endocrine control — active aggression (often predation) under noradrenaline control, and passive aggression (aggressive defence) under adrenaline control.

Clearly, aggression can be pain-provoked (Ulrich and Azrin, 1962); such aggression probably has significant survival value in that it causes the animal to respond vigorously to noxious stimuli in a way calculated to terminate them. Undoubtedly pain-provoked aggression has a genetic component, in that strength of aggressive response should be correlated with pain threshold.

We need to distinguish, of course, between intra-species aggression or fighting, i.e. agonistic encounters between conspecifics, and inter-species aggression, which is usually predatory behaviour. The two are normally elicited by different external stimuli, depend on different internal states, involve different movement patterns, and may involve different neural mechanisms (Hutchinson and Renfrew, 1966). In the case of intra-species aggression, genetic factors appear to interact with environmental events in a more complex and subtle fashion than in the case of inter-species aggression.

A good deal of aggression in animals is caused by the proximity of other individuals, so that, generally speaking, aggression is more common when population density is high (e.g. Southwick, 1969). In some cases, high population density leads to the development of a "behavioural sink" (Calhoun, 1962) which is characterised by a number of pathological behaviours.

Other internal and/or external factors are often involved in the instigation of aggression. The fact that the degree of proximity which elicits aggression may be affected by the internal state of the individual is a case in point. During winter, many small birds flock, and attack other individuals only when they come within a foot or so. During the breeding season, however, they attack any intruder over a wide area, the difference being due primarily to differences in endocrine state (Vowles and Harwood, 1966). Comparable changes also occur over the oestrous cycle and reproductive cycles in mammals (Noirot, 1972).

There is considerable laboratory evidence that the male sex hormone, testosterone, augments aggressiveness in the males of a wide variety of species and that ovarian hormones play a similar role in the females of some species. A relationship has been reported between adult fighting in males and ingestion of testosterone in infancy, and lack of fighting in males castrated before puberty. This suggests that male hormones act on the neonate to organise the neural structures which subserse aggressiveness. Edwards (1968), for example, reports that females administered testosterone on day 1, from day 60 on resembled male mice in tendency to fight in paired competition, when compared with males and control females, all groups from 60 days being administered increasingly large doses of testosterone. Edwards suggests that the normal differences between male and female mice is due to the stimulation the male receives from testicular hormones early in life.

Hormonal action, however, may be indirect; for example, the dominance order in bachelor groups of red deer is largely determined by antler size, although the shedding and growth of antlers is under hormonal control (Lincoln, Youngson and Short, 1970). There is also good evidence that central nervous system states comparable to those that must accompany normal aggressive behaviour can be induced by electrical stimulation of the brain in both birds (Brown, 1969) and mammals (Flynn, 1973).

Over and above hormonal factors, which may interact with external events to modify or potentiate aggressive behaviour, experience — particularly early experience — modifies the expression and intensity of the aggressive act. Among inbred strains of rodents, adult aggressiveness appears to be determined by a complex interplay of genetic and environmental effects. With mice, early experience which profoundly affects adult aggressiveness in one strain of mice have no effect on adult fighting in another (Ginsberg, 1967). Lagerspitz (1961) reports that success in fighting reduces or increases aggressive predisposition in mice. Again, mice and rats reared in groups fight less than do animals brought together after early social isolation. Group-reared animals, however, will fight strangers.

Similar results have been reported with dogs. There are a number of reports from Pavlov's laboratories (Klimov, 1929; Ivanov-Smolenskii, 1932) that the "weak" inhibitory type of dog does not necessarily show a pronounced passive-defence response (behaviourally shown in timidity or cowardice), although such a relationship was postulated by Pavlov as a link between nervous system type (temperament) and "personality". Rosenthal (1930) had earlier noted this lack of relationship, and suggested that it was due to the effects of early experience. In attempting to resolve this problem, Vyrzhikovski and Mayorov (1933), using a split-litter technique, one group of puppies being reared in a free environment, the other in social isolation from birth to 2 years, reported that the 4 dogs raised in social isolation showed pronounced passive-defence reflexes, although none belonged to the inhibitory type, as assessed by conditioning performance. None of the normally reared puppies showed passive-defence behaviour. Pavlov (1955, pp. 319–20) in reviewing these data, comments that social isolation 'disguises the real strength of the nervous system', i.e. that timidity may be a consequence of special features of the environment rather than an attribute of the weak nervous system. Krushinskii (1962) has supported these early findings in his report that the passive-defence reflex appears strongly in Airedales and German Shepherds raised in isolation, although the reflex is not carried by these breeds when raised under normal conditions.

Western data are in general agreement. Fisher (1955), for example, reports that a genetically predisposed aggressive breed of dog such as the wire-haired terrier does not show adult aggression when raised in isolation. Scott and Fuller (1965), from a review of a number of studies, suggest that under conditions of isolation from humans, breed differences in aggressiveness, and possibly in other temperament traits, tend to disappear.

It is also obvious that early experience can modify inter- as well as intra-species fighting (Kuo, 1967). Poshivalov (1977) reports that mice raised under conditions of isolation attack rats. Data suggest that the killing response of rats towards mice, which has been considered instinctive, can be eliminated by interaction between the species (Denenberg, Paschke and Zarrow, 1968). Adult fighting, which is regarded as species-specific behaviour having a genetical basis, is also markedly reduced by inter-species interaction. A number of experiments in which both test and control animals were from an inbred strain have reported significant differences in frequency of fighting between mouse litter mates raised by mouse mothers and mouse litter mates cross-fostered to rat mothers (Denenberg, Hudgins and Zarrow, 1964; Hudgins, Denenberg and Zarrow, 1968; Denenberg and Zarrow, 1970). Forty-six per cent of control mice fought at least once in the test situation, while only 4% of the experimental mice did so. The effect of early social experience is dramatically illustrated by the fact that the incidence of fighting can range from 0–78% as a function of social rearing (Hudgins, Denenberg and Zarrow, 1968). The studies of Denenberg *et al.* (1969) and Denenberg and Zarrow (1970) also suggest that the critical influence in reducing fighting is the maternal behaviour of the rat mother rather than biochemical or hormonal factors present in her milk.

Aggressive behaviour often occurs in situations which can be described as "frustrating", and some workers have therefore regarded frustration as the primary cause of aggression (e.g. Dollard *et al.*, 1939; Miller, 1959). It is certainly clear from a number of animal studies that aggression can be frustration induced (e.g. Azrin, Hutchinson and Hake, 1966). However, there is also evidence that frustration increases aggression only when the animal has been previously reinforced for reacting aggressively to frustrating situations (Scott, 1962). Thus it is possible that although frustration may increase the likelihood of aggressive behaviour, its actual occurrence depends on a number of other factors — certain external stimuli, inhibitory factors, life history and so on.

## C. AFFILIATION

Although a good deal of attention has been paid to sex and reproduction, psychogeneticists have shown comparatively little interest in affiliative behaviour, although it is obvious that sex and reproduction, the more "basic" emotions, seldom run their usual course without some prior affiliative behaviour. Sexual and affiliative behaviour, however, are separate and distinct, as a good deal of data attest (Beach, 1965, concerning dogs, quoted by Thompson, 1968).

To the writer's knowledge, no selective breeding data concerning affiliativeness have been reported, nor about strain differences in extent of affiliative behaviour. However, most ethologists regard this need as being deeply rooted in the biological properties of most living organisms. Species differ in their characteristic strength of affiliative tendency — dogs are more affiliative than cats, for example. Many observational studies report intra-species evidence that individuals differ in the strength of affiliative behaviour, which does not appear to be attributable to learning or deprivation.

At the most elementary level, one example of affiliation is the phenomenon of imprinting. Thompson (1968) reports evidence that the extent to which an animal will imprint on different objects depends on genetic factors. Again, there are considerable data portraying the profound effects, on development, of denial of social contact in early life, which suggest a genetic basis for this trait. The most illuminating studies are those reported by Liddell (1958) with kids and lambs, and, more particularly, by the Harlows with monkeys (1967). The Harlows note that infant rhesus monkeys show a compelling need to affiliate with others of their own age group — they employ the term " contact comfort" — and with their mothers, even when they are abusive or indifferent. Thompson, on this point, states

> 'Genotype must be at the bottom of much social behaviour ... Although a good deal of attention has been paid to sex, it is curious that little attention has been paid the more basic behavioural category of love or affection which must underlie these ... Hebb has made a strong case for the notion that the more complex the brain, the more sophisticated the social behaviour, and that in higher species .. such dimensions of affiliativeness as sympathy, empathy and altruism begin to emerge. Empathy has even been attributed to the rat. Be that as it may, much social behaviour must be referable to the basic makeup of organisms, including, of course, the genotype' (1968, p. 91).

The Harlows (1967), in similar vein, comment

> These examples illustrate the three basic reponses of primates — affection-affiliation, fear and social aggression. In fact, the responses usually emerge in that order as the infant monkey matures ... These responses are obviously not Pavlovian reflex reactions; rather they are complicated, inbuilt patterns of behaviour which can be modified by learning.

Compelling data suggest that rearing in isolation severely distorts development, an observation made originally by Kohler in 1925

> A chimpanzee reared in isolation is not really a chimpanzee at all

and underlined by Thompson

> 'Out of the primitive reciprocity that normally occurs between mother and infant emerges the adult forms of social behaviour or affectional systems — for example, heterosexual and maternal. Deprivation of contact comfort in early life produces an atrophy of these systems — poor mates, bad mothers, and indifferent companions' (1968, p. 90).

The notion that early affiliative experience is fundamental to many other complex forms of social behaviour is well documented for a variety of species. If adequate sexual performance is to develop, cats, monkeys and other species seem to require some kind of social interactional experience early in life. With humans, various types of deprivation in early life, including social, leads to aberrant social behaviour and personality difficulties (Langmeier and Matejcek, 1975). There are also indications that certain childhood social interactions are related to adult sexual behaviour (Sears, 1965).

However, while it seems obvious enough that sexuality and affiliativeness are closely interrelated, and are perhaps at the centre of much social behaviour, the degree of genotypic determination is unclear. Both are certainly part of the biological make-up in that they appear without the need for special training, although their emergence may require exposure to a certain kind of environment. Many animals actively seek affiliation even when they are punished for so doing; although punishment or threat may temporarily suppress the approach behaviour, this reappears immediately the threat is removed. It is also clear that there is some variability in expression of affiliativeness within species.

*Summary*

Although the animal data appear to be relatively straightforward, there are a number of problems of interpretation. Perhaps the most critical is that in some selective breeding studies we may not be selecting for the trait of task assumed. For example, Seligman (1970), from a review of the animal genetic studies, suggests that rats and other mammals come to a learning situation with a good deal of inbuilt bias to respond to particular types of reinforcement. It is simply not the case that any stimulus can be associated equally well with any reinforcement. The genes, so to speak, "programme for an expectancy". This might lead us to speculate, for example, on the degree to which social animals may have inherited expectancies which shape the development of their social contacts or bonds with conspecifics. It has been noted, for example, that young wolves, unlike many other species, when reared outside their normal social context, nevertheless form a typical wolf social group when assembled (Ginsberg, 1968). Contrast this with the behaviour of young monkeys when treated in a similar way (cf. Harlow and Harlow, 1966).

Another problem is the generality of the observed differences. Searle (1949), for example, using Tryon maze-bright and maze-dull rats, reports that in some learning tasks (escape from water maze), the maze-dulls showed superior performance to the maze-brights. Krechevsky (1933) reports that maze-bright rats (Tyron $F_7$) employed more spatial hypotheses and maze-dull rats more visual hypotheses in a multiple discrimination box. Presumably performance could be radically altered between groups by altering the availability of one or other set of hypotheses. Heron and Skinner (1940) report that animals differing in maze-learning ability do not differ in rates of extinction in a bar-press situation. Again, animals can be bred to maximise differences in immediate learning, i.e. in short-term memory, yet to show no differences in consolidation, i.e. long-term memory. Clearly, as Tryon points out, we usually select for a specific phenotype under a specific set of environmental conditions (cf. also Cooper and Zubek, 1958).

## Human Studies

### Methodology

Obviously breeding techniques are inappropriate with human Ss, although some instances, such as the Nazi Lebensborn programme (cf. Kraus and Kulka, 1958) have been recorded. Behavioural genetic data from human Ss have been derived from twin or sibling studies, in which attempts have been made to estimate heritabilities for well-established personality traits and psycho-physiological dimensions.

There are basically three approaches to the genetical analysis of human familial and twin data. The first, the "classical" approach, introduced a century ago by Galton, involves comparison of a sample of identical co-twins on traits or variables of interest with same-sex fraternal pairs or sibling pairs, the samples being matched on appropriate variables. Thus Mz pairs, genetically identical, are contrasted with genetically dissimilar pairs, pairs being of the same sex and age and family background. Many, but not all aspects of social experience are controlled within pairs. For a continuous trait which is quantitatively measured, the relative influence of genotypic and environmental contributions to the trait is usually estimated by comparison of variance within identical and fraternal twin pairs.

Various methods for determining heritability have been suggested in the literature. The best known is Holzinger's statistic

$$H = \frac{{}^r Mz - {}^r Dz}{1 - {}^r Dz}$$

which is claimed to provide an estimate of the proportion of variance accounted for by genetic factors. The significance level of H varies as the F ratio between Mz and Dz within-pair variances. There is general agreement, however, that these estimates are unsatisfactory, largely because the genotype/environment interaction term has been ignored or underestimated.

Interactions between genotypic and environmental factors are likely to be important for the interpretation of quantitative inheritance. An implicit assumption underlying many quantitative inheritance models, however, is that the effects, rather than being interactive, are additive, i.e. that if one genotype has a trait greater than another in one environment, it will also be the superior genotype in all other environments. Such a model always implies a logical relationship in which the relative ordering of the genotypes is the same in all environments.

Inbreeding data, however, clearly illustrate that total phenotypic variation should be partitioned into a portion due to environmental variation, one due to genetic variation, and one due to interaction between the two. The importance of the interaction term is most clearly demonstrated when given genotypes show different phenotypes in different environments. This is well illustrated, for example, in the experiment reported by Cooper and Zubek (1958). Following selective breeding of rats for maze-running speed, which separated fast and slow groups after a few generations, the experimenters raised later generations under different environmental conditions. The differences disappeared; all rats performed equally, irrespective of whether the environment was improved or worsened.

A second, and more sophisticated technique is that of Multiple Abstract Variance Analysis (MAVA), developed by Cattell (1960, 1965), which involves both the estimation of nature/nurture ratios, and some assessment of the importance of the correlation between genetic and environmental influences within the family as well as within the culture. Comparisons are made of between- and within-family variances of full and half-sib families, as well as between Mz and Dz twin pairs.

Finally, there is the biometrical genetic approach, first advocated by Fisher (1918) and later applied by Mather (1949) and Jinks and Fulker (1970). The method is discussed in detail in Jinks and Fulker (1970), and the reader is referred to this source for a full account. In brief, biometrical genetics attempts to assess the kinds of gene action and mating system operating in the population, and in this sense reaches far beyond the classical or MAVA approaches. After converting estimates of G (within- and between-family genetic components) and E (within- and between-family environmental components) to heritabilities, an attempt is made to relate these to the type of gene action involved. The simplest possible model assumes that all mating is random, and all gene action additive, dubious assumptions when we are dealing with personality variables. The most likely sources of deviation from random mating are inbreeding or positive assortative mating due to preferential mating of like phenotypes. In animals, it is relatively easy to determine the direction of dominance through controlled mating or employing inbred lines, and, for this reason, until comparatively recently, this method has been used almost exclusively with animal samples. Control of this sort with human samples is, of course, extremely difficult, although one method which has been employed has been to examine the scores of children of consanguineous matings, such as progeny resulting from cousin marriages.

The techniques of biometrical genetics have considerable advantages. Perhaps most importantly, these allow at least preliminary testing of the basic assumptions underlying simple genetic and environmental models, viz. that all groups represent a random sample of genotypes and environments present in the population, that there is no correlation between genotypes and environment, and no influence of genotype-environment interaction. The power of this model has been demonstrated by Jinks and Fulker (1970) in their re-analysis of personality and IQ data previously reported, and by Eaves (1973), Eaves and Eysenck (1975, 1976, 1977) and by Young, Eaves and Eysenck (1980) in their analyses of genotypic contributions to traits of extraversion, neuroticism and psychoticism.

There are a number of additional problems in twin study methodology. One is the very small samples of twins tested in most experiments. In a recent paper entitled "The power of the classical twin study", Martin *et al.* (1978) discuss the sample size required to accept or reject particular models of variation. They conclude that for many of the frequently encountered cases, 600 pairs of twins would be required to reject inappropriate alternatives. At least 200 pairs are required to achieve much more modest power. It is therefore doubtful, despite the apparent sophistication of many of the statistical analyses reported, whether such results advance our understanding of the origins of personality variation.

On the other hand, it may be that the case made out by the biometrical geneticists is overstated, reflecting their own frequent concentration on relatively soft data, such as questionnaires, which contain many sources of variation, including high error variance. For certain biological variables, very clear-cut results can be obtained from quite small twin samples, and we might expect this to become increasingly the case as more exact biological parameters of variation are identified. Nevertheless, from a genetics viewpoint, the use of larger samples, and samples which include not just twins, but other forms of kinship has undoubted advantages, since many parameters of interest in this field are continuous sources of variation, and subject to a complex interaction of environmental and genetic factors which the techniques of biometrical genetics are designed to disentangle, rather than following a simple mode of inheritance.

A second problem is the effect of differences in the prenatal environments of twins. For example, in the case of extraversion, the reaction of one twin to the other might originate in the intra-uterine environment where one twin takes up a position more favourable to development. "Competition" of this sort in the early lives of wild plants and animals is a commonly observed phenomenon.

The runt, for example, is often the result of this kind of effect. A strong case has been made for the intra-uterine environment producing strong competition (Burt and Howard, 1956; Burt, 1966). As Shields (1962) has shown, differences in birth weight, which, as a result of competition, can be quite pronounced, may result in the heavier, or "leader" twin assuming the more dominant role. This may be exaggerated in Mz pairs, who show greater weight differences at birth. Of interest also is the observation that Mz twins are more vulnerable to disease than Dz twins.

On the other hand, Mz, when compared with Dz twins, not only show greater similarity of genes, but also share more similar social learning histories. They are more apt to dress alike, to have common friends, to study together (Smith, 1965). The effects of shared genes, therefore, are confounded by those of shared experience.

There are additional factors, some additive, other subtractive, which might influence concordance estimates to an unknown extent. For example, many parents are mistaken about the zygosity of same-sexed twins (e.g. Freedman and Keller, 1963; Scarr, 1968), the percentage of misclassification ranging from 12 to 35% in adolescence. It has been claimed that up to one-third of all fraternal twins are being reared as identicals (Smith, 1965; Scarr, 1968). Again, as we have noted, it has been suggested that, within the diad, pairs of twins tend to adopt different roles, which periodically may be reversed, or that role-playing may be situational. These uncontrolled sources of variance must call into question some of the results of earlier studies reported.

Many of these problems, of course, would be resolved if we could compare samples of identical twins reared together and apart. A few such studies have been reported (Newman, Freeman and Holzinger, 1937; Shields, 1962; Burt, 1966; Eaves and Eysenck 1975). Comparisons of anthropometric, IQ and personality data from the first three studies are presented in Table 1. Heritabilities are remarkably similar; for personality measures, they are all relatively low. Figures for both separated and control Mz pairs are more similar than for Dz pairs.

An alternative is to study individuals adopted in infancy and foster-reared by non-relatives, which separates out the genetic transmission of the biological parents from the psycho-social transmission of the foster parents. For obvious reasons, most studies of this sort (e.g. Heston, 1966; Rosenthal *et al.* 1968) involve psychiatric disorder. A general finding is of a heavy concentration of psychiatric disability among fostered children of schizophrenic mothers. The Rosenthal *et al.* (1968) findings are particularly important in that they rule out toxic factors in the intra-uterine environment.

A somewhat different approach which has not found favour with behaviour geneticists is the methodology of testing for absolute values for inheritance of a

TABLE 1. *Estimates of hereditary (H) and environmental (E) determination of traits, from monozygous twins brought up apart and together and from dizygous twins: a comparison of data (from Cavalli-Sforza & Bodmer, 1971)*

| | H Values[1] | | | E Values[2] | | |
|---|---|---|---|---|---|---|
| | Shields (1962) | Newman, Freeman, and Holzinger (1937) | Burt (1966) | Shields (1962) | Newman Freeman, and Holzinger (1937) | Burt (1966) |
| **Height** | | | | | | |
| Females only | +0.89 | — | — | +0.67 | — | — |
| Males only | — | — | — | +0.89 | −0.54 | +0.33 |
| Both sexes | — | +0.81 | +0.93 | — | −0.64 | +0.33 |
| **Weight** | | | | | | |
| Females only | +0.57 | — | — | — | — | — |
| Both sexes | — | +0.78 | +0.83 | −0.62; +0.68 | +0.27 | +0.39 |
| **IQ** | | | | | | |
| Dominoes and vocabulary | +0.53 | — | — | — | — | — |
| Binet | — | +0.68 | — | — | — | — |
| Other | — | — | +0.86 | −0.04 | +0.64 | +0.40 |
| **Personality** | | | | | | |
| Extroversion | +0.50 | — | — | −0.33 | — | — |
| Neuroticism | +0.30 | — | — | −0.36 | — | — |
| Woodworth Mathews Neur. Ques. | — | +0.30 | — | — | −0.06 | — |
| Other | — | — | — | — | — | +0.95 |
| Educational attainment | — | — | +0.90 | — | — | +0.95 |

[1] Heritability estimates based on Mz/Dz comparisons, twins reared together. High H values imply high heritability.
[2] Environmental estimates based on comparisons between Mz twins reared together and apart: low or negative E values suggest high heritability.

trait, so that we can establish whether traits are more or less genetically fixed in one genotype than in others. From information about the genotype/ environment interaction, it should be possible to determine the extent to which different genotypes are affected by different environments, how susceptible each is at different periods of development, the extent of manipulation required to alter behaviour genotypically fixed, and how likely it is that an altered phenotype will spontaneously regress to its genotype — what Waddington has called its creode.

*Illustrative data from human studies*

The most convenient summary device is age-zone categorisation, although a number of studies show some chronological overlap.

A. NEONATAL AND PERINATAL SAMPLES

Comparatively little direct evidence is available from twin studies in this age range (0–12 months). Reasons for this are obvious enough. Standardised personality tests are inappropriate even at the 12-month level, and the alternative — developmental schedules — at this age provide only crude, comparative assessments of social, motor and speech development. Broad behavioural categories of greatest interest to personality theorists — dependency, affiliativeness, inter-personal responsiveness, emotionality, for example — arguably do not develop until considerable biological maturity has been reached, and are only weakly reflected in the behaviour of infants. Researchers, therefore, face the dilemma that at an age when temperament is expressed in purest form, test technology is inadequate to reliably measure behaviour, while at the chronological or developmental age when this is possible, the behaviour has already been steered by the experimental history of the subject. Postnatal effects, which all theorists recognise as important in personality development, have already occurred, and, as noted previously, it is sometimes difficult to estimate the interaction term, except from retrospective data, which tend to be unreliable.

A number of attempts have been reported to establish early and continuing differences between infants, suggesting inherited individual differences — one of the temperament criteria previously noted — ranging from frequency of smiling and laughing in the first year (Aldrich, Sung and Knop, 1945), sucking rate (Balint, 1948) and the quality of motor behaviour (Shirley, 1931), to broader behavioural categories such as activity level (Fries and Wolf, 1954). These dimensions usually have pronounced psychophysiological overtones. The extent of genotypic contribution to behavioural variance in such cases, is, of course, uncertain in the absence of twin studies, although there is the implicit assumption that environment has not yet had time to exert a major influence. As we shall see later, this is highly debatable. Dimensions such as irritability and emotionality could be strongly reflecting intra-uterine or very early post-natal effects.

The best-known attempts to dimensionalise human neonatal temperament are studies reported by Thomas *et al.* (1963), Korner (1964), Janis *et al.* (1969), Thomas, Chess and Birch (1968) and Escalona (1968). These authors have suggested temperament taxonomies of infant behaviour from studies of children from birth. The major dimensions identified, which are outlined in

Table 2, overlap to a considerable degree. Thomas *et al.* (1963) identified dimensions of response to novelty, distractibility, prevailing mood, intensity of reaction and rhythmicity. Thomas, Chess and Birch (1968) analysed their nine primary dimensions, measured annually over a period of 4 years, and extracted three second-order factors. Intensity of reaction, which is described as the energy invested in behaviour, corresponds to Janis *et al.*'s vigour of activity and Escalona's activity level, and therefore might be described as a dimension of basic arousal level or tonus. The second factor, adaptability, is described as the modification of initial pattern of response in the direction desired by parents or others, i.e. socialisation learning, and has a good deal in common with the Janis *et al.* and Escalona factors of social responsivity. The third factor, quality of mood, refers to basic emotionality, and includes two of Janis *et al.*'s factors, irritability and social responsivity, and elements of Escalona's factor of social responsivity.

From these data, there is clearly some agreement between the human and animal temperament taxonomies. This, by itself, of course, is not sufficient to support a genetic basis for these traits. Nor should we attach undue significance to the emergence of such clear-cut dimensions at a very early postnatal age. Nonetheless, there is some direct evidence of the temporal stability of the traits identified, and of their heritability.

Thomas and Chess (1978) report inter-year correlations for the first 5 years for the nine traits (Table 3). From the figures, as the comparison time span increases, the number of significant correlations is whittled down, except in the case of activity level and adaptability. On the whole, however, the consistency data are impressive, particularly when we consider the methodological problems involved in longitudinal studies of this type.

Thomas (1979), in collaboration with Chess, has reported further consistency data from follow-up of 136 Ss from infancy to their current early adult lives. From both quantitative and qualitative (case study) analyses, Thomas reports considerable stability of temperamental variables over this period. He does, however, underline the importance of the interaction between temperament, the child's abilities and motives, and environmental opportunities and demands, in shaping development. Temperament does not immutably steer development, nor does it follow a consistent linear course. Continuities and discontinuities occur and recur.

Conventional twin studies, which are obviously the most acceptable source of evidence of genetic contribution to personality, fall into two categories. Some researchers have attempted to measure relatively simple behaviours such as social smiling and fear response to strangers, which they claim provide the basis for subsequent development of the more complex behaviours such as dependency and affiliativeness. Others have employed broader dimensions,

TABLE 2. *Temperament dimensions derived from observations of neonatal behaviour (from Thomas and Chess, 1978. Reproduced by permission of Brunner/Mazel)*

| Escalona and Heider (1969) | Janis et al. (1969) | Thomas, Chess and Birch (1968) | |
|---|---|---|---|
| | | *First-order factors* | *Second-order factors* |
| *Activity level* the amount and vigour of bodily motion typically shown by an infant in a wide variety of situations | *Vigour of activity* intensity of motor activity — body movements, vocalisations | *Activity level* | *Intensity of reaction* the energy invested in behaviour |
| *Perceptual sensitivity* reactivity to sensory stimulation in general, and in specific modalities | *Irritability* ease with which child cries and whines, and effort needed to placate him | *Rhythmicity of biological function* | *Adaptability* ease of socialisation learning |
| *Motility* neuromuscular activity which leads to displacement in space — quantitative and qualitative aspects of body movement | *Stimulus satiability* rate of habituation, normally evidenced at about 3 months | *Approach/avoidance to new stimuli* | *Quality of mood* basic level of emotional responsivity |
| *Bodily self-stimulation* movement pattern which delivers direct stimulation to a body zone — thumbsucking, rocking etc. | *Threshold for attentional change* stimulus intensity and uniqueness required to attract attention — similar to "perceptual sensitivity" | *Adaptability* | |
| *Spontaneous activity* | *Social responsivity* degree to which the child elicits affectionate overtones from adults — smiles, babbles, laughs and coos when adult approaches | *Sensory threshold* | |
| *Somatic need states and need gratification* | | *Quality of mood* | |
| *Object related behaviour* infant's responses to perception of objects | | *Intensity of reaction* | |
| *Social responsivity* initially to mother, then to other social objects in the environment | | *Distractibility* | |
| | | *Persistence/attention span* | |

TABLE 3. *Inter-year correlations for each of the nine categories (N = 100–110)*
*(from Thomas and Chess, 1978. Reproduced by permission of Brunner/Mazel)*

| Category: | 1–2 | 1–3 | 1–4 | 1–5 | 2–3 | 2–4 | 2–5 | 3–4 | 3–5 | 4–5 |
|---|---|---|---|---|---|---|---|---|---|---|
| Activity | .30* | .21* | .26* | .16 | .30* | .31* | .23* | .26* | .29* | .31* |
| Rhythmicity | .44* | .39* | .21* | .15 | .32* | .03 | .07 | .10 | .09 | .37* |
| Adaptability | .38* | .22* | .18 | .07 | .46* | .37* | .25* | .54* | .33* | .51* |
| Approach/Withdrawal | .07 | .13 | .01 | −.03 | .11 | .14 | .06 | .30* | .07 | .33* |
| Threshold | .39* | .36* | .14 | .21* | .25* | −.03 | .09 | .18 | .19 | .11 |
| Intensity | .47* | .17 | .02 | .10 | .28* | .01 | .13 | .30* | .14 | .32* |
| Mood | .45* | .25* | .10 | .08 | .18 | .06 | .16 | .28* | .11 | .25* |
| Distractibility | −.05 | .13 | −.12 | .12 | .15 | .05 | −.06 | .12 | .37* | .14 |
| Persistence | .11 | .04 | .01 | .09 | .38* | .23* | .16 | .24* | .28* | .13 |

*Correlation is significant beyond the .05 level of confidence for respective N (N varies due to cases with no scored items in particular category for a given year).

such as those assessed by the Bayley Infant Behaviour Profile, which permits continuous assessment over a longer period of time.

Examples are the studies of 20 same-sex pairs of infant twins reported by Freedman and Keller (1963) and Freedman (1965) of social smiling and fear responses to strangers in the first 5 months of life, social orientation being scored as visual fixation time on the face, and frequency of social smiling, and fearfulness as fear of the investigator, these being considered to reflect basically tendencies to socially approach and avoid. Measures were also derived from the Bayley Mental and Motor Scales, and from the Bayley Infant Behaviour Profile. On this scale, which covers twelve categories of behaviour, responsiveness to persons and objects, fearfulness, goal-directedness, activity level and reactivity being the most critical, Mz pairs show smaller group differences than Dz pairs. Note that these sub-scales approximate the dimensions identified by Janis *et al.* and others.

In these studies, zygosity was not determined until after the observations were completed. In agreement with previous studies, for 6 of the Mz pairs, parents assumed that the twins were fraternal. The obstetricians involved were incorrect 9 times out of 19 in their assumptions about zygosity — as near as possible to random allocation. Observed behaviour differences, therefore, were not unduly influenced by parental attitudes about zygosity.

A series of recent studies by Matheny and colleagues (1975, 1975, 1976) reports some interesting results. In the first of these (Matheny, 1975), 20 Bayley Mental Test items, which were judged to be equivalent to items of Piagetian scales, were administered to 120 Mz and 85 same-sex Dz pairs, observations being made at 3, 6, 9 and 12 months. Mz pairs were more concordant than Dz pairs at 3 and 6 months for items related to prehension, object permanence and imitation. The total score intra-class correlations were 0.8 for Mz and 0.6 for Dz pairs, the difference being significant. These results support Piaget's assertion that sensori-motor capabilities are biologically based.

In a second study (Matheny and Dolin, 1975), Mz and Dz twin pairs were rated for adaptability in two settings, one unstructured, the other highly structured, at 9, 12, 18, 24 and 30 months of age. The Mz pairs were more similar in both settings than Dz pairs. In a third study (Matheny, Dolin and Wilson, 1976), in which intra-pair similarities on Bayley's Infant Behaviour Profile were calculated, the authors report higher intra-class correlations for Mz than for Dz pairs for almost all behaviours in the first year, a finding which replicates the earlier results of Freedman and Keller (1963) and Freedman (1965). In the second year, however, figures were roughly the same. The authors derived two behavioural clusters, composite scores for extraversion and for primary cognition. For extraversion, Mz twins showed higher heritability in the first year only, and for primary cognition, greater heritability in both first and second years. This presumably indicates greater genetic influence on the more cognitive behaviours.

Torgersen (1973, 1979) reports significant values for the 9 Thomas *et al.* temperament variables from a sample of 53 twin pairs (34 Mz, 16 Dz pairs, 3 uncertain zygosity). Details are shown in Table 4. The 53 pairs were assessed through interviews with mothers at ages 2 months and 9 months. In a follow-up of the same twin pairs at age 6 years, the same dimensions were examined, except for irritability, which proved too difficult to measure. The remaining eight dimensions showed significant heritabilities. However, Torgersen comments that when more conservative genetical methods were employed, differences were significant for five only of the eight categories — activity, approach/withdrawal, intensity of reaction, threshold and persistence.

While it seems reasonable to suggest, from these and other data, that

TABLE 4. *Differences as F-ratio between intrapair variances of weighted temperament scores in Mz and Dz twins at 2 months and 9 months (from Torgersen, 1979)*

|  | 2 months | | 9 months | |
|---|---|---|---|---|
|  | F-ratio | P value | F-ratio | P value |
| Regularity | 4.98 | < 0.001 | 12.86 | < 0.001 |
| Threshold | 2.82 | < 0.01 | 9.90 | < 0.001 |
| Approach | 0.83 | insign. | 6.77 | < 0.001 |
| Intensity | 2.55 | < 0.25 | 5.32 | < 0.001 |
| Activity | 1.52 | insign. | 5.26 | < 0.001 |
| Persistence | — | insign. | 4.40 | < 0.001 |
| Distractibility | 1.40 | insign. | 3.94 | < 0.001 |
| Mood | 1.54 | insign. | 3.31 | < 0.01 |
| Adaptability | 0.57 | insign. | 2.28 | < 0.05 |

genotype plays some role in the differential development of social or person orientation, precisely what mechanism might be involved is unclear. Some authors have suggested that the "cuddling" or "contact comfort" data, i.e. patterns of response to physical contact in young infants, might provide a clue. A number of these studies have been reviewed by Langmeier and Matejcek (1975). An example is the Schaffer and Emerson (1964) report that from a sample of 37 babies, 9 consistently resisted being cuddled and held by their mothers. Cuddlers appear to be less active, less restless, and slept longer than the non-cuddlers. It is suggested that these individual differences in the need for physical contact, or sentience need, could be in part due to gene differences, and there seems little doubt that such difference could markedly influence social development. Freedman (1965), Gottesman (1967) and Langmeier and Matejcek (1975) suggest that the cuddling/non-cuddling dichotomy predicts person orientation in older children, independently of maternal treatment. Note, however, the point emphasised by Freedman (1965), from his twin studies, that maternal treatment may so interact with the behaviour of the infant as to produce a healthy or pathological relationship.

The extent to which these "temperament" variables project in time to predict the universe of source and second-order traits which constitute the domain of adult personality is problematical. Data are limited, but a few studies present some relevant findings. Neilon (1964) and Murphy (cf. Escalona, 1968) tested groups of children on whom temperament profiles had been compiled by Shirley (1931) and Escalona and Heider (1959). The time elapse in the two sets of observations were 15 and 4 years respectively. In both cases, the later personality profiles were matched against the original observations by independent judges. Substantial agreements were reported, although there could be some question about the statistical evaluations.

The Kagan and Moss (1962) study, which is reported in more detail later, reports high stability of traits of dependency and aggressiveness from childhood to adolescence. Childhood data were retrospective. Dependency was stable for females, and aggressiveness for males, although the authors conclude that the differential stability of these traits between sexes is due largely to sex-role training.

A considerable amount of data has been reported on activity level, which is regarded by some (e.g. Escalona, 1968) as important in the moulding of the mother-child relationship, and to be related to traits of aggressiveness and dominance in later life. Some of the early studies (Fries and Wolf, 1954; Fries, 1954) reported that activity levels remain stable from infancy through adolescence. Two of the major longitudinal studies reported, those of Kagan and Moss (1962) and Schaefer and Bayley (1963) report similar results for this dimension, although other behaviours during infancy did not correlate with later behaviour. Thomas *et al.* (1963) and Escalona and Heider (1959), however, were unable to confirm this finding. The report by McGrade, Kessen and Latzendorff (1965) that activity level in neonates correlates significantly with length of labour suggests that activity level may be an acquired intra-uterine effect.

Response to novel stimuli has been investigated in a number of studies. Meili (1957a,b) reported that the manner in which infants below the age of 3 months respond to a visual stimulus foreshadows their response to the unfamiliar at later stages. Meili found a strong correlation between many of the adaptive and social characteristics of 4-year-olds and the same children's behaviour during exposure to novel stimuli in infancy, which latter he regards as "primary perceptual transactions". Similarly, Thomas *et al.* (1963) found that the response to novelty remains highly stable during the first several years of life, in terms of a consistent tendency to respond either with withdrawal and distress or a confident approach. Korner (1964) suggests that the way an infant deals with each developmental step may be inferred from a comparison of the baby's mode of dealing with familiar and novel stimuli, and a comparison of his behaviour when subject to drive tension, with his behaviour under optimal conditions of internal equilibrium.

There are some suggestions that certain temperamental traits relate to behaviour disorders in later life. Bergman and Escalona (1949), for example, report that a group of children who in early infancy showed marked hyper-sensitivity, which the authors interpret to mean lack of an effective stimulus barrier, so that ordinary levels of stimulation could prove overwhelming, developed psychiatric illness or behaviour disorders in adulthood.

The point is well illustrated by Thomas, Chess and Birch (1968) from a number of case histories in which temperamental characteristics such as distractibility, for example, play an important role in the aetiology of behaviour disorders. They conclude that:

> Children who develop behaviour disorders clearly indicate that features of temperament, together with their organisation and patterning, play significant roles in the genesis and development of behaviour disorders in childhood. No one of these temperament traits, on its own, influenced the course of the child's development. Rather, combinations of traits forming patterns or clusters resulted in the increased risk of developing behaviour disorders, and symptoms were found to be associated with differences in temperament. A given pattern of temperament did not, as such, result in a behaviour disorder. Its development was a product of the interaction between the child with given characteristics of temperament and significant features of the environment. Temperament, representing one side of the child's individuality, also interacted with abilities and motives, the other two facets, as well as with the environment, in determining the specific behaviour patterns which evolved during development.

Thomas and Chess (1978), from data assembled during the course of their New York Longitudinal Study (NYLS), identified a number of temperamental constellations — combinations of the nine temperamental variables — describing different personality "types". The Easy Child is characterised by regularity of biological function, positive responses to new stimuli, high adaptability, mild to moderately intense mood, usually positive. The Difficult Child, on the other hand, shows irregularity in biological function, withdrawal responses to novel stimuli, non-adaptability or slow adaptability to change, and intense mood expressions which are predominantly negative. The third type they describe as the Slow-To-Warm-Up Child, who displays relatively mild reaction intensities, either positive or negative, a tendency towards irregularity in biological function, relatively slow habituation to novel stimuli. These temperament constellations are thought to have an important steering influence on psychological development, and, importantly, to have predictive power in identifying children "at risk" for psychiatric disorder. This latter assumption is supported by data comparing the temperament profiles of "disturbed" under-5-year-olds — children expressing overt symptoms such as feeding problems, tantrums, stuttering and so on — with those of a "normal" group. The "active" clinical group (N = 34) showed highly significant differences from the non-clinical group (N = 66) in years 3, 4 and 5, on most of the 9 temperament variables. The former is characterised by high activity, irregularity of biological function, low threshold of response, non-adaptability, low persistence and distractability.

Along somewhat similar lines, Chess (1979) has discussed the importance of temperament in the development of the handicapped child. From observations on two groups, the first consisting of 243 children with congenital rubella gathered at ages 2–4 years and followed up to the age of 13–14 years, the second a group of mildly intellectually retarded children observed from the age of 5–11 years, she noted that a "poorness of fit" between the capacities, the temperamental characteristics and the behavioural styles of the child, and the expectations and demands of the environment, leads to distorted development and maladaptive functioning. For the physically handicapped child, an important variable is "plasticity of development", i.e. the efficiency with which the child learns to organise input from intact senses to cope with the environment. Chess also emphasises the increased vulnerability of the child who is burdened with physical or mental handicap and with the temperamental profile of the Difficult Child, and thus presumably lacks the repertoire of coping strategies more readily available to other temperament "types".


B. STUDIES OF "TODDLERS" AND OLDER CHILDREN

At a slightly older age (toddlers, 18 months–4 years), twin data available indicate that Mz are more similar than Dz pairs in attentive behaviour modulation and sociability, as rated by parents (Cohen, Dibble and Grawe, 1977), and in resistance to change, reflected in impulse control, measured by Matching Familiar Figures Test (Plomin and Willerman, 1975).

The most extensive data with this age group have been reported by Buss, Plomin and Willerman (1973). These authors selected four of the Thomas, Chess and Birch's (1968) temperament traits (or temperaments) — emotionality (level of arousal, intensity of reaction), activity (sheer amount of response output), sociability (tendency to approach others) and impulsivity (quickness of response) — dimensions which have also been identified in other studies (Vandenberg, 1967; Scarr, 1969; Mittler, 1971). In this study, the four dimensions were measured by ratings, on a 1–5 scale, of four sets of five items, assigned to dimensions on the basis of a factor analysis. The sample consisted of 147 twin pairs in the age range 4 months–16 years, with a mean age of 55 months. Results were analysed for the two groups — those below and those above mean age. Results are presented in Table 5.

In view of comments previously made about difficulty in determining zygosity, an interesting finding reported by these authors is that there was 93% accuracy in determining zygosity on the basis of the Nichols and Bilbro (1966) scale, compared with later serological techniques. Of interest also is the fact that intra-class correlations for emotionality increase with age, i.e. environmental influences make twins more alike in emotionality, while correlations for the remaining variables decrease with age, suggesting that, in these respects, environment acts divergently on twins. The authors also make the suggestion that different personality "types" are simply different combinations of temperaments — psychopaths, for example, are high on impulsivity and low on emotionality, the hyperkinetic type high on both

TABLE 5. *Heritability estimates for groups of male and female Mz and Dz twins on four temperament dimensions (from Buss, Plomin and Willerman (1973)*

|  |  | Boys | | | | Girls | | | |
|---|---|---|---|---|---|---|---|---|---|
|  |  | Mz | Dz | F | H | Mz | Dz | F | H |
| Emotionality | −55 months | .55 | .00 | 1.10 | .55 | .71 | .00 | 3.95 | .71 |
|  | +55 months | .87 | .46 | 5.67 | .76 | .81 | .38 | 6.35 | .69 |
| Activity | −55 months | .91 | .47 | 2.93 | .83 | .68 | .58 |  | .24 |
|  | +55 months | .73 | .00 | 4.47 | .73 | .70 | .00 | 9.24 | .70 |
| Sociability | −55 months | .76 | .42 | 4.43 | .72 | .59 | .36 | 2.03 | .36 |
|  | +55 months | .42 | .00 | 1.70 | .42 | .22 | .00 | 2.75 | .22 |
| Impulsivity | −55 months | .92 | .38 | 1.70 | .87 | .78 | .88 | 1.23 | .00 |
|  | +55 months | .86 | .00 | 4.40 | .86 | .88 | .65 | 4.85 | .66 |

impulsivity and activity. A personality typology of this sort has some resemblance to the Soviet typological approach, which we shall examine in the next chapter.

A good deal of data concerning possible temperament dimensions derive from observational studies. Smith (1973), Smith and Connolly (1972) and Blurton-Jones (1972b) have identified sociability (social maturity/participation) as the first component in a principal components analysis of observations of interactions within groups of 2–3 year olds. Smith (1973) reports negative loadings on this factor of crying and submissive behaviour. The second factor identified in these studies, which is orthogonal to sociability, contrasts manipulative with rough and tumble play. Unlike sociability, preference is to some extent sex-related. This supports some earlier views (e.g. McDowell, 1937) that girls prefer manipulative play, and boys active physical play, the latter being seen as a preparation for aggressive/sexual, and in some species, hunting behaviour. Smith (1973) suggests that manipulative object play represents genetic potentiality for tool use and tool making characteristics of primates.

The observation that there is little or no relationship between sociability and aggressive rough-and-tumble preference in small boys complements those of Beach (1965) regarding the relationship between affiliative and sexual/aggressive behaviour in male dogs. Although clearly affiliativeness is a necessary condition for the occurrence of sexual behaviour, the popularity of the male dog, reflected in the extent of his affiliative behaviour, does not breed success. It may be that sex differences in aggressive rough-and-tumble play are related simply to the pre-natal sex typing of the brain by circulating androgens. For whatever reasons, these behaviours appear to be under different gene control.

A number of longitudinal studies mentioned previously show that by the age of 3 or 4 years we can clearly identify dependency and aggressiveness (Kagan and Moss, 1960; Kagan and Moss, 1962), activity level (Fries, 1954; Fries and Wolf, 1954; Kagan and Moss, 1962; Schaefer and Bayley, 1963), response to novelty (Meili, 1957a,b: Thomas et al. 1963) as stable and relatively generalised personality traits. Thomas, Chess and Birch (1968) were able to trace their neonatal second-order factors of intensity of reaction, adaptability (social responsiveness) and quality of mood (emotionality) through the third and fourth years with little apparent change in trait content.

Block and Block (1979) report an interesting study in which children, in their fourth, sixth and eighth years, were rated by teachers (observations for 3 hours a day over a 5–9 month period) on a modification of the California Q-set, which is considered a useful datum for delineating overall personality structure, and, perhaps more importantly, for assessing developmental changes. The average intercorrelation for 100 Q items was 0.49, with several greater than 0.6, and a few reaching 0.7. When the items were grouped into broader categories using factor analytic techniques, the mean correlation rose to 0.56. Clearly, there is considerable stability of personality structure throughout the age range examined.

Twin studies with somewhat older children have consistently shown that the genotype contributes to individual differences in sociability, defined as a mixture of social introversion-extraversion, social anxiety, friendliness to strangers and social spontaneity. For example, Scarr (1968, 1969) has reported a study employing 52 pairs of 6–12-year-old girls (28 Dz and 24 Mz pairs), using the Adjective Check List and the Fels Child Behaviour Scales. Social apprehension, friendliness and affiliation show significantly higher within-pair similarity for the identical co-twins (Table 6). Judging from these data, hereditary factors influence the development of socialisation, and also account for variation in dependency and affiliative behaviour. However, it is equally apparent that social learning modifies the genotypic effects.

An interesting study is reported by Kagan and Moss (1962) which incorporates data from an earlier paper (Kagan and Moss, 1960) concerning the stability of dependency from childhood to adulthood. The sample consisted of 27 males and 27 females in their twenties, for whom retrospective data were available from years 3 to 10. Adult dependency variables — job security, emotional support from partner, tendency to seek support and advice from parents, tendency to withdraw in face of possible failure — were correlated with variables such as passive dependency, emotional dependency on female adults, and tendency to seek assistance from female adults, assessed in childhood.

TABLE 6. *Correlations for selected social-dependent behaviour in identical and fraternal twin girls: data derived from Adjective Check Lists completed by twins' mothers and ratings on the Fels scales by two experimenters (data adapted from Scarr, 1968, 1969)*

|  | Correlations | |
|---|---|---|
|  | Identical twins | Fraternal twins |
| *Adjective Check List dimensions* | | |
| Need affiliation | .83 | .56 |
| Anxiety | .56 | .03 |
| Need change | .70 | –.12 |
| Need autonomy | .40 | .11 |
| *Fels Child Behaviour Scales* | | |
| Rated anxiety | .88 | .28 |
| Rated friendliness | .86 | .36 |

Passive and dependent behaviours appeared to be fairly stable for females, but not for males. Kagan and Moss argue that the differential stability of dependency between sexes is a product of sex-role training. To the extent that this is true, aggressiveness, therefore, should show the reverse pattern, i.e., stability for males but not for females.

This is supported in the Kagan and Moss (1962) data on aggressiveness. Correlations are consistently higher in males — "behaviours which are incongruent with culturally defined roles, for example dependency in men and aggressiveness in women, will not be socially reinforced, and they will therefore exhibit poor stability over time". Further evidence that sex-role training affects aggressiveness is found in twin studies (Gottesman, 1963). Identical male twins closely resemble each other on dimensions of dominance and aggression, and differences between male fraternal and identical twins are large. It is claimed that genes predisposing male aggressiveness are socially reinforced, so that gene differences are exaggerated through experience. Differences in aggressiveness are much smaller among female identical and fraternal twins. Since aggressiveness in women is culturally punished, gene differences are presumably masked.

Olweus, in a series of studies (1973, 1974, 1977a,b) has reported striking data on the temporal stability of aggressiveness in boys. Classmates rated 201 boys in the sixth grade, and again 3 years later on a number of variables pertaining to aggression . Ratings were averaged over 3–10 raters. Olweus reports that the mean stability coefficient for the 3-year period was 0.66. When correlations were corrected for attenuation due to later unreliability, stability coefficients rose to approximately 0.80. In a second, similar study, in which 85 13-year-old boys were Ss, even higher stability coefficients are reported. In other studies in this series, it was observed that peer ratings, teacher ratings and self-ratings on a specially designed aggression inventory were all highly inter-correlated, suggesting the existence of a broad dispositional trait of aggression.

C. YOUNG ADULT AND ADULT SAMPLES

Most twin study data derive from young adult or adult samples, for which a great variety of personality tests is available. Twin methodology with these subjects, however, poses some special problems. Apart from the dubious validity of narrow heritability indices, there is the increased probability that older twins are separated — by marriage or occupation, for example. Age and separation appear to have some effect on the intra-class correlations reported (Canter, 1973), although there are discrepancies in the separation data reported. Shield's (1962) data, re-analysed by Jinks and Fulker (1970), indicate that twins reared apart are somewhat more neurotic than twins reared together. Canter (1973) reports that separated twins, either Mz or Dz, are less alike on measures of anxiety or neuroticism, while for extraversion, separated twins are more alike than non-separated twins, particularly the Mz pairs. Wilde (1964), on the other hand, reports separated Mz twins to be less alike on extraversion than non-separated twins, but the opposite for the Dz pairs. Increased heritability estimates for separated pairs for extraversion might suggest a subtractive effect of differential role-playing in non-separated pairs, an effect less likely in the case of anxiety/neuroticism. Insofar as the latter is concerned, however, the explanation could simply be that this trait has low heritability.

Adult twin studies can be conveniently reviewed under the following headings.

### 1. Sensory functioning

While it could be argued that sensory functioning offers a most promising area for human genetic studies, because of obvious dependence on identifiable anatomical structures and physiological mechanisms, little information has been reported, other than data on gross defects such as colour blindness, phenylketonuria (PKU), Down's Syndrome, for example. However, there are reports of a genetic component in critical flicker frequency (CFF) (Eysenck and Prell, 1951; Murawski, 1960; Vandenburg, 1962), although none in two-flash threshold or spiral after-effect (Hume, 1973), which have been used extensively in studies of the psychophysiology of personality. There also appears to be genetic contribution to a variety of perceptual-motor tasks – Embedded Figures, Street-Gestalt Completion Figures and Kohs Blocks Tests (Thurstone, Thurstone and Strandskov, 1955; Vandenburg, 1962), the size of after-image and Muller-Lyer Illusion (Smith, 1949), autokinetic movement (Eysenck and Prell, 1951), the perception of upright in Witkin's field-dependency Rod-and-Frame test and Thurstone's colour-form movie (Vandenburg, 1962), the latter purporting to demonstrate psychologically meaningful differences between persons reacting more to colour than to form. There also appears to be a genetic component in such motor skills as tapping speed (Newman, Freeman and Holzinger, 1937; Eysenck and Prell, 1951; Thurstone, Thurstone and Strandskov, 1955), pursuit rotor hand steadiness and card sorting (McNemar, 1933; Vandenburg, 1966), although it appears that the hereditary contribution is greater for the right hand than for the left (Thurstone, Thurstone and Strandskov, 1955; Vandenburg, 1962).[2]

### 2. Psychophysiological functioning

On a somewhat broader level, there is evidence for heritability of a number of psychophysiological variables, some of which are often regarded as indices of

[2]But see discussion, pp. 85–86, on this issue.

arousal. We should note, of course, that these indices do not inter-correlate very highly, which may call into question the utility of a concept of general arousal.

### (a) Cardiovascular measures

In line with earlier findings (e.g. Stocks, 1930) Miall et al.'s (1967) review concludes that blood pressure is multifactorially determined, and that environmental components are probably less critical than genetic. Subsequent data, however, have been equivocal, some studies reporting no significant differences between mean intra-pair variances for Mz compared with Dz pairs, using a single casual reading (Barcal, Simon and Sova, 1969; Downie et al. 1969), others a significant difference (Jost and Sontag, 1944; Kryshova et al. 1962; Osborne, De George and Mathers, 1963; Shapiro et al. 1968). Kryshova et al. (1962) report that blood pressure and skin temperature responses to hot and cold stimuli, and to bell and light, were very similar for both members of Mz pairs.

### (b) Heart rate

There are reports of a genetic component in heart-rate response both at rest (Mathers, Osborne and De George, 1961; Block, 1967: Shapiro et al. 1968; Hume, 1973), and in response to mildly stressful stimuli (Vandenburg and Falkner, 1965; Block, 1967; Shapiro et al. 1968). Jost and Sontag (1944), however, report no differences for resting heart rate. Lader and Wing (1966) report a significant difference in intra-class correlations between Mz and Dz twins when heart rate level was measured at the end of a habituation series.

### (c) Electrodermal measures[3]

Genetic effects have been reported for skin conductance response (SCR) (Jost and Sontag, 1944; Block, 1967), though there have been some failures of prediction (Vandenburg and Falkner, 1965). There is some support for a genetic component in skin conductance level (SCL) (Jost and Sontag, 1944) — a measure of tonic arousal — and for spontaneous fluctuation rate (SF) (Vandenburg, 1966; Rachman, 1960; Lader and Wing, 1966; Hume, 1973; Zahn,* 1977) which is claimed to be a measure of excitation/inhibition balance,

---

[3]Studies indicated thus * have employed schizophrenic Ss or Ss at high risk for schizophrenia. Whether or not results from such studies can be extrapolated to normal samples is problematical. It depends on whether we propose a continuity or discontinuity approach to mental illness; the continuity assumption that schizophrenia is an extreme form of introversion would permit such a generalisation, the discontinuity position that schizophrenics and normals are discrete, unrelated groups would not.

although this has been disputed, and for SCR latency (Rachman, 1960; Lader and Wing, 1966; Hume, 1973) although note the unpublished study by Bell, cited by Mednick* (1974) suggesting no significant genetic effects for SCL, SF, SCR latency or rise time. Concerning habituation rate of orienting response, some reports indicate genetic effects (Lader and Wing, 1966; Hume, 1973), others not (Rachman, 1960; Zahn,* 1977).

Recovery limb of the electrodermal response, which has recently been accorded some attention, presents a confusing picture. Zahn* (1977) reports that half recovery rate shows strong genetic influences, but not half recovery time, a surprising result in view of Mednick's* (1976) report that half recovery time identifies high risk Ss who have a schizophrenic spectrum diagnosis on most recent assessment, and Bell's data, reporting that half recovery time, but not half recovery rate, shows significant genetic effects.

Overall, it appears that SCL and SF have the strongest support for a genetic basis, although there is some evidence that latency, habituation and tonic responsivity may be genetically determined in part. Significant genetic effects for amplitude (SCR) appear doubtful.

*(d) Electrocortical responding*

1. EEG. A comprehensive review of genetic studies of human EEG is reported by Claridge and Mangan (in press), and only the sketchiest outline is attempted here.

Jule-Neilsen and Harvald (1958) reported practically complete concordance in normal EEG patterns and abnormalities in 3 pairs of Mz twins reared apart. Lennox, Gibbs and Gibbs (1945) claim a strong genetic component for EEG, as does Hume (1973) for resting alpha. Young and Fenton (1971) measured habituation of the EEG alpha-blocking response with repeated stimulation, and report significant intra-class correlations in 17 Mz pairs; although the latter were not significantly different from a group of 15 Dz pairs, they did differ significantly from a sample of thirty unrelated pairs of normals. Rust (1975) reports strong genetic influence for EEG amplitude, but not for latency, while Lykken, Tellegen and Thorkelson (1974) report that most of the EEG variance for frequency characteristics is genetic in origin.

The most comprehensive series of studies is that carried out by Vogel and his colleagues (Vogel, 1970; Vogel and Fujiya, 1969; Vogel and Schalt, 1979; Vogel, Schalt and Kruger, 1979; Vogel, Schalt, Kruger, Propping and Lehnert, 1979). A feature of this series is the identification of EEG "types", recognised as variants of the resting EEG pattern. Of the variants described by Vogel (1970), he suggests a fairly straight-forward autosomal dominant mode of inheritance for "low voltage EEG" and "quick (16–19Hz) alpha" variants. The results of these studies are summarised in Table 7.

In his most recent work, Vogel has considered the extent to which EEG "types" might be related to psychological differences, personality and cognitive performance. The "low voltage" group is described as being high on intelligence, especially spatial orientation, and as being normally extraverted, while individuals with "diffuse beta rhythm" are low in intelligence and poor in emotional control (Vogel, Schalt and Kruger, 1979).

2. Evoked potential. Some workers have chosen to investigate the cortical evoked potential as an approach to the study of EEG genetics.

The pioneering study was that of Dustman and Beck (1965), who report that members of their Mz pairs were more alike in their visual evoked potential responses than members of their Dz pairs. These authors make the interesting observation that at times the variability between twins on one occasion was less than the variability between occasions of testing for the one twin, suggesting that the variability of the visual evoked response itself is an important parameter.

TABLE 7. *Resting EEG variants, according to Vogel, with German and Japanese population frequencies (adapted from Vogel and Fujiya, 1969)*

|  |  | Population frequency | |
|  |  | German | Japanese |
| --- | --- | --- | --- |
| Low voltage EEG | Typical | 4.20% | 4.57% |
|  | Borderline | 2.25% | 2.14% |
| Monotonous α waves |  | 3.85% | 4.27% |
| Fronto-precentral β groups | Numerous | 1.47% | 0.68% |
|  | Rare | 0.45% | 0.12% |
| Occipital slow (16–19 cps) β (α-variant) |  | 0.60% | 0.42% |
| Diffuse |  | 5.54% | 4.03% |

Lewis, Dustman and Beck (1972) expanded their original investigation to include auditory and somatosensory as well as visual stimulation, using a sample of 44 Mz, 46 Dz and 46 unrelated pairs. Results were similar to those reported earlier. Other workers have tended to confirm these findings (Young, Lader and Fenton, 1972; Osborne, 1970; Rust, 1975).

In addition to these studies, which have been concerned with the shape of the evoked potential wave-form, Buchsbaum (1974) has reported a twin study of evoked potentials as part of a long series of investigations of the augmenting-reducing response. The sample was 30 Mz and 30 Dz twins pairs. He reports that all the evoked potential measures demonstrated a uniformly greater similarity between Mz than between Dz pairs, including the various slope indices of augmenting-reducing, as well as the individual amplitude parameters on which these are based. The significant differences recorded, however, are largely a function of low Dz correlations, which militates against a simple genetic interpretation for both the EP variables and the augmenting-reducing slopes. It is difficult, therefore, to draw any firm conclusions from these results.

*(e) Miscellaneous*

Lader and Wing (1966) report that intra-class correlations for integrated forearm extensor muscle activity were low for both Mz and Dz pairs. Somewhat more promising results have been reported for respiratory responses, Vandenburg and Falkner (1965) reporting a close concordance in Mz twins on a measure of respiratory response to intense stimuli, and Block (1967) significant intra-class correlations for respiratory period in Mz twins. Jost and Sontag (1944), however, found that intra-pair differences on this measure were similar in both Mz twins and sibling pairs, while neither of these differed from unrelated pairs.

*(f) Combined measures*

In a number of studies, attempts have been made to derive broad dimensions of psychophysiological functioning which might be more clearly related to personality dimensions or types than single psychophysiological measures.

The first study of this type was the Jost and Sontag (1944) report that a dimension of "autonomic balance", derived from the factor analytic work of Wenger (Wenger and Wellington, 1943) was more strongly represented in pairs of Mz twins than in pairs of siblings or unrelated controls. A similar type of general autonomic balance or level factor, probably reflecting tonic arousal level — the pacer stimulus referred to by Dember and Earle (1957) and the "optimal arousal flux" of Berlyne (1971b) — has since been identified by

Wenger (1948), Joyce (1966) and Mefferd (1966) — the latter two studies (unpublished) being cited by Cattell (1966) — Hume (1973) and Claridge (1973). In a number of these studies, a second factor of autonomic, particularly sympathetic, reactivity — "phasic arousal level" — has been identified (Freeman and Katzoff, 1942; Mefferd, 1966; Joyce, 1966; Hume, 1973). Martin and Rust (1976) have identified a factor of electrodermal responsivity from a factor analysis of a large battery of electrodermal measures.

Additional factors have been identified in some studies, but their content, not unexpectedly, depends on the particular psychophysiological variables included in the battery of measures. There seems to be some consensus, however, about a separate EEG dimension, involving alpha level and frequency of alpha blocking (Nebylitsyn, 1965; Pawlick and Cattell, 1965; Claridge, 1967, 1973; Hume, 1973) although precise interpretation of this factor remains in doubt. It may be to some extent an artefact of the large number of highly intercorrelated tests in the battery, which would tend to produce, in a principal components analysis, a separate EEG component. Claridge (1973) describes his EEG factor as reflecting arousal modulation. Hume (1973) and Claridge (1973) also identify a skin potential activity factor; Claridge (1973) suggests that this might reflect some aspect of cortical/subcortical relationships, perhaps concerned with feedback control mechanisms linking EEG with autonomic activity. Claridge (1973) interprets his fourth factor as perceptual responsiveness.

In a number of these studies, attempts have been made to determine genetic contribution to these psychophysiological dimensions, rather than to the single contributing measures. The factor, autonomic balance, seems to have considerable support, being more strongly represented in pairs of Mz than Dz twins, pairs of sibs or unrelated controls (Jost and Sontag, 1944; Hume, 1973). Claridge (1973) reports intra-class correlations for Mz and Dz twin pairs on his EEG factor, which he claims to measure arousal modulation, of 0.96 ($p < 0.001$) and 0.54 ($p < 0.05$), respectively, suggesting strong genetic determination of this factor. His other three factors, however, showed little evidence of genetic determination. Hume (1973) reports that the four intra-class correlations were significant for the Mz pairs, while for the Dz pairs, only those for factors 2 and 3 were significant. Autonomic balance and the spontaneous skin potential factor showed the clearest evidence for a significant contribution of genetic factors. The four factors together, however, accounted for less than half the variance, so that environmental factors have considerable scope, particularly on the raw measures on which the analysis was based. Hume claims that the composite measures represent major psychophysiological systems, and have various degrees of genetic determination. Insofar as their significance for behaviour is concerned, it is possible that these might provide a biological basis for personality variation, the interaction apparently varying situationally across individuals.

### 3. Personality functioning

Here we encounter a number of problems which make interpretation of results difficult. In the first place, researchers have used a variety of tests dealing with specific traits such as shyness, for example, and there is the assumption that trait names in different cases refer to the same underlying characteristics. Secondly, many tests have low reliabilities and validities, a problem exacerbated by different test methodologies — projective tests compared with questionnaires, for example. Finally, the majority of the reported work has employed adult samples, and there is the problem that twin separation and age may be important variables affecting heritability estimates (Canter, 1973).

With these caveats in mind, a number of clear trends have been reported. Although one of the earliest studies (Newman, Freeman and Holzinger, 1937) found little evidence to support any marked genetic contribution to personality, recent improvements in test methodology and psychometric sophistication have thrown up more promising results. Summaries of relevant work by Vandenberg (1960, 1966, 1967), Vandenberg and Falkner (1965), Mittler (1971), Canter (1973) and Eaves and Young (1981) point to the following conclusions.

Vandenberg (1967), from a review of fifteen studies (Table 8) reports a significant genetic contribution to extraversion, when interpreted as a dimension of sociability, which he suggests may be related to schizophrenia. He comments

> We have encountered time and time again evidence of a strong heritability component in sociability (or extraversion) and its opposite, introversion.

Subsequent studies are strongly supportive (Gottesman, 1967; Eysenck, 1967, Jinks and Fulker, 1970; Eaves and Eysenck, 1975; Horn, Plomin and Rosenman, 1976; Eaves and Young, 1981).

The Eaves and Young (1981) study is probably the most extensive review of the relevant twin and family data, with samples varying in size from 1,000 to approximately 25,000. These authors conclude that the shared family environment plays no detectable role in creating the similarities in personality observed between relatives, but that genetic and random environmental factors contribute roughly equally to measured differences in these dimensions. They also comment on the growing body of evidence suggesting that genetic and environmental determinants of personality cannot be regarded as constant

TABLE 8. *Summary of findings from twin studies using personality questionnaires (adapted from Vandenberg, 1967)*

| Author | Questionnaire | Personality traits | | |
|---|---|---|---|---|
| | | Mz significantly more alike than Dz | Mz and Dz equally alike | Dz more alike than Mz |
| Carter, 1935 | Bernreuter | Self-sufficiency<br>Dominance<br>Self-confidence<br>Neuroticism | Introversion<br>Sociability | |
| Vandenberg, 1962 | Thurstone | Active<br>Sociable<br>Vigorous<br>Impulsive | Dominant<br>Stable<br>Reflective | |
| Cattell *et al.*, 1955<br>Vandenberg, 1962<br>Gottesman, 1963a | HSPQ | Neuroticism<br>Surgency<br>Will control<br>Energetic conformity<br>Cyclothymia v. schizothymia<br>Social introversion | Dominance<br>Cyclothymia<br>Tendermindedness<br>Nervous tension<br>Socialized morale | Impatient dominance |
| Gottesman, 1963b<br>Gottesman, 1965<br>Reznikoff and Honeyman, 1967 | MMPI | Depression<br>Psychasthenia<br>Psychopathic deviate<br>Schizophrenia | Paranoia<br>Hysteria<br>Hypochondriasis<br>Hypomania<br>Masculinity-femininity<br>Introversion<br>Test-taking attitude | |
| Wilde, 1964 | Amsterdam Biographical Questionnaire | Psychoneurotic complaints<br>Psychosomatic complaints<br>Masculinity-femininity | | |
| Vandenberg *et al.*, 1966 | Myers-Briggs | Introversion | | Thinking-feeling<br>Judgement-perception<br>Sensing-intuition |

TABLE 8. (Contd) Summary of findings from twin studies using personality questionnaires (adapted from Vandenberg, 1967)

| Author | Questionnaire | Personality traits | | |
|---|---|---|---|---|
| | | Mz significantly more alike than Dz | Mz and Dz equally alike | Dz more alike than Mz |
| **Vandenberg et al.,** 1966 | Stern Activity-Index factors | Intellectual interests<br>Closeness<br>Sensuousness<br>Self-assertion<br>Applied interests<br>Orderliness<br>Expressiveness-constraint<br>Egoism-diffidence<br>Educability | Audacity<br>Motivation<br>Submissiveness<br>Friendliness | Dependency needs |
| **Vandenberg et al.,** 1966 | Comrey | Achievement need<br>Shyness<br>Compulsion<br>Religious attitudes | Dependence<br>Self-control<br>Empathy<br>Welfare-state attitude<br>Punitive attitude<br>Neuroticism | Hostility<br>Ascendance |
| Scarr, 1966a | Gough ACL<br>Fels Behaviour<br>List | Need for affiliation<br>Friendliness<br>Social apprehension<br>Likeableness<br>Counselling readiness | | |

TABLE 8. (Contd) Summary of findings from twin studies using personality questionnaires (adapted from Vandenberg, 1967)

| Author | Questionnaire | Mz significantly more alike than Dz | Personality traits | |
|---|---|---|---|---|
| | | | Mz and Dz equally alike | Dz more alike than Mz |
| Gottesman, 1966 | CPI | Dominance<br>Sociability<br>Self-acceptance<br>Originality<br>Social presence<br>Good impression<br>Socialization<br>Psychological mindedness | Status capacity<br>Sense of wellbeing<br>Self-control<br>Tolerance<br>Communality<br>Responsibility<br>Achievement via independence<br>Intellectual efficiency<br>Femininity<br>Flexibility<br>Psychoneurotic | Achievement via conformance |
| Brunn et al., 1967 | Special questionnaire and interview | Sociability<br>Frequency of drinking<br>Average consumption | Need for achievement<br>Neuroticism<br>Aggressiveness<br>Lack of control | |

throughout life, and that samples far in excess of those normally employed are required for the resolution of such subtle components of human differences.

Insofar as anxiety/neuroticism is concerned, both Vandenberg (1967) and Mittler (1971) suggest that the evidence is less conclusive. Nonetheless, a considerable number of studies report a substantial genetic component in neuroticism (Eysenck and Prell, 1951; Gottesman, 1963; Honzik, 1964; Scarr, 1966a; Jinks and Fulker, 1970; Shields, 1971; Eaves, 1973; Eysenck and Eysenck, 1975; Eaves and Young, 1981).

Jinks and Fulker (1970), in their re-analysis of previously published personality and IQ data, claim that a very simple genetical model is adequate to account for the differences observed by Shields in his twin study of anxiety/neuroticism. Assortative mating and additive gene action are indicated, suggesting that the evolutionary history of this trait involves natural selection for an intermediate optimum. Either extreme of the trait is at a reproductive disadvantage. For extraversion, however, a simple model is apparently not adequate, as Dz twins appear to react against each other, producing negative correlations. On the other hand, Young, Eaves and Eysenck (1980) report that the data for both neuroticism and extraversion are explicable in terms of a simple model which assumes additive gene action, random mating, and environmental effects within families. These personality results conflict with IQ data, which show strong directional dominance for high expression, so that, during evolution, individuals with high IQs have a reproductive advantage.

Finally, there is some support for genetic contribution to factors of exuberance and psychomotor speed (Cattell and Warburton, 1967), surgency (Gottesman, 1963a), dominance/assertion/self-confidence versus timidity, and activity/vigour/surgency versus depression (Vandenberg, 1967), and to broad traits of person orientation (Gottesman, 1967) and social apprehension (Scarr, 1966b). Nichols (1966) and Gottesman (1966) report heritabilities for dimensions measured by the California Personality Inventory, separately for males and females. For males, only dominance and extraversion gave high values in both studies, and, for females, only self-control.

Recently, a number of authors have attempted to measure the separate components of extraversion, either by employing separate sociability and impulsivity sub-scales of Eysenck's E scale (Eysenck and Eysenck, 1963a), or first-order source traits from Cattell's 16 P-F, which correlate to generate second-order factors of anxiety, neuroticism and extraversion — or secondary process — which are in most respects similar to Eysenck's E and N dimensions.

Canter (1973), for example, on the assumption that the sociability and impulsivity sub-scales of extraversion might have different descriptive, nervous-typological and genetic characteristics, derived intra-class correlations for Mz and Dz twin pairs on Eysenck's E and N, sociability and impulsivity subscales, and Cattell's source traits and second-order factors. She reports no significant genetic contribution to either E or N for total group, nor for separate male and female groups. However, genetic factors appear to make a significant contribution to sociability, though this applied more to female than to male groups. The evidence for impulsivity was much less convincing. This fits well with Vandenberg's (1967) finding. In his review of eight studies concerned with measuring sociability in various forms, only one (Carter, 1933) failed to provide evidence for a significant genetic contribution, while for impulsivity, two studies reported positive results, and one a negative result. Horn, Plomin and Rosenman (1976) also report that impulse control, as measured by CPI, has low heritability. On the other hand Eaves (1973) and Eaves and Eysenck (1975) report that both variables have strong genetic bases.

Lack of genetic contribution to impulsivity, defined as lack of control over egotistical impulses, or inability to delay need gratification, is puzzling, since the drives involved (aggressive and sexual, for example) have strong genetic determination. Failure of socialisation could be due to poor conditionability, which is claimed to be biologically based (Eysenck, 1967) or equally to chronically high drive levels, so high as to resist any environmental pressures to conform. In general, the effect of such pressures, except in the relatively few cases diagnosed as high P or psychopathic, would be to regress high and low impulsive Ss to the mean, i.e. to reduce the variance of impulsivity, with consequent lower and less reliable intra-class correlations, on which heritability estimates are based, since uncontrolled chance effects, such as measurement error, now exercise undue influence. In these circumstances, it would hardly be surprising if different studies report conflicting heritability estimates. In this connection, of interest is Eysenck's most recent statement that the impulsivity content of extraversion differentiates high and low P Ss; psychoticism is claimed to have greater than 80% heritability (Eysenck and Eysenck, 1976).

The second-order 16 P-F factors of neuroticism/anxiety and extraversion confirmed the EPI results in Canter's (1973) study. For first-order factors, the passive vs. apprehensive trait showed significant genetic effects for males, and tough-tendermindedness and trusting vs. suspicious traits significant effects for females.

Data concerning genotypic contribution to Eysenck's third personality dimension, psychoticism, or P, has only recently become available. Using modern biometric heritability statistics such as Eaves' refinement of Jinks and Fulker's (1970) method, P is claimed to have a heritability of 46% by Eaves (1973) and an additive heritability figure of 81% by Eysenck and Eysenck (1976). This is similar to the estimate for schizophrenia reported by Gottesman and Shields (1973), which, under Eysenck's definition of P, lies in the same dimension. Eaves and Eysenck (1977) report that 51% of the variation in P from a sample of 544 pairs of twins is due to environmental differences within families, but that the greater part (77%) of such environmental variation is due to random effects which are unlikely to be controllable. Also of interest is the Young, Eaves and Eysenck (1980) claim that for the psychoticism dimension, mating is non-random.

Little is known about the genetic basis of aggressiveness and dominance in humans. Crook (1937) reports low intra-family correlations for the dominance sub-scale of the Bernreuter Test. Carter (1933), in a twin study, reports an intra-class correlations for Mz pairs on the same scale of 0.71, compared to 0.34 for Dz twins of like sex, and 0.18 for Dz pairs of unlike sex. Gottesman (1967) on a similar measure derived from Cattell's HSPQ, reports heritabilities of 74% for males, and 0% for females. Note, however, in the case of females, the probable effect of sex-role training. Canter's (1973) analysis of Fould's hostility scale scores showed significant differences between Mz and Dz pairs on measures of self-criticism and intropunitiveness. Similar results have been reported by Vandenberg et al. (1966), using the Comrey personality and attitude scales. They found a significant difference between female Mz and Dz twins on a measure of punitiveness. This suggests tentatively that certain hostility factors are in part determined by genetic factors. On the other hand, it is possible that these findings represent the contribution of heredity to more stable personality dimensions associated with hostility, such as E, N and P.

In this general context, of interest is the finding that there is no greater concordance between Mz and Dz twin pairs on a number of Rorschach variables (e.g. Schachter, 1952), which suggests that the Rorschach test, contrary to certain claims, measures largely environmental factors. Also of interest is an indication of a hereditary component in "cognitive style" (Gardner, 1964) measured by variables such as field dependence (also reported by Thurstone, Thurstone and Strandskov, 1955; Vandenberg, 1962), levelling-sharpening, tolerance for unrealistic experiences, and extensiveness of scanning, for example.

In interpreting the results of twin studies, an important consideration is whether genetic variance for personality traits is age-related. This possibility has been suggested by a number of authors (Cavalli-Sforza and Bodmer, 1971; Gottesman, 1974); apparently this occurs in the case of IQ, where heritability for adults is much lower than for children (Rao, Morton and Yee, 1974; Morton, 1975). Obviously, this is a critical question, since researchers normally make the assumption that heritability for a particular trait in one age zone — usually adolescence or young adulthood — for all practical purposes is a valid estimate of heritability for both younger and older groups, i.e. is "true" heritability.

Data on this issue are limited and equivocal. Some authors (e.g. Partanen, Bruun and Markkanen, 1966; Buss, Plomin and Willerman, 1973; Claridge, Canter and Hume, 1973; Willerman, 1973) have compared data from younger and older subsets of their samples, but results have been inconclusive. Similar outcomes have been reported by Reznikoff and Honeyman (1967) and Horn, Plomin and Rosenman, (1976), who adopted the alternative strategy of administering to one age twin sample a personality measure for which twin data already existed for a different age twin sample. In both cases, adult and adolescent samples were compared. The personality tests employed were the Minnesota Multiphasic Personality Iventory (MMPI) and the California Personality Inventory (CPI).

Dworkin *et al.* (1976, 1977) report retrospective, longitudinal studies of adult twins, originally studied 12 years earlier, in adolescence, by Gottesman (1963, 1966). MMPI and CPI were administered to 42 adult twin pairs from an original sample of 178 pairs. Different patterns of significant heritability were found in adolescence and adulthood (Table 9). The patterns of adolescence-to-adult change is not inconsistent with results previously reported, independently for adolescent (Gottesman, 1963; Nichols, 1966) and adult (Reznikoff and Honeyman, 1967; Horn, Plomin and Rosenman, 1976) samples, using the same personality scales. More recently, Young, Eaves and Eysenck (1980) report a cross-sectional family study involving a nucleus of twin families comprising twins and both parents. They report a marked inconsistency of gene action

TABLE 9. *Scales with significant F ratios or* $R_{Mz} > R_{Dz}$ *in adolescence and/or adulthood (from Dworkin* et al.*, 1976)*

| | Scales with significant $Fs$ or $R_{Mz} > R_{Dz}$ | | |
|---|---|---|---|
| Inventory | Adolescence only | Adulthood only | Adolescence & Adulthood |
| MMPI | depression, psychopathic deviance, paranoia, schizophrenia, masculinity-feminity[a], hysteria[b], social introversion[b] | mania, K, ego-strength | anxiety[a], dependency[a] |
| CPI | sociability, self-acceptance, tolerance[a], social presence[b], socialisation[b], achievement via independence[d], intellectual efficiency[d] | sense of well-being, psychological mindedness | dominance, self-control[a], good impression[b] |

[a]significant in subsample only
[b]significant in entire adolescent sample only
[c]significant in female sub-set of entire adolescent sample only
[d]significant in subsample and female sub-set of entire adolescent sample only

between juveniles and adults for extraversion, psychoticism and lie score, but consistency for the neuroticism dimension.

No plausible explanation for age changes of this sort has been offered. Gottesman (1974) suggests that change might be a function of gene regulation, genotype/environment interaction and correlation, and/or epistasis (interactions between genes at two or more loci). The effect could be attributed to changes in the phenotypic variance as a function of shifts in environmental priorities and demand characteristics as Ss grow older. Again, if the assumption is made that greater concordance for Mz than for Dz twins is due in part to greater environmental similarity for Mz twins, we might expect this effect to disappear when twins separate in adulthood. We might recall evidence, however, that Mz twins are sometimes more alike when separated in adulthood than they were in childhood (Canter, 1973). Consider also the implications of those data reporting age changes in heritability as early as from first to second year of life (Matheny, Dolin and Wilson, 1976). Data to hand do not point to one or other, or any combination of the factors mentioned above, as the agent responsible for the changes recorded.

*Summary*

Despite the difficulties inherent in the methodology of selective breeding, behaviour genetic studies with animal subjects strongly suggest that emotionality/fearfulness, aggression and affiliativeness, which account for a good deal of the total repertoire of instinctive behaviour, have strong genetic components. In many studies, almost complete homozygosis has been achieved in relatively few generations. It is well to note, however, that the generality of these findings (i.e. the extent to which genotypic differences in one type of learning, for example, generalise to all learning situations) has been questioned, with some justification. In addition, it is clear that expression of these drives can be inhibited or distorted by environmental factors, particularly early experience, although the reasons for this are not entirely clear. The complexities of gene-environment interaction are as yet little understood.

With human studies, we encounter different, but equally vexing problems. Twin methodology, which provides the principal da a source, poses a number of problems. Estimates of narrow heritability, by common consent, are not entirely satisfactory, and the more sophisticated methods of biometrical genetical analysis are seldom employed. In addition, a number of factors — mistaken zygosity of twins, similar experiential histories, for example — add to and substract from the intra-class correlations on which heritability estimates are based, in unknown ways. These factors, in combination, call into question the acceptability of much data derived from early twin studies.

Some more recent and more careful studies, however, point to a number of clear-cut conclusions, which complement the animal data. Apart from a range of sensory functions and sensori-motor skills, which are not highly relevant to the present discussion, there is evidence for strong genetic determination of psychophysiological dimensions such as tonic and phasic arousal levels, and autonomic balance, and, less strongly, for factors of arousal modulation, and motor activity.

Attempts to dimensionalise human neonatal behaviour have suggested a number of dimensions similar to those described above. While we cannot assume that these are genotypic, in some cases it seems unlikely that environment has exerted a major effect, in view of sample ages (2–6 months), although in other instances responsivity levels could have been markedly influenced by either pre- or postnatal effects, or both.

At the level of adult personality structure, there is good evidence for a genetic component in sociability, or affiliativeness. There is less clear evidence for genetic contribution to anxiety or neuroticism, although very recent findings are more supportive. Little work has been reported on aggression and dominance, but what there is supports the animal findings that aggression has a strong genetic component. There appears to be a significant genetic contribution to P, psychoticism, Eysenck's third personality dimension. Measures of field dependence and cognitive style, which have some variance in common, also appear to have some genetic basis. Elucidation of this point, however, awaits critical studies.

A good deal of evidence, therefore, suggests that much human behaviour which we regard as reflecting important personality characteristics has strong genetic components, although environment must provide an appropriate context for actualisation of this genetic potential. In prospect, however, since it is clear that genetic variation for quantitative characteristics of social importance is probably due to a large number of polymorphic genes, only a relatively few of which have been identified, possibilities for more accurate genetic prediction of such traits will be limited until more sophisticated methodological and statistical techniques are employed in psychogenetic studies.

CHAPTER 2

# Typological Models

## Introduction

VIEWS of Soviet psychologists on the nature of human personality have varied considerably over the past 50 years. Whereas in the 1930s and 1940s personality was reduced to the sum of acquired knowledge, abilities and habits, that is, to experience, and in the 1950s to temperament, understood as the expression of a particular type of nervous system, a more recent trend, particularly among social psychologists, has been to emphasise the interaction between temperament and environment. Soviet psychologists strongly emphasise the plasticity of the mind and the power of the social environment to modify and improve individual capacities, a view in sympathy with classic Marxist theory, which underlines the importance of activity in socio-historical contexts in determining personality. The significance of the interaction between natural (i.e. biological) capacities and social and personal experience, which dates from earliest ontogeny, and takes different forms in different developmental periods, is expressed in such comments as "Man's nature is the product of history" (Rubinsteyn, 1957). In the historical process of development, the social, in one way or another, mediates, modifies and develops Man's natural capacities, so that Man, while altering external nature, at the same time changes his own nature.

Even allowing this strong interactional emphasis, however, a start-point in the study of personality is still the typological or temperament model, which has undergone a number of revisions since the publication, by Pavlov, of his final statement on human typology in 1935. Typological theory postulates the existence, in a highly organised nervous system, of a number of orthogonal properties or parameters describing the dynamics of excitatory and inhibitory processes, which, in various combinations, are the neurophysiological bases of individual psychological differences. The theory thus utilises central nervous system constructs, rather than secondary morphological or body type features, as emphasised, for example, in the theories of Kretschmer and Sheldon. Modern typologists take a dimensional rather than categorical view of type, type being regarded as a unique profile of points along a number of continuous dimensions. While certain combinations are considered to be more probable than others, any and all combinations are possible, a view which departs from the original Pavlovian notion of a limited number of types.

## Nervous System Typology

During the period under discussion, we can detect a logical progression in the development of typological theory. Pavlov's initial ad hoc theorising, based on animal data, from which he attempted to infer behavioural types along classic Hippocratic lines, was followed by a systematic programme of research with human Ss, mainly by Teplov and Nebylitsyn, designed to improve the content and construct validity of typological indices, employing new methodologies and psychometric techniques such as factor analysis, which refined and broadened the typological model. Recent work has centred on the relationships between typological properties and aptitudes — memory, "giftedness", for example — and the integration and interpretation of the large body of loosely related empirical data, in line with theories of nervous system functioning based on the findings of modern neurophysiology.

### (a) Pavlovian Model

Perhaps the most outstanding feature of Pavlov's theoretical system was his observation of levels of analysis and reaction to the environment by higher organisms, levels which corresponded to phylogenetic and ontogenetic development. The most basic level he described as that of the innate, species-specific unconditional reflex — "unconditional" because of its dependable, almost certain elicitation by the adequate stimulus. This level Pavlov considered to be mediated by neural pathways laid down in the evolution of the species. Learning, or behavioural plasticity, with its obvious advantage to the animal's adaption and the species survival, occupies the second level. Sensory input, regularly paired with stimuli eliciting unconditional reactions, come to signal the imminence of the biologically important unconditional stimuli, so that the animal reacts with appropriate conditional reflexes prior to the advent of such stimuli. This second level Pavlov named the primary or first signalling system. The third, highest, level of analysis of the environment, and reaction to it, occurs only in man. This is the level of speech — the "signal of signals" — an abstract system of symbolic representation of primary signals and unconditional stimuli, described as the "second signal system".

Pavlov postulated that two processes mediated the observed reflexive behaviour — excitation, the basis of all afferent expression of responses to stimuli, and inhibition, the basis of suppression of all responses, as for example, during extinction of conditioned responses and in sleep. It should be noted, of course, that although Pavlov wrote as if he were observing real cortical processes, his nervous system model, as Gray (1968) comments, really corresponds to Hebb's (1955) "conceptual nervous system" model, employing hypothetical constructs rather than direct neurophysiological observations of central nervous system processes. "Real" nervous system processes would require much more detailed anatomical specification than was available in Pavlov's day. Even to-day the relationship of known anatomic and functional brain systems to observed behaviour is far too little explored to explain behaviour using a real nervous system model (Gray, 1968; McCleary, 1966). However, if we remember that "excitatory" and "inhibitory" processes in Pavlov's theorising represent "conceptual nervous system" processes, they are perfectly compatible with modern physiological conceptions, since they are, in fact, summary organising statements at the behavioural level.

Early in his study of nervous system processes by the conditional reflex method, Pavlov observed consistent individual differences in the behaviour of his experimental animals. Initially, he ascribed these to typological variations in temperament, following the Hippocratic doctrine of four body humours. At a very early stage, "types" were defined in terms of behavioural portraits — "calm", "excitable", "heroic", "cowardly", for example. These impression- istic indices, however, were soon replaced by experimental indices derived from performance in conditioning experiments, setting the stage for more objective investigation of individual features of nervous system functioning.

Pavlov proposed three properties of the nervous system — strength, equilibrium and mobility. Teplov (1956) has fully reviewed the development of Pavlov's thinking about nervous system typology, and it will suffice here to describe briefly the content of these properties as outlined in Pavlov's last important statement on individual differences in "General types of animal and human nervous system activity" (1935).

Pavlov assigned a central role to strength — the capacity of the cortical cells to endure "extraordinary tension in their activity" due to the action of "powerful stimuli" (Pavlov, 1955, p. 316). Equilibrium, the second property, referred to the relative predominance of excitation or inhibition insofar as strength and mobility were concerned. Mobility described the ability of the nervous processes to 'keep pace with ... fluctuations ... of the organism's external environment ... in compliance with the demands of external conditions, rapidly to recede, to give preference to one stimulus, to excitation before inhibition and vice-versa" (ibid., p. 316). Pavlov's final temperament model was based on individual variations along these typological dimensions (see Corson and Corson,1976).

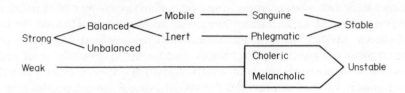

In this typological model, Pavlov made little reference to levels of environmental analysis. At no stage did he refer to the unconditional level of analysis, nor to the third level, the second signal system, as typologically descriptive constructs, except in a fleeting reference, in his speculations about human typology, to the distinction between "artistic" (relative predominance of first signal system activity) and "intellectual" types (relative predominance of second signal system activity). In general his typological theory involved only the conditional level of analysis.

### (b) "Middle" Version of the Typology

Studies of higher nervous activity in man were continued by Pavlov's students and contemporaries, Miasischev, Krasnogorskii, Ivanov-Smolenskii, Teplov and Merlin, and latterly by Nebylitsyn and Strelau. All these departed from the early Pavlovian typology in a number of ways. They all differed from Pavlov in assigning to the sub-cortex an important role in the development of CRs. Although Pavlov at times had acknowledged that unconditional reflexes may be organised and executed primarily at the sub-cortical level, he persisted in emphasising the cortical nature of conditioning.

Miasischev was perhaps the first to draw attention to properties of unconditional reflexes as individual features of higher nervous activity. The role of subcortical-cortical relationships was also noted by Krasnogorskii (1935, 1954) in his classification of Ss into "cortical", "subcortical", "balanced" and "energetic" types, which were considered to differ in levels of excitability in the cortex and subcortex. Ivanov-Smolenskii and his co-workers (Ivanov-Smolenskii, 1933, 1953; Kapustnik, 1930; Korotkin, 1930; Khozak, 1933; Kotliarevskii, 1933) using verbal, as well as various food and "orientating" reinforcements, classified four types of "closed-circuit" (conditional reflex) activity, using speed of formation as a criterion. Ivanov-Smolenskii was the first to assign to speed of CR formation the status of a separate property — in Pavlov's system this had been assigned either to balance (1928) or to strength (1935).

The mid-1950s marks a turning point in the development of typological theory. Renewed interest in the study of human, as distinct from animal, temperament, led to a search, initially by Teplov, and subsequently by Nebylitsyn, Merlin, Anen'ev and Klimov, for new methodologies, experimental techniques and response modes, and to the implementation of new techniques of measurement and analysis. Particularly important was the development of "involuntary" CR indices, i.e. measures claimed to be relatively free from influence by the second signal system, since a good deal of evidence attests that voluntary movements are the product of a long learning process affected through cortico-pyramidal connections (Sechenov, 1863; Luria, 1966a,b). A number of involuntary indices were developed, primarily the photochemical conditioned reflex (PCR) — i.e., the conditional reduction in light sensitivity using an auditory tone or red light as CS, and a disadapting flash of white light as US (Teplov, 1956; Maizel, 1956; Ravich-Shcherbo, 1956: Rozhdestvenskaya, 1959a) — and GSR (Yermolayeva-Tomina, 1963), vascular, EMG (Kolodnaya, 1963a), EGG (Nebylitsyn, 1961), visual phosphene (Nebylitsyn, 1960c), and motor (Leites, 1956; Nebylitsyn, 1960a,b) responses.

At this point in theoretical development, a number of problems emerged, and a considerable body of data relevant to these issues has been reported over the past 20 years.

The most urgent problem was that of defining more precisely the neurophysiological content of established properties such as excitatory strength, and of newer properties of uncertain status, such as lability and concentration, using new theoretical formulations which were being advanced around this time.

A number of factor analytic studies suggested that many indices thought to have common content did not load expected factors. For example, Melikhova (1964) reported that the reversal of CS signs, after the establishment of a stable CR, which was assumed to be a measure of mobility, loaded two factors which the author interpreted as equilibrium and strength of excitation, and did not intercorrelate with other mobility measures. No separate factor of mobility emerged from the analysis, although a number of so-called mobility measures were included in the test battery. Similar results have been reported in extensive studies by Rozhdestvenskaya et al. (1960) of indices thought to measure excitatory strength, by Borisova et al. (1963) in a study of mobility indices, and by Nebylitsyn (1965) in his report of methods for quick determination of nervous system properties. Paley (1968) reports that while seven of the variables he used to measure extinction with reinforcement and absolute threshold were correlated, and appeared to form a syndrome of nervous system strength, other "strength" measures failed to do so, nor did measures correlate across visual and auditory modalities, which contradicts the notion of a general factor of excitatory strength.

In addition, a number of failures of replication have been reported. For example, Teplov (1963) and Nebylitsyn (1966a) report highly significant correlations between measures of absolute threshold and excitatory strength, i.e., between lower absolute thresholds of sensation and thresholds of transmarginal inhibition, the stimulus intensity beyond which any increase in such intensity produces a response decrement. This finding led them to postulate that the effective range of responding in all systems is the same, different systems having different start-points, and thus different end-points, a fact which has important implications, particularly in the study of conditioning, which we shall discuss later (Chapter 11). However, Turovskaya (1963b), employing the same methodology, reports no correlation between these indices. Again, while Nebylitsyn (1960c) reports significant correlations between critical flicker fusion and visual sensitivity, which can be predicted within the framework of the law of strength, neither Turovskaya (1963b) nor Borisova et al. (1963) could replicate this finding. Nor could Golubeva (1964) replicate Borisova et al.'s (1963) finding of a positive relationship between EEG indices of lability and nervous system strength. She reports a highly significant, negative correlation.

The reasons for such inconsistencies and failures to replicate are not clear, particularly when we appreciate the methodological and technological sophistication practised in the laboratories of Teplov and Merlin, where a good deal of the experimental work was done. However, a number of possibilities come to mind. The first is that in some instances the response category may be too broad. For example, Golubeva (1973) reports that while photic driving in the beta-2 band (21–30 Hz) is a measure of lability, driving in the beta-1 band (14–20 Hz) indexes excitatory strength, the two properties being orthogonal. This may account for the discrepancy between the findings of Borisova et al. (1963) and Golubeva (1964) on the relationship between lability and excitatory strength, the difference lying in the frequency bands in which photic driving was measured.

Again, some of the contradictory data regarding mobility may be due to the type of reinforcement employed. The usual method of measuring mobility is for a stable discrimination to be established, following which the signs of CS+ and CS– are reversed. It has been reported that ease of reversal differs according to type of reinforcement, which, in turn, may affect the relationship of mobility to other properties. In mice, for example, the speed of development of motor CRs and the rate of reversal of CS sign are uncorrelated when food reinforcement is employed (Fedorov, 1961), but are significantly correlated ($p < 0.001$) when reinforcement is electric shock (Ermeev and Fedorov, 1963). The modality of the CS (Vatsuro, 1945, 1949) and response mode are probably additional sources of variance between and within species. Although data of this nature are not available from human Ss, there is no reason to doubt that similar constraints might exist at higher levels of nervous system functioning.

Finally, it is likely that orthogonality between properties varies between species, and, in humans, probably with age. For example, a considerable amount of data indicate that in man, rate of CR formation is uncorrelated with excitatory strength (e.g. Borisova *et al.*, 1963). However, significant correlations between these properties have been reported with other species — with cows, for example (Kokorina, 1964). It is entirely possible that the assumed structure of nervous system properties, based largely on animal data, will have to be revised in the light of studies of specifically human nervous system functioning.

There is also considerable evidence that the content of certain properties, and their interrelationships in humans, vary ontogenetically, and that developmental imbalance may be so pronounced that adult typological indices are inappropriate with children.

It is well established, for example, that nervous system strength (Chirkova, 1967) and external inhibition (Chudnovsky, 1963, 1967) are weak in young, particularly pre-school children, as is dynamism of excitation (Ravich-Shcherbo and Trifanova, 1967). This has an effect on assessments of balance according to strength and dynamism, since young children, as a group, appear to be more "excitable" or "weaker", because of general weakness of inhibition. Within groups, "true" balance can be camouflaged by developmental imbalance, and in particular cases, the validity of typological assessment, in any predictive sense, is unknown. Over time, however, excitatory and inhibitory strength, and presumably dynamism, become more equalised, within the limits of normal individual variability.

The same applies in the case of mobility. We might expect mobility of inhibition in young children to be relatively poor, since one aspect of the transformation — inhibition of the previously excitatory stimulus — should be difficult for young children, as it is for mentally defective Ss (Pevzner, 1959), because of inhibitory weakness.

Empirical data generally support these propositions. Leites (1972) for example, reports data from young children concerning positive and negative induction effects on reaction time (RT), which have been regarded as measures of mobility (Klimov, 1960) and of strength (Nebylitsyn, 1966a). With adults, the after-effect of both positive and negative stimuli results in increased RT latency (Klimov, 1967), a smaller but similar effect being shown by adolescent Ss (Polyakova, 1963a,b; Shchukin, 1963). With young children, however, the general finding is of decreased RT latency, indicating a general shift in balance of nervous processes towards excitation (Antonova, 1967; Leites, 1972). Antonova (1968) reports similar results from a longitudinal study. Again, while in adults there is strong evidence that mobility of excitation and of inhibition are uncorrelated (Nebylitsyn, 1965), Meyer (1963) reports a significant correlation between these indices in pre-school children. And while there is general agreement that there is little, if any, relationship between indices of balance, according to dynamism, and strength of excitation in adults (Nebylitsyn, 1966a), Utkina (1964) reports that these measures are significantly correlated in an adolescent sample. No immediate explanation for such findings suggests itself.

Part of the problem, of course, may simply be methodological. A good deal of the human data reported involve EEG measures, and it is known that EEG activity, such as frequency and regularity of the dominating rhythm, increases with age, which may be an important consideration when, for example, alpha-block or alpha-index is employed as a typological measure. The problem is somewhat more obdurate than this, however; Ravich-Shcherbo and Trifonova (1967) have reported that while frequency and index increase with age in the alpha and beta bands, in the theta band, these decrease.

Generally speaking, it is obvious that qualitative aspects of typological properties change in the course of development. Arguably, these changes are reciprocated by shifts in psychological functioning, if we accept the proposition that nervous system properties have an influence on mental functions such as memory (cf. pp. 316 ff). It may even be that in certain circumstances, developmental imbalance confers some benefit. For example, imbalance, insofar as dynamism of excitation is concerned, may account for the fact that, in certain instances, young children learn more quickly and more easily than adults.

Despite this, a considerable amount of research in Soviet laboratories over the last 20 years points to a number of fairly clear-cut conclusions, which, in effect, constitute a restructuring of the original Pavlovian typology.

1. Excitatory strength or endurance of cortical cells, measured by resistance to extinction with reinforcement (usually of PCR) is a consequence of low reactivity, and weakness a consequence of high reactivity or sensitivity of receptors and cortical projection areas (Teplov, 1956; Nebylitsyn, 1957a,b, 1959, 1960a, 1960b), rather than a function of amount of "excitable substances" in the cortical cells, a suggestion originally made by Pavlov. Nebylitsyn (1966a) reports a highly significant correlation ($r = 0.77, p < 0.001$) between lower absolute threshold and threshold of transmarginal inhibition, suggesting that the effective range of responding is similar in all reacting

systems, the difference between weak and strong systems lying in the minimal stimulus energy required to elicit a response. Caffeine has been shown to affect the weak, sensitive system more intensely than the strong system (Nebylitsyn, 1956, 1957a, 1957b, 1959; Nebylitsyn *et al.*, 1965; Rozhdestvenskaya, 1955).

Strength of the inhibitory process, which had received comparatively little attention, is now accorded the status of a separate property. Rozhdestvenskaya (1963) measured inhibitory strength by multiple repetition of differentiation, using the PCR method, and Yermolayeva-Tomina (1963) employed the same battering technique, i.e. multiple repetition of the differential stimulus, using GSR. As Teplov points out, however, there are some serious problems in measuring inhibitory strength, since the PCR method has obvious short-comings — it is often difficult to develop, is highly unstable and subject to spontaneous extinction — while the GSR is so intimately associated with orienting activity as to render conditioning interpretations very difficult (Nebylitsyn, 1966a; Teplov and Nebylitsyn, 1963).

2. The readiness with which the nervous system generates processes of excitation and inhibition in the formation of CRs is now referred to as dynamism of the nervous processes (Teplov and Nebylitsyn, 1963; Teplov and Nebylitsyn, 1966; Nebylitsyn, 1963b, 1966a, 1966b). This parameter had been variously interpreted by Pavlov, who at times considered it to reflect strength (1935), at other times balance of nervous processes (1928). Data from factor analytic studies (Nebylitsyn, 1963b; Rozhdestvenskaya *et al.*, 1960), however, showed this parameter to be orthogonal to strength.

Dynamism of excitation is defined by speed of formation of conditioned reflexes (PCR, GSR and EEG), and dynamism of inhibition by speed of formation of inhibitory reflexes — differentiations, conditioned inhibition (internal), delayed CRs and extinction of CRs. Various parameters of the EEG component (EEG alpha blocking) of the orienting reflex have been found to cluster together, and to reflect balance of the excitatory and inhibitory processes with respect to dynamism (Teplov and Nebylitsyn, 1966).

3. Although the construct validity of mobility has been the subject of considerable debate for a number of years, until the 1950s it had hardly advanced beyond the status of hypothetical construct.

According to Yakovleva (1938) Pavlov originally ascribed three meanings to the term "the speed at which they (the nervous processes) proceed, i.e. the speed with which they arise and then concentrate after the initial phase of irradiation ... their speed of disappearance when the stimulus has ceased to act ... the speed with which one process is replaced by the opposing process". In his subsequent writings, however, Pavlov emphasised the third meaning — "high mobility is the speed with which the organism, on external demand, yields, gives preference to one stimulation over another, substitutes stimulation for inhibition and vice-versa" (Pavlov, 1951–2, p. 268). A number of authors have suggested yet a fourth meaning — the speed of formation of both positive and negative CRs (Davidenkov, 1947).

Teplov (1956), in attempting to reconcile these different views, suggested that mobility refers to all aspects of nervous activity concerned with speed. However, in view of Ravich-Shcherbo's (1956) failure to find agreement between a number of mobility measures — e.g. speed of development of photochemical trace reflexes, visual after-image measures — he was forced to conclude that mobility is a compound rather than a unitary property (Teplov, 1963). Nevertheless, in general agreement with Krasuskii (1964) and Fedorov (1964), he suggested that alteration is a basic, if not the sole index of mobility — "in practice, mobility is that property of the nervous system which is characterised by alteration of stimulus signs" (Teplov, 1963, p. 37). Nebylitsyn (1966a), however, has expressed some dissent, noting that the alteration method confounds mobility with excitatory strength. In his typological model, mobility is an independent property orthogonal to nervous system strength and dynamism.

4. A good deal of the confusion about the content of mobility is due to the uncertain status of a relatively new property, lability, which has not been extensively investigated, but which clearly involves the speed with which the processes of excitation and inhibition arise in the nervous system.

The property is derived from Wedenskii's concept of functional lability, a term he used to describe the maximum number of impulses nervous tissue is able to produce per second in conformity with the rhythm of stimulations acting on the tissue. Wedenskii's arguments need not concern us here. It is sufficient to note that Ukhtomskii, who developed Wedenskii's original notion, defined lability as the speed with which a physiological structure is able to pass from a state of rest to a state of excitation, and vice versa, ready for the new response. Ukhtomskii (1937) and Golubeva and Trubnikova (1970) make the further comment that capacity to quickly arrest excitatory processes is directly proportional to S's capacity to differentiate perceptual input, a rather loose construct, which, however, may have something in common with the Western concept of perceptual and cognitive styles.

Teplov (1963) and Nebylitsyn (1973) define the property as the rapidity of nervous system activity, basically the speed with which the after-effect of an excitatory impulse is extinguished, and hence the speed with which one cycle of excitation is followed by another when a series of stimuli is presented. The most usual measures employed are the duration of the visual after-image (Ravich-Shcherbo, 1956), which was originally considered to be a measure of mobility, and efficiency of photic driving in the high frequency band (beta-2, 20–30 Hz) (Golubeva and Shvarts, 1965; Nebylitsyn *et al.,* 1965; Golubeva, 1973).

5. The property of concentration is an extremely tentative concept. Nebylitsyn (1973) reports that in a typical reaction time study, in which Ss were required to respond to signals of increasing intensity — a technique used in Teplov's laboratory to measure excitatory strength — consistent variations in response were observed after the influence of nervous system strength was partialled out by equating the intensity of the auditory signals in terms of individual Ss'auditory thresholds. This characteristic, which Nebylitsyn called concentration, was indexed by the duration and the sign of the inductive effects observed when double signal or choice RT methods were employed. No further confirmatory data have been reported (cf. Nebylitsyn, 1973).

6. The concept of equilibrium, or balance of nervous processes, is considered to be a secondary property derived from comparisons of levels of excitatory and inhibitory processes for any given property. Balance is the relative readiness with which the nervous system generates excitatory or inhibitory processes in the formation of CRs, in the speed of substituting one process for the other, and so on. A balance measure can be derived for all properties.

Theoretically, therefore, the Teplov-Nebylitsyn typology suggests a profile of 10 primary and 5 secondary properties — strength, dynamism, mobility, lability and concentration of both excitation and inhibition, and the equilibria between the excitatory and inhibitory processes for each property. These measures, taken in conjunction, are thought to provide a complete account of temperament.

### (c) Recent Extensions to Typological Theory

As mentioned previously, interest in typological research over the past 10 years has focused on the attempt to integrate the large body of empirical data accumulated, and to reconstruct the typological model more in compliance with modern theories of central nervous system functioning.

This interest has led to two important lines of enquiry, which are still proceeding, one concerned with the question of the "partial" nature of nervous system properties — a problem referred to by some of the earliest workers in this field (e.g. Ivanov-Smolenskii, 1935a; Krasnogorskii, 1935) — the other with a two-tier hypothesis concerning the structure of nervous system properties. It is postulated that while properties such as strength and mobility might provide a physiological basis for individual differences in aptitudes and various forms of mental activity, there are more general brain systems whose characteristic levels of activity determine individual differences in broad areas of personality functioning such as emotionality and activity level.

*1. The "partial" nature of nervous system properties*

The fact that inter-S variations in nervous activity do not necessarily correspond over different sensory and response systems had long been noted, as evidenced, for example, in the generally poor intra-S correlations between response thresholds across modalities. Data of this order led Teplov (1964) to comment that there exist "partial nervous system properties which characterise the functioning of separate regions of the cortex, as well as characteristics differentiating various sub-cortical centres." Thus the use of terms such as "strength", "nervous activity" "as if the entities which they denote are for the purposes of the theory ... undifferentiated wholes" (Gray, 1964c, p. 173) is unjustified. Nebylitsyn (1972) considered this problem to be one of the most important unresolved issues in the study of nervous system properties.

Evidence for partial variation in nervous activity over different brain regions has been reviewed by Teplov (1956), Umanskii (1961), Nebylitsyn (1966a,b, 1972) and Strelau (1972b). All agree on the use of certain parameters of the experimental situation — modality of the sensory stimulus employed as CS, or the two stimuli in an associated pair, type of US used as reinforcement, type of response elicited — as summary classification points of reference for data organisation. They differ only in the number of sub-headings used, and in the theoretical emphasis given to each category. Nebylitsyn (1966a) adopts perhaps the most theoretically logical summary device, noting simply the division between afferent and efferent brain structures, and further subdividing afferent structures into those concerned with conditional (CS) and unconditional (US) stimuli respectively.

i) UNCONDITIONAL AFFERENT

Teplov (1964, p. 123) notes that "typological properties of higher nervous activity turn out to be more or less different when they are based on different types of reinforcement". This was first indicated in Ivanov-Smolenskii's laboratory, where it was shown that the distributions of children among four types of "closing activity" differed according to the reinforcement used, whether alimentary, defensive, sexual or orienting/investigatory (Sinkevich, 1930; Korotkin, 1930; Kapustnik and Fadeeva, 1930; Khozak, 1933). Ivanov-Smolenskii (1935b) points out that "alongside the general synthetic type of higher nervous activity, or more correctly, closing activity, we may speak of a partial or component type, and in this way describe some separate function or other, for example, alimentary, defensive, sexual or orienting-investigatory, with respect to its relatively high excitability or its relatively greater or lesser readiness to acquire new conditioned connections" (1935b, p. 137, cited by Teplov, 1956, p. 123 of 1964 translation). As Teplov notes, Ivanov-Smolenskii's interpretation raises the important question of cortical-subcortical relationships, which was also the vinculum of Krasnorgorskii's (1935, 1954) typological system.

We should note that both these interpretations refer to that property now known as dynamism, and perhaps more importantly, that Ivanov-Smolenskii included the verbal (or second signal) system in his classification, distinguishing it with the term "general synthetic type of higher nervous activity". Ivanov-Smolenskii's later (1953) work was concerned mainly with this higher "synthetic" activity, measured by the motor method with verbal reinforcement, and he paid relatively little attention to the more basic unnconditional reflex systems. He considered the evolutionarily advanced and distinctively human activity of the cortical areas associated with speech and verbal association to be uniform within any subject insofar as basic nervous processes are concerned — "the higher and further from the instinctual foundation the conditioned connections are studied, the nearer we approach to an evaluation of the general or synthetic type" — whereas "the more primitive, the simpler and the older the unconditioned reflexes ... the more clearly the component or partial type stands out" (1935b, pp. 137–8, cited by Teplov, 1964, p. 123).

It is perhaps surprising, in view of the acknowledgement in early Soviet typological research of the importance of differential sensitivity to reinforcement type, and in view of the frequent references to this fact by Soviet typologists (cf. e.g. Nebylitsyn, 1966a), that little attempt has been made to incorporate this variable into the typological model. For example, Nebylitsyn, in his 1966(a) book, in which he reports most of the important research completed in his and Teplov's laboratories in the previous 20 years, although aware of the implications of the work of Western physiologists on reward and punishment centres in the mid-brain, cites as referent indices of dynamism of excitation (the speed of development of conditioned reflexes), the photo-chemical reflex (PCR), conditioned EEG reactions, and GSR conditioning. Reinforcement in all cases is sensory — a flash of light in the case of PCR, visual and auditory stimuli of moderate intensity in the case of EEG, and a muscular press, following Merlin's (1958a) methodology, in the case of GSR. In few, if any, cases, are "biologically significant" USs (pain, food, sexual) employed. Apart from Strelau's (1972b) study, almost all the critical research on individual features of human psychophysiological responses to different reinforcements has been reported by Western psychologists, notably by Gray (e.g. 1970; 1971a). A review and appreciation of this work will be postponed until the chapter on sources of variance in conditioning (Chapter 10).

ii) CONDITIONAL AFFERENT

We can point to variations in higher nervous activity across different CS modalities not only within, but also between species. Vatsuro and his co-workers have shown that chimpanzees form conditional reflexes several times faster to kinaesthetic than to visual CSs (Vatsuro, 1949), that in dogs mobility is higher for auditory than for visual stimuli (Vatsuro, 1945; Vatsuro and Shtodin, 1947; Vatsuro and Kolesnikov, 1948) whereas in monkeys, visual mobility is higher than auditory. On this evidence, Vatsuro (1949) formulated his "principle of leading afferentation" which states that specific analysers play a leading role in the organisation of higher nervous activity, these leading analysers differing from species to species. This principle, of course, does not allow for intra-species variation in the leading analyser role, since it is argued that type of leading or dominant analyser is a species-specific characteristic determined by problems particular to each species. Vatsuro pointed out that in man the separate analysers no longer have this particular significance, i.e. a species-specific leading role, which is now assumed by the second signal system, so that particular intra-individual analyser variations may make their influence felt as personality differences (Teplov, 1956; Nebylitsyn, 1966a).

Of course, leading afferentation can refer to any property. There are no intra-S data suggesting that any one modality is dominant for all properties within the individual. We might argue that the problem is irrelevant insofar as dynamism is concerned, since when biologically significant USs are employed, both the modality and intensity of the CS seem of lesser importance than when sensory conditioning is involved. The same applies to lability and concentration, so that the important properties, as far as this question is concerned, are strength and mobility. Possibly the critical issue is one of which property, as well as modality, has greater significance for survival of the species under consideration. For some, sensory acuity, visual or auditory, may be the important variable, for others, the capacity to adapt to changing environmental conditions. Evidence available to this point with human Ss refers mainly to strength-sensitivity and mobility.

Nebylitsyn (1957b) has reported that strength of nervous system differs according to the modality involved. Measurement of strength in auditory and visual modalities by three methods — the caffeine version of induction, extinction with reinforcement and the effects of caffeine on absolute thresholds — indicates that inter-S differences were consistent within, but not between modalities. Inter-analyser differences occurred in about one-quarter of the sample, these differences being large in about 12% of cases. A number of authors have reported inter-analyser differences in absolute sensitivity, particularly with auditory and visual thresholds (Wertheimer, 1955; Nebylitsyn, 1957b; Turovskaya, 1963b; Ippolotov, 1966, 1967; Paley et al., 1966; Strelau, 1972b; Mangan, 1974). Ippolotov and Mangan employed tactual, as well as visual and auditory threshold measurements. None of the correlations in any of the research reported was significant except the auditory/visual coefficient reported by Ippolotov. However, Rozhdestvenskaya, Golubeva and Yermolayeva-Tomina (1969a) report, from a factor analysis, evidence of a general factor of strength loading both visual and auditory threshold measurements, and two modality specific factors. This structure is also suggested by Rusalov (1972a).

Strelau (1972b) measured both auditory and visual mobility, employing a GSR measure, the US being electric shock, the CSs blue and green lights, and tones of 120 and 1200 Hz, respectively, with 10 Ss. He reports no significant correlations between auditory and visual mobility.

Mangan (1978c) reports no correlation between measures of auditory, visual and tactual mobility, using a simple RT procedure, the signal stimuli being blue and green lights, high and low tones, and air puffs differing in quality. While Strelau measured both mobility of excitation and of inhibition, Mangan measured only mobility of inhibition.

Strelau (1972b) also reports a relevant experiment concerned with dynamism, or speed of conditioning, using a GSR response, and a discrimination schedule, S+ and S− being different coloured lights, and reinforcement being shock, temperature (heat) and a strong voluntary muscle contraction. Agreement in type designation is reported in 2 from 36 cases. No agreement is reported in 44% of cases. Strelau reports, however, a significant relationship between speed of conditioning and the (subjectively rated) physiological intensity of the US.

iii) EFFERENT

Considerable evidence now attests that response as well as stimulus specification affects typological assessment. The earliest report of this is Arkangelskii's (1924) description of a dog in which "a marked difference was observed in the action of the inhibitory process according to whether motor or salivary responses were recorded" (Teplov, 1956, p. 123). The only similar study in the Soviet animal literature is that of Alekseeva (1953), involving two dogs, in which CS and US modalities were held constant, and nervous system properties measured using salivary and motor responses. Results were approximately similar for both response modes.

Data from human studies are equally sparse in the Soviet typological literature, which again is surprising in view of the importance attached to variations in nervous system properties attributable to response mediating structures by typologists such as Nebylitsyn (1966a).

Strelau (1972b) reports three experiments. In the first study, no correlation is reported between two strength measures, one involving increased RT latency under multiple repetition conditions, the other a measure derived from the Kraepelin test, which involves simple arithmetical problems performed over a considerable period (80 minutes). The second and third studies report no correlation between strength measures of EEG extinction with reinforcement and extinction with reinforcement of the PCR, and between two RT measures involving, on the one hand, vocal response, and on the other, key pressing.

Interest in western psychophysiology in this problem has suggested large individual differences in responsivity of different effector structures. The extensive work of Lacey and colleagues (Lacey, 1950; Lacey and Van Lehn, 1952; Lacey, Bateman and Van Lehn, 1953; Lacey and Lacey, 1958b, 1962) has established the principle of response specificity in individual reactions to stress. Lacey (1950) demonstrated that individuals in experimental stress situations exhibit idiosyncratically specific patterns of autonomic reactivity. For example, some Ss were maximally reactive in heart rate response, others in blood pressure, others in skin conductance, inter-correlations amongst different autonomic variables within Ss being low. This characteristic has become known as the principle of individual relative response specificity (Lacey and Lacey 1958b). These individual, highly specific, relative activation hierarchies are reliable upon immediate re-test (Lacey and Van Lehn, 1952) and across different stress episodes (Lacey, Bateman and Van Lehn, 1953; Lacey and Lacey, 1958). The principle of individual response specificity has received ample independent confirmation (Wenger et al., 1961; Schnore, 1959), and has been shown to apply to conditioned response phenomena (Cadoret, 1963).

The relevance of this principle to the question of partial typological characteristics is obvious. We should note, however, some limitations in the usefulness of the concept. Firstly, all the relevant studies have been confined to stress situations, and it is a good question whether the phenomenon also occurs in non-stressful situations, i.e. whether the individual reaction patterns are consistently reproducible from stress to more subjectively pleasant forms of emotional arousal. The responses of the autonomic system to aversive stimulation are relatively generalised and non-specific, thus allowing maximum scope for the operation of individual response specificity. In the case of appetitive stimulation, however, the response elicited may be specifically and functionally related to the reinforcing stimulus — i.e. salivation to food, genital vasocongestive responses to erotic stimuli. In these cases, although other autonomic responses probably occur, they are likely to be peripheral to the main function.

However, some stimulus-specificity has been reported even for autonomic responses in differing stress situations, or under conditions of high arousal. The notion that different stimuli can excite qualitatively different patterns of activation across multiple physiological systems has historical roots in William James's contention that different emotional states are differentially represented in patterns of peripheral physiological activity. Subsequent research has vindicated his position with respect to some of the stronger emotions at least. Ax's (1953) classic study differentiated fear and anger in humans according to patterns of activity in heart-rate, muscle tension, systolic and diastolic blood pressure, respiration, skin conductance, finger blood content and temperature. Schachter (1957) confirmed the results of differential patterning in a wider group of subjects, using pain as an emotional stimulus, as well as anger and fear. Sternbach (1960) differentiated startle patterns from those obtained by cold pressor stimulation, exercise and noradrenalin infusion, using a range of measures similar to those employed by Ax, except that muscle tension indices were replaced by measures of facial temperatures. Wolff and Wolff (1947) reported markedly different stomach reactions in a patient with a gastric fistula during anxiety as opposed to anger or resentment.

In addition, evidence has accumulated which suggests that even relatively mild non-emotional stimuli may have their own qualitatively distinctive patterns of peripheral physiological activation. The study reported by Davis, Buchwald and Frankman (1955), and subsequent studies by the same authors (Davis and Buchwald, 1957; Davis, 1957) differentiated patterns of activity in response to auditory, tactile and visual stimuli, using measures which included pressure pulse, volume pulse, balistocardiogram, heart-rate, vaso-motor tone, skin resistance, respiration and muscle action potentials. Some of the tactile stimuli, which included pressure, touch, cold and tickle, produced different reaction patterns, even within the same stimulus modality, as did certain visual (pictorial) stimuli of differing thematic content.

These considerations impose some restriction on any classification of the main variables directing the organisation of individual differences in nervous system properties over different stimulus and response systems. It would seem that with certain stimuli, mainly appetitive, the efferent and unconditional afferent variables should be subsumed under the same general class, since certain URs can only be elicited by specific USs. A natural constraint on response factors is imposed by the US — food in the mouth evokes salivation and chewing responses, not sexual responses. This US enforced constraint is in contrast with the relative independence from the US of the analysers carrying the CS. Generally speaking, any sensory stimulus may be coupled with any UR.[1] Thus, in most instances, the principal sources of variation are the CS and the US, the form and quality of the UR and CR being determined by the type of US employed.

This is not to deny, of course, the importance of concurrent autonomic responding during the action of the CR and UR. Possibly these systems enter

[1]There is evidence of a high degree of cue specificity in certain CS-US pairings; however, the data are somewhat controversial, and, in any event, are not of critical importance in the present context.

into concomitant CR relationships with external stimuli during every type of conditioned activity, as Gantt suggests (Gantt, 1943, 1944, 1953). However, in view of the non-specific nature of these autonomic responses, such patterns might be viewed more logically as a sub-dimension of the US–UR activation system, their significance in any situation probably varying (inversely) with the specificity of that system. Such an attitude would recognise the existence, simultaneously, of stimulus-response and individual response specificity. Clearly the non-specific subdimension would assume greatest significance in studies employing aversive reinforcement, generating pain and fear, and in studies involving conflict and neurotic behaviour (Gantt, 1942, 1943, 1944, 1953), and least significance where the reinforcement is appetitive.

## 2. Partial and general nervous system properties

Clearly, stimulus and response specificity are important sources of variance in typological assessment. These impose checks on the system, an important consideration if we accept the premise, derived from cybernetic analysis of self-regulating systems, that some limit must be placed on the interrelatedness between parts of the system for behaviour to be adaptive. Such constraint increases possibilities for compensation, and thus produces a reserve of plasticity.

This concept of self-regulation in nervous activity, effected largely through afferent-efferent synthesis, is a classic formulation in Soviet physiology, dating back to Sechenov, and explicitly acknowledged by a number of authors. As early as 1928, for example, Bernstein formulated his notion of sensory correction, which anticipates the modern concept of feedback. He substituted the concept of reflex circle for reflex arc, closed at its periphery, to emphasise the fact that afferent signals, as feedback from organs performing the action, are a control mechanism for correcting such action. At the same time, within the mainstream of Pavlovian theory of higher nervous activity, Anokhin was also emphasising the role of self-regulation in reflexive activity, thus anticipating the ideas of psychological cybernetics. His concept of "acceptor of action", as one of the principal functional elements in the overall activity of the brain, emphasised the interaction of central activating and effector structures in generating programmes of action for goal-directed behaviour. This theoretical development broadened and complemented the notion that neural mechanisms are the ultimate foundations of behavioural acts (Anokhin, 1969).

In a very broad sense, this concept has greatly influenced the development of typological theory, suggesting the possibility of general, unitary, neurophysiological dimensions regulating and integrating the functioning of the brain as a whole, in addition to partial properties characterising particular regions of the cortex. This division was first proposed by Teplov (1956, 1964) who suggested that general properties might underlie human temperament (personality), while partial properties are of relevance in the case of special aptitudes. If this turns out to be the case, a critical question is whether there is one type of strength, for example, which characterises particular centres, and is the basis for certain sensory-cognitive and mental functioning, distinct from strength treated as a general property, which is involved in every action, and thus should be considered a dimension of temperament.

There are, of course, a number of possibilities, and different theorists have adopted different views. We might simply assume a general type, concerning, for example, strength or mobility or dynamism, which reflects the activity of both the cortex and the sub-cortical centres, a view compatible with Pavlov's original theorising. In such a case, sources of variance, which account for the data inconsistencies reported, would be S's motivation, his cortical tonus, and so on. Secondly, we might argue that there exist only special properties — we are referring, in this case, to the strength, mobility, dynamism of the excitatory processes in the centre to which the stimulus is addressed, or where responses are registered. A question here, however, is how far we should extend this notion of specificity. A sobering thought is Nebylitsyn *et al*.'s (1965) suggestion that mobility, *vis-à-vis* night and day vision, could have different neurophysiological content!

Again, possibly there are special properties which characterise particular nerve centres, and, in addition, dominant centres which are of central importance in the behaviour of the individual. This is, in fact, an extension of Vatsuro's concept of dominant or leading afferentation. Finally, we might argue that there are general properties, plus special properties which are, in all essential respects, independent. This is the most commonly accepted view amongst present-day typologists. Strelau (1972b), for example, suggests that the general property has a functional, integrative significance, the partial properties characterising sensory or response systems. At simple behavioural (e.g. reflexive) levels, partial properties come into play because only one or two centres may be involved. When behaviour is "biologically significant", however, in that it is concerned with S's survival or adaptation, activity probably involves a number of additional centres, and a general property is more likely to be involved.

The most explicit theory of general and partial nervous system properties, and of their integration in complex behavioural repertoires, is that of Nebylitsyn (1966a, 1972, 1973). In his earliest statement (1966a) on this issue, he made the very general suggestion that nervous system properties might be determined by a synthesis of the functional characteristics of the cortex and subcortex, in which the general activating reticular mechanisms play an important role. In his subsequent theorising (1972, 1973), however, he has attempted to describe more precisely the neurophysiological substrate of general properties.

He begins with the premise that the surface of the cortex can be divided into two large regions, the posterior or retro-central region (including parietal, occipital and temporal lobes) and the anterior or antero-central region (the frontal lobes), which differ structurally, morphologically and functionally. The posterior cortex is concerned with stimulus processing — stimulus discrimination, analysis and synthesis, and heteromodal interaction — these functions being integrated by a complex of interneuronal connections, which serve as the morphological basis for intra-cortical projections and inter-analyser associations. The posterior cortex represents an intra-cerebral system which transforms sensory data into images of external reality within the brain, thus serving as the neurophysiological bases of perception, concepts, memory traces, i.e. of all those aspects of mental functioning which ultimately depend on sensory mechanisms (Nebylitsyn, 1972).

On the other hand, the complex of antero-central formations is concerned with higher forms of environmental interaction. These, particularly the pre-central (motor), pre-frontal and mediobasal zones, mediate afferent, and especially efferent connections with the analysers, and with the structures of the paleocortex, thalamus, hypothalamus and the BSRF. They are, therefore, intimately involved in a range of functioning from the comparatively primitive (e.g. homeostatic equilibrium) to complex activities such as motivation, the initiation and control of emotional excitement, and thus constitute the morphological substrate of temperament. There is also evidence, however, that the most anterior pre-frontal regions mediate the programming and regulation of motor acts, as components of conscious goal-directed behaviour (Anokhin, 1949; Luria, 1963b, 1966a), integrating information from the receptors and the thalamus through afferent connections, and exerting efferent control over structures in the posterior cortex, the limbic brain and the sub-cortex (Nauta, 1964; Zambrzhitsky, 1959). In addition, the frontal lobes have an important bearing on certain aspects of problem solving (Luria and Tsvethova, 1966; Livanov et al., 1966a,b; Giannitropany, 1966), such that the whole strategy of an intellectual, as distinct from a sensory act, is organised by the anterior regions of the brain.

On this evidence, Nebylitsyn (1972) considers that the frontal cortex, and its associated structures, constitute a single brain apparatus, a regulatory system involved in the planning and regulation of behaviour, i.e. concerned with drives and motivation, attention, intelligent planning, intellectual giftedness. As such, it is a central component of higher forms of human behaviour and, therefore, personality. In addition, he notes that the regulatory system might also be closely connected with the mechanisms of verbal regulation, of vigilance, mental fatigue and tension, which are important factors in work efficiency.

By contrast, the functional properties of the perceptual (posterior) system relate only to specific aspects of individuality, i.e. to those involving sensory mechanisms and their psychological projections. For example, certain combinations of nervous system properties in the visual system might relate to visual memory, but have little relevance to behaviour as a whole, and cannot therefore be considered as the neurophysiological basis of personality.

It seems fair to comment, however, that Nebylitsyn offers little empirical support for these propositions, particularly for the postulated relationship between partial/general properties and specific/general intellectual operations. Initially the problem is a definitional one. For the sake of argument, ought we to include in the general intellectual category S's basic problem-solving strategies? Such strategies, conventionally labelled speed or tempo, persistence, carefulness, for example, have been identified by Western psychometricians (e.g. Eysenck, 1947; Mangan, 1959) and have been regarded as work-attitude, temperament factors. In line with Nebylitsyn's notion that the general property is concerned with "intelligent planning", one would have to answer "yes". However, Kalyutkin, Zyryanova and Sukhobskaya (1972) report that these problem-solving strategies are significantly correlated with partial properties of strength and dynamism. Again, would we regard incidental and intentional recall as involving general or specific levels of intellectual functioning? There is evidence that efficiency of recall is related to the partial property of lability (Golubeva, 1972b; Paley et al., 1966). The question really is — how specific is specific?

In his last (1973) paper, Nebylitsyn attempted to expand his theory of general nervous system properties based on morphological structures located in the anterior cortex, which play an overall purposive, goal-directive and integrating role in organising and integrating behaviour. Empirical support derives from EEG data concerning amplitude and frequency, and the periodicity and stability of EEG patterns obtained from occipital and frontal cortical sites. Factor analysis revealed that, while amplitude and frequency factors could be equally well measured from both sites, independent periodicity and stability factors emerged at frontal and occipital sites. On this basis, Nebylitsyn implies mutually independent physiological factors, each with its own particular operational characteristics. Of importance is the fact that EEG amplitude and frequency parameters were common to the entire cortex, while the stability and periodicity factors neatly subdivided into two factors. Nebylitsyn (1973) suggests that EEG measures of stability and periodicity are indices of nervous system strength, the work capacity of the neuronal populations producing a given brain wave, which reflects the content of the two most important components of the strength syndrome — the effect of repeated stimulation of moderate load, leading to exhaustion, and the action of distracting stimuli.

In this paper, Nebylitsyn (1973) identified the two main parameters of temperament — general level of activity and emotionality, which he considers to account for almost all the variance of temperament. His description of level of activity has something in common with Eysenck's description of extraversion (E); the equivalence of emotionality and neuroticism (N) hardly warrants comment.

Nebylitsyn identifies two discrete structures in this cerebral regulatory system which mediate temperamental characteristics. The mean level of excitation in the reverberating circuits in the fronto-reticular system, which includes the frontal section of the cortex, together with the reticular formation of the mid-brain and certain other sub-cortical structures, determines the tempo, amount and variety of the individual's actions and movements. The reticular formation is the generator of excitation, while the frontal section acts as the modulator, capable of both dampening and stimulating the initial activity of the reticular structures by means of a feedback system. The brain system which is physiologically relevant to emotionality, the second temperament dimension, is the limbic structure, as the primary generator of emotion, and the frontal section of the cortex, particularly the mediobasal and orbital sections, which acts as the modulator of emotional expression.

More recently, Simonov (1979) identifies four brain structures which he considers to be involved in emotionality and in the organisation of goal-directed behaviour. The frontal parts of the neo-cortex mediate orientation to signals with high probability of reinforcement, the hypothalamus the satisfaction of dominant need. The hippocampus is claimed to mediate reactions to signals of low probability events, while the amygdala is concerned with the creation of a "dynamic balance" between competing needs and motivations.

Nebylitsyn's theory, therefore, postulates a vertical organisation of morphofunctional brain systems — the brain analysers, including the sensory projection areas, CS and afferent structures, which determine individual variations in aptitudes and abilities; and two general brain systems, the fronto-reticular and the fronto-limbic, whose rostral sections are located in the antecerebral or frontal cortex, and whose general activity level locates individuals along the two most important temperament dimensions, activity level and emotionality. The dynamics of nervous processes in each of these systems is determined by the same set of properties — strength, dynamism, mobility, lability and concentration — which vary in different systems, and which are the neurophysiological bases of individual differences in aptitudes or abilities and temperament.

He suggests that these systems have a multi-stratified structure. At lower levels of organisation, distinctive features of the system are the automatic, probably genetically fixed, processes of self-regulation, which ensure smooth efficient functioning. At higher levels, we note the conscious, voluntary nature of these processes, which are executed with the aid of speech and "verbal thought". Take, for example, the case of memory. Lower operational levels may be represented by elementary processing and coding of information, which may occur without conscious participation, and which are reflected in phenomena such as reminiscence. On the other hand, higher levels are characterised by voluntary, conscious, goal-directed selective remembering, which is subject to verbal regulation. Nebylitsyn suggests that analogous multilevel operations can be observed in psychological categories such as perception, attention, emotion, for example. Importantly, properties of the nervous system will be differently expressed at these different levels. There is no reason to expect, for example, that dynamism will have the same content at the level of the individual neuron as at higher levels, which are created when neurons aggregate to become part of an integrated structure.

However, while Nebylitsyn's theorising is plausible enough, and is not at variance with modern concepts of neurophysiology, he can offer little firm empirical support for his propositions. The only evidence he cites for general brain systems mediating temperamental dimensions is his report that Ss who are very active physically (e.g. in terms of tempo, tapping rhythms) tend to have more prominent high frequency components in frontal EEG leads (in the beta-2 range, 20–30 Hz). Since a number of authors have suggested that high frequency EEG rhythms are produced by ascending activating influences from reticular structures to the cortex, he proposes that fronto-reticular interaction is the critical factor underlying individual differences in activity level. No evidence relating to the postulated fronto-limbic brain system is offered.

### Genetic Studies of Nervous System Properties

An obvious question arises of the extent of genetic contribution to nervous system properties. Pavlov (1928) clearly assumed a high degree of determination: "Temperament ... is the general basic character of the nervous system". And since the basic character of the nervous system was for him represented in the complex of nervous system properties, which are genetically coded, temperament constitutes the genotype.

Teplov (1956), on the other hand, while recognising temperament as the psychological expression of nervous system properties, so that the latter can be considered the substrate of temperament, expressed some doubt about the simple equating of the two. He considered that while nervous system properties might be "natural" properties, they are not necessarily inherited, since they might be influenced by pre- and postnatal factors, particularly intra-uterine influences, and by the results of early social experience. Teplov was conscious of the latter possibility in view of the evidence from Pavlov's laboratories that strong nervous system types raised in social isolation showed marked passive defensive reflexes (timidity), which had previously been considered a behavioural index of the inhibitory or 'weak' type of dog. More recent evidence is strongly supportive. Hecht *et al.* (1976), for example, report that rats raised in isolation show reduced resistance to stress, and Burakova (1976) that dogs raised in isolation from the age of 3 months evince slow and unstable development of CRs. Since early experience can disguise the real strength of the nervous system, Teplov refrained from the use of the term "genotype".

According to Teplov, the interaction of temperament and early environment, which he describes as "character", with aptitudes, constitutes personality. Typological differences underlie individual psychological differences in both character and aptitude. Nervous system properties, however, are not properties of individuality, *per se.* They are physiological, not psychological entities. And while, physiologically speaking, they have unique functional significance, they have multiple psychological significance, since, in the course of development, they enter into the formation and functioning of systems of conditioned responses which define psychological parameters of individuality.

*Selective Breeding Experiments*

The problem, of course, could be resolved by direct test for heritability of temperament dimensions and nervous system properties, using selective breeding techniques. However, although concern with behavioural genetics has a long history in the Soviet Union, surprisingly little material on this issue is available either in original or in translation. One of the few publications is by Fedorov: *Genetika Povedeniya* (*Behaviour Genetics*) (1969), which is a collection of original research, rather than a comprehensive survey of the field. Studies report inheritance of "emotionality" and susceptibility to audiogenic seizure, which parallel Western findings, and, of more immediate interest in the present context, studies of the inheritance of the nervous system properties of mobility and strength.

The data on mobility are of particular interest. The task was right and left turning in a T-maze to sound and light respectively, reinforcement being electric shock. After establishment of a stable CR, signal values were reversed. The number of trials to achieve criterion was taken as the index of mobility. This is the transformation measure, which we shall discuss in greater detail in Chapter 8.

Two pure lines of white rats were employed as Ss, the Wistar line, and the Krushinskii-Molodkina line. Number of trials to achieve transformation differed significantly between strains, the Wistar line being considerably slower (N trials 28.1 versus 17.4). Cross-breeding techniques established that mobility is inherited, low mobility being dominant. From other data reported, it appears that the Wistar strain shows high strength of nervous system, in addition to low mobility.

In this connection, of interest is work reported on the genetic basis of stress tolerance. Yumatov and Sotselyas (1979), for example, report that resistance to cardio-vascular disturbance as a result of prolonged immobilisation stress differs between different strains of rats, suggesting a genetic basis. At the same time, other studies have shown that an animal's nervous system strength determines individual differences in a wide range of EEG and somatic disturbances to stress, whether this is induced by immobilisation (Kolomeytseva, 1979) or hypoxia (Troshikhin and Nosar, 1976). These observations fit the human data on stress tolerance.

*Twin Studies*

Some genetic studies of mental processes and nervous system functioning were carried out in the 1930s in the Institute of Medical Genetics in Moscow (cf. Luira, 1978a), but in the mid-1930s such work was proscribed by the Central Committee of the Communist party. It is only recently that human genetic studies have again become respectable in the Soviet Union.

Thus, only limited data are available on heritability of nervous system properties and of higher-order mental functioning, using standard twin study methodology. Insofar as typological properties are concerned, perhaps the most informative data are those reported in the series of investigations described in the biennial publication of the Institute of Psychology, Academy of Pedagogical Sciences, Moscow (1978), the Institute in which Teplov and Nebylitsyn carried out their earlier investigations. These studies extend some initial work on heritability of excitatory strength and mobility reported by Shlyakhta (1972), Vasiletz (1974), Ravich-Shcherbo (1974) and El'kin and Khoruzheva (1975), and take account of a number of previously disregarded methodological and statistical problems (cf. Dubinin, 1971). In the section *Problems in genetic psychophysiology*, four studies are reported from Ravich-Shcherbo's group dealing with the properties of excitatory strength, mobility, lability and dynamism, the nervous system properties which have been most carefully researched by the Moscow group.

The first study is that of Shlyakhta and Panteleyeva, in which excitatory strength was measured by three classic indices — the EEG version of extinction with reinforcement, the reaction time (RT) method, and photic driving to low frequency stimuli. Summary data for the RT and photic driving indices are shown in Tables 10 and 11. It is worth noting that in the 33–56 year group, the twins had lived apart for at least 10 years, had families, and, in most cases, worked in different professions.

From the data reported, there is little evidence for genetic contribution to nervous system strength measured by the EEG variant of extinction with reinforcement. Correlations for Mz twins differ little, if at all, from those for Dz twins. The authors, however, point to a number of methodological problems, previously referred to by Shlyakhta (1975), which may account for failure of prediction.

For the photic driving and RT indices, however, there is clear evidence of considerable genetic involvement, particularly for the RT measure. Also of

TABLE 10. *Intra-class correlations for twin pairs
(14–16 years) using the photic driving index
(from Shlyakhta and Panteleyeva, 1978)*
$(**p<0.025, ***p<0.01)$

| Pairs | N | 4 imp/sec | 5 imp/sec | 6 imp/sec |
|-------|----|-----------|-----------|-----------|
| MZ | 19 | .69 | .64 | .53 |
| DZ | 22 | .24 | −.11 | .24 |
| NR | 19 | −.05 | −.24 | .01 |
| F |  | 2.45** | 3.08*** | 1.62 |

TABLE 11. *Intra-class correlations for
twin pairs in three age ranges using an
RT index (from Shlyakhta and
Panteleyeva, 1978)* $(***p<.01)$

| Age | Pairs | N | r | F |
|-----|-------|----|------|----------|
| 8–11 | Mz | 20 | .91 |  |
|  | Dz | 20 | −.14 | 12.67*** |
|  | NR | 24 | −.13 |  |
| 13–16 | Mz | 20 | .67 |  |
|  | Dz | 20 | .41 | 1.79 |
|  | NR | 22 | −.28 |  |
| 33–56 | Mz | 23 | .94 |  |
|  | Dz | 20 | .09 | 15.17*** |
|  | NR | 20 | .11 |  |

interest is the substantially higher correlation for the younger, compared with the older children, although the correlation is greatest for the oldest group.

The second study, reported by Vasiletz, concerns mobility, measured by transformation, sensory after-effects, and by personal tempo, three well-verified methods for measuring mobility. A choice RT paradigm was employed, offering three alternatives, stimuli being randomly presented in a long sequence with random ISIs. This method has been used by Borisova (1969), and is an adaptation of a technique originally suggested by Khil'chenko. An earlier study by Panteleyeva (1977), using a similar (RT) technique for measuring transformation with 20 Mz and 20 Dz pairs, had reported Mz pairs to be more similar in total number of errors, anticipatory EMGs, and RT latencies.

Vasiletz's summary data are presented in Table 12.

Vasiletz reports little correlation between the indices of mobility, which raises the question of whether we can assume a unitary dimension of mobility. From the data presented (Table 12), significant F ratios are reported for three of the four error-scored transformation measures (indices 13, 14 and 16) for the 33–55 year group, for the four "general" transformation measures (indices 17–20), for the 7–11 year group, such measures presumably combining both the positive transformation (indices 1–12) and the error scores, and for the tempo measure (index 25) for both groups.

It is difficult to unequivocally interpret these data. Lack of support for a unitary dimension of mobility is one problem. The tempo score, which, for both groups, shows strong genetic determination, is now regarded more as a measure of lability. On the other hand, the F ratios for "general" transformation mobility for the 7–11 year group — arguably the most valid mobility measure — indicate a high level of genetic involvement, although there is some evidence (cf. Klonowicz, 1979) that, with age, environmental factors (e.g. training, experience) may exert an increasingly greater influence on transformation ability.

In the third contribution, Panteleyeva and Shlyakhta report a twin study of lability, lability being defined as the speed of initiation and termination of excitation (Teplov, 1963; Borisova et al, 1963; Turovskaya, 1963b; Nebylitsyn, 1966a) and thus distinct from transformation mobility. Lability measures were critical flicker fusion (CFF), photic driving to high frequency stimuli, and measures of optimal and maximal tempo, derived from the Tenning test. The latter, which purports to measure "psychical tempo", has been regarded by a number of authors (Belyaeva-Exemplyaskaya, 1961; Geon, 1961; Latmarizova, 1947) as measuring mobility, but by later authors as measuring strength and lability (Weinstein and Zhiv, 1973) or lability (Lepikhova, 1974) of nervous processes.

TABLE 12. Intra-class correlations and F ratios for twin pairs in two age groups on mobility scores (*p < 0.05, **p < 0.01) (from Vasiletz, 1978)

| Age | Pairs | N | Transformation index | | | | | | | | | | | | Transfor. errors | | | | "General" transfor. | | | | After-effects | | | | Tempo |
|---|---|---|---|---|---|---|---|---|---|---|---|---|---|---|---|---|---|---|---|---|---|---|---|---|---|---|---|
| | | | 1 | 2 | 3 | 4 | 5 | 6 | 7 | 8 | 9 | 10 | 11 | 12 | 13 | 14 | 15 | 16 | 17 | 18 | 19 | 20 | 21 | 22 | 23 | 24 | 25 |
| 7-11 | Mz | 20 | .27 | .29 | .17 | .18 | .36 | .32 | -.14 | -.11 | -.13 | -.26 | .35 | -.13 | .10 | .54* | .06 | .07 | .16 | .40 | .01 | .27 | .09 | .16 | .03 | -.05 | .68* |
| | Dz | 20 | .06 | .36 | .14 | .28 | .39 | .48* | .24 | .07 | .07 | -.22 | -.22 | -.05 | -.62* | .04 | .21 | .03 | .42 | .30 | .03 | -.19 | .46* | -.12 | -.36 | -.18 | .03 |
| F ratios | | | 0.8 | 0.7 | 1.3 | 0.8 | 0.9 | 0.3 | 0.2 | 0.4 | 0.5 | 0.5 | 1.1 | 0.7 | 0.4 | 3.0** | 1.0 | 1.7 | 2.6* | 4.1** | 5.9** | 5.2** | 0.3 | 0.7 | 0.9 | 1.0 | 4.1* |
| 33-55 | Mz | 20 | .28 | .27 | .32 | -.05 | .00 | -.11 | -.16 | .29 | .10 | -.09 | -.03 | -.05 | .22 | .24 | .27 | -.02 | .49* | .38 | .08 | .21 | .06 | .38 | .31 | .18 | .90 |
| | Dz | 20 | -.02 | .21 | .24 | .46* | .18 | .35 | -.22 | -.08 | -.25 | -.10 | -.10 | -.10 | -.06 | -.05 | .14 | .06 | .01 | -.14 | .49* | -.13 | -.04 | -.21 | -.43* | -.04 | -.16 |
| F ratios | | | 1.5 | 0.9 | 0.7 | 0.4 | 0.2 | 1.7 | 1.3 | 1.1 | 1.1 | 1.9 | 0.6 | 1.1 | 2.2* | 3.5** | 1.6 | 3.0** | 1.3 | 1.0 | 1.6 | 1.7 | 1.0 | 3.0** | 1.0 | 0.8 | 9.7** |

Mobility indices

Results are shown in Tables 13a and 13b.

CFF appears to have strong genetic components in the three age groups. The same is true for photic driving and tempo measures for the 13–16 year group. However, the authors suggest, in line with previous findings, that maximum tempo is probably not a measure of either mobility or lability, the measure being more closely linked with strength of the nervous system (Vasiletz, 1974).

The fourth study, reported by Shibarovskaya, concerns dynamism of excitation and of inhibition, i.e. the speed of formation and extinction of conditional responses, using a broad range of EEG measures. Results are summarised in Tables 14, 15 and 16. Table 14 presents resting EEG data for alpha-amplitude and index, and for frequency and summed energy of rhythms throughout the normal EEG range. Of particular interest are the significant F ratios for alpha amplitude and index, alpha frequency and summed energy in the alpha band. These data provide evidence for genetic involvement in certain

TABLE 13a. *Intra-class correlations and F ratios for CFF in the three age groups (from Panteleyeva & Shlyakhta, 1978)* $(***p<0.01, **p<0.025)$

| Age | Pairs | N | CFF | F |
|-----|-------|-----|------|--------|
| 9–11 | Mz | 20 | .78 | |
| | Dz | 20 | .35 | 2.95** |
| | NR | 24 | .12 | |
| 13–16 | Mz | 20 | .84 | |
| | Dz | 22 | −.01 | 6.3*** |
| | NR | 22 | −.14 | |
| 35–86 | Mz | 23 | .72 | |
| | Dz | 20 | −.30 | 4.64*** |
| | NR | 20 | .15 | |

TABLE 13b. *Intra-class correlations and F ratios for photic driving and Tenning Scores in the 13–16 year group (from Panteleyeva & Shlyakhta, 1978)* $(***p<0.01, *p<0.05)$

| Age | Pairs | N | Photic Driving imp/sec | | | Tenning | |
|-----|-------|-----|------|------|------|--------------|--------------|
| | | | 18 | 25 | 30 | $T_{opt.}$ | $T_{max.}$ |
| 13–16 | Mz | 20 | .81 | .60 | .30 | .78 | .69 |
| | Dz | 22 | .24 | .29 | .23 | .15 | .25 |
| F | | | 4.0*** | 1.78 | 1.1 | 3.86*** | 2.42* |

TABLE 14. *Intra-pair correlations for 30 Mz and 26 Dz pairs, aged 11–12 years on four EEG indices (from Shibarovskaya, 1978)* ($*p< 0.05, **p < 0.025, ***p < 0.01$)

| Index | | Mz | Dz | F |
|---|---|---|---|---|
| Alpha amplitude | | .80 | .33 | 3.35*** |
| Alpha index | Beginning | −.04 | .03 | |
| | End | .56 | .11 | 2.02* |
| Frequency of rhythms | delta | .65 | .07 | 2.66*** |
| | theta | .85 | .82 | |
| | alpha | .87 | .48 | 4.0*** |
| | beta$_1$ | .24 | .38 | |
| | beta$_2$ | .30 | .51 | |
| Total energy of rhythms | delta | .66 | .57 | 1.26 |
| | theta | .78 | .54 | 2.09* |
| | alpha | .81 | .53 | 2.47** |
| | beta$_1$ | .89 | .79 | 1.91 |
| | beta$_2$ | .71 | .18 | 2.83*** |

TABLE 15. *Intra-pair correlations for 30 Mz and 26 Dz pairs, aged 11–12 years for alpha-blocking responses to auditory stimulation (from Shibarovskaya, 1978)*

| | | Mz | Dz | F |
|---|---|---|---|---|
| 1st stimulus Presentation | Latency | −.06 | .26 | |
| | Persistence | .55 | .37 | 1.4 |
| Mean Values | Latency | −.41 | .33 | |
| | Persistence | .35 | .01 | 1.52 |
| Speed of Extinction | | .50 | .04 | 1.92* |

TABLE 16. *EEG indices of conditioning for 30 Mz and 26 Dz pairs, aged 11–12 years* ($**p<0.015, ***p<0.01$)

| | | Mz | Dz | F |
|---|---|---|---|---|
| Trials to criterion CR | | .15 | −.26 | |
| Conditioning index | | .30 | −.05 | |
| Alpha-blocking | Latency | .35 | −.04 | |
| | Persistence | .76** | .03 | 4.04*** |
| | Index | .69** | .25 | 2.42*** |

resting EEG indices which Nebylitsyn (1972, pp. 89–96) claims to reflect balance of nervous processes according to dynamism. He reports that high dynamism of excitation is expressed in low-amplitude, high-frequency alpha-rhythm, with frequent periods of desynthronisation (low alpha-index), and high dynamism of inhibition in high-amplitude, low-frequency alpha-rhythm which is registered uninterruptedly (high alpha-index). Data involving theta and beta indices were inconclusive.

The data reported in Table 15 and 16 indicate that genetic influences are most clearly shown in two of the alpha-block indices which are claimed to measure dynamism of excitation — alpha-index and persistence in alpha frequencies — in habituation of the orienting response, a measure of dynamism of inhibition, and in certain aspects of conditional-orienting EEG reaction. Thus genetic factors seem to be clearly involved in indices which reflect speed of CR formation and extinction, and the dynamics of generalised subcortical activation. These findings are in broad general agreement with those earlier reported by Shlyakhta (1972).

### Studies of Higher-order Psychological Functioning

In view of the data cited above, the question arises of the extent to which higher-order psychological functions and neurophysiological processes which are thought to be related to nervous system properties are subject to genetic influences.

Some relevant studies have been reported. Of interest is Mikheyev's (1972) report of less variability and higher heritabilities for Mz pairs in recognition and short-term memory tests, using a paired-associate technique in auditory, visual and tactual modalities. Mz superiority was greater for recall than for recognition tasks in all modalities.

A number of twin studies have been reported investigating proof-reading ability — a measure of "voluntary attention" (Mosgovoy, 1978) — which has been shown to be related to excitatory strength (Yermolayeva-Tomina, 1960), and mobility (Akhimova, 1971). Glukhova and Vorobeva (1974) report heritability coefficients of 0.7 for number of errors, and 0.75 for time required to complete the task, findings which are replications of earlier work by Schwartz (1970). Mosgovoy (1974) reports a similar study of proof-reading performance by 20 Mz and 14 Dz twin pairs aged 9–16 years. Significantly higher Mz intra-pair correlations are reported for number of errors, efficiency under distracting conditions, time taken, and speed and accuracy.

In the fifth study from Ravich-Shcherbo's group, Mosgovoy (1978) examined similar parameters of voluntary attention in 130 twin pairs — 25 Mz and 25 Dz in the age ranges 10–11 and 14–15 years, and 15 Mz and 15 Dz pairs in the age range 20–50 years. The proof-reading material was Landolt's rings, and parameters of voluntary attention were distribution (efficiency in identifying rings with breaks at two points), steadiness (efficiency in identifying rings with a break at one point only) and shifts (efficiency in identifying rings where the response criterion changed every two rows). Number of errors, time taken, and the ratio, errors over time, were measured for each of these parameters.

Results are shown in Table 17. For the 10–11 year group, the intra-pair similarity for Mz twins is significantly higher than for Dz twins for all measures. In the 14–15 and 20–50 year groups, however, significant differences are reported only for the steadiness parameter. Differences seem to depend on Ss' developmental level, as well as on genetic contribution. The latter exerts considerable influence on all aspects of voluntary attention in the 10–11 age group, but it is critical with older age groups only for steadiness.

Of interest is the twin study of individual differences in resting EEG reported by Meshkova and Smirnov (1978). Its importance lies in the claim, which has some support in the typological literature, that EEG parameters reflect basic properties of the nervous system (Nebylitsyn, 1972), which determine to a large extent the dynamic features of a number of mental processes — the individual's emotional make-up (Ol'Shannikova, 1974), aspects of intellectual and behavioural activity (Krupnov, 1971; Mosgovoy, 1973) and memory functioning (Luria, 1962; Golubeva, 1976), for example.

In both the Eastern and Western literature, however, there is some disagreement about the extent of genetic contribution to individual EEG features. Some authors claim complete dependence (e.g. Vogel, 1970; Cernacek and Podivinsky, 1972; Davis and Davis, 1976), their findings being derived from twin studies using standard methodology. However, more

TABLE 17. *F ratios and heritability coefficients for the three parameters of voluntary attention (from Mosgovoy, 1978)*

| Age of twins (years) | Statistical parameters | Distribution | | | Steadiness | | | Shifts | | |
|---|---|---|---|---|---|---|---|---|---|---|
| | | N | T | N/T | N | T | N/T | N | T | N/T |
| 10–11 | F | 3.42** | 2.95** | 3.24** | 3.25** | 4.27** | 4.20** | 5.08** | 4.01** | 4.89** |
| | H | 0.71 | 0.66 | 0.69 | 0.69 | 0.76 | 0.76 | 0.80 | 0.75 | 0.80 |
| 14–15 | F | 1.38 | 1.56 | 1.36 | 4.00** | 1.96* | 2.84** | 1.71 | 1.94 | 1.86 |
| | H | 0.27 | 0.35 | 0.26 | 0.75 | 0.49 | 0.64 | 0.42 | 0.50 | 0.46 |
| 20–50 | F | 0.65 | 0.30 | 0.95 | 2.45* | 0.82 | 4.66** | 1.84 | 0.61 | 1.66 |
| | H | — | — | — | 0.68 | — | 0.76 | 0.43 | — | 0.38 |

$*p \leqslant 0.05$; $**p \leqslant 0.01$.

sophisticated analyses have suggested that genetic determination of EEG parameters is far more complicated (Inouye, 1961; Kamitake, 1963; Young, Lader and Fenton, 1972; Shlyakhta, 1975; Meshkova, 1974). We should also note the report by Meshkova (1974) that genetic influences, insofar as resting EEG is concerned, are more pronounced in the right than in the left hemisphere. She claims that certain left hemisphere EEG features develop in post-natal ontogeny under the influence of environmental and social factors, largely speech and specific motor activity associated with the right hand. This is suggested in a study reported by Panashchenko (cited by Kol'tsova, 1973) who reports that training the fingers of a child to execute precise movements stimulates speech development and, at the same time, considerably alters resting EEG parameters in the relevant hemisphere.

Meshkova and Smirnov (1978) examined a number of EEG parameters, using a sample of 20 Mz and 20 Dz pairs aged 18–26 years. The EEG measure employed was the coefficient of local non-stationariness (CLN) devised by Klyagin and Kovalev (1974), CLN being derived from a broad spectrum of EEG amplitudes. Generally speaking, CLN of resting EEG is regarded as an index of level of alertness. This measure has been used in a number of studies. For example, Klyagin and Kovalev (1974) report a correlation between CLN of resting EEG and strength of the nervous system, and Kovalev, Smirnov, and Rabinovich (1976), a relationship between CLN of background EEG and intensity of certain emotions, such as joy and rage. CLN in the frontal sections of the brain appears to be positively correlated with aggressive behaviour and CLN of the central sections with the expression of elation and joy.

Meshkova and Smirnov (1978) report highly significant correlations and F ratios (Table 18) for MZ pairs for all 13 leads taken together ($K_\Sigma$) and for right hemisphere ($K_d$), compared with left hemisphere, correlations for left hemisphere CLN and for both anterior and posterior sites being much less significant. Correlations for Dz pairs were non-significant. These data thus suggest that level of resting EEG activity is, to an extent, under genetic control for the cortex as a whole, being a stable characteristic of nervous system functioning. These findings support results from other Soviet studies (e.g.

TABLE 18. *Intra-pair correlations and F ratios for summary CLNs (\*p < 0.05) from Meshkova & Smirnov, 1978)*

| Twins | $K_\Sigma$ | $K_d$ | $K_S$ | $K_a$ | $K_p$ | $\dfrac{K_a}{K_p}$ |
|-------|------|------|------|------|------|------|
| MZ | .658* | .606* | .415 | .342 | .276 | .097 |
| DZ | -.096 | -.042 | .042 | -.026 | -.171 | .107 |
| F | 3.32* | 3.52* | 1.47 | 0.99 | 2.14 | 0.16 |

Shibarovskaya, 1978; Mikheyev, 1979), and from Western studies which we have already reviewed.

On the other hand, the degree of inter-hemispheric asymmetry reported suggests that genetic influences may not be uniform over the whole brain, or at least that activity in certain areas may be modified by environmental factors, probably during early development. Genetic influences seem to be more pronounced for the right than for the left hemisphere. Under normal conditions, it is the right hand which receives the most training, and it thus seems reasonable to anticipate changes in the activity of left hemisphere EEG as a consequence of such training. The bio-electric activity of the right hemisphere is also less subject to influences imposed by language development, and for this reason may be more directly under the control of genetic factors.

These results raise a number of important points concerning the relative influence, on nervous system properties, of strictly genetic effects on the one hand, and, on the other, of environmentally modifiable developmental or maturational processes which may lead to a progressive alteration in phenotypic variation with age. In a very broad sense, they tend to support the evolutionary genetic interpretation formulated by Orbeli (1949) and Davidenkov (1947), which proposes that the phylogenetically older functions are more dependent on genetic factors, and have become more refined by selection, the more recent organs and functions being more highly variable, since they are influenced to a considerable degree by social and personal experience. Meshkova and Smirnov suggest that their findings endorse Davidenkov's (1947) view that the right hemisphere mediates primarily imaginal, concrete and first signal functioning, the left hemisphere verbal, abstract-logical and second signal functioning, a view shared by a number of other authors (e.g. Luria, 1962; Gazzaniga, 1970; Kok, 1975), and one which is not greatly at variance with current Western views on this issue (cf. Ornstein, 1972).

This throws up two further points which may have implications for genetic studies of nervous system properties. It has been argued that nervous system characteristics, particularly those measured by EEG activity, become stable only at certain developmental periods. Data reported by Ravich-Shcherbo and Trifanova (cited by Nebylitsyn, 1972, pp. 114–15) describing EEG activity in groups of 5-, 10- and 13-year-old children, for example, indicate that while mean frequency and summed energy in alpha and beta bands increase with age, in the theta band, these indices reduce, as does alpha-index, which, on the average, decreases from 71.3 at age 5 to 48.3 at age 13. Overall, in the age range studied, they suggest the gradual development of the property of dynamism of excitation. As synaptic connections mature, there is an increase in speed of transmission of excitation in the reticular structures. In a later study, however,

Ravich-Shcherbo and Shibarovskaya (1972) report no change in the structure of dynamism between ages 8–9 and 14–15.

There is obviously a good deal of uncertainty about regression of genotype on age with regard to nervous system properties and functions. Certain effects have been noted by a number of authors (e.g. Obratsova, 1964; Chudnovsky, 1967; Kolarova, 1968) and are clearly indicated in some of the studies reviewed. For example, Shlyakhta and Panteleyeva report a reduced contribution of genotype to nervous system strength with increasing age in the lower age range when an RT strength measure is employed. However, the general finding is that excitatory and inhibitory strength increase with age. Reduced genetic contribution is reported by Vasiletz insofar as "general" transformation is concerned. We might also refer here to the Klonowicz (1979) report that in an older sample (of university students) transformation ability seems to be greatly influenced by S's training and experience over a relatively short period of time (2 years). On the other hand, Panteleyeva and Shlyakhta's lability data suggest stronger, rather than weaker genetic contribution for CFF with increasing age.

A diminishing role for genetic factors in phenotypic variation has been noted by Mosgovoy (1978) for certain aspects of voluntary attention. These results agree with earlier data reported by Luria (1962), who, in a study of memory processes with pre-school and school-age children, reports a progressive reduction in genetic contribution. This reduction is more pronounced in tasks involving what Luria describes as "voluntary verbal regulation of behaviour". The greater the child's command of language, the smaller the genetic contribution. In Mosgovoy's study, however, this reduction does not apply equally to all aspects of voluntary attention. Steadiness, which involves concentration on a single cue, has strong genetic determination even in the oldest group. Why this should be so is a matter of conjecture. However, it has been claimed that this particular attentional parameter reflects mobility of nervous processes (Akhimova, 1971), although the mobility measure employed would now be regarded as an index of lability. If so, we might expect the genetic contribution to remain constant, or even increase, with age.

Some animal work has been reported on this problem. While these data may be of somewhat limited value, since many of the growth functions are likely to be species-specific, we can cite the Kozlova, Rogatnykh and Sergeyeva (1979) study by way of illustration. In a study of strength, equilibrium and mobility, employing both alimentary and defensive reinforcement, these authors report that in 3–4-month-old dogs, the excitatory process was either strong or medium for both types of reinforcement, but at age 1–2 years, responses to defensive reinforcement were relatively stronger. Equilibrium, insofar as strength was concerned, increased with age, but mobility of nervous processes became more "unbalanced" with age.

In view of these uncertainties and contradictions, it is arguable whether it is legitimate to test for genetic contribution during certain periods of growth, when the immature, highly plastic nervous system is probably subject to relatively transient environmental influences, even though it may be true that maturational processes are under genetic control. Much more data are required before we can begin to answer the question of age related changes in genetic contribution to the catalogue of temperamental, i.e. nervous system characteristics underlying individual psychological differences.

Clearly the particular concern of Soviet research with developmental as well as strictly genetic influences on central nervous system functioning reflects a commitment to activity theory of development and personality organisation. It raises many interesting questions. The recency with which behaviour genetics research has been revived in the Soviet Union, together with a certain amount of uncertainty surrounding the measurement and interpretation of aspects of the theory of CNS activity which guides their work, must, for the moment, leave many of these questions unanswered. Nevertheless, the empirical data which have emerged so far do add important evidence in support of a genetic contribution to nervous system characteristics underlying individual psychological differences, particularly to properties of strength, lability and dynamism of the nervous system.

## The "Behavioural" Typology of the Warsaw Group

From the early 1970s, the theorising and empirical work of the Warsaw group, under the direction of Jan Strelau, has made considerable impact on typological theory. In 1969 Strelau established a Laboratory of Individual Differences at the University of Warsaw, which, to some extent, continued and extended the work of the Moscow group. However, Strelau had been exposed to other influences, particularly that of Tomaszewski, and this added new dimensions to his typological thinking.

### Strelau's temperament model

Strelau defines temperament as a set of traits manifested in energy level, and in the temporal parameters of reaction (Strelau, 1974a). His main temperament dimension, reactivity, describes the relationship between stimulus intensity and response amplitude, a relationship predictable from the Law of Strength. In this sense, his concept is similar to the Pavlovian notion of nervous system strength-weakness.

There are, however, some fundamental differences. Perhaps most importantly, while strength is thought to reflect only characteristics of the central nervous system, specifically the cortex, reactivity involves, in addition, the autonomic nervous system and the hormonal system, which have their own operational characteristics, and which inter-relate in a variety of ways (Strelau, Klonowicz and Eliasz, 1972; Eliasz, 1979).

The physiological mechanisms of reactivity (see later) co-determine level of activation. Stimuli of physically equal intensity are responded to more strongly by low-reactive than by high-reactive Ss. Thus reactivity enhances or dampens stimulation. This determines, according to Eliasz (1973a; 1979), the dynamics of respondent, and, indirectly, of operant behaviour. The latter, which he describes as "activity", is the typical, individually determined intensity and duration of behaviours organised to ensure a specific level of activation, taking into account both individual reactivity, and an individually specific, and genetically fixed optimal level of arousal. This latter concept is similar in all essential respects, to those earlier described by Hebb, Leuba and Berlyne (optimal stimulation, optimal arousal flux).

Thus, according to Strelau, reactivity and activity aspects of energy level are regulated by two closely related mechanisms — reactivity by a mechanism whereby stimulus intensity is transformed into central arousal, and activity by an acquired behavioural mechanism, which is consolidated in cortical and subcortical structures, learned strategies for enhancing or dampening stimulation, thus regulating level of arousal to ensure optimal activation. This activity mechanism is formally programmed in what we might describe as preference for certain types of work, in cognitive "styles", personality "traits" (Eliasz, 1973b; 1979). Eliasz (1979) has suggested that the strength and duration of operant (activity) and respondent (reactivity) behaviours are inversely proportional.

In addition to reactivity and activity, certain temporal aspects of behaviour — reaction time, mobility (speed of switching from one reaction to another), stability and tempo of reaction and rhythmicity of response — contribute to the description of temperament (Strelau, 1974a). A core concept is obviously that of mobility. We have discussed the construct validity of this property in a previous section. In addition to simple "speed of switching", i.e. "transformation mobility", however, Strelau has been concerned with the opposite pole — "secondary function" or perseveration, i.e. the continuation of a response after the eliciting stimulus has terminated. Cognitive inertia, rigidity, are roughly similar concepts. Something like this has been implicated in most theories of temperament — Kretschmer (1921) for example, refers to rigidity-plasticity.

On the methodological side, Strelau has developed a temperament inventory (STI), which is claimed to measure excitatory strength (reactivity), inhibitory strength, the equilibrium of these processes, and mobility of nervous processes.

He reports (Strelau, 1972a) that these questionnaire-derived behavioural measures correlate highly with the psychophysiological indices of the same properties developed by the Moscow group.

More recently, Strelau has also been concerned with validating temporal parameters of behaviour, which is of particular interest in view of the difficulties experienced by Soviet typologists in establishing the construct validity of mobility. Gorynska and Strelau (1979) describe a 108-item inventory, sampling a wide spectrum of emotional, intellectual, verbal and motor behaviour, which measures 6 temporal aspects of behaviour — two perseveration measures (response persistence and recurrence), reaction mobility (the minimal time necessary to respond differentially to successive stimuli) and three measures of what the authors describe as "liveliness" — reaction time, regularity and tempo.

Factor analysis revealed two factors, one loading the two perseveration measures, the second, the three liveliness measures. Mobility loaded both factors about equally, but with opposite signs. The authors also report highly significant correlations between the six scales and mobility scores from the STI. Perseverative traits appear to be stronger in females, liveliness traits in males. On the basis of this analysis, Gorynska and Strelau conclude that mobility is determined by two different psychophysiological mechanisms, one conceived as speed of response elicitation (liveliness), the other as speed of response extinction (perseveration). The interaction between these mechanisms determines ease or difficulty in adapting response to change in stimulus conditions. Note that these are the two aspects of lability, which, according to Nebylitsyn, is independent of mobility.

It is clear, therefore, that Strelau's concept of mobility differs appreciably from the classic Pavlovian view. The mechanisms mediating speed of elicitation and extinction of excitation are independent. There is also the consideration, referred to by Strelau (1977), that behavioural mobility, as measured by STI, while correlating with mobility as measured by the experimental techniques employed by the Moscow group, appears to have additional content. This he adduces from the fact that although experimentally determined indices of transformation mobility do not correlate highly with any of Guilford's fluency and flexibility of thinking tests (although Mangan (1967b, 1978c) has reported such correlations), high correlations have been reported between these measures and mobility measured by STI (Strelau, 1977; Klonowicz, 1979). We shall return to this point later. At this stage it is sufficient to note that a number of temporal aspects of responding, which historically have been considered important temperament variables, can be subsumed under two independent physiological mechanisms mediating speed of elicitation and extinction of nervous processes.

*Temperament and personality*

In construing the relationship between temperament and personality, Polish typologists have been influenced by the theory of action/activity advanced by Tomaszewski (1963), which is, in fact, an extension of Vygotsky's views. Personality is regarded as a "central system regulating and integrating activity" (Reykowski, 1977), appropriate regulative mechanisms being formed in the course of activity in specific socio-historical contexts.

Strelau's group has identified a number of factors which modify and facilitate the growth of these regulative and integrative structures, and has advanced a number of speculations, and reports considerable research, on the nature of the developing relationships between temperamental variables and such structures.

(a) REACTIVITY

The specific strengths and magnitudes, i.e. energy level, and the temporal characteristics of primary drives and emotional mechanisms aroused by sensory input from both external and internal stimuli, are perhaps the most critical factor. Some infants are more active than others, some react more strongly to weak stimuli under objectively similar environmental conditions. Such individual differences in reactivity exert a 2-fold effect, steering and modifying new forms of conditioned adaptive behaviour acquired through experience.

The consequences of such differences can be profound. As a number of Western authors have also pointed out (e.g. Danziger, 1976) socialisation is a reciprocal process. Lively, passive and anxious withdrawing infants are treated differently by parents, and this eventually may lead to the formation of certain cognitive structures and motivational mechanisms. In turn, the effects of a whole range of environmental stimuli are modified by the child's temperamental traits. Depending primarily on the child's reactivity or energy level, these factors can exert strong or weak, short-term or long-term effects. As we pointed out in our discussion of genetic influences on animal behaviour, what appear to be identical environmental treatments for two individuals can produce quite different consequences. The effects of similar punishment regimes, for example, appear to depend on individual reactivity, as studies by Merlin (1955) and Utkina (1964) have shown. They report that "strong", low-reactive pupils respond to negative grades with high arousal and increased effort to achieve better grades, while weak, high-reactive pupils, in similar circumstances, withdraw, and tend to give up.

Thus, strength of temperament traits will determine, to some extent, how strong an influence the environment will exert. Such effects might be expected to lead eventually to different behavioural patterns and thus to different personality structures.


(b) NEED FOR STIMULATION

From the beginning, individually specific stimulation requirements show up as individual differences. According to Strelau (1974a) and Eliasz (1974a,b,c), within the context of a socially-prescribed system of rewards and punishments, high-reactive individuals prefer non-stimulating situations and activities, while low-reactive individuals seek and organise activities to enhance stimulation. In order to promote optimal level of arousal, the individual must choose such situations, or undertake such activities, which will both reach and sustain such an optimum, and, at the same time, will confer benefits concomitant with his interests and needs, and with the expectations of relevant persons and groups. Such patterns of approach and avoidance may be formalised in habits and behavioural stereotypes, i.e. in personality structure.

Following this general line of enquiry, Strelau has reported a series of studies (Strelau, 1970b, 1974b, 1975a) examining the temperamental determinants of work style, involving, for example, the ratio of principal to auxiliary actions, pacing, choice of conditions, whether stimulating or non-stimulating. According to Strelau, reactivity determines work style preferences, since high reactive individuals are sensitive to all types of stimuli, have strong orienting responses, and reduced resistance to strong stimuli.

Further work has suggested much more complex relationships between temperament and work style. Eliasz (1974c) has reported that low-reactive individuals prefer active self-regulatory styles — to use Nuttin's (1965) concept of self-regulation — as a means of reducing discrepancy between expectation and achievement. The more active the self-regulatory styles, the more persistently S works at his task, the higher his N/Ach, the more effectively he strives to improve performance, the more realistic his expectations. Where such activity and attitudes lead to success and satisfaction, these are "consolidated" in personality structure. On the other hand, high reactive individuals prefer a passive style of self-regulation, which has opposite behavioural manifestations.

Eliasz has suggested that frustration and neuroticism modify the relationships described above, since high level of either increases activation, and thus should decrease individual need for stimulation. The fact that neurotics show a lowered need for stimulation is well supported in both the Western (McReynolds and Bryant, 1956; Berlyne and Lewis, 1963; O'Leary, 1965) and Polish literature (Eliasz, 1974a). Eliasz proposes, therefore, a complex set of relationships between reactivity, N, and self-regulatory style, degree of activity or passivity depending also on the level of frustration encountered. In non-frustrating conditions, low N/low reactive Ss should prefer an active self-regulatory style, while high reactive/high N Ss should opt for a passive style. In frustrating conditions, however, high reactive/low N Ss and low reactive/high N Ss, who, under neutral conditions, show no style preference, now show a preference for a passive style. Eliasz (cf. Strelau, 1980) reports confirmatory data from 15–17-year-old male samples.

Other studies from the same source suggest clearly that differences in reactivity are related to preference for situations differing in degree of stimulation (Eliasz, 1974c) and to differences in preference for particular styles of action (Strelau and Krajewski, 1974; Klonowicz, 1974a; Strelau, 1975a). It is also evident that in different situations, irrespective of the amount of stimulation offered, high and low reactive Ss perform equally well if they are permitted to choose their own individual styles of action (Klonowicz and Czyzkowska, 1974; Strelau, 1975a). These styles might be regarded as compensation techniques for under- or over-stimulation. Klonowicz (1974b), on the other hand, has shown that where Ss do not have a choice of work style, reactive Ss work better in monotonous situations, and low reactive Ss better in highly stimulating conditions. She has proposed a concept of psychophysiological cost to describe the consequences of performing in settings whose stimulation properties, for whatever reason, are not attuned to S's level of reactivity.

A number of additional findings relevant to the low reactivity-high need for stimulation/high reactivity-low need for stimulation hypothesis have been reported, exploring a broad range of behaviours in a variety of contexts. These studies have in common the assumption that high reactive individuals will avoid high levels of arousal of whatever origin, whether induced, for example, by emotional tensions, by stress, risk-taking, conformity pressure, discrepancy between real and ideal self-image. These are briefly summarised below.

1. Reaction to stress seems to be related to S's reactivity level, a finding which agrees with the animal and human data reported from Soviet laboratories. Maciejczyk (1974) reports that low reactive pilots are more resistant to stress than high reactive pilots. It has also been reported that high reactive individuals are more prone to ulcers of the digestive tract than low reactive individuals (Jastrzebska et al., 1974).

2. Some recent work has explored the possibility that high reactive Ss should be less capable of tolerating high levels of emotional tension, and, as a consequence, tend to avoid stressful, conflict situations, or, in such situations, adopt behavioural/cognitive strategies aimed at reducing such tension.

Kozlowski (1977) reports that low reactive Ss are risktakers. The underlying rationale is that risk-taking produces emotional tension. Highly reactive individuals will avoid situations causing emotional tension, and so will avoid risks. The opposite is true for low reactive individuals.

3. Bialowas (1976) has reported that high reactive Ss yield more to conformity pressure in an Asch/type setting, since they are less able to tolerate cognitive dissonance which generates emotional tension (Festinger, 1957; Reykowski, 1977). Those high reactive Ss who do not conform are significantly more state-anxious, as measured by Spielberger's state-trait anxiety inventory (STAI), than those who yield to pressure. If we regard level of emotional tension, measured by anxiety level, as an index of psychophysiological cost, then under conditions of group pressure, which is clearly a stressful situation, highly reactive individuals probably pay a greater psychophysiological price than low reactive Ss, particularly if they choose not to yield. Yielding reduces cost, and thus contributes to psychological comfort.

Bialowas's findings support hypotheses previously advanced by Klonowicz (1974b) and Strelau (1970b), and some Western research suggesting a relationship between anxiety level and susceptibility to conformity pressure (Mangan, Quartermain and Vaughan, 1959, 1960; Vaughan and Mangan, 1963).

4. Strzalkowska (1977) has examined tolerance of discrepancy between real and ideal self-image, such discrepancy being thought to relate to emotional tension (Reykowski, 1976, 1977), and to degree of maladjustment, as a function of reactivity. Contrary to expectations, however, high reactive Ss disclosed greater real-self/ideal-self discrepancies than low reactive Ss. While it is possible that results were confounded by N, clearly other factors are involved.

One possibility is that highly reactive individuals, when faced with social evaluation, react more strongly to negative judgments than low reactive Ss, because of their overall sensitivity. The consequent loss of self-confidence, increased fear of failure, could lead to lower self-esteem, which, in turn, increases the discrepancy between real and ideal self-estimates. Grzegolowska (1978; cited in Strelau, 1980) has offered an alternative explanation. She suggests that one method of regulating stimulation inflow is through acquisition of patterns of cognitive function specifically aimed at reducing anxiety. Defence mechanisms can be viewed in this light. In effect, they can modify temperamental traits such as reactivity. However, no strong empirical support has been offered for these speculations.

5. The hypothesis relating stimulation-seeking to reactivity level has also been employed to investigate the problem of psychopathic deviance. It has been suggested that psychopaths are characterised by a low level of cortical arousal, which motivates them to seek strong and variable stimulation to obtain an optimum (Quay, 1965). A number of experiments have been reported, exploring different aspects of this problem.

Skzpek (1969), for example, has reported that under conditions of perceptual isolation psychopaths show increased preference for complex stimuli, the preference remaining constant after a period of arousal, while neurotics, under similar conditions, show increased anxiety, and a decreased preference for complexity.

Gawecka and Poznaniak (1979) compared groups of psychopathic prisoners, neurotic patients and normals in amount and type of stimulation-seeking. They examined the significance of length of imprisonment, and whether there are differences between those prisoners who opt to live in single cells, compared with those who are confined to single cells as a disciplinary measure, or those who opt to live in communal cells. Also examined were questions of any relationship between frequency of self-injury and need for stimulation in psychopathic prisoners, whether psychopaths are less reactive than neurotics, and whether highly reactive neurotics and psychopaths differ from low reactive neurotics and psychopaths in type and amount of stimulation sought.

The authors used Gawecka's stimulation-seeking questionnaire, which measures fear stimulation (risk-taking, danger, physical and social threat), social (the presence of others), sensory-motor, intellectual-cognitive and changeability-diversity (an atmosphere of "something happening") stimulation. In addition, a scale of autostimulation measured phantasy, imagery, creative thinking, day-dreaming. Reactivity was measured using Strelau's TI.

Psychopath prisoners, compared to neurotics, show a significantly higher level of demand for sensory, social and fear stimulation, but not for intellectual-cognitive stimulation, changeability-diversity, and autostimulation. Prolonged imprisonment decreased the need for social stimulation, but increased that for sensory stimulation, change-diversity, and intellectual-cognitive stimulation, this result applying mainly to young prisoners. Neurotics, compared to psychopaths, were significantly more reactive, with psychopaths being more differentiated in this respect.

*Reactivity mechanisms*

Obvious questions arise as to the nature of reactivity mechanisms, whether they are subject to change in the course of development, and, if so, to what extent is this relevant to the question of the temporal stability of reactivity.

There is evidence of compensatory effects aimed at restoring optimal level of arousal under conditions of sensory deprivation and over-stimulation. These involve primarily changes in sensitivity to stimuli (Fiske and Maddi, 1967). Zuckerman (1964, 1971), Tranel (1962) and Zubek (quoted by Zuckerman,

1971) report that under deprivating conditions Ss resort to day-dreaming, to irrelevant motor behaviour, presumably in an attempt to increase arousal. This is accompanied by hormonal changes — increase in adrenaline and noradrenaline secretion (Frankenhaeuser *et al.*, 1971) and increased secretion of thyroid hormone (Zuckerman, 1971), which enhances nervous system sensitivity (Strelau, Klonowicz and Eliasz, 1972). Ss with relatively greater adrenaline secretion perform better under monotonous conditions, which is in line with the finding that adrenaline is effective in raising blood glucose level (Mandler, 1975). This, in turn, increases sensitivity to stimuli. There is, therefore, some evidence for the operation of physiological adaptive mechanisms resulting in the lowering of sensitivity threshold in the case of stimulation deficit.

Under conditions of over-stimulation, there are good reasons to believe that sensitivity to stimuli is decreased. We might infer this from Gray's (1971a) theory, which postulates a negative feedback loop in the ARAS and the septo-hippocampal system — the system concerned primarily with threat of punishment and frustrative non-reward — such that increasing arousal in these structures results in lowered activation, the raising of sensitivity thresholds, and thus reduction in the subjective intensity of stimulation.

Such adaptation effects, however, are probably relatively short-term. There is evidence that long-term deprivation produces a switchover from the "hormonal re-tuning", i.e. the active mechanism described by Zuckerman and Frankenhaeuser *et al.* to a more passive adaptation (Dubos, 1965). Overall sensitivity is reduced, there is increased tolerance for intense (e.g. pain) stimuli. The "Law of Strength" is negated.

We can only guess at the mechanisms involved in such reactivity control. The inhibitory transmitter GABA is a possibility, judging from recent evidence that valium (diazepam group of minor tranquillisers) works through increasing the level of GABA, via peptides. Again, since individual differences in pain thresholds are known to be related to encephalin levels, encephalin release could monitor a somewhat slower control — around 20 minutes (Levine, Gordon and Fields, 1978). In the case of control of the order of several days, this could be due to induction of enzymes, to changes in receptor numbers (Snyder, 1977) as in opiate addiction.

In the case of prolonged over-stimulation, a similar sort of process, but reversed, seems to occur. Passive adaptation now results in sensitivity increase — hyper-sensitivity — with accompanying reduced tolerance for intense stimuli.

Eliasz (1979) suggests that the shift from active to passive regulation is due, in both cases, to fatigue in the physiological mechanisms compensating for substantial declines or elevations in activation level. The speed with which such shifts occur is a function of both the persistence and the degree of discrepancy between required and actual stimulation.

Overall, then, a picture emerges of a complex interaction between environmental stimuli and the functioning of these reactivity mechanisms. How quickly such mechanisms adapt to short-lived discrepancies is a function of their lability, which, apparently, is quite marked. Adaptation occurs within minutes (Klonowicz, 1974b; Sataloff, Vassallo and Menduke, 1972a,b; Frankenhaeuser *et al.*, 1971; Mandler, 1975). Such rapid adjustment gives the appearance of a high degree of temporal stability of temperament traits. It is only when the differences between actual and optimal stimulation is exaggerated that we need to postulate alteration in the physiological mechanisms themselves which determine the ratio of response amplitude to stimulus strength.

*Temperament and intellectual functioning*

The Warsaw group has been concerned with certain aspects of the relationship between temperament and intellectual functioning. Their views, however, differ somewhat from those of Soviet psychologists, who have differentiated natural biological abilities from human abilities, the latter being shaped by socio-historical rather than genetic factors, the former being closely related to temperament traits (Leont'ev), since they are based on the same physiological mechanisms.

Strelau (1977) considers that the role of temperament traits is expressed in the dynamics of intellectual processes and mental activation, and in the speed of mental processes. He has reported (1977) that mobility, as measured by STI, is related to levels of flexibility and fluency of thinking measured by Guilford's tests, a finding which is also (weakly) supported by Klonowicz (1979). She regards transformation mobility as a basic dimension, a view which is shared by Kozielecki (1968) and Trzebinski (1973). These authors maintain that intellectual abilities such as fluency, flexibility and originality are responsible for both the final outcome and the efficiency and rationality of thought processes.

Two further studies in this area are of particular interest. Klonowicz (1979), from a comparison of first and third year humanities and engineering students on fluency and thinking flexibility tests, suggests that transformation ability is subject to specialisation due to individual training, judging from changes in performance over a 2-year period in the groups studied. The second study, by Kozcielak (1979) compared a group of 100 inventors and non-inventors — shipyard workers — selected on the basis of "creative projects" submitted over a one-year period. Ss were compared on measures of flexibility and temperament scores from the STI. The inventor group scored significantly higher on all thinking flexibility tests, and showed significantly stronger STI inhibition and mobility. Her results point to significant relationships between technical inventiveness and flexibility of thinking, mobility and strength of excitation, and, to a lesser extent, strength of inhibition. Mobility thus appears to play a significant role in thinking flexibility, a point also made by Mangan (1967b, 1978c) and Strelau (1977).

In other studies Lewicka (cited by Strelau, 1980) has reported a relationship between Eysenck's E-I dimension and development of crystallised intelligence. Matczak (pers. comm.) has reported that preference for a particular cognitive style appears early in ontogenesis, is relatively independent of cognitive capacity, and is probably co-determined by temperament and situational factors. Sosnowski (1978) has shown that when level of stimulation is optimal, verbal behaviour is freer and more fluent than when level of stimulation deviates from optimal.

Worth mentioning in this context is a series of animal studies, running parallel with the human work, examining reactivity and need for stimulation in rats (Matysiak, 1977, 1978, 1979a,b). He reports that stimuli in different modalities have different stimulation values, that there are marked individual preferences for different modalities of sensory stimulation (Matysiak, 1979a). According to Matysiak, there are two independent forms of stimulation control — one increasing the level of incoming stimulation, the other reducing this inflow. The fact that frequency of turning on a light under conditions of sensory isolation, and the frequency of turning off a bright, continuous light source — techniques which have been employed by Barry and Symmes (1963) and Goodrick (1970) — are highly and negatively correlated, suggest marked individual differences in need for stimulation.

### Summary

Soviet typological theory is very much in a state of flux. Three new properties — dynamism, lability and concentration — have been added to the original Pavlovian model. Nervous system properties are now regarded as "partial", i.e. they are thought to reflect properties of particular receptor and cortical structures. In addition, some recent work suggests that they may be intimately related to psychological processes such as memory and reasoning. Over and above these partial properties, two general brain systems are postulated, which determine basic temperamental traits of activity level and emotionality, which account for a major part of the variance of temperament. These traits have something in common with Western personality dimensions of extraversion and neuroticism.

A number of comparatively recent genetic studies of nervous system properties, employing twin methodology, suggest strong genetic contribution to the properties of strength, mobility and lability, to certain EEG parameters, and to psychological functions such as voluntary attention, which are thought to be shaped by typological properties.

Strelau's group, in proposing their reactivity/activity model, have made considerable advances in typological research. Strelau discusses temperament as a set of relatively stable traits expressed in energy level and in the temporal characteristics of reaction. Inventories for measuring energy level, represented primarily by the factors of reactivity and mobility, and temporal aspects of responding have been developed.

On the theoretical side, the Warsaw group has proposed a model of personality which has as its core concept the notion of stimulation control to promote optimal conditions for efficient intellectual and emotional functioning. Optimal activation level is considered to be individually specific and genetically determined. Such stimulation control is co-determined by S's reactivity, i.e. by the innate responsivity of the reacting systems and tissues, complemented by various hormonal steering or balancing mechanisms, and activity, characteristic types and intensities of learned behaviour which harmonise with individual stimulation requirements, and which are reflected in choice of cognitive styles and work conditions. Individuals seek comfortable physical and psychological conditions, and avoid conflict and discrepancy situations which are likely to create too high levels of emotional tension or activation, either overtly, or through the agency of defence mechanisms.

Thus personality, which is the system regulating and integrating activity, can effect temperament, and vice versa. However, since personality is formed in the context of social experience, in certain instances behaviour may become stereotyped and "non-functional". For example, if achievement need has become functionally autonomous, a conflict may develop between the motive to behave in previously reinforced ways, which has now lost its positive valence, and the desire to behave in ways more consistent with current stimulation needs. This is one aspect of behavioural dynamics which is at present attracting the interest of typological theorists of this school.

CHAPTER 3

# Human Typology and Higher Mental Processes

*Man is by no means a leather sack filled with reflexes, and the brain is not a hostel for conditioned reflexes which just happen to arrive there together.*
L. S. Vygotsky (1968)

## Introduction

THROUGHOUT his life, although working almost exclusively with dogs as experimental animals, Pavlov's interest turned increasingly to human mental phenomena of consciousness and thought.

> Only one thing in life is of real interest to us — our psychical experiences (1928, p. 80).
>
> The most important ... of the oldest acquisitions of psychology as a science is the establishment of the existence of connections between subjective phenomena ... and then the connection between thoughts, emotions and impulses to action (1935, p. 607).

His insistence that mental activity is dependent on nervous processes in no way meant that he denied subjective states, nor that he reduced thought and consciousness simply to nervous activity; rather he insisted that, if the mechanisms of mental states are to be studied, they must be regarded as expressions of nervous activity. However, it was not until the late 1920s that he worked directly and systematically with human mental processes, in the diagnosis and threatment of mental illness. His theory of human typology, therefore, was outlined in only the most sketchy detail.

### (a) The Second Signal System

Language occupies a central role in Pavlov's theory of human typology. It is the "last new principle in the activity of the cerebral hemispheres" (1941, p. 93). "It is precisely speech which makes us human" (ibid, p. 179). However, he never specifically addressed himself to the problem of the function of language, of how and why the first signal system evolved into the second, a point which was not lost on subsequent theorists. As Orbeli, Pavlov's successor,

100

complained "The second signal system did not just drop from heaven" (1950, p. 15).

Pavlov, although not avowedly a dialectical materialist, presumably was in sympathy with the theory of language development expounded in the Marxist science of society. Engels had pointed out that labour, the fashioning and use of tools, produced the essential differences between man and other animal forms. The development of manual dexterity was accompanied by changes in the relationships between people, and by changes in physiological and nervous system structures. Tool making and fashioning objects with tools involve social activity, and social activity — the fact that it encouraged the discovery of more and more of the properties of environmental objects — led to the formation of words, speech, language.

> Men in the making arrived at the point where they had something to say to one another. The need led to the creation of its organ: the undeveloped larynx of the ape was slowly transformed ... and the organs of the mouth gradually learned to pronounce one articulate letter after another. (Engels, 1940, p. 279).

This theme has been recapitulated by a number of Eastern and Western theorists. Vygotsky, one of the major protagonists in the "battle for consciousness" in the Soviet Union in the 1920s and 1930s, also asserted that man is shaped by the tools and the instruments he uses. Neither the hand, nor the mind, of itself, amounts to very much. He cites Bacon's apophthegm, "Nec manus, nisi intellectus, sibi permissus, multam valent; instrumentis et auxilibus res perficitur" which aligns him squarely with the earlier view, boldly expressed by William James, that function creates organ. Thus the historical determination of man's intellect and consciousness. However, while Vygotsky might be described as a functionalist or as an instrumentalist, perhaps even as an Act psychologist, his views clearly transcended both the historical materialism of Marxism, and the functionalism of the Dewey–James school.

The speech mechanism also plays a decisive role in making possible abstractions, generalisations, reasoning and consciousness.

> It is said that thoughts arise without ... the language shell, in, so to speak, a naked form. But this is absolutely wrong. Whatever the thoughts that may arise in the mind of man, they can arise and exist only on the basis of words and phrases. Bare thoughts, ... free of the "natural matter" of language, do not exist. Only idealists can speak of thinking ... without language (Stalin, 1951, p. 36).

The function of language is thus two-fold — communication, and as a stimulus to problem-solving and thinking, which significantly affects man's adaptation to, and control over the environment. Pavlov's theorising about the second signal system, however, was restricted to the second problem area.

According to Pavlov, words — elementary motor-speech responses — signalise objects and their attributes, and thus represent "an abstraction from reality, and make possible the formation of generalisations, which indeed constitutes an extra, essentially human, higher mentality" (1941, p. 93). A word redintegrates the complex of sensory traces which would result from the direct action of the object or event designated by the word, a characteristic first noted by Berkeley, and emphasised by Sechenov (1863). Since words are abstractions from particular things and events, man can react, or inhibit response to the environment in terms of both sensory stimulations and abstractions from these — derived from both his own experience and the experience of others — thus greatly increasing adaptability. This system of conditioned reflexes to language Pavlov called the "second signal system", by contrast with the first system of sensory signals.

The underlying mechanism of verbal conditioned reflexes, according to Pavlov, is the association, by the cortex (specifically the frontal lobes), of sense stimuli with the nerves and muscles of the speech organs. These, in turn, send kinaesthetic stimulations to the cortex, where they may be connected with other conditioned verbal signals. This second system consitutes the nervous apparatus of thought — or communication with self by means of silent speech — of consciousness and mental processes generally. During ontogeny, the formation of speech conditioned reflexes, and their transformation into higher-order configures of meaning by the synthesising and analysing activity of the cortex, results in highly complex hierarchies of verbal associations, which, at the highest level, involve the capacity to form abstract, logical connections, and thus confer potential for inductive reasoning.

Superficially, there seems to be some contradiction in Pavlov's statements as to whether words, as CSs, are subject to the same laws, in general, that govern conditioned sense stimuli. For example, in a 1927 paper, he notes that language allows "neither qualitative nor quantitative comparison with any conditioned stimuli in animals" (p. 357), and, in a 1933 paper, that the advent of language involves a "new principle of neural action" Again he notes

> After it is learned, human speech, unlike second-order conditioning, remains constant (relatively unextinguished). That is, our words are not conditioned reflexes — the process here is different 1949, Vol. 1, p. 240).

However, in 1935, shortly before his death, he wrote

> The essential laws governing the work of the first signal system necessarily regulate the second system as well, because it is the work done by the same nervous tissue (1941, p. 179).

Clearly, Pavlov recognised that there are special applications and forms of these laws, i.e. new principles within the same basic framework, which characterise the work of the second signal system. This is the view taken by Bykov (1953)

> As a CS, word ... is much more diversified than any of the others (sensory stimuli), and *in this respect*, cannot be either qualitatively or quantitatively compared with conditioned stimuli in animals (p. 55).

The fact that words have incomparably greater potential for connecting and associating places them on a much higher level than conditioned sensory stimuli. Thus there is both a continuity and a discontinuity in the higher nervous activity of man and animals — a continuity since the nervous activity of both is the product of conditioned reflexes, a discontinuity because man has, in addition, the apparatus of the speech organs. We note also that in identifying this new principle of abstraction and generalisation, Pavlov refers to "analysis and synthesis of these new generalised signals" (1941, p. 114), suggesting higher forms of verbal conditioning, configuring and thinking.

A good deal of the early experimental work on second signal activity centred on the basic question of whether, as Pavlov asserted "speech is as real as CS to man as all other stimuli". While it is true that words are labels with the capacity to evoke images, and while image is like the real stimulus in certain respects, labels are not. Word is a representation, not an analogue, and it is only in the process of conditioning that it acquires the affective quality of the image it denotes. Additionally, of course, such verbal representations have the power to access associative networks formed by past experience, so that, under certain circumstances, they may acquire greater affective significance than the sensory stimuli they denote. The question thus broadens into an enquiry into the circumstances in which words can become adequate or more than adequate substitutes for CSs, and into the extent to which laws governing the formation and extinction of sensory CRs, cortical analysis and synthesis, irradiation and concentration, i.e. the laws of excitation and of inhibition which regulate higher nervous activity as a whole, also govern the functioning of the second signal system.

Research has suggested that word, in a functional sense, can be equivalent to the sensory stimulus which it designates. In the general context that interoceptive responses, as well as exteroceptive, can be conditioned to exteroceptive CSs (Bykov, 1953; cf. review by Razran, 1961b), it is clear, from both Soviet and Western data, that verbal stimuli presented by experimenter, or self-produced verbal stimuli, can substitute for sensory CSs in both exteroceptive and interoceptive conditioning. Bykov (1953) cites a number of illustrative experiments involving simple classical conditioning procedures. In the first, the CS is the ringing of a bell, the US an electric shock, and the UR hand withdrawal. After the establishment of a stable CR, the spoken or written word "bell" produces the CR. Thus the word stands for the bell, and evokes the reflex or conditioned response which has been temporarily connected with the actual sensory sound (or sight) of the bell. Experientially, therefore, the word "bell" has become a verbal CS, signalling concrete bells of whatever type.

Self-produced verbal stimuli can also become effective through stimulus generalisation from an externally produced CS. Hudgins (1933), Razran (1935), Kotliarevsky (1936) and Menzies (1937) have demonstrated that once a stable CR has been established, S is able to elicit the CR by simply naming (vocally or subvocally) or imagining the CS. Kotliarevsky (1936), using pressure on the eyeball as US for heart rate retardation, with a bell as CS, reported that generalisation extended not only to the word "bell" announced by E, but also to the word enunciated by S.

The effect has also been demonstrated in young children. Voigt (1968), in a review of the literature, comments

> the results (Hudgins) were confirmed by Kotliarevsky (1935). He reports successfully conditioning both dilation and constriction in children, using the same stimuli as Hudgins, and also found that the conditioned pupillary responses could be evoked by E's verbal command (p. 976).

Clearly the second signal system is more functional that the first system, in that a word such as "bell", as an abstraction from all real bells and bell sounds, stands ready for a reflectory signal to do the work of a range of sensory stimuli, which can vary along a number of physical dimensions (e.g. size, shape, timbre, periodicity). This constitutes a reserve of plasticity, since what is true of "bell" holds true for hundreds and thousands of other words, and more importantly, for their combinations in phrases and sentences.

Additionally, in classical conditioning, words, or "thoughts", may override, and, in certain circumstances, displace the sensory CSs they denote. Razran (1935), in his conditioned salivation study with humans, notes: "After a great deal of training, the thought of the conditioned stimulus was a more effective conditioner than the conditioned stimulus itself".

This phenomenon is convincingly demonstrated in an experiment, attributed to Ayrapetyants, and reported by Bykov (1953). Warm water was introduced into S's bladder via a catheter, and pressure changes in the bladder registered on a meter. S could see manometer pressure readings, and "learned" the gauge readings matching his subjectively experienced desire to urinate. After several trails, the gauge was disconnected. Following this, when S was told that the gauge was showing the previously established critical point — bladder full — he felt the desire to urinate, although there was, in fact, very little water in his bladder. Importantly, if S "thought" that the gauge was registering zero, considerable quantities of water could be introduced into his bladder without him showing any desire to urinate.

There are a number of other reports illustrating the same general point. Bykov (1953) describes an experiment in which a vasodilation CR was stabilised, employing a classical conditioning paradigm, with a bell as CS, and a warm (110°F) stimulus as US. The sensory CS was then replaced by a verbal instruction "I am going to ring the bell", which elicited the vasodilative CR. Subsequently, S experienced a 150°F stimulus, which produced a mild pain reaction, expressed as a vasoconstrictive response. Following this, S was instructed "I am going to apply the warm stimulus", but, instead of the 110° coil, the 150° stimulus was applied. S's response, however, was not the unconditioned vasoconstrictive response, but the verbally conditioned response of vasodilation. On post-experimental enquiry, S disclosed that he had experienced warmth, not pain, i.e. that he had subjectively experienced the response conditioned to the verbal signal, rather than the UCR. S's second signal system, therefore, suppressed and replaced the unconditioned "innate" reflex.

Kondrat'eva (1974) describes an experiment in which the law of strength was pitted against instructions for S to react fastest to signals of lowest intensity (40 dB, compared with intensities of 60, 80, 100 and 120 dB) to which, according to the law of strength, the longest RT latency should be expressed. Results showed that the effectiveness of sensory signals is determined both by their physical properties and by their subjective significance. Roughly similar results have been reported by Raevskii (1972) in a choice RT experiment, where it is clear that excitation in the projection areas is under the control of the second signal system. According to Raevskii, verbal instructions activate the second signal system mechanisms, so that when sensory stimuli are presented later, the nerve impulses are conducted to the proper "address". Note, however, that the steering function of second system signals is dependent, to some extent, on S's developmental level. Belyaeva (1979), for example, reports an experiment involving motor conditioned reflexes to auditory and verbal stimuli which clearly indicates greater negative induction of the second by the first signal system in 4–5-year-old children, but greater negative induction of the first by the second signal system in 6–7-year-olds.

It has been claimed that second signal stimuli can excite unconditional responses in a variety of response modalities. Linetskii (1961), for example, reports increase in rate of urine secretion simply by suggesting to S, under hypnosis, that he is drinking water. This is an extension of work by Platonov, a student of Bykov, who, in his (1959) book, reports data which he claims to show that

All processes occurring within the organism are actually reflected in man's cerebral cortex. The internal environment of the organism can therefore be influenced by the cerebral cortex. Under certain conditions, verbal stimuli can evoke a series of simple and complex physiological responses ... it is thus possible to influence water or carbohydrate metabolism, hunger and satiety, secretions in the gastro-intestinal tract, thermoregulation, vasomotor activity, trophic responses. Finally, we can provoke endocrine-vegetative changes, influence instinctive and emotional activity, and even channel the immunifacient processes in the desired direction (p. 420).

Bykov (1953), in reviewing the data from verbal conditioning experiments, comments

Similar facts convinced us that the very conception of unconditioned reflexes should be broadened. Under normal circumstances, every unconditioned reflex becomes "covered", as it were, with conditioned reflexes of varying complexity.

From earliest age, conditioned reflexes of both the first and second system knit together with the innate unconditioned reflexes to form fused reflexes. Such fusions Bykov describes as "complex-reflex" acts. Thus the 3 levels of higher nervous activity in man — UCRs, and CRs of the first and second signal sytems — form a functional whole, although the whole is subordinate to its highest expression. The cortex manages overall functioning, not as an agent exercising external control over lower functions, but by entering into and becoming part of them. This is what is meant by the "compulsory interweaving" of conditioned (including verbal) and unconditioned reflexes. It is possible that the degree of cortical control is in part a function of the state of S (e.g. hypnotic compared with waking state) and the type of UR involved, in that URs from the viscera appear to be more "controllable" than those having more specific, i.e. "conscious" feedback.

However, given that normal Ss ontogentically develop a system of complex reflex acts awaiting linkage with sensory stimuli, does the activation of such systems — e.g. through verbal instructions — produce immediately in the cortex the necessary conditions for the development of sensory conditioning? Rather surprisingly, as Anokhin (1958) complains, despite the theoretical importance of this problem, little real interest has been shown by Soviet typologists in the nature of the verbal instruction at the physiological level.

Available evidence suggests that the formation of afferent-efferent connections through instructions in humans is many times faster than development of connections in animals (Narbutovich and Podkopaev, 1936), hardly surprising in view of the much greater speed with which concentration of nervous processes occurs in humans (Teplov, 1964). The fact that the frequency of dominant alpha activity is considerably higher in man than in other species (rat, cat, rabbit), i.e. that time constants in human cortical elements are smaller, implies that man is more "sensitive" in this respect. However, the structural correlates, as well as the underlying neuronal mechanisms of afferent-efferent connecting appear to be identical (Chuprikova, 1967).

In animal conditioning studies, the excitability of the cortical points to which the two stimuli — usually the CS and US — are addressed, is the critical element (Kogan, 1960; Livanov, 1962). There is evidence of increased excitability in food reward centres (the lateral hypothalamus) (Kupalov, 1960), and in brain areas mediating punishment (Nikolaeva, 1953, 1955) during appetitive and aversive conditioning, so that the salivary UR occurs more rapidly after application of the CS, and the intensity of punishment required to produce the withdrawal response diminishes as the CR is strengthened. Asratyan (1962) has demonstrated a heightened excitability at cortical US sites during conditioning. There is also evidence of heightened excitability at the site of application of the CS (Nikolaeva, 1953; 1955), so that as the CR is established, the strength of CS required to elicit the CR diminishes considerably.

Indirect supporting data are also available from EEG studies. It appears that with increase in the number of CS–US pairings, at the CS site photic driving improves, and occurs at lower flash intensities (Dumenko, 1955), and that there is increased amplitude and frequency of evoked potentials (Artem'ef and Bezladnova, 1952; Danilova, 1956; Galambos, Sheatz and Vernier, 1956; Zagorul'ko, 1958). Also of interest is the finding that evoked potentials during conditioning of a defensive CR to electric shock are intensified in the appropriate area of the sensori-motor cortex (Sommer-Smith et al., cited in Gedevanishvili, 1960). Heightened excitability in cortical structures is also suggested in the appearance, at both CS and US sites, of high frequency, high amplitude EEG spikes in response to stimuli applied during conditioning (Meshchevskii, 1955; Rabinovich, 1960), which, although generalised, are more prominent in the second and fourth cortical layers. CFF also seems to improve during the course of conditioning (Livanov, 1962). In this connection, it is important to note that increase in excitability at particular cortical sites does not occur immediately — at times up to 50 pairings are required (Nikolaeva, 1953, 1955). Increase in excitability, however, always precedes the appearance of the CR (Danilova, 1966; Nikolaeva, 1953, 1955).

The precise mechanisms mediating excitability are obscure, though they obviously involve the non-specific activating systems of the reticular formation and the thalamic structures. It is likely that a link is formed, at the thalamic level, between simultaneously acting relay cells in the non-specific efferent pathways for both CS and US, so that ultimately presentation of the CS alone activates the relay cells of both CS and US, and thus the cortical representation of the US due to the action of the CS alone. This is deducible from a number of observations;

direct stimulation of non-specific structures facilitates conditioning (Cherkes, 1958); conditioning is accompanied by electrical changes in both the cortex and non-specific structures (e.g. Gastaut and Roget, 1962; Jouvet and Hernández-Péon, 1957); during conditioning, an arousal reaction which can be excited in the cortex by direct stimulation of non-specific activating structures is always observed (Morrell and Jasper, 1955; Yoshii, Pruvot and Gastaut, 1957, e.g.). All these observations point strongly to recruitment of non-specific activating structures during conditioning.

In human conditioning studies, there is evidence, paralleling the animal data, of increased excitability at CS and US sites (Alekseyenko and Blinkov, 1955; Gyurdzhian, 1954; 1955; Maruseva and Christovich, 1954) involving reduced GSR, alpha-block and vascular response latencies to a CS (Sokolov, 1958a,b), increased CFF and photic driving to low frequency flashing lights (Danilova, 1959; Sokolov, 1958a, b), and reduced latency of alpha-blocking (Jasper and Cruikshank, 1937; Knott, 1939). Chuprikova (1972) also reports increased excitability at both afferent and efferent sites to which paired stimuli are addressed.

Where simple instructions are given, there is evidence, even in very young children, of quite specific EEG patterns (Zaitseva, 1975), which are modality-specific — different patterns, for example, are expressed to "listen", compared with "look" (Khrizman, 1975). Considerable evidence also attests that where afferent-efferent connections are established by verbal instructions, such as in RT experiments, excitability in the appropriate motor analyser is heightened. EMG records show increased excitability both when instructions are presented (Bassin and Serkova, 1956), and throughout the course of the experiment (Kolodnaya, 1957), particularly after presentation of a warning signal (Boiko, 1964). There is also evidence of recruitment of non-specific activating systems following instructions, when measured by EMG (Bassin and Serkova, 1956) and GSR and alpha-block measures (Sokolov, 1958b). Nauta (1971) has also reported increased activation in the cortical area to which the signal is addressed.

The difference between the human and the animal data is that when temporary connections are established by verbal instructions, heightened excitability in afferent and efferent structures, and in the non-specific reticular structures (the latter depending largely on the perceived effectiveness of the US), appear on the first application of the CS, sometimes before, as during the instruction period (Bassin and Serkova, 1956). It seems clear that instructions, which activate previously learned associations, immediately create foci of enhanced or diminished excitability at the cortical locus of both CS and US (Shinchko, 1959; Boiko, 1961) and in the appropriate effector structures. Such increase in excitability is a necessary physiological condition for CR formation.

## (b) Symboling

An obvious gap in Pavlov's human typological theorising concerns higher-order conditioning, problem-solving and thinking. The first describes a level of functioning not necessarily mediated by verbal symbols or language, but, which arguably, may be image-driven, and which can be distinguished from problem-solving and from thinking, which, at higher symbolic levels, may involve dimensions of meaning over and above the denotative content of language. As Razran comments "Configuring — perceiving, is, in a way, a second-signal system, Pavlov's second signal system being really a third" (Razran, 1971, p. 270).

### Higher-order conditioning

We can identify two forms or levels of higher-order conditioning, sensory preconditioning, the "association of associations", and configuring. There is a considerable amount of relevant data reported in the Soviet and Western literature of these issues.

#### i) SENSORY PRECONDITIONING

Sensory preconditioning, involving both forward and backward sequences, was first reported by Panferov (1926) in salivary conditioning with children, and by Narbutovich and Podkopaev (1936) in salivary and aversive (shock) conditioning with dogs. Since that time, the phenomenon has been demonstrated in many species, using a variety of CSs, stimuli in the associated pair, and USs (Rokotova, 1952, 1954; Sergeyev, 1956). Shinchko (1959, 1969) reports comprehensive data from human Ss. Sensory preconditioning was shown by most Ss, using combinations of two to four sensory or verbal preconditioned stimuli, one of which was later paired with salivation, swallowing, hand withdrawal, eye blink, respiratory change or vasoconstrictive URs, produced by administration of sugared beets, unavoidable shock, corneal air puffs, and a device preventing breathing for 30 seconds. Ss' verbal reports showed that they were unaware of the relationship between the associated stimulus and the UR, although they were aware of the relationship between the associated and the to-be-conditioned stimuli, and between the latter and the UR.

The effect is shown by children from an early age. Kazatkin, Mirozyants and Khokhitva (1953) report various types of sensory pre-conditioning in 46–222-day-old infants.

American studies, dating from Brogden's original (1939a) study, report strikingly similar results (cf. review by Kimble, 1961). The majority of these studies have employed human Ss, and CRs have tended to be more complex. Perhaps the most significant findings from both sources is that ease of sensory preconditioning correlates well with position on the phyletic scale, and, not surprisingly, that backward sequences appear to be fully effective only in man and apes, i.e. in higher animals; congruent with this is the finding that sensory preconditioning is abolished only when the higher regions of the cortex — the association, but not the sensory projection areas — are ablated (Thompson & Kramer, 1965).

ii) CONFIGURING

Configuring, or compound stimulus conditioning, involving inter- and intra-analyer synthesis, has been extensively reported in the Russian literature since Palladin's (1906) original study. The essence of compound stimulus conditioning is that the compound, which may be a combination of 2, 3 or 4 stimuli in the same or different sense modalities, has CR efficacy, while the individual elements, in isolation, fail to elicit a CR (Babkin, 1910; Nikolaev, 1911). Different forms of compound CSs have been employed — simultaneous (or complex), in which the CS is typically 2–4 stimuli presented at the same time, successive, where 2 to 4 CSs are applied at intervals of several seconds (chains), and the dynamic stereotype, successive compounds of 4–8 CSs, of which, normally, all but one are paired separately with the US, one being left unpaired. Approved methodology is differential contrast, which involves extinction of component stimuli, and prolonged CR training with compounds, omitting differential contrast, the former being the more usual method of producing configuring or compound without component conditioning.

The fact that conditioning of this type can occur suggests that something is formed in the compound which is not contained in the components. In this connection, Beritoff (1932) refers to an emergent neural-CS centre, mediated by short axon stellate cells in cortical layers 3 and 4 located at the end of the afferent brain, which he postulates as the producer of imagery (1961). Konorskii and Lawicka (1959) note that

> the cortical representation of the compound of conditioned stimuli cannot be simply considered as composed of the particular centres representing each element of the compound. The compound stimulus must be viewed as a stimulus different from its component stimuli (pp. 195–6).

Soviet ablation experiments, which have not been replicated in the West, suggest that configuring is mediated by higher cortical regions. We should note that differential conditioning, with which configuring has sometimes been confused, can be retained even following decortication.

A number of illustrative experiments on human configuring can be cited from the Soviet and Western literature. Shastin (1925), in a salivary conditioning experiment with three young children (one 4-year-old, two 6-year-olds) blindfolded his Ss a few seconds before presenting an auditory CS; he found that the children salivated to the compound CS (blindfold plus auditory stimulus) but not to either alone. Zaklyakova (1965) presented four auditory stimuli — buzzer, bell, metronome, whistle — to three groups of five Ss over a period of 8 days in three sequences. With the first group, the stimuli were presented in random order, with the second, in the order described, with the third, in reverse order. Subsequently, eye-blinks were conditioned to the successive compound stimulus (buzzer-bell-metronome-whistle) using corneal air puff as US. A control group with no previous experience of the auditory stimuli was employed. Conditioning to the compound stimuli occurred significantly faster in the second experimental group.

A considerable amount of data on configural conditioning has been reported in the American literature by Razran (1938) and by Grings and his associates (cf. review by Grings, 1969). Compound conditioning, using a variety of compounds and usually the GSR response, has been demonstrated many times in groups of college students.

From the data reported, sensory preconditioning and configural conditioning have much in common; they occur only in higher animals, being mediated by brain centres higher in evolution than those which mediate sensory conditioning, and both are forms of sensory-sensory learning involving the activation of sensory-orienting reactions. One important difference is that sensory preconditioning involves only sensory-sensory learning, while configural conditioning involves interaction with reinforcers.

Pavlov considered the formation of the dynamic stereotype the highest achievement of the dog's brain, and, except for the second signal system, possibly of the brain in general. However, at no stage did he offer a detailed analysis of the phenomenon, other than to point out that Petrova's data emphasise the importance of internalisation in rendering higher animals relatively autonomous of their surroundings. Razran (1971) suggests that this form of learning may be the evolutionary mechanism transforming neurone behaviour into neuro-cognition.

We need to ask, of course, whether the laws governing the formation of sensory CRs also apply to sensory preconditioning and the formation of the dynamic stereotype. Information on this point is not available, except indirectly, from a number of experiments Pavlov describes in relation to experimental neurosis and psychopathology (1941). He notes experiments in which already established dynamic stereotypes were altered in dogs with different types of nervous system. The ease with which the stereotype can be altered is a function of the stability of the stereo type (i.e. number of times reinforced), the nature, order and complexity of the components, and the type of nervous system. Pavlov reports that even the strong equilibrated type of nervous system found it difficult to change an already established dynamic stereotype (p. 99). With the extreme types, the excitable and the weak, chronic, pathological conditions develop when the nervous system is stressed, i.e. when a strong dynamic stereotype is altered. The outcome is similar to that following "collisions" between excitatory and inhibitory processes. The excitable type becomes more unrestrained and nervous, the weak type more depressive and withdrawn. Thus the strong and equilibrated types are more able to tolerate alteration of the components of the stereotype than the unequilibrated — excitable or weak — types. With the latter, neurosis may develop. Strength and equilibrium, and, to a lesser extent, mobility of nervous processes, determine the ease with which alteration of the dynamic stereotype is tolerated by dogs.

Over and above these data, there are a few studies reporting the cohesion of stable stereotypes, and the consequences of attempted alteration. Selivanova (1979), for example, reports that changes in the spatial arrangement of conditioned and unconditioned stimuli in stable stereotypes in dogs lead to experimental neurosis with long-lasting disturbances in situational conditioned reflexes and in short-term memory.

We might infer from some of Pavlov's comments, and, indirectly, from data reported by later workers, that similar nervous system characteristics determine the ease with which the original stereotype is formed. There are solid theoretical grounds for arguing that the formation of stereotypes depends, in the first instance, on strength of irradiation, as opposed to concentration. As we shall see later (Chapter 8), this depends, in turn, on differences in strength and balance of nervous processes. Moderate levels of strength and balance create optimal conditions for concentration, with the result that the associative networks are more circumscribed, discrete. On the other hand, extremes of strength and balance favour irradiation, and, as a consequence, more pervasive, generalised stereotypes. In one important sense, therefore, individual differences in levels of irradiation and concentration may determine the modes in which experience is laid down. It seems obvious, for example, that any tendency to form "loose" stereotypes may impede the transformation of simple CS–CR links, since the "adequate" CS is probably not a simple, discrete stimulus activating highly specific afferent-efferent links. It could also be argued that mobility of nervous processes, which has been regarded as a fundamental nervous system property, is more a behavioural consequence of these more basic properties, high mobility being associated with concentration (i.e. moderate levels of strength and balance) and circumscribed stereotypes, and low mobility with irradiation (very high/low levels of strength, and imbalance), and more or less unstable stereotypes.

On this basis, we might expect that the principles governing both the formation and the alteration of dynamic stereotypes are similar to those governing associative linkage in general, and the development of sensory CRs in particular. There are, however, a few discordant notes. For example, Dumenko (1975) reports that during elaboration of a dynamic stereotype (in dogs) changes in EEG background activity during inter-stimulus intervals are different from those observed during formation of ordinary conditioned reflexes, suggesting special mechanisms. Pavlov has also suggested that in the alteration, and presumably formation of dynamic stereotypes, an additional, "mental" element is involved. He notes

> It would seem strange to me, if, on the ground that only associative activity is ascribed by the psychologists to the dog, this nervous task (alteration of the dynamic stereotype) should not be considered a mental one. (1941, p. 99).

Precisely what this involves, however, is a matter of conjecture.


*Problem-solving*

Is problem-solving simply an outgrowth of configuring, and thus a configure of configures, or, phenomenally, an image of images? Or does it involve "insight", a higher level of symbolic functioning?

The image as the phenomenal core of perception is a strong tradition in Western psychology. "Perception is image", claimed Bühler (1907), elaborating on the Aristotelian dictum 'thought is image'. As Razran (1971) notes, however, "neural perception-like action" must precede the sensory pattern before the latter can be phenomenally achieved, so that perception, as distinct from sensation, is a neuro-cognitive category of mind.

Pavlov notes, in somewhat similar vein

> Sensation is a kind of purer physiological stimulation ... perception, however, is what arises in the brain when the stimulation ... is connected with other stimulations and old traces. It is this that enables us to get an idea of an external object. Such is perception. The final result of internal elaboration constitutes its very essence (1955, p. 580). Perception, if considered profoundly, is simply a conditioned reflex (ibid., p. 581).

To Pavlov, then, perception was image plus contextual variables. Image is what we perceive, and although evoked by the immediate stimulus, it embraces the representations of all events contiguous to previous experience with the same stimulus. As we shall note later, this additional element is an important aspect of thinking and higher nervous activity.

In man, problem-solving, which involves perception of what-leads-to-what, is often mediated by language. Possibly the benefit conferred by language is evident not so much during the initial configuring, but in carrying over the relationship to new situations, although we might regard this as a "thinking" process, akin to Spearman's concept of "g", which involves the generalisation of abstracted relationships. Probably we need to make a distinction between the capacity to generalise, which is determined by the process of irradiation, and that generalisation which is dependent on the steering of the stream of consciousness by efferent activity, mediated, in the first instance, by language. In many of the animal problem-solving tasks cited in the literature, while it is clear that, after extensive practice, sub-human primates, for example, can link together a series of associations into a behavioural chain, leading to some desirable outcome, this is not easily transferable to new situations, i.e. the linked associations are, to a great extent, situation-specific.

A prime example is the behaviour of the very sophisticated and conceptually trained chimpanzee, Raphael, from Pavlov's laboratory. Raphael learned to extract a cup from a box with a stick, then fill the cup with water by turning a spigot on a jug in another part of the laboratory, and then to douse a flame barring a banana in a food dispenser. According to Pavlov, he had learned "associations of associations" through extensive experience with the material. However, during one summer, after spending a considerable period of time on a raft on Lake Ladoga, when confronted with the food dispenser and the defending flame on his raft, and the jug on another raft 3 metres away, he was highly frustrated until he managed to join two poles, cross over them with the cup, extract water from the jug, recross, and extinguish the flame to get the food. He made no attempt to use the water on which the raft floated, although previously he had learned to scoop water with the cup to cool himself. Vatsuro, in describing his behaviour, comments that since Raphael did not possess a second signal system, i.e. language or symboling, he was, to all intents and purposes, idealess. On the other hand, as Razran (1971) notes, a number of studies have demonstrated that microcephalic children, while inferior to apes in performance of concept formation tasks, nevertheless learn more words in a comparatively short time than any chimpanzee from many years of training. More recent evidence suggests that the slowness of language learning by sub-human primates may be due to lack of voluntary motor control over respiratory, laryngeal and buccal muscles, judging from the highly sophisticated levels of signal language achieved by some Ss.

On a number of occasions Pavlov vigorously rejected the view of Yerkes, Köhler and the Gestaltists, that mental processes in chimpanzees differ qualitatively from the associative higher nervous activity of other animals, the difference between the mental activity of chimpanzees and man being only quantitative.

> They (Yerkes and Köhler) regard this activity (problem-solving) as a manifestation of a special intelligence of apes, and sharply distinguish it from the activity of dogs, which they regard as an associative process .... What is the difference between ape and dog in this respect? ... Raphael's success is due, above all, to the highly developed mechanical

possibilities of his body ... we find nothing, absolutely nothing, that had not already been observed by us in dogs. This is a process of association followed by a process of analysis ... and accompanied by an inhibitory process which facilitates differentiation (1955, p. 559). There you have the whole of Raphael's man-like activity; his entire behaviour is based on analysis and association (ibid, p. 562).

Pavlov is scornful of the Gestaltists claim that their apes went away, "meditated at leisure", "found a solution". "This is absolute nonsense" (ibid, p. 562). The hiatus in activity is due entirely to fatigue.

Their somewhat complex behaviour is a combination of association and analysis, which I consider to be the foundation of the higher nervous activity .... The same can be said of our thinking.

"Beyond association there is nothing more in it" (ibid, p. 563). According to Pavlov, what distinguishes ape intelligence from the problem-solving activity of a child, or our own inventions, is "only the poverty of associations" (ibid, p. 567). Insight initially consists of elementary associations, and then of complex associations between these, to form chains of associations. "Association is knowledge, it is thinking, and when you make use of it, it is insight" (ibid, p. 589).

Pavlov considered Raphael's problem-solving behaviour to be initially imitative, and subsequently, image-driven. This is well illustrated in one task, in which Raphael was required to slide open the lid of a box containing food, using differently-shaped sticks to fit the round, quadrangular or triangular openings in the lids. Following a demonstration by E, using one stick, and one lid, Raphael quickly mastered the task. According to Pavlov, he formed an association between the visual image of the stick and the success of the action. As the experiment proceeded, however, and differently shaped openings were presented, Raphael persisted for a time with the previously successful stick, then resorted to trial and error, until gradually a second phase developed, viz. "a connection between the images of the sticks and (the images of) the shapes of the openings" (ibid, p. 561). Gestalts do emerge, but associations form gestalts, not vice versa. Other examples of chains of associations forming gestalts are the delayed reflex and the dynamic stereotype.

Insofar as the ability to respond to a relationship is concerned — an ability which Köhler regarded as evidence of a higher form of cognition differentiating apes from lower forms — Pavlov, in this Wednesday discussion, cites an experiment, with S. V. Kleshchev, demonstrating, with dogs, the formation of a conditioned reflex to stimulus relations, as quickly as to an isolated stimulus.

Thus, since apes, like dogs, but unlike humans, possess no second-signal system, no new principle of conditioning — or learning, or thinking, or intelligence — governs the mentality of apes. "Cognitive" behaviour of this sort is subject to the laws of excitation and inhibition which regulate nervous activity as a whole — those governing the formation and extinction of CRs, cortical analysis and synthesis, irradiation and concentration.

Vygotsky suggested a somewhat different interpretation of Köhler's results, which certainly indicate, in apes, an embryonic intellect, primitive "thinking" in the proper sense. According to him, however, this in no way relates to speech. Ape ingenuity in finding detours for the solution of a problem, their "inventions" in making and using tools, although undoubtedly involving rudimentary thinking, belong to the prelinguistic phase of thought development. In his general theory, Vygotsky maintained that thought and speech spring from different roots. They develop along quite different lines, although the two growth curves, both phylogenetically and ontogenetically, cross and recross. In young children, there is demonstrably a prelinguistic phase in the use of thought, and a preintellectual phase in the use of language.

Importantly, the close correspondence between thought and language development in man is not evident in higher anthropoids. In dealing with human intellectual and linguistic development, Vygotsky's basic theme is that dialogue is internalised into inner speech and thought. Inner speech is not due to suppression of egocentrism, as Piaget asserted, nor can it be regarded as "subvocal speech" (Watson), muscular tremors in the larynx, a speech reflex inhibited in its motor part (Bechterev), or, as Goldstein suggests, everything that precedes the motor act of speaking, including Wundt's "motives of speech", and the indefinable non-sensory and non-motor speech experience. It is a specific formation with its own laws and complex relations. It is speech for oneself. External speech is for others. The latter is the instrumenting of thought into words, its materialisation, its objectivisation. In inner speech, the process is reversed. Speech is transformed into inward thought. To this extent, therefore, thought development is determined by language, that is, by the linguistic tools of thought and by the socio-cultural experience of the child. The child's intellectual growth is contingent on his mastering the social means of thought, i.e. language.

Köhler maintained that lack of speech — "that infinitely valuable technical aid" — and the paucity of images — "that most important intellectual material" — explains the difference between ape and primitive man, making "even the slightest beginnings of cultural development impossible for the chimpanzee". Vygotsky comments, however, that the ape does have a fairly rich language of his own (32 speech elements, or "words"), and a system of linguistic communication based on an extensive repertoire of gestures expressing affect and social emotions, some of which appear to be a transitional form between grasping and pointing. Pointing gestures are the first stage in the development of speech, a level which is not normally achieved by animals. Ape "speech", however, is not concerned with intellectual reactions, with thinking. It originates in emotion and is clearly a part of the total emotional syndrome, far removed from intentional or conscious attempts to inform or influence others.

Köhler introduced the term insight (Einsicht) to describe the intellectual operations accessible to both chimpanzee and man. However, from his behavioural descriptions, it is clear that the actual physical presence of a sufficiently simple situation is a necessary condition for the functioning of the chimpanzee's intellect. There is no evidence that apes reach the stage of objective representation in any of their activities. For example, none showed the slightest intent to represent anything in their "drawings". As Koffka points out, by insight Köhler meant seeing in the literal sense, and only by extension seeing in the sense of understanding relations, comprehending. The intellectual reaction is steered not by memory traces, but by the situation as visually presented. There are inherent limitations of imagery. Even the best tool to solve a given problem has no utility for the chimpanzee if he cannot see it simultaneously or quasi-simultaneously with the goal, a point also heavily underscored by Pavlov in describing Raphael's behaviour.

It is obvious that Vygotsky had little sympathy with the rather simplistic view of the second signal system espoused by Pavlov. For him words, language, was not simply a redintegration of the qualities of the sensory stimuli, but something much more — a mediating structure through which such stimuli were filtered, and interpreted in terms of the individual's experience, his social activity, his social goals and motivations. Although this was never explicitly stated, from this point of view there are no grounds for assuming any similarity between the laws governing the operation of the second and the first signal systems. Nor did he have much patience with nebulous terms such as insight in accounting for the problem-solving behaviour of apes. For him, concept development is a highly complex process, involving progress from "heaps", to complexes, to pseudo-concepts, to true concepts; the latter, and the language which infuses and instruments them, give power and strategy to cognitive activity. Nothing like this is observable in apes. Nor is there anything akin to man's capacity to create higher-order structures which in effect replace and give new meaning to the conceptual structures which themselves are sign-posts *en route* to higher-order mastery. Once a new structure has been incorporated into the child's thinking, it recruits the older concepts into the intellectural operations of the higher type.

*Thinking*

What about thinking — "associative memory" — in Razran's terms the outcome of acquired symboling involving the neurocognition of meaning? To what extent is it imageless, to what extent mediated and steered by imagery, sensory and verbal? This question, of course, merges into psycholinguistics, which is beyond the scope of this book. However, we need to examine, however superficially, some basic concepts in this area *vis-à-vis* the theory of higher nervous activity and human typology.

A strong structuralist tradition is evident in the thinking of Sechenov and Pavlov. Sechenov (1863) — in agreement with the views of Locke and Hartley — maintained that thought and imagination, "ideas", originate in sense impressions. These elements are subject to higher order synthesis — the "reflection" on pure sense data of Locke, the apperception or creative synthesis of Wundt, the "attention" of Titchener. In all cases, however, thought or consciousness was regarded as implicit in the totality of sensory elements.

Sechenov was perhaps the first to suggest that all psychical phenomena are expressed in muscular activity, whether in words, or in actions. Psychical activity is initiated in sense stimulation, and culminates in muscular activity. But what about the middle section of the reflex? How are sense stimuli and muscular activity connected in the brain? Sechenov postulated brain centres which augment or inhibit the muscular phase of the reflex arc, a view which was expanded by Pavlov in his theory of conditioned reflexes. According to Sechenov, when the muscular phase is enhanced, we have emotion, when it is inhibited, we have thought. "In a thought, we have the beginning of a reflex, and its continuation; only the end of the reflex (i.e. the movement) is apparently absent" (1935, p. 320). Sechenov believed that all psychic phenomena — sensation, perception, thinking, will, motivation, memory, love — can be accounted for within the framework of the reflex arc.

Bekhterev (1907), and following him, Watson and the behaviourists, suggested that thought processes depended on the inner activities of the musculature of speech. Thought and imagination, therefore, are simply implicit muscular behaviour, symbolising lines of overt action. They note, however, a distinction between passive and active language, the former describing (conditioned) responses to words, the latter the use of words describing the development of language as a social tool. Words are learned initially as separate units, then are integrated into higher units. Overt language is gradually replaced by internal language, implicit language activity, "silent speech". For the behaviourists, therefore, thinking consisted of speech movements on a small scale, which substitute for overt acts. No longer do we encounter "ideas", but speech movements of the elements involved in thought. Thought processes, therefore, are described in terms of language.

Another, and different point of view was expressed by the Wurtzburg school, postulating elements of experience — "conscious attitudes" (Bewusstseinslagen) — not reducible to sensations and images. These bear some resemblance to the "imageless thoughts" described by Stout (1896) to the "transitive states" referred to by William James in his discussion of "stream of thought", and to the "perceptual reaction" of Woodworth (1915).

Sechenov and Pavlov adopted a position half-way between these extremes. Neither entirely equated thought with language. Both railed against animistic concepts such as "insight", "intuition". Sechenov's much quoted statement that "Thought is the first two-thirds of the psychical reflex" (1863, p. 503) clearly expressed his view that while thought involves receptor and central neural action, it does not involve explicit effector action. He also observed, however, that during development, effector action is inhibited first as gross motor movement, then as verbal behaviour. This in no way excludes the possibility that at certain developmental stages, or at certain levels of cognitive processing, thinking is at least accompanied, if not directed by implicit or silent speech.

Pavlov, in his later theorising, was quite explicit in his views on thinking "The entire mechanism of thinking consists of the elaboration of elementary associations, and in the subsequent formation of chains of associations" (1955, p. 593). The complexity of the associative networks is obviously an important factor "As associations grow and increase in number ... thinking becomes more profound" (ibid, p. 594). At this stage, an additional element is added "This, however, is only half the process. It is what the philosophers, including Locke ... call synthesis" (ibid, p. 594). The other half is cortical analysis. In describing this process, he draws an analogy from his experiments with dogs, in which differentiation initially produces temporary irradiations — generalisation — then response inhibition to the generalisation stimuli, so that "the real connection becomes more and more precise" (ibid, p. 595). This is what happens in human thinking.

> The habits of scientific thought consist, above all, in obtaining ... a more precise connection and in the subsequent rejection of all accidental connections .... The process of thinking begins with associations, with synthesis; then analysis joins in. The latter is based ... on the analysing capacity of our receptors, of the peripheral endings, and ... on the process of inhibition which develops in the cerebral cortex and sorts out that which does not correspond to reality from that which does (ibid, p. 595).

Pavlov had little to say about the relation of thought to language. His postulate that the second-signal system, unique to man, involved a new neural principle was in the nature of a generalisation, not supported by empirical data. It was left to subsequent workers in the fields of higher nervous activity (the study of the physiological basis of perception, learning and thinking), and psycholinguistics, which are separate research and teaching disciplines in the Soviet Union, to investigate this problem. However, Soviet psycholinguists have been more directly concerned with the problems of language teaching in a

multilingual society, and workers in perception and learning with developmental aspects of these processes, so that concern with the problem has tended
to be peripheral rather than direct.

Western psychology tends to favour the Wurtzburg approach to thinking, an
emphasis also acknowledged in certain schools of Soviet psychology — the
influential Georgian "Set Psychology" school, for example. In general, while it
is recognised that the kinaesthetic sensations which often accompany thinking
are obviously due to general or linguistic muscular action, few now consider
these to be an integral part of thinking. Similarly, there is now a general
consensus that, as thinking becomes more practised and abstract, imagery
becomes less clearly identifiable as a component. "Meaning" — whatever the
term connotes — assumes greater functional significance at higher levels of
abstracting.

However, we should mention that in Soviet psycholinguistics, which has
been shaped by the psychological theory of Vygotsky, considerable importance
is attached to the intimate relationship between language and thinking
(Vygotsky, 1968; Luria, 1968; Zhinkin, 1966, 1967; Leont'ev, 1977). Contrast
this with the views of American psycholinguists, based on the transformational
generative grammars produced by the Chomskian revolution, in which no such
emphasis can be detected. Luria (1968), who has provided strong empirical
support for Vygotsky's language-thought model from extensive neuro-
linguistic data, refers to "the coding of thought into a verbal utterance after
passing through the stage of inner speech" (p. 210-11). Zhinkin (1966) claims
that inner speech does not necessarily employ a speech-movement code, rather
that it has its own unique code in which "visual ideas and a variety of schemata"
are significant elements (p. 20).

Generally speaking, Soviet psycholinguists distinguish between "inner
speaking", a latent physiological activity of the articulatory organs, which may
(although not necessarily) imitate processes occurring during real speaking,
"inner speech", basically a code to solve some communicative (usually
cognitive) task, which may be accompanied by inner speaking, and "inner
programming" of an utterance, the employment of an inner speech code to plan
an utterance, or to retain its content in short-term memory. Obviously,
relationships between thought, speech, and inner speaking, inner speech and
inner programming are highly complex, and details need not concern us here.
However, we might note in passing the developmental significance of
articulatory kinaesthesis, and its later generalisation and differentiation in
relation to symboling and thinking, which is indicated in Soviet research
reporting that motor reproduction of articulation plays a highly important role
in speech learning at its inception (Lyakh, 1968a,b).

In considering the role of language and thinking in human typology, a number of obvious questions arise. How do words, as abstractions, and their combinations, in propositions, interrelate to form complex associational networks? As higher levels of abstraction are realised, how and to what extent does language move away from direct reflection of image? Are higher levels of symboling mediated by neural centres independent of those centres carrying concrete images of words, as has been suggested by Beritov (1932) and Konorski and Lawicka (1959) in the case of compound sensory CSs and their components? If so, what new principles are involved?

Data bearing on these issues are limited. There is no direct evidence of higher nervous centres mediating higher configures of "meaning", although, on the basis of Luria's (1966a) extensive evidence that frontal lobe functioning is essential for complex stimulus processing and orienting activity, we might suggest these structures as a possible site. There is, however, some indirect evidence on this point. Data have been reported suggesting a relationship between age and intellectual ability and the modes and limits of phonetographic (sensory) and meaning (semantic) generalisation for both words and propositions, and, from the Soviet data on thinking, some indications of the relative significance of verbal compared with sensory CSs in conditioning and discrimination learning.

Insofar as phonetographic and semantic generalisation are concerned Razran (1971) has drawn extensively on both Soviet and Western sources in generating a model which seems to fit the reported data. He postulates a two-level structure of symboling. The first is a concrete level, in which symbols are "units of intra-organismic neurocognitive meaning and extra-organismic linguistic communication". As we have previously noted, words can substitute for sensory CSs, and can create the conditions — in terms of excitability in the appropriate cortical projection and efferent centres — for CR formation. A second, abstract level involves the integration or transformation of such units into higher and essentially independent configures carrying additional meaning — as in the case of sensory configures — while linguistic communication phases continue to play an instrumental role. These higher configures — sememes — imply the emergence of a new phase of "symbolic neurocognition", and, in turn, are integrated into higher configures of meaning, known as propositions. Arrays of sentences come to serve identical or nearly identical semantic or logical propositions organised as neurocognitive wholes, or logisemes. Thus symboling gives rise to three ascending levels of thinking — a specific symbolic level, in which meaning is still bound up with the effector units of languages — which Razran denotes as symbosemic — a semantic level, in which ultimate units of identical as well as related meaning are served by different linguistic units, and a logisemic level, where general logical propositions dominate language.

Most of the data relevant to phonetographic and semantic generalisation
have been derived from classical conditioning experiments in which words and
sentences have been used as CSs (cf reviews by Razran, 1961b; Maltzman,
1968). The "dynamic transfer" of a CR, i.e. the transfer and extinction of CRs
from sensory stimuli to their word designations has been well established
(Traugott, 1934; Seredina, 1956b; Marushevsky, 1957; experiments cited by
Bykov, 1953). Note, however, that transfer from first to second signal system is
easier than the reverse (Harris, 1960), which seems to require extensive
experience of first to second system transfer. This may reflect one of the
operational characteristics of language, particularly in propositional form, viz.
to retain the "sense" of individual stimulus items, without necessarily
redintegrating *in toto* their individual sensory components. In the
latter event, sensory chaos would develop, with cortical overload the
inevitable outcome. Presumably this is what Pavlov meant by the
synthesising and analysing capacity of the cortex, although he was referring
specifically to sensory chains. In modern terminology we would refer to a
gating interface, possibly mediated by the hippocampal and temporal lobe
structures.

The reported data point to the following conclusions.

1. What has been referred to as "elective generalisation", i.e. word to word
CR transfer, to transfer of autonomic responses from one symbolic cue to
another which is related in some definable way, has been shown to follow verbal
dimensions (e.g. Razran, 1939, 1949, 1949a, 1952; Riess, 1940, 1946; Lacey and
Smith, 1954; Grush *et al.,* 1973). Chen-Jung (1973) reports differences in
orienting response magnitudes and habituation rate to changes of verbal
meaning, none to changes in form. Greater transfer from CS words to their
synonyms than to homonyms has been reported, employing salivary (Razran,
1939) and GSR (Riess, 1946) CRs. However, type of transfer appears to vary
with the chronological and development level of S (Reiss, 1940, 1946). Reiss
(1946) reports greater transfer to antonyms and homonyms than to synonyms
in young Ss, and that this relationship reverses with older Ss. This is consistent
with the findings of Luria (1959) and Luria and Vinogradova (1959); the latter
report semantic generalisation in their normal group, semantic and
phonetographic generalisation in their retarded group and phonetographic
generalisation only in their severely retarded group. This is also not inconsistent
with the findings of Schwartz (1948, 1949, 1960) that transfer of vasoconstrictive and pupillary CRs occurs to phonetographically related words only early in
conditioning, while semantic generalisation occurs throughout the whole
course of conditioning. This relationship between type of generalisation and
age and ability level of subjects, however, has not always been supported.
Freeman *et al.* (1972), for example, report signal value generalisation along

both semantic and phonetographic dimensions with their group of normal adults.

Mednick (1957) has reported transfer among words related in terms of word association norms; transfer has been demonstrated from a vocalised nonsense syllable to a subvocal word (Menzies, 1941; Noble, 1950) and as a generalisation based on mediated verbal similarity (Hartman, 1963).

2. Transfer within larger verbal units has also been demonstrated. Razran (1949) reports salivary CR transfer of propositionally equivalent, but sententially different sentences, and Vinogradova (1957) that when motor and salivary CRs are conditioned, using a discrimination schedule, US+ being the word "good" and US– the word "error", when true and false statements are substituted for these words they are responded to in terms of the original conditioning. Acker and Edwards (1964) differentially conditioned vaso-constrition to the words "good" and "bad", and report transfer to words evaluated on the good-bad scale of the semantic differential.

The phenomenon of semantic transfer seems to require that Ss will form a conceptual model of the semantic category of the original stimulus to which they are conditioned. In terms of Osgood's (1953) theory of mediated generalisation, which is considered by many to underlie the phenomenon of semantic generalisation, verbal stimuli produce mediators which in turn come to elicit responses as a result of conditioning. S's subsequent responsiveness to the test stimuli (words) is thus the degree to which test words elicit the mediating responses.

3. An interesting set of data, reported by Razran (1971, pp. 279–81) emphasises the point that, within the constraint that the efferent system of language seldom fully reflects the afferent neurocognition of meaning, nevertheless the structure of the latter is reflected in the organisation of language. What he is referring to is the referential relations of single units contained within propositions.

Razran cites data from his own studies (Razran, 1952) and from El'kin (1955). El'kin conditioned finger withdrawal to shock, CS being the sentence "Student vyderzhal ekzamen" (The student passed the examination), and reports 86% transfer to "passed", 50% transfer to "examination" and 10% transfer to "student". With more emotional stimuli, El'kin reports 100% transfer to each of the two words in the sentence "Vklyuchaya tok" (I am turning on the shock). Razran (1952), using a salivary conditioning technique, reports approximately similar transfer to different linguistic units in three matched sentences, none with apparent affective connotation (e.g. "Ya Dal Yemu novy myach" — I gave him a new ball). Transfer to the subject varied between 9 and 18%, to the predicative verb, 30 and 46%, to the direct object, 26 and 28%, although such differences were not evident in a control study of the conditioning efficacy of individual words. While such data should be regarded as tentative, they do suggest that, unlike compound stimulus conditioning, the changed functional significance of the components of grammatical organisation is a function of the compounding, rather than of the original inequality of the components, and that grammatical organisation pertains to the interaction of generalised higher configures, and not to specific words.

Studies concerned with aspects of combined (verbal-sensory) conditioning with young Ss have thrown up interesting data suggesting the dominance of verbal over sensory symboling from the earliest age. For example, studies from Kol'tsova's laboratory (Kol'tsova, 1967) suggest that with groups of 8–15-month-old infants, the verbal component in a combined verbal-sensory CS has greater CR efficacy, and that, generally speaking, second-signal (i.e. verbal or symbolic) conditioning does not follow the laws of simple conditioning and generalisation. The number of ways in which a particular object — e.g. a doll, or book — is experienced, both verbally and tactually, seems to be more important than stimulus-response repetitions. Reinforcement or pairing with biological USs is not required. Lyakh's (1968a,b) data, which are too extensive to report fully here, show clearly that in groups of 2–8-month-old infants, articulation with and without vocalisation of the Russian vowel sounds "a" and "oo" produces significant differences between groups in imitative articulation and spontaneous vocalisation. Certain compound stimuli are more effective than others (vocalisation appears to be the crucial element) in initial learning, resistance to extinction and rate of differential conditioning. With slightly older children (3–10 years), evidence from the American literature suggests that the older the child, the more readily can he reverse the rule of his learned discrimination. This would be anticipated only on the assumption of a dominant role for symboling.

In general, it appears that man's higher-order symboling steers his linguistic, perceptual and conditioning behaviour. Even Pavlov, who had little enough to say on this matter, affirmed that "Thoughts (of humans in conditioning experiments) about 'what is done to them and why' inhibit the formation of conditioned reflexes"(1949, Vol. I, p. 244). Concepts dominate percepts, the primary sources of information about the world. They are more stable and veridical, since concept formation involves the averaging out of variations due to environmental inconstancy of whatever origin.

### (c) Signification and Signalisation

A recurring question in our discussion of higher nervous activity is whether we can account for this activity in both animals and humans in terms of a single principle, viz. signalisation. Pavlov clearly recognised both a continuity and a discontinuity in the higher nervous activity of man and animals — a continuity in that both are products of conditioned reflexes, a discontinuity in that the second signal system, which is unique to man, confers an immeasurably greater potential for connecting and associating, for thinking. But does this require an additional explanatory principle?

Pavlov, despite some inconsistencies and contradictions in some of his writings on this issue, never fundamentally deviated from a simple, one principle (signalisation) model. Other views on the relationship of psychological processes such as thinking, logical memory, to higher nervous activity, however, have been expressed in the Soviet literature. Perhaps the most explicit are those of Vygotsky (e.g. 1960, 1972), whose theories have recently become very influential in Soviet psychology. Writing in the late 1920s, he maintained that while the fundamental and most general activity of the cerebral hemispheres of both man and animals is signalisation, the most fundamental and general activity distinguishing man from animals, psychologically speaking, is signification, that is, the creation and use of artificial signs which permit man to master the signal activity of the cerebral hemispheres.

It could be argued that Vygotsky, by his emphasis on the ways in which, and the extent to which, man has shaken free from the yoke of stimulus-response conditioning, was the real architect of the second signal system. As we have noted, Pavlov regarded this system as a reflection of reality in the sense that word is a higher-order signal of signals, adding not a new dimension, but a wider scope to higher nervous activity, thus counteracting, to some extent, the excessive rigidity of his earlier theorising. Vygotsky, however, proclaimed that man actively creates a mediator between himself and the physical world, a structure through which the stimulus signals of the physical world are filtered. Man reacts to sensory signals in terms of his own idiosyncratic conception of reality. This construction, the second signal system, is shaped by society and by social activity.

On the other hand, the system of connections formed in the animal brain on the basis of contingent signalisation is a copy, a reflection of the natural ties between "all types of natural agents which signal the appearance of immediately beneficial or destructive events". In this sense, nature determines behaviour, adaptation is passive. The conditional reflex principle, however, cannot explain all, or even most human behaviour, as Pavlov asserted, since man's adaptation is active, involving the alteration of nature and of his own behaviour. Active adaptation presupposes a complex structure of artificial connections amongst environmental stimuli which signify behaviour, so as to create new connections in the brain, connections which are subordinate to man's will, to his needs and aptitudes. Man masters nature, rather than vice-versa. "Natura parendo vincitur" pinpoints the sense in which Vygotsky believed that in mastering nature, man masters himself, for it is the internalisation of overt action which constitutes thought. Vygotsky therefore clearly distinguishes elementary and higher psychological processes, between which there is a qualitative gap, an observation originally made by Kornilov in 1925. Elementary processes are explicable in physiological terms, as chains of reflexes, and schematic cortical/subcortical connections. Higher processes, however, have to be explained in socio-historical terms. Vygotsky suggests that man's mastery of nature can be understood only through consideration of his social nature. In the process of social activity, man has created and developed complex systems of psychological connections, without which neither work nor social relations would be possible. Social behaviour requires a new regulatory principle guiding the determination of social behaviour through signs. Of all the regulatory systems, speech is pre-eminent. Through speech, man controls his own behaviour and that of others.

Vygotsky makes a clear distinction between the situation in which one person influences another through language, and that in which, in his words, "the key and the apparatus are in one pair of hands", the apparatus being the cerebral cortex, Pavlov's "magnificent signalling apparatus", the key to this apparatus being the signal system of speech. The first case, he suggests, may appear, superficially, to fit the conditioned reflex pattern, an assumption usually made by reflexologists when discussing the role of word, the oral command, in conditioning experiments. However, the passive creation of connections by auditory signals explains only the response to human speech by animals, and by the young child at an early developmental stage. Understanding speech is obviously much more complex, approximating the second case, in that psychological connections may be formed within the same behavioural systems. Here we are concerned largely with issues of autostimulation and self-mastery.

Vygotsky lays great emphasis on the difference between active and passive formation of artificial connections, as well as that between artificially created and naturally occurring connections. He notes

> It may be said of an animal that it is attracted by food, but it cannot be said of a stick that it "took itself" into a monkey's hand to reach a piece of food lying outside the cage. Similarly, it cannot be said of a man who ties a knot (in his handkerchief), as a reminder, that the information memorised itself by him (1960).

In effect, the man is actively constructing the process of memorisation by forcing an external object to remind him of something. In this lies a fundamental characteristic of higher forms of behaviour. In more elementary forms, something is remembered; in the higher form, man remembers something. In the first case, a temporary link is formed through the concurrence of two stimuli which simultaneously affect the organism. In the second case, the man deliberately forms a temporary link through the actual creation of stimuli.

This, then, is the essence of the dialetical or qualitative leap referred to by Kornilov and Vygotsky. It allows a change in the quality and type of stimulus-response relationship. It has its origin in a fundamental new element in human mental functioning — a "stimulus-means". Language, enumeration, calculations, plans can all be regarded as instances of such "stimulus-means", stimuli not given, but created by man, on his own initiative, through which he establishes new stimulus-response relationships which allow behaviour to occur. Not for man the fate of Buridano's ass, who, when faced with an irresolvable approach-approach conflict situation, starved to death. In such a situation, the normally functioning human may flip a coin, thus forcing a choice between the two stimuli. Such strategies, of course, can be external or internal. As the individual internalises rules of conduct, he resorts more frequently to internal stimulus-means, such as verbal codes in memory. The defining characteristic of man's behaviour is, thereore, that he is able to personally influence his relationships with environmental stimuli, and through this agency, to change his behaviour, subjugating it to his own control.

In distinguishing signalisation from signification, Vygotsky employs the analogy, suggested by Pavlov, of the telephone switchboard. Where two lines are directly connected, this corresponds to the unconditioned connection. Where the call is relayed with the help of temporary connections we refer to a conditioned connection. If we wish to grasp the essential differences between signalisation and signification, however, we should consider not only the switching mechanism, but also the operator. This added feature, which refers to the needs, purposes and goals of the operator, denotes signification. Thinking, imagination, creates artificial or preferred images, and behaviour is then selected to realise these images.

Vygotsky comments that the use of signs, in one sense, is analogous to the use of tools. Both are forms of mediated activity. The essential difference between them lies in their different use. The function of a tool is to conduct man's influence on the object of his activity. It is externally oriented, a means of man's external activity aimed at mastering nature, and must lead to a change in the object. On the other hand, a sign, which is an auxiliary means of solving psychological problems — to remember, to compare, to choose, for example — changes nothing in the object of the psychological operation. It is a means of internal activity aimed at man's mastery of himself. To this extent, expressions such as "Language is the tool of thought" are misleading. Signs, of which words are only one, although admittedly important class, are the means by which man "operates" on his environment to advance his personal goals and objectives.

Thus, according to Vygotsky, there are real qualitative differences between the behaviours of man and animal. These differences he attributes to their different evolutionary and cultural histories, i.e. to characteristic features of passive rather than active adaptation, the one being governed by the principle of signalisation, the other by signification. The latter, which distinguishes a good deal of higher-order psychological functioning, and is thus descriptive of much human behaviour, refers both to the process of connecting artificially created signs, and to the fabrication of sign structures (as in the case of memory aids), which serve to activate, at some future time, and, to a degree, trans-situationally, established associative links. Whether the operational character-istics of such processes differ from those known to describe signalisation to the extent that new laws and principles need to be invented to account for these, however, is problematical.

### (d) Artistic and Thinking Types

Pavlov viewed the problem of human types as a complex issue, due to the greater intensity of nervous system processes, and to the social character of human environment. Thus nervous system properties, while providing the basis for type determination, are modified by early social influences to the extent that strength-weakness or mobility of cortical cells alone will not determine how adaptable a nervous system will be under changing conditions. These considerations led Pavlov to employ two additional criteria in human type determination — the interrelationship between cortical and subcortical activity, on the one hand, and between the first and second signalling systems on the other. On the basis of the predominance of one system over the other, or their balance, this relationship being determined in the course of development, he derived three general types — thinking, artistic and middle types.

Animal behaviour is obviously dominated by the first signal system, the effect of any stimulus being determined by neural pathways laid down between CRs and URs during development. Thus the emotional content of sensory signals is determined reflexively by whatever URs they evoke — e.g. food, defense and reproduction. In this sense, much animal behaviour has unconditioned emotional content, in that the animal reacts to a stimulus on the basis of whatever immediate effect it promises, in line with previously established conditioned reflexes. There are no other phenomena to which emotions can be opposed.

With humans, emotion is contrasted with ideas of verbal abstractions, both being different aspects of consciousness, of the reflection of objective reality in the human mind. The role of ideas is primarily to reflect objects and processes, while the primary role of emotions is the evaluation of the significance for the individual of the objects reflected in ideas. Every idea, therefore, has more or less of an emotional tone. There is no emotion without idea, no idea without emotion. It is the emotional aspect of the reflection which mobilises arousal and motivates to action.

The higher nervous activity underlying emotions and ideas, and their interrelationships, involves the sensory and speech systems of the cortex, and the system of unconditioned reflexes in the subcortex. Since ideas are verbal abstractions, or a product of abstraction and synthesis which is mediated by the manipulation of second signals or verbal ability, the underlying nervous activity is mediated by the second or speech system. Emotions, on the other hand, are primarily the interrelated work of the first or sensory signalling system and the subcortical unconditioned system.

The majority of human Ss fall into the middle or balanced category. Their emotions, during the course of development, are increasingly regulated by the second system, i.e. reality testing develops in the course of social experience. Within this constraint, the middle type can be strong, mobile and equilibrated, to varying degrees. In addition to the middle type, however, there are the extreme, though not pathological types, the "intellectual" type, in whom abstract ideas are partly divorced from concrete imagery and emotions — the cloistered academic living in the rarified realm of abstraction is the prototype — and the "bohemian" or "artistic" type, in whom imagination and emotion are partially exempt from the regulating influence of ideas or verbal abstractions. In terms of underlying higher nervous activity, the intellectual type represents a predominance of the second signal system, the artistic type a predominance of the first signal system and the subcortical processes. In both cases there is a degree of dissociation between the different signal systems.

Pavlov developed his theory of human nervous system type in relation to the problem of human neuroses. He wrote

> Constitutional neurasthenia is a form of general weakness occurring in the middle human type. Hysteria is the result of general weakness in the artistic type; psychasthenia (is) a product of weakness in the thinking type (1941, p. 163).

Neurasthenic states result from acute or prolonged overstrain of the nervous processes, through conflict, physical and mental exhaustion, for example. The first stage of neurasthenia is characterised by a weakening of the inhibitory process, shown behaviourally in impulsivity, irritability, lack of self-control. In the second stage, excitatory processes weaken; this is shown behaviourally in general tiredness. The excitatory processes are pathologically labile; they are easily evoked, but rapidly exhaust. In the third stage, heightened inhibitability and lowered reactivity develop as a function of irradiating transmarginal inhibition.

Psychasthenia and hysteria, characteristic of the thinking and artistic types respectively, were considered by Pavlov to involve derangement of the dynamic relationships between the first and second signalling systems. Psychasthenia he viewed as the pathological extreme of the thinking type, and hysteria the pathological extreme of the artistic type. The former is characterised by heightened rationality, a plethora of socially unnecessary inhibitions and very weak emotions, indicating a morbid predominance of the second over the first signal system. Abstract thought takes precedence over more direct signals of reality, so that words and rationalisations seem more real than sense experience and action. The psychasthenic tends to withdraw from reality, to shut himself away in an ideal world of his own making. The real world, however, threatens his fantasies, and he may develop obsessions, which are forms of local neuroses.

Hysteria, the general neurosis of the artistic type, is characterised by highly emotional or imaginative thinking, a tendency to substitute fantasy for reality, and by rash and impulsive actions. The pathological disturbance of higher nervous processes underlying hysteria is a predominance of the first signal system over the second, and of subcortical activity over cortical. As the normal regulating influence of the second signal system over the first diminishes, the activity of the latter becomes chaotic, and is characterised by pathological fantasies and unrestrained emotional behaviour. This can lead to such stressing of cortical and subcortical cells that there is great increase in irradiating transmarginal inhibition, which may pass through the various hypnotic phases between wakefulness and sleep — equalisation, paradoxical and ultra-paradoxical phases — with their particular clinical syndromes of suggestibility, catalepsy, twilight states, anaesthesia, and paralysis. Hysterics, therefore, are particularly susceptible to the inhibitory states of partial sleep or hypnosis.

Thus, in his human typological theorising, Pavlov was concerned primarily with the pathogenesis of general neuroses. The 3 distinctive forms he identifies — neurasthenia, psychasthenia and hysteria — all result from overstrain of the cortical processes, producing dissociations between the cortical signalling systems, and between these and subcortical activity. They are peculiarly human, in that they all involve, in one way or another, the human speech system of signalling. We should note, however, that any form of neurosis can occur under appropriate conditions in any one of the 3 types. Type implies heightened, rather than exclusive, susceptibility.

Treatment involves restoration of the healthy functioning of the underlying higher nervous activity, the interrelations between the cortical signalling systems, and between the cortical and subcortical processes. Pavlov's clinic claimed that bromide, combinations of bromides and caffeine, and particularly sleep therapy were the most effective ways of treating neuroses. According to Pavlov, sleep inhibition, which can be produced by drugs or suggestion/

hypnosis (Platonov, 1959), can be partial in depth and extensiveness, and can develop in restricted regions of the cortex. One part of the cortex may be inhibited, another part excited. It is interesting to note that this phenomenon of differential excitability in the cortex was subsequently proposed by Oswald (1962). The waking section of the cortex, which Pavlov called the "sentry post" in the first signal system, the "rapport zone" in the second, may be maintained in a state of heightened excitability, due to the surrounding inhibition. As the excitability of the wakeful section becomes relatively greater, verbal suggestion becomes more and more effective. The opportunity for reconditioning under these conditions is considerably improved. The system of conditioning therapy, based on these techniques of suggestion and hypnosis, remains an important aspect of Soviet psychiatric practice.

## Summary

Comparatively little work has been reported on the relationships of nervous system properties to higher order conditioning, to configuring and symboling, particularly to language and thinking, which, according to Pavlov, constitutes the second, exclusively human, signal system. The extent to which relationships demonstrated in the first, conditional, signal system can be generalised to second signal system activity is problematical. It is clear that words can substitute for, and at times displace, the sensory CSs they denote, thus introducing a reserve of plasticity into human behaviour. Something more than this, however, is involved in human adaptation. As Vygotsky emphasised, adaptation is active rather than passive, signification rather than signalisation being an essential ingredient in man's mastery of nature. This suggests that there are, in fact three, rather than two, signalling systems, a point also made by Razran, and implied in Bykov's concept of fused reflexes. The first involves BSRF structures, where perception, via cortical activation, cannot be dissociated from unconditional reflex responsivity. This is Pavlov's first system. At a second level, we need to postulate a system where BSRF and unconditional reflexes are inhibited, probably via the diffuse thalamic system, thus allowing perception to occur in the absence of response. This seems a necessary though not sufficient neurological condition for the development of "consciousness", "awareness" in the widest possible sense. Finally, there is Pavlov's second system, which is essentially a representational system, but efferent rather than afferent, involving speech elements, which permits both communication and the active construction of reality. Association of neural events at this level creates a world representation which can be manipulated by language so that simulations permit the evolution and selection of optimal behavioural strategies, i.e. thinking and intelligent planning.

CHAPTER 4

## *Interactional Approach to Development*

'*A man can become a man only when he is raised in human society*'.
J. A. Comenius: The Great Didactic, 1657

'*In tracing the cultural development of mental functions, we are, at the same time, mapping the path of development of the personality*'.
L. S. Vygotsky (1960)

### Introduction

IN PREVIOUS discussion, we have frequently referred, in passing, to the important role played by reciprocal interactions between genes and environment from earliest age — transactions in which one influences, and, at the same time, is influenced by the other — in shaping personality. It is surely axiomatic that personality growth can only be evaluated in the context of a system of mutuality between the child and the social environment which he engages. We noted, however, that this term is excluded from classic heritability estimates, which thus must be regarded as suspect. Again, it seems difficult to account for the awkward regression of genotype on age without recourse to such interaction. Undoubtedly it is a core concept in the reactivity/activity model proposed by the Warsaw group. The notion that reactivity and activity meld to provide levels of stimulation appropriate for optimal development, consistent with the individual's genetically determined optimal arousal level, underlines the extent to which both genes and environment are prescriptive in steering personality development.

Apart from an acknowledgement that social learning is a reciprocal process, however, the Warsaw group has not yet addressed itself specifically to the question of the ways in which the biosocial needs of the child are actualised in development. And while we can detect a recent move towards a more transactional approach to personality by certain Western personality theorists such as Endler and Magnusson, and Staats, for example, their approach is anything but developmental. It is perhaps not surprising, therefore, that typologists, who are, in any event, more psychophysiologically oriented, have

132

made few attempts to formally incorporate this term into mainstream temperament/personality theory.

Reasons for this differ between West and East. In Western psychology, personality and developmental psychology have been regarded historically as separate disciplines. The effects of early experience in moulding personality have been emphasised mainly by psychoanalysts in their attempt to account for maladaptive behaviour in adulthood. Many of the assumptions underlying psychoanalytic theory, however, have proved so unacceptable to psychologists of different persuasion that psychoanalytic postulates, derived largely from clinical observations, have had comparatively little impact, or have proved highly controversial. Consider, for example, the initial ferment occasioned by Bowlby's (1951) contention that the long-term separation of a child from his mother in early life irreversibly reduces his capacity to form stable relationships in later life.

Soviet typologists have shown equal disinterest, but for different reasons. Their typological research over the past 30 years has focused on methodological issues, and on attempts to interpret data in line with modern theories of neurophysiology. From the late twenties, however, there has been a clear recognition (by Pavlov, Teplov, Bykov, e.g.) of the importance of early experience, and of the extent to which such effects are reflected in adult behaviour. Bykov (1953), for example, refers to "fused" reflexes, integrations of basic biological dispositions, overlaid by experience. Nebylitsyn (1972) is quite explicit on this point.

> . . . nervous system properties exert only a relatively small influence on the dynamic aspects (tempo, speed, intensity) of human response under normal circumstances. They are determined to a much greater extent by the regulating influences of the social environment (p. 294).

The situation changes when S is stressed, and must maintain performance under conditions of frustration, boredom, distraction, sensory overload, fatigue.

> Extreme conditions . . . expose natural qualities in the individual's nervous organisation . . . the most basic of these are nervous system properties (p. 294).

Clearly, if genetic potential is to be realised, the child's environment must offer appropriate physical and psychological stimuli to permit increasingly differentiated contact with the world of objects and people, so as to encourage the acquisition of sensori-motor skills and personal-social goals. These stimuli interact over time with maturational processes to promote growth, adaptation and redintegration, i.e. to produce the more or less stable structures of personality.

But what are these contextual stimuli? And can we identify "innate" biosocial needs to which such stimuli are instrumental? Understandably enough, these have been differently conceptualised by Soviet and Western theorists — they issue from differential theoretical models, which, in turn, have been nurtured in different psychological and philosophical traditions. As we shall see, however, there is some degree of unanimity.

## Western Views

Developmental psychology has surprisingly little to offer in this regard. Some information can be gleaned from the neonatal observational studies we have already described, such as that of Thomas, Chess and Birch (1968), which have been the launchpad for some of the developmental schedules recently devised. Undoubtedly, however, the deprivational literature has provided the most informative data, largely because a critical problem in this area is the identification of those biosocial needs which are so crucial in the lifespace of the infant that their denial, in severe enough form, and for a long enough period, leads to developmental retardation and distortion in personality.

In their theory of psychological deprivation, Langmeier and Matejcek (1975) identify three categories of important biosocial needs — sensory and sensory-cognitive, emotional/affectional (mainly maternal) and personal/social.

### A. Sensory and Sensory-cognitive

We can conveniently review relevant material under two headings.

i) From birth, there is evident need for a certain level of external stimulation, for a certain amount and complexity of stimuli, to maintain an adequate level of attentiveness and activity. This optimal input level, which is actively sought after by the child, and which has been described as the "pacer stimulus" by Dember and Earle (1957) is that level which elicits positive emotional tone, and encourages exploratory behaviour.[1] When the input from the environment is below this optimal level, the child may become apathetic, and in severe cases show symptoms of "hospitalism", while at too high levels, stress and exhaustion may result from over-stimulation, with consequent behaviour instability.

A considerable amount of evidence (cf. Langmeier and Matejcek, 1975), suggests an inverted U function relating complexity and amount of stimulation to attentiveness and curiosity, and to emotional tuning and stability. Preferred arousal level is represented by the top of the inverted U curve, and, relative to this preferred level, the emotional state of the child changes from positive to

---

[1]Note the similarity of this view to that expressed in 'activity' theory.

negative tuning as a function of increasing stimulus demand. It seems that optimal arousal level, which profoundly affects both the child's physiological status (biochemical individuality, metabolism, immunology) and psychological status (emotional tuning, spontaneous activity, aspects of learning and attention, curiosity, tolerance of stress and frustration, for example), is genetically fixed and ontogenetically invariant, although there is some evidence that this can be affected by chronic nutrient and psychological features of the environment (Lát, 1962).

ii) The need for sensory-cognitive structuring, for meaningful sequences or order of stimuli, as a condition for effective learning. We observe, at a very early age, attempts by the child to find meaning in the hierarchical arrangement of stimuli, and motivation to discover their functional value, and the meaning and direction of change.

Evidence for drives of curiosity and of mastery or competence derives initially from some early conditioning studies with neonates, which indicate that conditioned responding persists even in the face of obstacles or negative consequences (White, 1959; Scott, 1957). The most convincing data, however, are from more recent studies, which report that while increase in the "interest-value" of UCSs — the use of flashing lights, jack-in-the-box, for instance – appears to have little effect on acquisition rates, reinforcement schedules other than continuous greatly accelerate conditioning. An implication is that it is the schedule rather than the reinforcement *per se* which is the motivating factor, that the actual problem-solving is the true motivation for infants in learning situations.

Papousek's (1969) findings are perhaps the most informative. In his experiment, the infant could turn on a light by turning his head to the left; once this had been learned, the response frequency for left-head turning dropped. However, when the contingency was changed to right head turn/light on, immediately following a non-reinforced left head turn there was a burst of left head turns, followed by detection of the right head turn/light on contingency. This, in turn, was followed by a brief, high rate of right head turning, which then subsided. Behavioural signs of pleasure and joy, which were not associated temporally with head turning, suggested that problem solving is its own reward.

A number of studies have demonstrated a quite surprising degree of problem solving efficiency in young infants. For example, Siqueland and Lipsitt (1966) stabilised a discrimination of head turning to one side when a buzzer was sounded, and head turning to the other side when a bell sounded. The two contingencies were then reversed. Subjects, who were one-day-old infants, were able to make this discrimination reversal in very few trials. This suggests that all the neural structures required for stimulus and response identification, and for stimulus-response selection, are available in the intra-uterine environment, long before the infant's actions have any consequence.

However, it is also clear that learning ability can decline if not exercised. This has been clearly demonstrated in both animal and human studies. For example, Blakemore and Mitchell (1973) report that kittens raised in visual environments, consisting entirely of horizontal or vertical stripes, up to the age of 4–5 weeks, lose their vertical or horizontal striate cortex detectors, not apparently through atrophy, but through the recruitment of all detectors to the one function. Papousek's (1967a) data from human infants, which illustrate the same general point, are presented in Table 19. From these data, it seems that the development of learning ability depends on an interaction between an innate set of mechanisms and the opportunity to use these in a psychologically meaningful way.

TABLE 19. *Comparison of the conditionability of 2 groups of infants of approximately similar age. Group A were subjected to conditioning procedures from birth, group B from age 3 months (from Papousek, 1967a)*

| Group | Mean age in days at beginning of test | Mean trials to criterion |
|-------|---------------------------------------|--------------------------|
| A | 107.54 | 94.63 |
| B | 105.92 | 176.23 |

Various aetiological factors which might underlie curiosity and competence drives have been suggested. Hebb's (1949, 1955) incongruity hypothesis (basically an OR (orienting reflex) approach, which we shall discuss in some detail later) is perhaps the most plausible account. He proposed that perceptual experiences deposit patterned traces, and that exposure to novel perceptual input generates conflicting impulses in the nervous system. If the resulting discrepancy between the familiar stimulus configuration and the new stimulus is large, the resulting high neural excitation leads to avoidance and/or fearfulness. On the other hand, if the discrepancy is small, approach and active efforts to explore the novel stimulus are more likely. Discrepancy limits, of course, appear to be fixed by genetically-determined psychophysiological characteristics. Primary dishabituation, and the speed with which the novel stimulus is itself habituated, is dependent on strength of internal inhibition, excitatory strength of nervous system, and the strength of external inhibition (Chapter 7), which, in the Soviet typology, are basic nervous system properties.

There is some empirical support for the incongruity hypothesis. For example, young infants devote more visual attention to novel and complex patterns than to familiar ones, and novel stimuli and the pursuit of novel tasks produce greater excitation (e.g. Berlyne, 1966; Lewis *et al.*, 1966). These and similar data suggest that novelty and complexity constitute a source of motivation that is independent of primary need state.

To the extent that curiosity and competence drives are part of the repertoire of basic human drives, it is obvious that the environment must offer the child stimulus structures which are sufficiently varied by distinguishable contingencies to allow him to explore and discover physical and social relationships.

### B. Emotional/Affectional

The need to control for postnatal maternal effects — by cross-fostering, for example, — has been emphasised in the animal literature. Important behavioural traits in adulthood, such as level of aggressivity, have been shown to be partly determined by maternal influences (Denenberg, Hudgins and Zarrow, 1964; Hudgins, Denenberg and Zarrow, 1968; Denenberg and Zarrow, 1970). Direct evidence from human studies on this point is lacking, for obvious reasons. However, some relevant data are available from observational and retrospective studies. Generally speaking, the most significant postnatal effects occur in those instances where primary need satisfaction is not fully met by direct physiological process, but involves the intervention of a second person, normally the mother, over a considerable period of time. Arguably, it is the immature somatic development of the child, which must be compensated for by maternal behaviour, which is the critical factor.

It is generally acknowledged that from the age of about 4–5 months, one of the important developmental needs is for an object of specific affectional attachment, which is a prerequisite for feelings of security (cf. Langmeier and Matejcek, 1975). Although initially this object is normally the mother, who becomes the embodiment and substitute for the whole environment, so that all the child's activities and interests are concentrated on his relationship with her, subsequently, other significant objects of social worth — the father, the family as a whole, the peer group, the cultural model and so on — assume increasingly important roles. This need is generally recognised, but differently labelled, in different cultures — dependency need, attachment need, affiliative need, need for love, for example. If this drive is to be satisfied, the environment must provide sufficiently stable and permanent objects, offering a warm emotional bond and uncritical acceptance of the child in his life space. Depending on the severity of denial and the strength of the need, the effects of denial range from the affectionless psychopathy described by Bowlby (1951) to an increased vulnerability to emotional stress.

At a slightly older age, there are a number of specific effects which arise from the reactions of caretakers to the ways in which the child attempts to satisfy his primary needs. These are viewed by some theorists as significant factors in personality development.

Caretakers invariably make demands on children with regard to time, place and method of feeding, elimination and satisfaction of sexual impulses. Toilet training, as the first experience of impulse control, is claimed by some to be important in the development of the central controlling mechanism of personality, the ego. Feeding and sentience needs are also assumed to have important developmental roles. Frustration of feeding needs, for example, is suggested as a fundamental developmental experience which begins to teach a child about separate external objects. In addition, feeding is a time of intimacy and warm sensual contact, which may be important for subsequent development of feelings of security.

Caretakers' reactions to elimination, feeding and sexual needs are viewed by some theorists as important in the aetiology of anxiety. Freud originally postulated that anxiety initially occurs in the individual as the result of sudden, diffuse stimulation occurring at birth.[2] This, however, is closely followed by a fresh source of danger, the possibility of deprivation of physiological need. Later, according to theory, this fear may become attached to actions by influential adults, which implicitly carry the threat of physiological deprivation, and thus give rise to a threat reminiscent of the primary anxiety.

Later theorists abandoned the notion of primary anxiety occurring in the first months of life, and maintained that anxiety originates in the social process, and that it cannot therefore arise before the child develops an awareness of his status relative to the environment. Anxiety begins when the young child realises his own helplessness, and the degree to which he is dependent on others for protection and survival. The growth of anxiety is thus a consequence of the threats and punishment which are used to control the child's primary need behaviour, particularly elimination and sex. The threat, however, is not one of physiological deprivation, but of frustration of dependency needs, of the need for protection and support. Aspects of such training influence self-attitudes, particularly those relating to guilt and shame. Adults can communicate feelings of disgust about elimination and sex, which, if introjected, can become the nucleus of a deprecatory self-concept. There is no evidence that man is biologically predisposed to develop negative attitudes about natural physio-

---

[2]Freud also maintained that the pattern of physiological response to birth was reproduced by the individual throughout his life, in response to stress. This could be regarded as the first crude statement of the individual response stereotype principle expounded by the Laceys in the 1950s.

logical processes. These are learned by the child from the reactions of others to his primary need behaviour.

We can contrast this view with learning theory approaches to anxiety, which emphasise both experiential and biological components. Theorists such as Dollard and Miller (1950) regard anxiety as a learned drive, based on an innate propensity to avoid pain. It is not the reaction of others to primary need behaviour which is the important variable, but the actual strength of the avoidance drive. If, for example, the infant is sensitive to pain, then presumably avoidance responses will be stronger, and any anxiety based on these more pronounced. Anxiety develops through the attachment of pain to a particular stimulus through association, and, if the fear reaction is strong enough, it may generalise to objects or situations which are similar to the original fear-provoking stimulus. Individuals who are exposed in early life to intense fears or conflicts are likely to show a high predisposition to anxiety in later life, i.e. to show high levels of trait anxiety.

We note, however, that in many cases the fear-provoking stimulus may be the threat of withdrawal of maternal love and support, that the strength of the avoidance response may be in part dictated by the child's dependency needs, and that this could generalise to other situations and relationships. Dynamic and learning theory approaches to anxiety, therefore, while appearing superficially to be different, share a good deal of common theoretical ground.

## C. Personal/Social

Finally, we should refer to the child's need for primary values, for objects and goals which are relevant to the growth of his personal identity and self-fulfilment. While this is generally recognised as an important need in adolescence, undoubtedly the pattern is laid down early in life. The critical factor here is probably a history of successful striving, a point which has been emphasised by Guilford and Cattell, which presupposes the provision, by parents, of realistic goals, and discriminating schedules of reward and punishment, leading to the recognition and acquisition of personal, social and physical competence. The child needs confirmation of his worth, and approval of assumed social roles, as a necessary precondition for effective personality integration. Effective models should help him to discover goals and values, to appreciate complex roles inside and outside the family, and to evaluate his tentatively emerging, but energetically demanding, awareness of ego identity. "Evaluative acceptance" seems a good description of this necessary condition for the development of personal integrity in human development.

These sensori-cognitive, emotional and social stimuli may be deficient to any degree, producing deficits or imperfections in personality development, ranging from mildly to severely maladaptive. The experimental and deprivational literature provide many examples. Contrived reduction in visual, auditory and tactual stimulation in mature adults, for example, produces relatively severe but transient distortions of imagery and thought. Prolonged, severe social isolation and maternal deprivation in young animals appears to have a profound deleterious effect on adult capacity to form stable, permanent social and sexual relationships (Harlow and Harlow, 1962) and affects the intensity and mode of aggressive and dominance behaviour. More recent evidence, however, indicates that the effects may not be as irreversible as first thought (Clarke and Clarke, 1976). In any event, the extent to which animal findings can be extrapolated to humans is a matter of some dispute. Clearly, critical experiments with human infants are impossible for ethical reasons, and we are thrown back on "social" experiments which have been reported from time to time, and on the relatively few cases of severe isolation and criminal neglect which have been reported (cf. Clarke and Clarke, 1976). Inferences from clinical to normal cases have obvious drawbacks.

We must emphasise, of course, that the critical stimuli described above should be considered in the context of the individual child and of the society in which he lives. While we might argue that these stimuli will be much the same in all human societies, particular needs are experienced with different degrees of urgency in different cultures. In some, for example, withdrawal and passivity are valued, in others activity and enterprise are preferred. We can assess the effects of denial, therefore, only in terms of generally accepted values in a certain culture, social class and individual family.

## D. Maturational Variables and Personality Stratification

Whether or not the environment possesses these contextual features, of course, is irrelevant unless the child is capable of responding in an appropriate manner. There must be maturational sequences of sensory and morphological changes, which, interactively with environment, stimulate the growth of increasingly more and more complex, sophisticated and differentiated input (stimulus) and output (response) systems.

The notion of developmental stages is as old as child psychology. What is implied is that the same environmental influence will have a different impact, depending on the stage in which it is brought to bear. For example, attachment to a maternal figure, it is claimed, must take place within a certain developmental stage, at an intensity considered optimal, or it will not occur at all, or be distorted. Similarly, the effectiveness of different types of stimulation is greater at some developmental stages than at others. For example, visual-motor co-ordination appears to be most plastic to environmental stimulation between 1.5 and 5 months (White, 1963; White, Castle and Held, 1964); social responsiveness, on the other hand, is readily reinforced by appropriate stimulation after the age of 3 months, but probably not before (Lennenberg, Rebelsky and Nichols, 1965). Again, although 4- and 5-month-old infants show a fleeting stranger response and a more lasting selective responsiveness to their mothers, real discrimination between the mother and all other persons occurs at about 6 months of age. Much work on early learning suggests that new behavioural integrations are tied to a biological timetable in a highly discriminating manner.

This epigenetic view of personality is influential in most current theories of child development. Developmental epochs, of course, do not necessarily coincide with chronological age zones. The former are demarcated in terms of process — coping patterns and modes of functioning which emerge and delineate different stages. Developmental theorists conceptualise such processes in rather similar ways, but terminology differs. Piaget, for example, uses concepts of assimilation, accommodation and equilibration; Gesell refers to reciprocal interweaving, developmental direction and functional asymmetry; Thompson uses concepts of differentiation, growth and organisation, which, superficially at least, have a more compelling parsimony, and, for present purposes, appear more useful.

Thompson (1968) analyses differentiation, his core concept, in terms of three clearly identifiable stages, in which different levels of input/output differentiation make prepotent certain forms of learning. The first of these stages is characterised by low levels of both input and output differentiation, so that the neonate can neither differentiate the sensory input, nor organise responses into stable hierarchies or habits. At this stage, according to Thompson, the only form of learning possible is habituation, i.e., the inhibition of repetitive, non-signal, or distracting stimuli. Since the child's capacity for both operant and respondent conditioning is limited — or so it is claimed — the critical need at this age is for an adequate supply of appropriately structured stimuli to maintain attention and alertness, to encourage curiosity and search.

Following certain morphological changes, discriminability in sensory systems on the input side increases. There is some dispute in the literature, however, about the precise nature of some of these changes, and the age at which they occur. For example, flexible accommodation has been claimed to develop at around 4 to 5 months, until which time the child can focus only at about 19 cm (Haynes, White and Held, 1963), which is thought to be the mean distance from the mother's face to breast. Slater and Findlay (1975), on the other hand, report accommodation at different distances in 2-month-old babies. However, they present no data on speed of accommodation, nor on clarity of image (the object may be blurred) so that the original Haynes, White and Held (1963) statement may still hold good — that around 4 to 5 months is the age at which flexible accommodation with clear vision of objects spatially located at different distances is known to occur. The behavioural consequences of this are uncertain, although clearly it allows the child, who is still physically immobilised, to more effectively "penetrate" the social environment.

Of course, vision may not be the only, nor indeed the most critical modality involved in the child's "recognition" of his mother — tactual, auditory, gustatory and olfactory discriminations may also play important roles. Macfarlane (1974), for example, has reported efficient olfactory discrimination (head-turning response) of the mother's breast pad at 6 days of age. In view of the older evidence — more an inference — (e.g. Escalona, 1968) that olfactory discrimination is general does not emerge much before 7 months of age, there is the interesting possibility of genetic coding to recognise the smell of the mother's breast and/or milk from birth. There may also be other sensory discriminations which serve to mediate the relatively stable relationship a child has with his mother from birth.

It is generally conceded, however, that at about 5 months of age the child co-ordinates sensory systems so that objects become "permanent". Perhaps it is in this sense that the mother is now recognised, and her absence vociferously responded to. Such sensory integration is probably a necessary condition for the development of the anaclitic bond, which occurs around this time, and is claimed to play an important role in development (e.g. Bowlby, 1951; Spitz, 1954a,b).

On the output side, while it is clear that most of the efferent components of the autonomic nervous system must be fully functioning from the earliest age to make possible the critical life-sustaining behaviours such as sucking and grasping, somatic development is still immature, and must be compensated for by maternal behaviour. In this second stage, when input differentiation is high, and output differentiation low, the dominant form of learning is considered to be mainly affective or classical conditioning.

In the third stage, both forms of differentiation have reached a comparatively high level, and instrumental conditioning becomes possible. Now, effective cues come to elicit instrumental or coping responses, i.e. behaviour aimed at reducing the unpleasantness, or increasing the pleasantness of the affective response. This, according to Thompson, is the period of shift from the reflexive to the instrumental, a shift to greater voluntary control, which probably involves increase in cortical inhibitory control. Such increase of inhibitory control with increasing age has been noted in animals and children, and is generally described in terms of a transition from involuntary to voluntary activity. Hebb (1949) refers to this development as increase in central autonomous processes.

Thompson makes the point that what happens in one stage determines what happens in the next and succeeding stages, and that it is the residua of these developmental stages which constitute the developmental stratification of personality. Thus, any need, drive or motive must involve, and should be assessed in terms of three major components — a temperament component, an affective component, and an instrumental meaning component.

While Thompson's formulation has an attractive simplicity, however, and while it may be true that certain types of learning are prepotent at different developmental levels, two considerations, in particular, raise doubts about the robustness and applicability of his model.

i) Developmental processes operate more in parallel than in series, and there is considerable evidence that there is a much greater degree of overlap between processes than is envisaged by Thompson. We might argue that while different behavioural integrations cannot anticipate certain maturational events, when these latter occur, the newly available learning becomes assimilated or incorporated into the total response repertoire, interacting with other, "older" behaviour patterns. Such is the process of growth, of higher-order organisation of response sequences. This point has been emphasised by Bruner (1973), who suggests that, given the limited processing capacity of the child, a complex action is achieved only when the relevant subroutines have been acquired, so that processing capacity is free to fit the "modular" into a serial programme, which, with practice, becomes smoothly flowing. These subroutines, such as, for example, those aspects of reaching, grasping and transporting involved in drinking from a cup, may become available at different developmental times.

Thus, while it is clear from both Soviet and Western sources that there is a peak of classical conditioning around 5–6 years of age (Razran, 1935), and while it is true that decline of classical conditioning beyond the sixth year is paralleled by increase in symbolic activity and voluntary control, the assumption that lack of response differentiation limits operant conditioning prior to this age is highly debatable. In the first place, considerable evidence suggests that very young infants are capable of respondent conditioning and discrimination reversal of a relatively high order. In slightly older children disuse may lead to atrophy; it is not the case that the relevant neural structures have not yet developed. Secondly, when speech develops, the potential for operant control is greatly increased. A good deal of operant control and active avoidance in humans is effected through language.

The period from 1 to 4 years is the time when the child is subjected to the strongest socialisation pressures, when dependency needs are strongest, and thus the opportunity for emotional conditioning greatest. Whether a child of this age is more subject to emotional conditioning because of limited response differentiation, or more amenable to such conditioning because of strong dependency ties, therefore, is a good question.

ii) Recent research shows quite clearly that infants are capable of complex behaviour — such as guided reaching, grasping and tracking — at a much earlier age than was previously assumed. Reaching, for example, like walking, begins well before birth. All the components of reaching and grasping can be elicited in foetuses at the conceptual age of 14–16 weeks. Visually initiated reaching can be elicited in new born infants (Bower, 1973), while some discrimination of distance has been reported in 2-week-old infants (Bower, 1972). Of interest is the observation (similar to that concerning rate of conditioning) that infants who experience reaching every day from birth show no decline in reaching — unlike unpractised neonates — which suggests that decline is a function of disuse.

Insofar as tracking is concerned, data indicate that 8-week-old infants will anticipate the reappearance of an object which has disappeared behind a screen (Gardner, 1971; Bower, Broughton and Moore, 1971). This is not due to inability to arrest eye and head movement, but represents a general response to moving objects. When objects other than that which disappeared behind the screen emerge from the other side, infants of about 20 weeks show disruption of tracking as they look back for the original object (Bower, Broughton and Moore, 1971).

These comments nothwithstanding, Thompson's views are of value in directing our attention to the developmental sequences of learning experiences, which are initiated by maturational changes in sensory and neural structures, and which, interactively with certain environmental features, lay down pathways which canalise development to produce some of the personality constellations we observe in adults.

## Soviet Views

It is difficult to establish precisely what Soviet authors mean by "personality". However, it seems to refer to an amalgam of aptitudes and needs, such as those described by Bozhovich (1976), for example, the need and aptitude for work, for social interaction, for life perspectives (neglecting primary needs such as hunger, need for warmth and so on, and sensori-cognitive needs such as adequate level of stimulation, which are critical in the first year of life), of abilities such as memory and thinking, and of neurophysiological variables such as nervous system properties. Elementary mental and neurophysiological processes, which have their own developmental logic and maturational history, are mediated and shaped by appropriate activity, to produce an individual whose values and goals, consciously projected (i.e. his personality), are in harmony with those socially and culturally prescribed.

Even the most perfunctory scanning of the Soviet literature underscores the emphasis that Soviet personality/developmental theorists place on the genotype $x$ environment interaction in shaping personality. Difficulty in operationalising and conceptualising this complex term, however, is perhaps the very reason why Soviet psychology, in the opinion of some leading educationalists (e.g. Davydov, 1976) still lacks a general theory of mental development comparable, for example, with Piaget's theory in scope and level of sophistication. Davydov notes particularly the dearth of theories concerning the development of aptitudes in the child, of the effects of group activity on personality development, the fact that Soviet developmental psychology touches only peripherally on mental development in later periods, for example, in adolescence and young adulthood.

The rationale underlying this strong interactional approach to child development is obvious enough. Most Soviet theorists, including Pavlov, have shown at least sympathy with, if not full acceptance of, the theory of cognitive development embedded in the Marxist science of society. This implies that labour, involving initially the fashioning and use of tools, significantly enriches interpersonal relationships, this being paralleled by changes in physiological and nervous system structures. Discovery of the properties of environmental objects through social activity led to the formation of language, which, in turn, made possible abstractions, generalisations, reasoning and consciousness, processes which direct man's adaptation to, and control over the environment, and thus constitute the core of personality.

As a consequence, an important guiding principle in Soviet psychological theory, a view which figures prominently in the writings of Anen'ev, Luria, Vygotsky, Leont'ev, Rubinsteyn, Smirnov, Teplov, for example, is the assertion that mental phenomena can be studied only in the context of man's activity in the real world. Consciousness is formed, developed and actualised in the course of activity. This is a direct expression of Lenin's theory of reflection, which insists that mental phenomena, which are intimately linked with neurophysiological phenomena in a single, unified system, are diverse forms of subjective reflection of objective reality. Activity in the real world, i.e. "appropriate" activity, implies that the content and mode of such activity are determined largely by the needs which mark particular developmental periods. In line with Vygotsky's original model, there is some consensus in the Soviet literature that we can clearly delineate six developmental stages, each with its unique maturational and activity characteristics (cf. El'konin, 1971; Bozhovich,

1976). Orderly progress through these stages gives the child's mental development an internal unity (El'konin, 1971).

The first period, from 0 to 12 months, is marked by primary needs (for food, warmth, movement), by needs associated with the functional development of the brain (e.g. need for stimulation), and finally, by social needs. Denial of these needs generates restlessness, satisfaction evokes heightened "vital tone", i.e. increased level of attentiveness, and intensification of cognitive and motor activity, which Bozhovich (1976) describes as the "animation complex".

Insofar as social development is concerned, this is the period in which direct emotional contact crystallises the child's need for emotional/social contact with others. Vygotsky notes that at this time the essence of the social situation is that all the infant's behaviour and activity are realised through the mediation of, or in co-operation with, an adult. When no adult is present, it is equivalent to taking away the infant's arms and legs, his means of locomotion, of altering his position, of seizing desired objects. Thus, in normal circumstances, the caring adult, usually the mother, becomes the focus of the infant's entire, immediately perceived environment, the object towards which all things gravitate.

As a result, the content of the mental life of the infant during this period is characterised initially by affectively coloured sensations, later by globally experienced, affectively toned impressions. The infant's consciousness gradually acquires emotional components linked with immediately perceived external events. During this developmental period, perception dominates in the conscious mind of the infant, and the act of grasping as the basis for action with things develops.

Towards the end of this first year, the infant's consciousness expands, individual psychological functions begin to differentiate, the first general sensory impressions consolidate, the infant may begin to use elements of words to name objects. At this time, the infant's needs become more attached to specific objects, which thus acquire motivational properties — when they enter his perceptual field, they activate latent needs and excite adaptive behaviour. Herein lies the source of the situational dependence of the infant in the first year of life.

In the second developmental period (1–3 years) manipulation of objects, speech development and visuo-motor learning assume great significance. The child's behaviour ceases to be regulated by adult structuring of external stimuli. He is now motivated not only by directly perceived impressions, but also by images and ideas evoked by memories. Memory begins to play an increasingly active role in mental development, gradually assuming a dominant position in restructuring the child's behaviour and consciousness. As motivating ideas and images increasingly free the child from total subservience to external stimuli, he becomes more aware of himself as subject rather than object (the process of self-recognition), then of himself as the executor of acts (the process of self-awareness). According to Bozhovich (1976), this is the first clearly identifiable moment in the development of personality. The emergence of this new systemic structure is signalled by the appearance of the word "I", indicating a new attitude to the world of people and things. The child is able to independently satisfy more of his needs, to communicate, to perform activities not mediated by adults.

This self-awareness, of course, emerges only gradually in the second and third years, the transition from self-recognition to self-awareness being facilitated by social activity. This shift is thought to mark the beginning of development of the ego system, which incorporates both rational (cognitive) and affective components. The former implies knowledge of oneself, of one's separate and unique identity, recognition of one's active rather than reactive role in the environment. This is largely dependent on the development of new sensori-cognitive systems. The latter describes an attitude about oneself, which is predicated on the emergence of a new structure, that of self-esteem. Initially, these emerging structures appear to operate independently. For example, the rational element is lacking in the first self-evaluations, which are steered almost entirely by the child's need for adult approval to keep intact his emotional well-being. Eventually, however, these systems and structures converge and interact at that point in time which Vygotsky and others describe as the 3-year-old crisis. At times, the conflict between what "I want" and what "I must do", which, behaviourally, is expressed in obstinacy and negativism, and in distorted attitudes towards normative behaviour, may be severe, and may have long-term consequences.

Development in this 1–3 year period is thus thought to culminate in the emergence of a central personality structure, the ego. All subsequent personality development is steered by the growth of self-awareness, which, however, has different components and features at different developmental stages.

Play activity characterises the 3–7 year period, such activity encouraging the development of symbolic functioning and imagination in the child. This orients him to the general purpose and meaning of human acts, and emphasises aspects of self-discipline and control in human relations.

The period 7–11 years, which is marked by entry into school, is a period of study activity. Through this, the child acquires a theoretical orientation to the environment, which enables him to perceive valid objective qualities and patterns, and to develop the psychological prerequisites for abstract, theoretical thinking, the capacity to construct internal plans of action, the ability to reflect on possible consequences of actions. This period is characterised by the emergence of a new internal systemic structure, viz.

awareness by the child of himself as a social individual, which carries with it recognition of new status, and of socially meaningful activity to reinforce this status.

The period of 11–17 years is characterised, in its first phase (11–14 years), by the emergence of the capacity to be guided by goals which lie beyond the immediate context, and by the ability to actually set goals. The enabling activity is communication within a system of social useful activity, which includes sport, artistic effort, work. An important feature is recognition of, and acceptance of group norms and standards. The second phase (15–17 years) is marked by study and occupational activity, which shape particular cognitive and occupational interests, and facilitate the planning of future action, and the development of moral ideals. In this period, the child should acquire an awareness of life perspectives. A concept of himself, of what he wants to be, of what he wants to accomplish in his life, are important components of this awareness, and thus of further ego development.

Davydov (1976) observes that the end product of development through these periods is the person possessing certain qualities which form the basis of his general outlook and moral fabric, which are basically prerequisites for an active life as a productive being and as an effective member of society. He recognises certain basic needs and aptitudes — primarily the need and aptitude for work, through which a person is able to efficiently organise and improve his labour, the need and aptitude for establishing social contacts, providing the basis for development of mature moral standards and ideals, and the need and aptitude for making intelligent and prudent decisions about life's problems and about future orientation. Activity through which these aptitudes can be maximised can be categorised in two ways. The first group comprises those activities which instruct the child about the motives and norms of inter-personal relationships, which encourage an understanding of human behaviour, through which certain needs and drives, particularly appropriate to infant and adolescent stages, take shape. The second group comprises types of activity concerned with learning socially appropriate ways of interacting with objects of our material and intellectual culture, through which the intellectual and cognitive aptitudes of the pre-school and the younger and older school-age child, in particular, are formed.

Davydov (1976) suggests that each of the three broad developmental stages — 0–3 years, 4–10 years, and 11–17 years — can be subdivided into two phases, the first phase in each stage featuring a dominant activity from the first group, the second a dominant activity from the second group. In the second phase of each stage, according to El'konin (1971), the child develops cognitive abilities on the basis of the needs and motives shaped in the previous period.

There is a general recognition amongst Soviet developmental psychologists of "critical periods" at 3, 7 and 11 years (Blonsky, 1961; Vygotsky, 1972; Davydov, 1976). While developmental changes, on the whole, occur slowly and smoothly, there are relatively short periods in which major psychological modifications and personality changes occur. During these critical periods, behaviour is often tempestuous and impulsive. Children are difficult to manage.

The extent and duration of these crises, of course, depend on a variety of life circumstances, and there are large individual differences in the intensity, and the duration of the conflicted period. Generally speaking, however, these are periods in which negativistic behaviour predominates. Vygotsky comments:

> During these periods, in contrast to the more stable periods, activity is more destructive than constructive. The progressive development of the child's personality tapers off and effectively grinds to a temporary half during these periods of crises. All the achievements of the previous stage, all that had distinguished the child at that particular age fades, atrophies, decays, disintegrates. During these periods, the child loses much of what he has previously acquired, rather than acquiring something new (Vygotsky, 1972, p. 119).

During crises periods, however, constructive activity does take place, and gradually the rudiments of a new, more appropriate kind of activity emerges. It is really in the pre-critical phase that development slows down, that the child's inner life, according to Vygotsky, becomes a wasteland. The content of the critical phase proper is a search for a new concrete form of appropriate activity. When this new kind of activity is assimilated into the behavioural repertoire, which occurs during the post-critical period, the new form of activity is enriched by relevant actions and goals, and through it, various mental processes are actualised. This marks the advent of a period of stable development. The characteristics of critical periods are thus outward manifestations of qualitative changes in the child's activity, and in the nature of his mind.

Of course, these new structures which emerge and are assimilated do not surface immediately, but function as a type of internal structure or framework. They are enveloped by an outer fabric of overt actions, motivations and functions which determine the direction and mode in which the mind is further shaped in each period, and provide a central core which gives the individual mind its unique, unified structure.

> As such, these new structures of critical periods fade away as the next age period sets in, but they continue to exist in latent form within it, not, however, leading an existence of their own, so to speak, but only as part of those ongoing processes under the surface which, during stable periods, suddenly give rise to new structures (Vygotsky, 1972, p. 122).

There have been some suggestions about the psychological mechanisms governing the emergence and assimilation of new, more appropriate types of activity. According to Leont'ev (1975), this occurs when a new reinforcement transforms the original motive. For example, a child may initially do his homework promptly so that he can go out and play. However, as a consequence of getting good marks for his efforts, which enhances his self-esteem, he will begin to do his homework for this reason; thus the act of doing homework has acquired a new motive.

> Acts become richer and richer. They outgrow, as it were, the activities of which they were a part, and enter into conflict and contradiction with the motives which originally gave rise to them. As a result, motives become goals. There is a change in their hierarchy, and new motives, new types of activity are born; previous goals are psychologically discredited, and the actions corresponding to them either cease to exist, or become mechanical operations. (Leont'ev, 1975).

Appropriate shaping through reinforcement is generally recognised as an important educational goal. Leont'ev (1972) comments:

> Does not the art of education consist in the creation of a proper combination of comprehensible motives and actual motives, and in the ability to attach at the proper time a higher significance to the successful result of an activity, so as to effect a transition to a higher kind of actual motive, by which the individual may guide his life?

Up to this point, we have been emphasising the role of activity in personality organisation. There is no suggestion, of course, that maturation is unimportant. According to Vygotsky, the child's mental development proceeds along two parallel lines. The first is the process of maturation, that is, the refinement and perfection of the systems and tissues which constitute the organic basis of any mental process, and secondly, cultural development, which involves the emergence of new mental structures. For example, when a child learns to master language, the structure of his mental processes undergoes change. These processes become mediated, and thus more perfected and productive, i.e. become "functional".

The work of Vygotsky's school in areas of language development, thought, memory, perception and attention suggests that during ontogeny, as the child learns cultural forms of conduct and behaviour, genuine qualitative changes occur in the functions themselves, and in their interrelationships. These new structures cannot be reduced to elementary psychological functions. They are complex integrative structures which operate as internal mechanisms directing the child's behaviour and activity, his relationships with others, his attitudes towards his surroundings and to himself. Elementary psychological functions such as perception, thinking, memory, have their own logical development, and each, through a complex integrative process, is transformed into higher mental functions — categorical perception, logical memory, conceptual thinking, voluntary attention. Such higher mental functions, which are fusions of elementary functions, have their own unique characteristics not derivable from the separate components. They are stable structures broken down only by old age or pathological process.

A good example is the development of memory, and its relationship to thinking. A considerable amount of data, using Vygotsky's double stimulation technique — various memory aids are provided, the functional development of memory being indicated by choice of particular aids — suggests that in the first year of life, mental functions have not yet become differentiated. They depend directly on perception, and operate only within this context. Thus, to all intents and purposes, memory is recognition. As the child develops, however, perception is subordinated to other functions, particularly memory, then thinking, such functions being now more attuned to the aims of the child's development as a bio-social whole. This ultimately gives rise to a special kind of memory with its own special structure, viz. logical memory. It is not simply memory plus reasoning, but a unique, qualitatively different function.

Similarly, thinking, early on, amounts to little more than memory. As the mind develops, however, memory becomes richer and more variegated, until finally it is replaced by discursive thought. At a certain stage of development, thinking actively participates in memorisation and recall, and transforms them into more or less conceptual processes. Vygotsky (1956) concluded that in early childhood memory dominates in the structure of thought. As the child develops, however, the relationship changes — memory becomes logical, and memorisation qualitatively different, an observation also reported by Leont'ev, Smirnov and Zinchenko. As such functions emerge and take shape, they subordinate all other functions, thus steering the integrative processes occurring during this developmental stage. That is, they determine the structure and specific features of the child's consciousness, viewed as a system.

Further development involves changes not so much in the structure of these higher mental functions, as in the "interconnections". These interfunctional structures, which characterise later developmental stages, are labelled psychological systems, complex integrative structures which have unique structural and functional features.

What we would describe as personality is a stable psychological system at a high integrative level. What characterises this structure is the ability to pursue a line of action independently of immediate constraints, such action being guided by consciously posed goals. It is the quality which transforms man from the slave to the master of his environment, and of himself. It is the basis of the active rather than the reactive nature of human behaviour. The central component of such a system is the will, which has no correlate amongst elementary mental functions. It incorporates in its structure not only consciously posed goals, but also higher mental functions such as emotional memory, imagination, moral feelings. It is through this system, which may vary during the course of a person's lifetime as a consequence of acquired experience, that all responses are mediated, and thereby acquire a conscious and voluntary character. Thus the psychological description of personality involves study of the evolution of motivation, of affective goals, of internal plans of action which enable a person to structure his motivational space. Of obvious importance is the formation of motivational systems which have affective components derived from the person's beliefs, his moral sentiments, his needs, which, in certain instances, can be in conflict. Soviet developmental psychologists recognise the role of defence mechanisms in conflict resolution, and point out that an important educational goal is the harmonious relationship between cognitive and affective processes, i.e. between what is controllable and what is not controllable by the conscious mind. The resultant is the emergence of a "core", which, in all essential respects, is similar to what in the West is described as the ego system, or simply the ego.

There seems to be some unanimity, therefore, that personality, like mental processes generally, develops in the context of activity — specifically social activity — in the real world. As Marx and Engels comment: "The real spiritual wealth of the individual depends wholly on the richness of his real relationships" (Works, Vol. 3, p. 6). This being said, what significance do Soviet personality theorists attach to genetic determinants of personality, for example, to nervous properties?

There is some evidence of a strong environmentalist or anti-genetic bias (e.g. Lomov, 1977), firmly entrenched in the assertion that there are no genetic limitations on potential for intellectual development, that personality traits are not irreversible. On the other hand, there is a clear acknowledgement of the importance of the development of those systems and tissues which constitute the organic basis of any mental process, these neurophysiological variables being intimately linked with mental phenomena in a single unified system. The important qualification is that these processes can be shaped and modified through activity. Thus, simple genetic coding of developmental sequences is rejected. This is clearly illustrated in the strong criticism of that aspect of Western theories of development, proposing that intellectual development is steered by fixed, pre-determined ideational organisations of S's actions, such programmes being rooted in the individual's biological and physiological structures.

Soviet theorists, on the whole, maintain that these structures change as activity itself develops. For example, Markova and Abramova (1977) cite Nebylitsyn's (1966a) comment, which we have previously noted in a different context, that "Human abilities are formed and developed in accordance with specific psychological laws. They are not given from the outset in the characteristics of nervous system organisation" (p. 361) to support the hypothesis that "naturally" conferred human abilities and aptitudes are organised and realised in the process of activity. Given the reality of nervous system plasticity, a central concept in Pavlov's theory, these authors hypothesise that the involvement of the child in different types of active intellectual, perceptual and social activity corrects and reshapes psycho-physiological characteristics, a point which, incidentally, has also been made by Ax (1974, cf. pp. 452–53). As the child progressively masters activities, the relative importance of organic characteristics and nervous system properties decreases. This is particularly relevant at certain developmental stages, particularly adolescence, which, according to Anen'ev, is characterised by optimal performance in all functional systems, including the psychophysio-logical. At this time, it is suggested that nervous system properties assume a quite different role. Precisely what this involves, however, is unclear.

Generally speaking, it seems that the zeitgeist is now strongly influenced by Vygotsky's views, expressed more than 40 years ago — that new systemic structures are formed during ontogeny, these being created by S's assimilation of the products of human culture; that mental or psychological features which are "natural", i.e. possibly determined by nervous system properties, are mediated in the process of activity and social contact through the socially elaborated system of signs; that this mediation alters the content and the structure of these functions, the result being mind, a phenomenon unique and specific to man as a social being. Activity thus plays a dominant role in human mental development, higher mental processes and functions being the result of internalisation of interpersonal forms of communication, which, in turn, is related in some way, as yet undisclosed, to the formation of new physiological structures.

## Summary

What we have referred to as contextual stimuli, i.e. those providing an appropriate context for the actualising of genetic potential, have been touched on only very briefly in this chapter. A complete account would require a separate volume. We will simply note, at this juncture, some unanimity in both the Soviet and Western developmental — particularly the deprivational — literature that an adequate supply of sensory stimuli, the provision of a warm, emotional bond with a caring figure, and experience with, and opportunity to acquire complex social roles, all these being quantitatively and qualitatively consonant with the maturational level of the child, are necessary, though not sufficient conditions for the development of effective learning, of emotional stability and security, of effective personality integration in the society in which the child develops. There can be little argument that these are important sources of environmental variance in personality.

Equally noteworthy is the broad agreement in the identification of critical periods in development. Terms such as "3-year-old crisis" and "Oedipal conflict" identify similar developmental moments. Opinions about underlying mechanisms differ, of course, but the similarities are striking. In this connection, it is interesting to recall that from 1924 to 1934, when Vygotsky, Leont'ev and Luria were attempting to reconstruct Soviet psychology from first principles, a good deal of their thinking was infused by psychoanalytic theory. Examples are Luria's 1925 paper "Psychoanalysis as a system of monistic psychology", and his 1932 monograph, *The nature of human conflict*. This important influence tends to be overlooked, primarily because the conceptual models these theorists adopted grew out of the socio-historical theory of the Vygotsky school, and were couched in language which is thoroughly Pavlovian, and because the relationship of some aspects of Freud's theory to Marxism has been, and continues to be, a contentious one. Nevertheless, psychoanalytic principles which shaped thinking in Western developmental psychology were also influential in the Soviet Union in the period when much theory building was occurring.

There are, of course, obvious differences in the two approaches. Perhaps most importantly, while both emphasise the significance of "residua" from previous developmental stages, in both the broadest possible sense, and in the particular instance that unresolved conflicts at certain crisis periods have specific, deleterious effects on subsequent personality organisation, this aspect is perhaps more strongly emphasised by Soviet educational and developmental psychologists than by their Western counterparts. Developmental features, according to Vygotsky, are essentially restructures, qualitatively new features appearing for the first time at particular ages, features which are basically re-organisations of personality structures and activity formed at earlier stages. These are the products of the demands placed on the individual by society, and by the social objectives guiding the development of those capacities peculiar to that particular age.

The difference, we suppose, is rather one of emphasis, stemming from the different ideological viewpoints of the theorists involved. Be that as it may, Soviet developmental theory is more thoroughly interactional than Western theory. Social and biological events are regarded as having no unique identity and significance, of themselves. Their importance lies in their interactive role in the context of appropriate activity. While Western theorists acknowledge the significance of interaction effects, these tend to be treated more superficially, and do not occupy a central place in current approaches to personality organisation and development.

# PART 2

# Typology and Personality

IN RECENT years, considerable research interest has centred on the relationship between typological properties and personality dimensions. In large measure, this has been due to the availability, in translation, of works such as Sokolov's *Perception and the conditioned reflex* (1958a), and the writings of Teplov and Nebylitsyn, the most authoritative of Soviet differential psychophysiologists, in Gray's *Pavlov's typology* (1964b), and in *Fundamental Properties of the Human Nervous System* (1966a). Much of the work reported has involved relationships between various orienting response (OR) parameters, particularly habituation rate, which is regarded as a measure of extinctive or internal inhibition, and excitatory strength of the nervous system, to personality measures such as Eysenck's extraversion (E) and neutoticism (N) dimensions, thought to reflect speed of development of inhibition, and arousability. Little attention has been paid to mobility, the third nervous system property, which, however, was accorded scant regard in Pavlov's laboratories, and about which there is little worthwhile information, and none to the properties of lability and concentration.

For convenience, in Chapter 5 we shall briefly describe current state-trait and interactional theories of personality. In the remaining chapters, the content of the different nervous system properties and their relationships to personality dimensions will be described, and some interpretations attempted.

# CHAPTER 5

## *Theories of Personality*

During a visit to Europe shortly after World War II, R. B. Cattell met Kretschmer, and told him of his factor work, in particular that he had found a leading factor which he named *"cyclothymia-schizothymia"*. On hearing this, Kretschmer remarked, *"Ach, Herr Cattell, now I believe in factor analysis"*.
Quoted by E. Howarth (1976)

## Introduction

IF WE employ an arguably over-inclusive criterion, we can describe two main approaches to personality — state-trait and social learning theories. State-trait theory is usually associated with a factor model of personality structure, although controversy has centred round the question of the minimum number of factors required to account for the maximum proportion of behavioural variance. Some state-trait theorists, notably Eysenck, claim that the personality dimensions identified by factor analysis are reflections of broad biological dispositions, genetically based. Methodologically, his theory is both nomothetic and idiographic, and theoretically, both structural and, in one sense, functional, being concerned with the why as well as the how of individual differences in personality. On the other hand, other state-trait theorists, such as Cattell and Guilford, refer only in passing to the biological foundations of their source or higher-order personality traits.

Social learning theories of personality attach little importance to the biological determinants of behaviour. Even where these are acknowledged, as, for example, in the social behaviourism approach of Staats, interest focuses on the mechanics, the how. Nonetheless, such approaches, except in the extreme case of "situationism", are functional in a different sense, in that they are concerned primarily with the processes underlying the development of behavioural systems. According to Staats, for example, these are processes of classical and instrumental conditioning operating within the constraints of a broad transactional or interactional model, to produce group and individual structures, which, interactively, constitute "personality". Nevertheless, neglect of biological "springs of action", as one sub-system of P, the person in the person $x$ situation interaction which all interactional theories emphasise, greatly depreciates the role of individual differences in personality.

## State-trait Theories of Personality

The most elegant and productive state-trait/biological theory is that of Eysenck. This theory, which attempts to establish the biological underpinnings of personality dimensions derived from extensive factor analyses of questionnaire items, has been systematically developed over a period of 30 years. During this time, a number of pertinent issues have been raised, two in particular. The first involves the stability and the representativeness of Eysenck's factor structure, compared with those postulated by other state-trait theorists such as Cattell and Guilford. The second concerns the significance of the revisions and amendations to Eysenck's biological theory proposed by Gray, Claridge and Zuckerman. It is not suggested, of course, that the views of these authors are simply addenda or footnotes to Eysenck's theory. Each has his own area of particular interest and competence. However, only those aspects of their theories germane to present and particular issues will be touched on.

### Eysenck's Model

Three distinct periods can be identified in the development of Eysenck's theory. In the first period (1947–1955), Eysenck reported factor analyses of data demonstrating that extraversion and neuroticism, his two dimensions of personality, differentiated two major neurotic types, dysthymics and hysterics (cf. Hildebrand, 1953). Data were initially derived from rating scales, questionnaire items and objective tests (e.g. suggestibility, persistence, level of aspiration) administered to patients at the Mill Hill Emergency Hospital.

Extraversion is described as follows:

> The typical extravert is sociable, likes parties, has many friends, needs to have people to talk to, and does not like reading or studying by himself. He craves excitement, takes chances, often sticks his neck out, acts on the spur of the moment, and is generally an impulsive individual. He is fond of practical jokes, always has a ready answer, and generally likes change: he is carefree, easy going, optimistic, and likes to "laugh and be merry". He prefers to keep moving and doing things, tends to be aggressive and lose his temper quickly: altogether his feelings are not kept under tight control, and he is not always a reliable person.

Since extraversion and introversion are regarded as idealised end-points of a continuum, introversion is described in opposite terms.

Neuroticism — emotionality or anxiety — an orthogonal dimension, refers to degree of emotional arousability. Since emotion acts as a drive, N is a multiplier, particularly in emotion — producing situations, potentiating the existing response tendency, $_sH_r$.

From about 1953 on, the various Eysenck personality questionnaires were developed — the MMQ (measuring neuroticism), the MPI, based on the Guilford scales, from which non-orthogonal E and N scores could be derived, the EPI, measuring orthogonal E and N dimensions, various children's and psychoticism scales (PEN and PQ), and finally the EPQ, which provides E, P, N, and L measures. During this period, separate (though correlated) impulsivity and sociability components of extraversion were identified.

The original theory relating dysthymia–hysteria to E–I sparked off a good deal of controversy as to whether this dichotomy provided a valid basis for selecting criterion groups. A number of studies in which the MPI was given to neurotic sub-groups showed that while dysthymics were low on E and high on N, as theory, hysterics did not score particularly high on E. The argument, therefore, was that hysterics could not be used as a criterion group. However, Eysenck subsequently reported that psychopaths are a more obviously extraverted group, and thus a better criterion group for E. The problem, of course, was in part due to discrepancies between the objective test data and the questionnaire data.

At this point, Eysenck began to analyse personality in a stratified manner, as in the case of intelligence, employing factor analysis to demonstrate different levels of generality of description from traits to types, his preference being to work at the level of types.

In the second period, from 1958 to 1967, we can detect attempts to explain the biological basis of the descriptive dimensions referred to in previous research. The basic model invoked Pavlovian constructs of excitation/inhibition balance, which generally showed that test results correlated in the expected manner with questionnaire measures, for both unselected samples and for extreme scorers of the E–I dimension. Drug manipulation, sedation threshold and behavoural inhibition studies (e.g. perceptual after-effects, vigilance, psychomotor performance) all pointed to the same general conclusion — that extraversion-introversion was measuring excitation-inhibition balance. These findings were important since they provided a systematic account of the biological basis of personality. In addition, they accounted for some individual differences in human performance, and, to some extent, bridged the gap between personality and general experimental psychology.

However, in this middle period the theory appeared to hold up better for neurotic than for normal samples. Because of the concentration on the E dimension, N tended to be neglected. Thus, the theory moved away from the original empirical aim of compiling evidence about the dynamics of normal personality.

We should also note, in this period, Eysenck's important studies of motivation, attitudes, psychosomatics, criminality and behaviour therapy, and his brief excursion into the domain of psychoticism, shown in factor analysis of symptom items.

Eysenck's third period, from 1967 to the present time, marks a distinct shift in emphasis. In the middle period, there had been some concern with conditioning and personality, the E relationship to personality being important for several reasons, primarily the understanding of the dynamics of personality development. Eysenck theorised that the rapid conditioning of introverts led to withdrawal and guilt, and to the development of introverted neurotic symptoms as a result of "surplus" conditioning. This, in turn, led directly to Eysenck's involvement with behaviour therapy as a way of dealing with this surplus conditioning. However, Eysenck's theorising over this issue pinpointed his difficulty in dealing with N. Spence's argument that N or MAS is an important variable in conditioning posed problems, since N and E were assumed to be orthogonal. Eysenck argued that introversion was measured by MAS, or at least that part of MAS which accounts for differences in eyeblink conditioning. The empirical finding is that MAS correlates with both E and N.

From 1967 on, Eysenck recast his behaviour theory in arousal terms, with considerable emphasis still on Pavlovian constructs. His theory proposed that E reflects differences in ARAS arousal, and N differences in limbic arousal. P is assumed to be a major personality variable influencing individual differences in performance. He now emphasised zone analysis, on the grounds that results may depend on aspects of the experimental situation, as the Eysenck and Levy (1972) results confirm, under-arousing conditions favouring Is over Es. Thus Eysenck argues for more careful selection of Ss and experimental conditions. Although impulsivity and sociability are differentiated, the significance of the two variables for biological theory is not yet evident. The Eysenck and Levy study suggests that impulsivity is the causal factor, although the bulk of evidence indicates that sociability has a stronger genetic component than impulsivity.

Psychoticism, or P, is a collection of behavioural indices which characterise Ss across nosographic categories ranging from "normal" to clinical syndromes such as "schizophrenic" or "psychotic". A continuous underlying distribution of P is assumed, on which nosographic labels can be located. P is thus conceived as one of three orthogonal coordinates (P, E, and N) which conjointly determine the location of an individual with regard to personality.

P is thought to represent a genetically determined predisposition which interacts with environmental factors, as well as other genetic factors (such as IQ), the interaction determining a "threshold" of predisposing conditions above which the behavioural manifestations of P become clinically detectable. The P scale tests for the strength of this predisposition, so that high values of P are expected to correlate with overt signs of abnormality, such as clinical syndromes, alcoholism and the like. Given his underlying genetic model, and using modern biometric heritability statistics such as Eaves's refinement of Jinks and Fulker's (1970) method, P is claimed to have a purely additive heritability of 81%, which is comparable with the heritability for schizophrenia (Gottesman and Shields, 1972), which, under Eysenck's definition of P, lies on that dimension.

Eysenck maintains that P, as measured by the EPQ, shows a higher score for males than for females, and offers the explanatory suggestion that P is determined by sex hormones, such as testosterone (leading to higher P) and oestrogen (leading to lower P). This is thought to also fit the observation that there appears to be an age-sex regression, whereby male P rises and female P falls with sexual maturity, although female P rises to meet male P during the menopause.

## Cattell's Model

It is unnecessary to attempt a full description of Cattell's very extensive work on personality, and only the sketchiest outline is presented here.

Cattell derives 16 source traits from the IPAT 16 PF Test (1957), which are claimed to give a full description of personality. These tests, many of which are based on earlier Guilford tests, intercorrelate to generate major second-order factors of anxiety, extraversion, radicalism, tendermindedness and superego (Gorsuch and Cattell, 1967), which thus reflect the theoretical alignment of the correlated personality traits assessed by the 16 PF (Cattell, Eber and Tatsuoka, 1970). Adequate construct validity has been demonstrated by identifying the psychological characteristics of high and low scoring Ss on the 16 scales, and then demonstrating predictable differences between clinical, psychiatric, educational and occupational groups on such characteristics.

Cattell's factor structure, however, has been criticised on both empirical and theoretical grounds. Rorer (1972) has commented on the mass of contradictory facts. For example, the four supposedly parallel forms of the 16 PF do not intercorrelate very highly (Bouchard, 1972). The primary factor structure which Cattell postulates has proved extremely difficult to replicate. Tupes and Christal (1961) and Norman (1969) have reported a five factor solution, Howarth and Browne (1971a) a 10 factor solution. Adcock, Adcock and Walkey (1974), Karson and O'Dell (1974) and Adcock and Adcock (1977) have also reported contradictory findings.

Howarth (1972, 1976, 1980) has been Cattell's most trenchant critic. He points out that Cattell does not even employ his own criteria — scree test and eigenvalue greater than 1.0 — in establishing factors. He himself insists on the much stricter criterion — at least five loadings in excess of 0.4 if obliquely rotated — for there to be an interpretable factor. Howarth (1976) claims that only 3 of Cattell's original (1947) factors meet this criterion — dominance, superego and parmia. From his own earlier (1972) study, Howarth reports a seven factor solution — cooperativeness/considerateness, phlegmatic vs. surgent, emotional maturity, extraversion/sociability, superego adjustment/emotionality, unidentified. Perhaps most informatively, what actually emerged from Howarth's (1976) study were factors which closely resemble Eysenck's factors, particularly at second-order level — extraversion, cognition, anxiety$_1$ and anxiety$_2$.

It is fair to point out that Cattell continues to attach greater significance to his source traits, regarding Eysenck's second-order factors as "pseudo-second orders", "space deformed". However, there is now a firm consensus that Cattell's second-order factors of extraversion and anxiety are almost identical with Eysenck's E and N dimensions (cf. Eysenck and Eysenck, 1969; Royce, 1973). It is also clear that the superego factor identified by Cattell (Cattell, Eber and Tatsuoka, 1970) is very similar to Eysenck's third dimension, P. The complex structure of Cattell's factors can be reduced, in essence, to combinations of Eysenck's four major factors. For example, ego strength is not apparently a simple source trait, as Cattell suggests, but combines low P, high E, low N and high L. According to Eysenck and Eysenck (1976), combinations of scores on these dimensions accurately reproduce the Cattell score.

This being agreed, what is the significance of Cattell's theorising in the present context? Simply that it may reveal somewhat more of the content of the second-order factors than Eysenck's account. Insofar as extraversion is concerned, there are apparently five source traits loading this factor — affectothymia, dominance-submission, parmia, group dependence, surgency, and possibly eroticism (Adcock, 1976). One of the genetic components, threctia, which is highly and negatively correlated with dominance-submission, at the introvert pole reflects a low fear threshold and a high disposition to fearful responding — thus being similar to Gray's more neurophysiologically based concept of introversion — and, at the extravert pole, a low anger threshold and susceptibility to threat. The factor space enclosed by these axes would presumably generate a controid of flight-fight. A second genetic component is a subdimension of surgency, defined as resilience, a quality reflecting S's capacity to bounce back from depressive setbacks (Adcock, 1976).

There are also a number of culture-dependent traits which contribute to extraversion. Affectothymia, or "kindliness" (similar to the earlier trait of cyclothymia) derives from Guilford's agreeableness, and is probably a generalised affection arising from early familial experience. Warm, friendly experience in the family is introjected, and expressed subsequently in an outgoing, wanting to meet, to interact, attitude, i.e., sociability. Surgency or F refers to resilience or bounce, recovery potential, which derives from a history of successful striving. This determines, in part, the degree of ego enhancement experienced, which, in turn, contributes directly to S's hedonic level. Such experience leads to a generally optimistic, sociable, extraverted outlook.

Cattell's concept of extraversion thus interactively combines experiential and biological components. It is a product of S's "interest in social contact, his tendency to dominate others, his low degree of social timidity, the extent to which early experience has made him seek group support, and his tendency to surgency" (Adcock, 1976, p. 107). In his system, the biological contribution is presumably smaller than that suggested by Eysenck and Gray. Perhaps we should say that the environmental contribution is given added weight. Threctia, or timidity, particularly in the social sphere, results from conditioned effects in relation to the fear drives. Dominance similarly relates to anger (Adcock, 1976). Affectothymia and surgency certainly include considerable environmental variance. As a consequence, we might expect extraversion to predict conditioning rates less well, except in aversive conditioning situations, where threctia plays a dominant role.

Insofar as anxiety is concerned, Cattell views this as a multiplier, a view similar to those expressed by Eysenck and Gray. High emotionality suggests high levels of reactivity in the autonomic nervous system, which potentiates the response S is predisposed to make on the basis of the trait-determinant of extraversion.

### Guilford's Model

Guilford and Zimmerman (1956) report fifteen dimensions of temperament, a number of which are similar to Cattell's source traits. These load on broad higher-order factors of exvia-invia and anxiety. However, unlike Cattell, who factors the scores of clusters or packages of items, followed by oblique factor rotation, Guilford concentrates on item factoring and orthogonal rotation. An obvious disadvantage is that orthogonal rotation of a large number of primary factors is less likely to approach simple structure than the Cattell solutions.

A controversy which has arisen is Guilford's claim that Eysenck's E scale represents an artificial combination of two of his orthogonal primaries, social activity and restraint (rhathymia), from the Guilford-Zimmerman Temperament Survey. The details and the history of this controversy need not concern us here. We might comment, however, that considerable data suggest that extraversion represents a second-order combination of two correlated primary factors, sociability and impulsiveness (Eysenck and Eysenck, 1963a) both these elements being important features of Eysenck's description of extraversion (Eysenck and Eysenck, 1975). Guilford (1975, 1977) claims that

Eysenck's own data support the orthogonality of sociability and impulsiveness, the latter being regarded by him as the opposite pole of his factor of rhathymia. Guilford (1977) argues that rhathymia, and, by inference, impulsiveness, is more correctly described as being related to thoughtfulness, another of his factors.

However, while Bendig (1962) reports that social activity and impulsivity are separate factors, other studies do not support Guilford's contention. Vagg and Hammond (1976), for example, in an investigation of the Guilford, Cattell and Eysenck factors, found only Eysenck's E and N factors to be invariant, Eysenck and Eysenck (1977) report a multifactorial structure for impulsiveness, each of their personality factors being related to different subfactors of impulsiveness. Note also the finding of Strelau and Terelak (1974) that Guilford's rhathymia and activity scales load a common factor with extraversion.

## Conjoint Studies

Data from a number of conjoint factor analyses of items from the Eysenck, Cattell and Guilford questionnaires provide information on the instrumentality of the different factor models described. One example is the studies reported by Sells, Demaree and Will (1970, 1971) who conjointly factored marker items for 15 Guilford and 17 Cattell factors. The factors derived from the 600-item matrix were content homogeneous, but source factor heterogeneous. Results, therefore, do not favour either Cattell's or Guilford's model. Nor do the traits appear to be particularly stable.

In addition to the extensive studies reported by Eysenck and Eysenck (1969) which indicate that second-order factor solutions of the type proposed by Eysenck best account for the inter-item analyses of the Cattell, Guilford and Eysenck questionnaires, other large scale studies are in general support. Vagg and Hammond (1976) partially replicated Eysenck and Eysenck's (1969) findings. The Sells, Demaree and Will (1970) results did not support Cattell or Guilford primary factor structures. The first two primaries to emerge, emotional stability and social extraversion, are clearly Eysenck-type factors. Similar results were obtained by Browne and Howarth (1977), who factored 401 questionnaire items derived from many source inventories, using 1003 Ss. Again the first factors to emerge were sociability and adjustment/emotionality. Of interest is Howarth's (1980) report that 12 of the Browne and Howarth (1977) factors line up with 12 of the factors described in French's (1973) list of personality factors, this latter inventory being thought to represent an important consensus. Finally, we might note the review of replicated factor structures reported by Royce (1973) (Figure 2). Of the limited number of

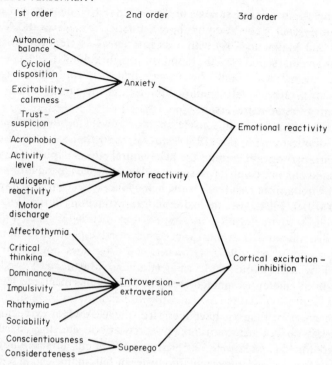

Figure 2. Royce's (1973) conceptual synthesis of temperament and emotionality structure.

second-order factors which have been shown to exist, three of these closely resemble those proposed by Eysenck and Eysenck (1975).

Thus, from a considerable amount of evidence, it appears that the Cattell and Guilford primary factor structures do not account for additional variance to that taken up by Eysenck's second-order factors. In addition, their factors appear to be inherently unstable, and, arguably, redundant. In evaluating the results of studies attempting to relate temperament to personality, therefore, it seems prudent, in our opinion, to attach greater weight to those employing higher-order personality dimensions assessed by questionnaires such as the EPI.

## Amendments to Eysenck's Biological Theory

### Gray's model of the psychophysiology of personality

Gray employs many of his individual contributions to learning theory, such as the fear = frustration, hope = relief hypothesis, in fashioning his theory concerning the psychophysiology of personality. He suggests two modifications to Eysenck's conditioning theory. Firstly, he replaces the ARAS of Moruzzi and Magoun (1949) with a more extensive system comprising the ARAS, the medial septal area, the hippocampus, the orbital frontal cortex, and all interconnections. Secondly, he suggests that "susceptibility to signals of punishment", rather than "conditionability", is the causal variable determining introversion-extraversion.

Gray's theory is based, in considerable part, on the behavioural effects of sodium amobarbitol. Miller (1951) demonstrated that small doses (15–20 mg/kg intraperitoneally) reduce the behavioural effects of punishment in rat approach-avoidance conflict (passive avoidance), while having little effect on reward. Amobarbitol also reduces the behavioural effects of frustrative non-reward (Miller, 1964), and, therefore, retards extinction (Barry, Wagner and Miller, 1962), attenuates PR acquisition and extinction (Wagner, 1963), and impairs discrimination learning owing to increased responding to the negative cue (Ison and Rosen, 1967). However, the drug does not impair simple approach or active avoidance learning (Kamano, Martin and Powell, 1966). Amobarbitol, therefore, antagonises only the punishment mechanism in learning.

Amobarbitol is thought to have its effect on the ARAS. However, small doses (20 mg/kg) do not depress running to reward or shuttle-box behaviour (Kamano, Martin and Powell, 1966). Gray (1970) points out that amobarbitol also acts on the hippocampus and the cluster of cells in the medial septal area which serves as a pacemaker for the hippocampal theta rhythm (Stumph, 1965). Lesions in these areas have effects comparable to those of amobarbitol (Butters and Rosvold, 1968).

From investigations of the effects of driving and blocking theta rhythm, Gray reports that the threshold for septal theta-driving is greatly raised by 20 mg/kg amobarbitol intraperitoneally, especially at 7–8 Hz, which is the natural frequency in the rat exposed to frustrative non-reward. Much smaller effects were found at 6 Hz (the natural frequency for consuming the reward) and at 9–10 Hz (the natural frequency for running towards the reward) (Gray and Ball, 1970).

Theta-driving at 7.7 Hz increases extinction rate, and creates a "pseudo-PR extinction effect" on random trials. That is, theta-driving has an opposite effect to amobarbitol. Theta-blocking on unrewarded trials reduces resistance to extinction in PR, and septal lesions, disrupting theta rhythm, reduce the PR extinction effect.

Orbital frontal lesions in primates have a similar effect to medial septal lesions (Butters and Rosvold, 1968). In man, frontal cortex lesions, alcohol and barbiturates have an extraverting effect (Eysenck, 1967). Gray thus postulates that level of introversion is determined by the degree of activity in the negative feedback loop consisting of the ARAS, together with the orbital frontal cortex, the medial septal area and the hippocampus.

Gray suggests that the Teplov—Nebylitsyn typology may be explicable in terms of arousal levels (Gray, 1967). He also suggests that transmarginal inhibition may be accounted for by his hypothesised feedback loop, which he compares with Eysenck's cortical inhibition system, cortical inhibition being higher in the extravert (i.e. less behavioural inhibition). He also maintains that his hypothesis that introverts are more susceptible to punishment and frustrative non-reward is concordant with Eysenck's views on the nature and cause of psychopathy and dysthymic disorders.

## Claridge's model of schizophrenia

Claridge has been concerned primarily with developing a model of schizophrenia, but some of his findings and interpretations have implications for biological theories of personality.

Claridge (1967) attempted to account for certain empirical findings with schizophrenics, in particular that with such patients, rather than differences in absolute values, the covariation between psychophysiological measures is opposite in direction from that observed in neurotics. Essentially the model proposed two systems, which normally work in parallel, but in schizophrenics become "dissociated". The first system is the tonic arousal system, a system similar to that which Venables and others have described as autonomic arousal, i.e. a mechanism concerned with maintaining the individual's level of emotional reactivity. The second system Claridge describes as "arousal modulation", a mechanism which he assumes to have two properties. The first is to control, through filtering, the level and quality of sensory input from the external environment; the second is to regulate, through negative feedback, the level of tonic arousal. Arousal modulation might have a good deal in common with what Venables describes as "cortical arousal".

More recently, Claridge has simplified this model. Data from schizophrenics have demonstrated more explicitly an altered covariation between autonomic activity (tonic arousal) and measures of perceptual sensitivity (e.g. two-flash threshold). The model now emphasises that schizophrenics show inappropriate levels of perceptual sensitivity to the external environment, given their level of tonic arousal, which, it is argued, parallels the symptomatology of schizophrenia, in which there is inappropriate matching of emotion to perceived stimuli. Thus, the sensory input processing side of "arousal modulation" is retained, although the nature of the feedback mechanism whereby sensory processing is linked to arousal is left unexplained.

Claridge appears to have abandoned his earlier notion of dissociation between the two hypothetical processes in schizophrenia. There are a number of reasons for this. In the first place, the two systems do covary systematically in schizophrenics, but in a direction opposite to that expected. Thus to talk about "dissociation" may be misleading, though in severe cases the processes can be effectively dissociated from an adaptive point of view. Secondly, similar forms of covariation to that reported in schizophrenics can be observed in some normal individuals either under LSD, or high on rated psychoticism. Hence, he espouses the notion of "psychotic-like" and "neurotic-like" forms of covariation between tonic arousal and perceptual sensitivity, which form the nervous typological basis of personality variations associated with high loadings on descriptive dimensions of N and P.

*Zuckerman's sensation-seeking model*

Zuckerman's theory of sensation-seeking (Zuckerman, 1974, 1975) has some similarity to Eysenck's biological model. Zuckerman argues that individuals differ in their need for stimulation in order to maintain optimal arousal, such need being determined by differences in cortical arousal. We might note that similarity of this construct to need for stimulation postulated by Strelau's group, and its importance in determining levels of both sensory and emotional reactivity, which we have described in detail in a previous chapter. Note also the similarity between this and the related phenomenon of augmenting-reducing (Petrie, 1960), augmenters showing a greater increase in EEG evoked potential amplitude than expected to increasing stimulus strength, reducers the reverse. Zuckerman (1975) argues that such arousal differences underlie differences in behaviour variously described as thrill-, adventure- or sensation-seeking. However, unlike Gray or Claridge, Zuckerman (1975) reports a questionnaire measure of his theoretical dimension, which he claims to be independent of other major personality inventories including those of the Eysencks. His dimension, however, obviously bears some resemblance to the arousal models of Claridge and Eysenck. More importantly, Eysenck and Eysenck (1977) and Paisey and Mangan (1980) report that an extraversion factor accounts for the bulk of the variance of impulsivity and sensation-seeking items.

## Social Learning Theories of Personality

In addition to the question, which we have just considered, of the most viable state-trait theory of personality, we also have to ask the question — one which has been increasingly aired in the literature — of whether a state-trait approach to personality, as such, is justifiable. This is a perennial debate in personality theory, dating back to Thorndike, who rejected the notion of broad, general traits of personality, suggesting rather independent and specific stimulus-response bonds or habits. State-trait theories, by contrast, generally postulate that a consistent history of reinforcement creates consistent forms of behaviour, i.e. behavioural traits and types.

### *Situationism*

Social learning theory as expounded by Bandura and Walters (1963) and Mischel (1968) has been described as "situationism" (Alker, 1972; Bowers, 1973; Ekehammer, 1974), a type of radical behaviourism which excludes personality (and, to a lesser extent, the person by situation interaction) as causal mechanisms.

A number of early experiments concerned with trans-situational consistency of conduct, as, for example, the studies of Hartshorne and May (1928, 1929) and Hartshorne and Shuttleworth (1930), claimed to show the situational specificity of behaviour described as honesty, deceit, self-control. The inference from these and similar studies is that we cannot refer to broad general traits of "honesty", and, by analogy, to traits of "extraversion", "neuroticism", "sensation-seeking" and so on, the individual's behaviour being largely directed by situational and interactional (person by situation) variables. This argument has recently been resuscitated by Mischel (1968, 1969, 1973a,b, 1977, 1979), who proposes that the (claimed) inconsistency of personality is due largely to the specificity of behaviour.

Eysenck and Eysenck (1980), in rebuttal, have pointed to a number of considerations which Mischel has ignored. These we shall briefly enumerate. The first concerns the actual data base. Epstein (1977) has pointed out that consistency correlations (behaviour across situations) can vary from 0.37, roughly the figure quoted by Mischel, to 0.81, depending on the number of observations. Data from studies cited have often been grossly misinterpreted. For example, Hartshorne and May, in their classic studies (1928, 1929), report that the average intercorrelation of 23 sub-tests employed as part of the total character score was 0.23, a figure which is cited as evidence for the situational specificity of honesty. The authors themselves, however, make no such inferences. They report that when they combined sets of tests into a single score, reliability increased to 0.73. They conclude

> Just as one test is an insufficient and unreliable measure in the case of intelligence, so one test of deception is quite incapable of measuring a subject's tendency to deceive . . . if we use ten tests of classroom deception, however, we can safely predict what a subject will do, on the average, when ten similar situations are presented (1928, p. 135).

Secondly, the situational specificity of behaviour may depend rather much on the methodology employed. Block (1977) reports that self-report (S) and rating (R) data are usually reliable and comparable, while objective test (T) data — from which, incidentally, Mischel's evidence for low reliability coefficients is derived — are often unreliable and inconsistent. Mischel, however, handles this difficulty by suggesting that the postulated generalised traits may be more a reflection of the observer's construction of behavioural consistency than of actual consistency in the subject's behaviour. Another relevant point is the specificity of the response-equivalence class from which data are collected, which is an arbitrary choice on the part of the experimenter.

Perhaps the strongest counter-argument to Mischel's critique, however, is the high heritabilities reported for major personality dimensions such as E and N, which we have already reported (pp. 43 ff.), and the impressive evidence for consistency of personality traits from childhood to adulthood (pp. 35 ff.). Also of relevance in this connection is the extent of genetic influence on cross-situational consistency and person-situation interaction. There seems little doubt that individuals do differ in the extent to which their behaviour is consistent from one situation to another, but to what extent is this genetically or environmentally determined? Dworkin (1978) reports a study of 54 Mz and 34 Dz 30-year-old twin pairs, selected from the sample of 178 same-sex pairs of high school age administered the MMPI and the CPI by Gottesman (1966) examining self-reported anxiety and dominance and responses to the Snyder (1974) self-monitoring scale across twelve situations, anxiety and dominance being assessed by the S–R inventory method of Endler, Hunt and Rosenstein, (1962). Dworkin reports significant genetic variance for the Snyder self-monitoring scale, for variability across the S–R inventory of anxiety situations scales, but not for the S–R inventory of dominance situation scales. Genetic covariation between self-reported cross-situational consistency for anxiety and dominance suggests that there is a genetic pathway accounting for their significant phenotypic correlation.

Insofar as person-situation interaction is concerned, Matheny and Dolin (1975) report that although correlations of "adaptability" scores with an infant twin sample between two different settings are low, Mz twin pairs are more similar than Dz twin pairs in their pattern of adaptability between situations. This suggests that there are genetic influences on the pattern of change in trait across two different situations; to the extent that such interactions are under genetic control, they cannot be reconciled with situationist approaches to personality. There is, of course, the problem of whether the same trait was being measured in the two settings. If not, the data, rather than referring to genetic influences on the person-situation interaction, would speak to genetic influences on the organisation of personality traits within-individual (cf.

Dworkin *et al.*, 1977). There is also the consideration, one which we have noted previously, that genetic influence on personality traits varies as a function of age (Dworkin *et al.*, 1976).

Dworkin (1979) reports a further study in which anxiety and dominance were measured across a set of twelve situations in an adult twin sample. Evidence of significant genetic variance for anxiety was found for the person-situation interaction, and for the person-mode of response interaction. For dominance, evidence of shared sibling environmental influences was found for the person-situation interaction. From this, and the evidence previously cited, it appears that factors influencing the person-situation interaction vary, depending on the traits studied. As in the case of cross-situational consistency, anxiety appears to be more subject to genetic, dominance to environmental, influence.

It seems fairly obvious that state-trait theory is the only major personality theory which can comfortably accommodate the data referred to above in their personality models. However, even if, for the sake of argument, we do accept the main thrust of Mischel's argument, that cross-situational behavioural measures usually produce correlations no greater than 0.30, thus accounting for approximately 10% of behavioural variance (a figure reported by Sarason, Smith and Diener (1975) from a review of a large number of studies), are the necessary implications those which Mischel and others would have us believe? We might comment that conduct criteria are very complex, and that while any particular personality trait, by itself, might not account for more than 10% of behavioural variance (in any event, a substantial portion!) appropriate combinations of traits might, and often do. As we have previously noted, while any one of the 18 scales of the California Personality Inventory, or any one of the 16 source traits from the 16PF, which have low reliability coefficients, might not, by itself, contribute much to measured consistency, higher-order factors such as Eysenck's E and N, which subsume many source or primary factors in various combinations, do give high consistency values. In any event, it is worth pondering the fact that few, if any, state-trait theorists assume a one-to-one correspondence between internal traits and behavioural indices, most regarding state and trait constructs as intervening variables which permit a parsimonious description of the functional relationships between independent and dependent variables. As illustrated in Fig. 3, where we have three independent and three dependent variables, if we postulate a unifying intervening variable, such as extraversion or neuroticism, we reduce the number of functional relationships from 9 to 6. Considerably greater parsimony is achieved when we are dealing with four and five independent and dependent variables.

This being said, there is little doubt that situational factors often do account for a significant proportion of behavioural variance. But state-trait theorists

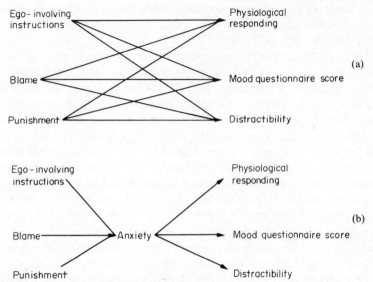

Figure 3. Two ways of describing interrelationships among independent and dependent variables: (a) without postulating an intervening variable; (b) with postulation of an intervening variable (from Eysenck & Eysenck, 1980).

would accept this proposition, as they would the importance of the interactions between the situation and the person, a point emphasised by Magnusson and Endler (1977). As Eysenck and Eysenck (1980) point out, however, this does not imply that these interactions reflect idiosyncratic and theoretically unpredictable relationships. Situational factors are likely to be no more consequential than person factors, and probably the observed interactions between person and situations are both theoretically predictable and replicable.

Of course, the obvious question arises of the proper interpretation of the interaction term. While Mischel emphasises the idiosyncratic organisation of the behaviour within-individual, and thus the uniqueness of stimulus equivalence for each person, state-trait theorists such as Eysenck and Eysenck (1980) point to instances of theoretically compatible and replicable interactions between situational and individual difference variables. One such is the observation, replicated in eight studies (cf. Allsopp and Eysenck, 1974) that the Yerkes—Dodson prediction that performance in simple learning tasks is interactively determined by arousal level and task difficulty, can only be sustained if we take into account the interaction term incorporating the well-substantiated finding that introverts have higher levels of cortical arousal than extraverts. This is likely to occur in any situation in which one personality group, say introverts, show one direction of effect, with extraverts showing the opposite direction (Shigehisa, Shigehisa and Symons, (1973). A similar type of interaction occurs in the case of anxiety, where, for example, the interaction between instructional stress and trait anxiety appears to facilitate or decrement performance (cf. Costello's (1964) review of seven studies). In such cases, neglecting the interaction terms simply inflates the error variance, while reducing the main effects portion of the total variance to a much lower figure. On the other hand, where such variables are considered, much of the so-called error variance is seen to be main effect by personality interaction variance.

Criticism of state-trait theories of personality based exclusively on cross-situational consistency data derived from a limited range of experiments seems naive. As Eysenck and Eysenck (1980) comment, the perspective is limited, at times irrelevant. The data lend themselves to a somewhat more generous interpretation. In any event, there are other, more realistic criteria by which such theories may be judged. Nevertheless, situationism has redirected attention to the importance of situational and person by situation interactional variables as sources of behavioural variance additional to that taken up by personality differences. In addition, on an important, but different front, concern with these sources of behavioural variance has ushered in a new generation of interactional social learning theories of personality, such as those described by Endler and Magnusson, and Staats, which have considerable relevance to the question of the acquisition of rules of social-moral conduct, which we shall be considering in Chapter 11.

### Situation Analysis

An important issue for situational and interactional theorists is the development of a classificatory system for situations as well as for individuals, which involves analysis of the ways in which individuals interpret different kinds of situations. To the extent that behaviour is determined by situation, dimensions along which situations vary are prime sources of individual differences.

A number of attempts to conceptualise and measure social situations have been reported. Wish and Kaplan (1977), for example, employed objective ratings, and multidimensional scaling, to generate the following situational dimensions — friendly/hostile, co-operative/competitive, tense/superficial, equal/unequal, formal/informal, task-oriented/socio-emotional. Argyle et al. (1979), employing a slightly different approach, have attempted to dimension-alise situations in terms of appropriate sets of rules. However, it appears from their results that situations vary greatly in terms of the number of agreed rules.

Some rules meet universal requirements, others do not. Few rules, in fact, are cross-situational.

Bem and Funder (1978) have attempted to characterise situations in terms of a set of template-behaviour pairs, i.e. a set of personality descriptions (Q-sorts) of hypothetical "ideal" persons, each one associated with a particular behaviour. The Q-sort description of a particular individual is then matched against each template, and the individual is predicted to express the behaviour associated with the most similar template. The authors have employed this technique to predict behaviour in delay-of-gratification, mixed-motive game, and forced-compliance situations.

In this context, however, it may be necessary to differentiate "voluntary" and "involuntary" social interactions. Arguably, only the latter lend themselves to the types of analysis suggested above. The former may be steered more by individual reactivity and activity requirements, a point which has been emphasised by Eastern European and some Western theorists (e.g. Bowers, 1973; Epstein, 1979; Furnham, 1981).

### "Interactional" Theories of Personality

Some recent developments in social learning theory have emphasised the importance of the person by situation interaction term in accounting for behavioural variance and personality organisation. These "interactional" theories of personality describe one attempt to resolve the schism between the classic behaviouristic assertion that personality is a dependent variable, i.e. an effect (Keller and Shoenfield, 1950), and the traditional conception of personality as a cause of an individual's behaviour. Over the past 15 years, distinct, but converging viewpoints, can be detected. The first is described as "interactional psychology" theory of personality, the second as "behavioural interaction" theory of personality, the latter incorporating principles underlying social behaviourism as articulated by Staats (1963, 1970, 1975, 1980).

### Interactional Psychology

Personality and interaction, as causal mechanisms in behaviour, are considered foundation principles of the new interactional psychology (Endler and Magnusson, 1976), towards which both Bandura and Mischel have gravitated in their more recent theorising. Bandura (1969) has acknowledged the principle of behavioural interaction, recognising that the individual's behaviour affects the social environment, the latter in turn affecting the individual's behaviour, the two processes being labelled reciprocal influence and reciprocal determination, or simply determinism. Bandura has also formulated a concept of personality, P, referring to "cognitive and other internal events which can effect perceptions and actions" (Bandura, 1978). He refers to the construct of self-efficacy, similar to the more familiar construct of the self-concept. Mischel (1973a), in similar vein, espouses principles of personality and person by situation interaction in his later theorising, employing terms such as cognitive and behavioural (social) competencies — behavioural repertoires describing cognitive and emotional personality constructs, which, however, are not described in any detail. As an aside, we might note, in view of the substantial theory renovations by Bandura and Mischel, that both claim that it was never their intention to exclude concepts of personality and person by situation interaction from social learning theory; nevertheless, social learning theory, until 1968, had these characteristics of radical behaviourism (Bower, 1973).

Interactional psychology, as described by Endler and Magnusson (1976) has a number of defining attributes. The first describes a multidirectional interaction or feedback between individual and situation as a determinant of behaviour. The second asserts that the individual is an intentional, active agent in this interaction — self-direction is a critical aspect of theory. The third and fourth principles assert, on the person side of the interaction, that cognitive factors are the essential determinants of behaviour, although emotional factors do play a part, and that on the situation side, the psychological meaning of the situation is an important determining factor. We might refer here to the comment by Endler and Magnusson (1976) — one earlier made by Rotter (1954) — that consistency in behaviour across situations, something which Mischel (1968) had rejected out of hand, is a function of the individual's choice of the situation. As we have noted previously (Chapter 2), this is an important principle guiding the theorising of the typologists of the Warsaw school.

### Behavioural Interaction Theory

A more positive approach to the contributions of person, situation and person by situation interaction to the variance of behaviour than the arguably reluctant admissions of some of the interactional theorists such as Mischel and Bandura is the theory of Staats (1963, 1970, 1975, 1980) who describes his approach as behavioural interaction theory, derived from principles of social behaviourism. Social behaviourism is a functional theory employing principles of classical and instrumental conditioning in what is claimed to be a new theoretical structure of three function learning. This approach was first demonstrated in a theoretical analysis of language and motivation (Staats, 1963), emphasising the function language has for an individual in his behaviour rather than the way language is learned, which tends to be the thrust of classic behaviourist analysis of language. Staats has attempted to outline the repertoires which constitute language, claiming that the individual's reasoning, his planning, his self-concept, his intelligence, are composed of such repertoires (and others), which in fact constitute, in large part, the individual's cognitive personality processes.

Insofar as emotions and motivations are concerned, social behaviourism has attempted to develop a theory employing these as personality constructs, the basic proposition being that the individual learns a system of stimuli which elicit emotional responses — i.e., the individual's reinforcement system — which has personality functions in that it determines how he behaves. Thus, the concept of personality embodies a basic behavioural repertoire consisting of the various stimuli which elicit emotional responses, positive and negative, in the individual. The way in which the individual learns to respond is his personality, but this, in turn, is moulded by the environment's responses. Clearly a central principle is the interaction conception. Behaviour is both an independent and a dependent variable, a cause and an effect.[1]

The four defining characteristics of the simple interactional psychology model outlined above are fully acknowledged by Staats. There are, however, important differences between the two approaches. Neglecting a number of methodological and theoretical issues which are of limited relevance in the present context, important differences lie in the nature of the environmental, personality and interactional constructs which both theories employ. Staats complains that interactional psychology does not identify an existing theory, or innovate a new theory to account for ways in which the environment shapes learning to form personality. The latter concept itself, probably as a consequence, is poorly defined, as we noted above. Finally, the nature of the person/situation interaction is not specified.

Staats himself (1970, 1975, 1980) has attempted to fashion a theory incorporating analysis of the three important elements. In specifying the environmental conditions important in the learning of personality, Staats employs instrumental and classical conditioning concepts to account for the basic functions that stimuli can have — emotional, rewarding and directive. The environment, of course, is instrumental at two stages — at the point of original learning of behavioural repertoires, and in later situations, where the effects of person/situation interactions become important. Personality is conceptualised as involving both language-cognitive development and function, and the emotional-motivational aspect. The latter system consists of

---

[1]Note the striking similarity to Rubinsteyn's view, cited earlier (p. 53).

all the stimuli — social, sexual, aesthetic, and so on, and the words representing these stimuli — which elicit emotional responses in the individual, the nature of the system determining personality "type", whether extravert or introvert, writer or carpenter, heterosexual or homosexual, for example. Thus the individual's emotional-motivational structure is a system of learned stimuli steering instrumental behaviour, in that it elicits attitudes (the A function), has reinforcing properties (the R function) and has directive or incentive properties (the D function). This ARD system affects the way the individual learns new attitudes, his perception of what is rewarding and punishing, and steers his overt behaviours. ARD (personality) differences ensure that individuals have different experiences, and emit different responses, when faced with the "same" environment.

Finally, social behaviourists have elaborated various types of interactions (cf. Staats, 1975) in which similar principles apply — person/environment interaction, person/behaviour interaction, referring to ways in which personality repertoires can affect the individual's later behaviour (e.g. language-cognitive repertoires involved in reasoning, planning, self-direction of all kinds) person/person interaction, where each person can serve as an attitude-eliciting, reinforcing and directive stimulus for the other, and finally, person/group and group/group interactions. In the latter case, Staats maintains that groups, like individuals, have ARD systems, which combine with individual ARD systems to produce highly complex interactions.

Staat's analysis of types of interaction, however, omits reference to those person-specific traits which many personality theorists consider to be important sources of individual differences in personality. One model of person-situation interaction which incorporates this term is Howard's (1979) model (Figure 4). $B = f(E)$ represents the pure situationist model — behaviour is determined by environmental contingencies; $B = f(P)$ describes a pure trait theory model — person-specific traits are explanatory variables; the phenomenological position is represented by model b, $E = f(P)$, i.e. the situation itself is cognitively constructed through processes of perception; $P = f(E)$

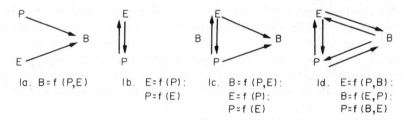

Figure 4. Four models of person-situation interaction (from Howard, 1979).

represents social learning theory — differences among people stem from variation in their environmental histories.

These four models, in various combinations, probably account for the major sources of interactional variance. They can certainly account for the interaction concepts of, for example, Buss (1977), who, following Overton and Reece (1973), proposed two mutually contradictory definitions, metaphysically incompatible mechanistic and "organismic" models. The former, according to Buss, has determinate structure, is inherently passive (reactive), and displays unidirectional linear relationships between dependent and independent variables. This is essentially Howard's model a. The latter, which is represented in Howard's model b, is active, underscored by psychological purposes and goals, and is basically bidirectional. Howard combined these models in models c and d; in the latter, mutual causation exists amongst the three variables.

Different theorists have adopted one or other of these models to advance idiosyncratic views about the importance of different elements in the person-situation interaction, and regard these models as mutually exclusive. They are not incompatible, however, as Merlino (1975) and Howard (1979) have pointed out. For example, models c and d are particular instances of relationships exemplified in a and b. The organismic model extends, rather than contradicts, the mechanistic model. It may be that different models have particular utility in steering development in different periods, or in the actualisation of different forms of behaviour. For example, in Kohlberg's (1968) theory of mental development, a mechanistic model is employed to explain early acquisition of behaviour such as reading, an organismic model to account for the later development of formal logical relationships. Again, it may be that a mechanistic model describes the formation of habits, an organismic model the development of adaptive behaviour. It is surely unnecessary to comment that restrictive models such as those described in models a and b, particular instances of processes and interactions which can be subsumed under more general models of wider applicability, advance neither theoretical development nor our understanding of the highly sophisticated interactions through which human behaviour is canalised and consolidated.

While it is perhaps true that the interactional models of personality we have described are not wholly convincing, nevertheless they have redirected attention to important mechanisms of personality formation and social learning, i.e., to the transaction between individual and environment, the one acting on and simultaneously being acted on by the other, the process being interpretable, and the outcomes predictable, in terms of established principles of classical and instrumental conditioning. As such, they have some affinity with "activity" models of personality originally advanced by Vygotsky (1960), and latterly by Leont'ev (1975) and Davydov (1976).

## Questionnaire Methodology

In the following three chapters, we shall be describing, in some detail, the empirical, or inferred content of excitatory and inhibitory strength, dynamism and mobility, and, more briefly, of lability and concentration. We shall also review studies attempting to relate these nervous system properties to personality dimensions such as Eysenck's extraversion, neuroticism and psychoticism, and to Cattell's 16 PF variables, and to less well validated dimensions such as field dependence-independence. Since most of the data are derived from questionnaires, however, at this point we should at least note questions posed by some Western personality theorists, and by most typologists, of the extent to which questionnaire techniques reliably elicit underlying attitudes, and assess performance, which do, in fact, reflect personality-temperament traits.

There are at least two aspects of this problem. The first involves sampling, sampling referring to both the range of personality-temperament characteristics assumed to exist in the population, and to the population of possible questions intended to elicit responses reflecting such characteristics. In certain questionnaires, populations of characteristics and of questions may be restricted, and not necessarily well matched.

The problem is particularly cogent when a questionnaire is of the forced choice type, and is context freed, i.e., not situation specific. Recently, a number of personality theorists have seriously questioned the extent to which subjects' verbal statements about themselves are, in fact, accurate descriptions of their behaviour, or a description, in good or bad faith, of their feelings about their behaviour. We can, of course, take account of the incongruity between attitudes and behaviour, rather than assuming one to be indicative of the other, by the use of such techniques as Osgood's semantic differential, or Bannister and Mair's repertory grid method. However, such techniques imply a discontinuity model of personality rather than the continuous dimensional or threshold model favoured by Eysenck and Cattell.

Secondly, with the development of questionnaire methods for measuring nervous system properties, the question arises of whether these properties are validly and reliably represented in the different forms of overt behaviour — social, occupational, for example — which are amenable to questionnaire-type measurement.

This reduces to the question of whether the content of questionnaire-derived dimensions is the same as that derived from laboratory tests. Strelau (1972a) has claimed that his STI temperament dimensions correlate highly with similar laboratory indices employed by Nebylitsyn. However, Nebylitsyn has emphasised the partial nature of nervous system properties; measures of visual and auditory absolute thresholds, for example, which are standard measures of excitatory strength, do not correlate very highly. The same applies to mobility, which is also modality-specific. There is the additional problem that ergographic strength measures do not load a factor defined by auditory and visual strength measures — the latter, despite only moderate intercorrelation, having some common variance (Rozhdestvenskaya, Golubeva and Yermolayeva-Tomina, 1967) — so that we may have to differentiate strength in afferent and efferent structures.

If laboratory strength tests measure (partial) afferent sensitivity, and questionnaire strength items refer largely to maintained physical/motor activity, and to distractibility, which is, in fact, the content of many of the Strelau items, it is possible that personality traits such as extraversion could relate in one way to laboratory strength measures, and in a different way to questionnaire-derived strength assessments, or that impulsivity and sociability subscales relate in different ways to the reactivity and activity aspects of excitatory strength.

As yet, these issues have not been resolved. However, implications should be kept in mind when we attempt to evaluate the typology/personality research described in this section.


## Summary

It could be claimed that the trait position, the situational position and the interactionist position are not different approaches, identifying three different solutions to the same problem, rather solutions to three different problems. The trait theorist is concerned with consistent behavioural tendencies in individuals over a sample of situations, the situationist with the effect of situations over a sample of individuals, the interactionist with the behaviour of people possessing certain attributes in situations having certain attributes. The situation and the person are interdependent, the meaning of any stimulus, either sensory or social, being determined as much by the individual's cognitions and perceptions as by its objective characteristics.

Unfortunately personality theorists usually adopt one particular stance. Social learning theorists such as Staats, for example, tend to underestimate the significance of person-specific traits, and, as a consequence, underplay the importance of biological variables. Biological theorists, on the other hand, tend to minimise the importance of the person-situation interaction term. Neither model can command universal respect. Each has its limitations, each its strength. The reader is left to make his own judgement about the respective merits of the different approaches.

As a final comment, it has been suggested that in certain circumstances — for example, under stressful conditions — the individual sloughs off what Asratyan describes as tonic or adaptive reflexes, Bykov as complex-reflex acts, responding in harmony with his basic biological predispositions. Nebylitsyn (1972) comments that it is probably only in such circumstances that "natural" nervous system properties direct, in any absolute sense, the individual's behaviour. While the importance of situational analysis, i.e., S's perception of the situation, has rightly been stressed by interactional theorists, the possibility that such perception may, and probably does, disrupt adaptive mechanisms in certain situations, regressing the individual to his basic biological "self" — and the implications of this — has never been seriously considered by interactional theorists.

# CHAPTER 6

## *Strength of the Nervous System*

*The significance of strength of the nervous processes is clearly shown in the fact that in the (environment) there arise ... unusual, extraordinary developments, powerful stimuli ... And the nervous cells must endure this extraordinary tension in their activity.*
I. P. Pavlov (1955 p. 316)

### Introduction

STRENGTH of the nervous system .refers to the endurance or the working capacity of the cortical cells — the extent to which asymptotic level of response can be maintained when cells are subjected to repeated or protracted stimulation of moderate intensity, or to single presentations of "ultra-strong" stimuli.

Very early in his speculations about nervous system functioning, Pavlov suggested that cortical cells can lapse into an inhibitory state — a "refractory condition", "non-excitation" — as a result of hammering, i.e. prolonged application of a CS.

> ... concentrations of stimulation at one point, or, as we say in the laboratory, the hacking away at one cell, causes this cell to pass into a refractory state, a state of inhibition, unexcitability (Pavlov, 1915).

Pavlov considered this phenomenon "an extremely important property of the higher brain mass".

In his study "Internal inhibition and sleep — one and the same process", Pavlov first suggested that the weak nervous system is characterised by rapid onset of inhibition, and that the speed of development of protective inhibition in the cortical cells is a criterion of nervous system strength, a view he maintained thereafter.

> We can easily conceive of nervous systems which, either from birth or as a result of environmental pressures, possess a small reserve of excitable substances in the cortical cells, and which, therefore, easily lapse into an inhibitory state (Pavlov, 1951–2, p. 62).

182

Similar views are expressed in "Inhibitory types of nervous systems in dogs" (1928) and "Several problems of the physiology of the cerebral hemispheres" (1928), and, following Rickman's (unpublished) studies in the 1930s, were formalised in the typological proposition that excitatory strength refers to the working capacity of cells, reflected in thresholds of transmarginal or protective inhibition.

From about 1933 onwards, there also appeared in Pavlov's writings reference to inhibitory strength. In his paper "Essay on the physiology of higher nervous activity" (1951-2, p. 202), he notes that weak cells are incapable of enduring both intense stimulation and " ... continuation of the inhibitory process". In his 1935 paper "General types of higher nervous activity in animals and man" indices of strength of the inhibitory process are listed, particularly "how long the cell can endure a continuous inhibitory process" (1951-2, p. 283).

Other than this, however, Pavlov had little to say about inhibitory strength. At no time did he consider in any detail the effect of continuous hammering of the cortical cells by an inhibitory stimulus. By analogy with transmarginal inhibition, presumably a type of transmarginal excitation should develop, possibly some form of hysteriosis, or heightened excitability of the central nervous system, which is known to occur following inhibition or fatigue in certain afferent systems. Other than pointing out that there is a weakening, or unpredictability, or complete cessation of CR activity through over-stressing of the inhibitory function, however, Pavlov is silent on this point. Perhaps his most important observation about inhibitory strength was his comment that predominance of excitation reflects strength, and predominance of inhibition weakness of the nervous system. This suggestion — that the strong inhibitory type is also the weak nervous type — had considerable implications for subsequent typological theorising.

There are a number of problems, still unresolved, in the Pavlovian theory of strength-weakness. One is the question of the cellular processes and mechanisms which are thought to mediate excitatory strength. Pavlov suggested two possibilities — that strength is a function of the amount of "excitatory substances" present in the cortical cells, and/or of the "functional destructability" of such substances. The latter would imply that the "weak" type is more sensitive or reactive than the "strong" type, as well as being less enduring (Nebylitsyn, 1966a ). Secondly, there is in Pavlov's writings the statement that working capacity can be measured both by the single presentation of an ultra-strong stimulus, and by repeated applications of moderately intense stimuli — the "battering" technique. As Teplov (1956) points out, however, there are no grounds for assuming that the same neural substrate underlies the inhibition generated by these two procedures. This issue, of course, is one aspect of the more fundamental problem of identity between different types of inhibition — internal, external, transmarginal, reactive and satiation — a problem which remained for Pavlov and subsequent theorists a vexing question.

## Indices of Nervous System Strength

The original typological model proposed basic properties of strength and mobility of both excitation and inhibition, and secondary properties of equilibrium. Initially, emphasis was placed on equilibrium according to strength, and it was from studies of this property that indices of excitatory and inhibitory strength, which are described in both large and small standards (Podkopaev, 1952; Kolesnikov and Troshikhin, 1951), were derived. However, while in large standard experiments the use of caffeine and ultra-strong stimuli, and bromide and prolongation of differentiation were suggested as indices of excitatory and inhibitory strength respectively, the authors of the small standard, while proposing the caffeine test as a measure of excitatory strength, suggested speed of formation of differentiation (rather than prolongation) as an index of inhibitory strength (Kolesnikov and Troshikhin, 1951). Subsequently, a number of authors employed speed of development of positive and inhibitory CRs as a measure of excitatory and inhibitory strength (Voronin, Sokolov and Bao-Khua, 1959; Biryukova, 1961; Merlin, 1958a,b; Gurevich and Kolesnikov, 1955, *inter alia*). A number of additional indices, such as speed of OR extinction, and error ratios in the positive and negative phase of differentiation, have also been suggested.

We should note at this point, however, that Pavlov never specifically referred to speed of CR formation as a strength index, although this would be a reasonable inference from many of his statements suggesting that strong systems condition quickly, and weak systems slowly. For example, in "General types of higher nervous activity in animals and man", he notes that in strong dogs "CRs form quickly, after two or three trials, quickly attain a large amplitude, and remain stable, no matter how complex the reflexive system", while in weak dogs "it is completely opposite; CRs form very slowly, after about ten trials, their amplitude increases slowly and they never stabilise, fluctuating to zero, no matter how simple the reflexive system" (1955, p. 318). Pavlov never resolved the problem of the typological significance of the speed of CR formation, other than proposing a direct relationship between predominance of excitation and speed of CR formation. This uncertainty subsequently created a good deal of confusion; different typological theorists have suggested that speed of formation of positive and inhibitory CRs is related to strength, to equilibrium, or to mobility of nervous processes.

A considerable amount of data from Teplov's laboratory, however, indicates that speed of CR development is independent of both nervous system strength (e.g. Barkhudaryan, 1956; Kokorina, 1963; Nebylitsyn, 1963b; Borisova *et al.*, 1963) and mobility (Borisova *et al.*, 1963; Yermolayeva-Tomina, 1963; Ravich-Shcherbo, 1956), i.e. that strength, mobility and dynamism of excitation and inhibition are orthogonal nervous system properties. Insofar as strength is concerned, since methods for measuring this property (in dogs) developed by the Pavlovian school — the maximum tolerable dose of caffeine, and the effects of ultra-strong stimuli — are obviously inappropriate with human Ss, these authors have developed two sets of indices, one involving the very brief action by ultra -strong stimuli (usually with caffeine), the other repeated presentation of moderately intense stimuli. For excitatory strength, the former include the repetition, exhaustion and caffeine variants of the induction method, the latter, the various forms of extinction with reinforcement, photochemical and EEG; for inhibitory strength, the only index developed was one involving repeated presentations of the differential stimulus.

## Excitatory Strength Indices

### Induction methods

Briefly, it has been demonstrated (Teplov, 1937, 1941) that a supplementary, additional light stimulus located at a short angular distance from the test spot affects perception threshold for the test stimulus. With weak and strong intensities of the additional stimulus, threshold perception is enhanced, due to irradiation of excitation from the point in the cortical projection area on which the radiating energy from the additional stimulus falls. With moderately intense additional stimuli, however, threshold perception is decremented, due to the development of a zone of negative induction around the stimulated cells of the cortex. This inverted U relationship provides empirical support for Pavlov's contention that "with weak stimulation irradiation occurs, with medium stimulation there is concentration, and with very strong stimulation, irradiation recurs" (1951–2, p. 329).

To measure threshold changes during high intensity of the additional stimulus, Rozhdestvenskaya (1955) employed the caffeine method, which has been used traditionally by the Pavlovians to stimulate the excitatory process, and to differentiate strong and weak nervous systems. In theory, caffeine should transform a moderate into a strong focus of excitation in the weak, but not the strong system. Insofar as the induction method is concerned, caffeine should thus produce no effect in the strong system, while in the weak system it should induce a strong zone of irradiated excitation round the source of the moderately intense additional stimulus, i.e., positive rather than negative induction. As a result, threshold perception should be enhanced.

Data reported by Rozhdestvenskaya (1955) and Nebylitsyn (1956) are strongly supportive. Different doses of caffeine in weak and strong systems produced the expected results. Rozhdestvenskaya's graphs clearly show stages at which a stimulus is transformed from one of (absolute) medium intensity to a (subjectively) very strong stimulus, producing irradiation. Using this technique, she was able to locate her Ss on a strength-sensitivity continuum. Rozhdestvenskaya (1959b) reports similar results using the repetition and the exhaustion variants of the induction method.In both cases, the excitatory focus of the additional stimulus was strengthened. In explanation, it was suggested that in the repetition method, multiple presentation of the additional stimulus produced gradual summation of excitation in the stimulated cells. In the exhaustion method, in which frequent threshold measurements were taken, the fatigued state developing in the stimulated cells was thought to lower thresholds of transmarginal inhibition (TTI), so that presentation of the inducing stimulus at the end of a long series of threshold measurements should differentiate Ss in the same way as the caffeine and repetition variants. Rozhdestvenskaya (1959b) and Rozhdestvenskaya et al. (1960) report a high level of agreement between the three indices.

The nature of the processes underlying these strength measures is unclear. Nebylitsyn (1966a) suggests that the weaker the nervous system, the more intense the inhibition developing in the stimulated cells. According to the law of negative induction, in the area adjacent to the developing inhibitory focus, a zone of excitation emerges, which potentiates the excitatory focus from the additional stimulus. Since the intensity of the inductive excitation is determined by the intensity of the developing inhibition, the weaker the nervous system, the greater the inductive excitation. Where excitation from the additional stimulus and from the latent induction summate, in weak Ss there is a transfer of the excitatory focus of the additional stimulus beyond the threshold of irradiation, which produces a heightening of sensitivity. In strong Ss, on the other hand, the summated excitation fails to reach the irradiation threshold, and sensitivity is unchanged.

*Extinction with reinforcement*

This method consists of the multiple presentation of CS and US, with short inter-trial intervals (ITI), following formation of a stable CR. This produces functional exhaustion in the stimulated nerve cells, rate of exhaustion being determined by the threshold of transmarginal inhibition. This was one of the earliest methods for testing strength utilised in the Pavlovian laboratories. However, following studies by Petrova (1934), suggesting lack of agreement between this and other strength measures, this method was omitted from standard experiments.

However, following redefinition of the strength dimension, a number of experiments carried out in Teplov's laboratories, employing photochemical (Yermolayeva-Tomina, 1959, 1960; Rozhdestvenskaya *et al.,* 1960; Nebylitsyn, 1957b, 1959) and EEG (Nebylitsyn, 1961b, 1965) variants of this method, extinction with reinforcement has been shown to correlate highly with strength measures employing induction (Rozhdestvenskaya *et al.,* 1960) and other procedures (Turovskaya, 1963b; Nebylitsyn, 1963b; Nebylitsyn *et al.,* 1965).

*Inhibitory strength*

Only a few studies in the literature are concerned with the development of indices of inhibitory strength. Pavlov mentioned prolongation of differentiation as a measure of absolute inhibitory strength, and this was the method employed almost exclusively in experiments with dogs. For example, in salivary conditioning, the number of drops of saliva secreted during the action of a prolonged differential stimulus was considered to be an index of "disinhibition", and thus of inhibitory strength-weakness. There is some evidence that multiple repetition (Fedorov, 1961a) and increasing the physical intensity (Guseva, 1959, 1961; Zeval'd, 1964) of the differential stimulus produces the same effect.

Rozhdestvenskaya (1963a) has reported data measuring the effect of prolongation and multiple repetition of the differential stimulus on absolute visual sensitivity, using the photochemical method. She concluded that under these conditions, the differential stimulus retains its inhibitory quality with strong Ss, but that with weak Ss the differential is transformed into an excitatory stimulus. Yermolayeva-Tomina (1963) compared a number of orienting and conditioned GSR indices with measures of prolongation and 15-fold repetition of differentiation, and on the basis of her results concluded that disinhibition through prolongation of differentiation is a function of balance of nervous processes, rather than inhibitory strength, occurring exclusively in Ss showing a predominance of excitation.

Karpilova (1964), in animal experiments, has reported that different nervous system types exhibit different limits of delay inhibition, an observation also recorded by Guseva (1959, 1961), who tested the limits of differential inhibition in dogs by increasing the intensity of the differential auditory stimulus. Strong nervous system types showed initially an excitatory phase, followed by disinhibition of differentiation, and an increase in all CR activity, such increase being directly proportional to the intensity increase in the differential stimulus. On the other hand, weak types displayed increased "general" inhibition, without loss of differentiation, accompanied by a gradual decline in amplitude of salivary CRs and an overall decrease in all CR activity. Guseva (1961) also reports that the threshold of disinhibition is lower in animals suffering experimental neurosis and in senile animals. In man, caffeine increases the limits of inhibition of delay in inhibitory types, an effect also shown by excitatory types after ingestion of bromide.

From these results we could argue for disinhibition as a measure of the strength of conditioned inhibition. It is thus the inverse of transmarginal excitation, which was regarded by Pavlov as the boundary of conditioned excitation. According to Barkhudaryan (1964), all forms of conditioned inhibition are localised in the cortical site of CS representation. When inhibition intensifies, it irradiates to other analysers, and also to regions of cortical representations of USs, and sub-cortical areas. In the disinhibition phase, the inhibitory stimulus produces excitation in the "receiving" part of the sensory projection area.

### The Concept of Strength-sensitivity of Nervous Processes

As previously noted, there was an apparent conflict in Pavlov's views about the processes mediating nervous system strength. Pavlov had suggested that cortical cells differ from other nerve cells by reason of a larger supply or greater reactivity (i.e. more rapid "functional destructibility") of the "excitable substances" in these cells. He also suggested that differences in reactivity might differentiate weak from strong cortical cells, although generally he attributed such differences to the actual amount of such substances in these cells. This is clearly expressed in his 1925 paper "Inhibitory type of nervous system in dogs" (1951–2, p. 68) and reiterated in "Some problems of the physiology of the cerebral hemispheres", in which he states: "in the excitable type the cells are strong and richly endowed with excitable substances, whereas in the inhibitory type, the cells are weak, and contain very little of this substance" (1951–2 p. 102). In accepting the latter alternative, Teplov (1956) proposed that the weakness of the nervous system is a consequence of its high reactivity. This is the reason for the low working capacity of weak cells — they have lower absolute thresholds, react more strongly and quickly in the moderate band of stimulation than the strong system, and show more rapid onset of transmarginal inhibition.

This hypothesis has been strongly supported in a series of experiments from Teplov's laboratory, reporting significant negative correlations between sensitivity in the visual system, measured by lower absolute threshold, and strength measures (induction, extinction with reinforcement, slope of the RT curve) in a number of response modalities, usually EEG and motor (Nebylitsyn, 1956, 1959, 1963b; Nebylitsyn *et al.*, 1965; Rozhdestvenskaya *et al.*, 1960; Turovskaya, 1963b). Nebylitsyn (1960c) reports highly significant correlations (+0.53 to +0.75) between visual rheobase (the electro-excitability of the eye) and absolute visual threshold, and four strength measures — extinction with reinforcement and three induction methods. Similar results have been reported with animal Ss. Bobrova (1960) and Neumyvaka-Kapustnik and Plaskin (1964) report negative relationships between motor rheobase and nervous system strength, determined by caffeine tests and ultra-strong stimuli.

In a series of experiments exploring the relationship between strength and sensitivity, Nebylitsyn has used a reaction time (RT) method. Ample evidence suggests that response latency is inversely related to stimulus intensity (e.g. Woodworth and Schlosberg, 1955). Nebylitsyn, therefore, assumed that reduction in RT latency as signal intensity increases is an example of the operation of the law of strength, decrease in latency being equivalent to increase in response magnitude, up to a limiting value. Beyond this point, which defines the threshold of transmarginal inhibition, response magnitude decreases, generating the well-known inverted U function.

In his first study, Nebylitsyn (1960a), using varying signal intensities (range 0.02–2000 lux for vision, 45–120 dB SPL for audition), reports that the slope of the curve relating RT to signal intensity is steeper in its approach to its fastest RT for the strong than for the weak group, strength being measured by extinction with reinforcement of the photochemical reflex (PCR). These data are presented in Figure 5. Nebylitsyn proposed that the greater excitability of the weak nervous system allows it to respond near maximally at a lower level of signal intensity than the strong, but less excitable system. Similar results have also been reported by Turovskaya (1963b) and Borisova (1965), using induction techniques, and by Nebylitsyn *et al.* (1965), in three experiments employing the EEG variant of extinction with reinforcement for measuring strength.

In order to control for differential responsivity in the efferent or motor systems in some of the experiments reported, Nebylitsyn adopted the scoring convention $t/t_{min}$, which is the ratio of response latency at each signal intensity to the minimal response latency (usually to the most intense stimulus). The curves of $t/t_{min}$ ratios are almost identical with those derived from raw RT scores (Nebylitsyn, 1960a). Caffeine does not affect the steepness of the slope for either group, but displaces both curves in the direction of greater sensitivity (Figure 6). Correlation of the summed $t/t_{min}$ ratios with maintained CR magnitude, indexed by the PCR (Nebylitsyn, 1960a) and EEG (Nebylitsyn *et al.*, 1965) versions of extinction with reinforcement, gave coefficients of +0.65 and +0.59 respectively.

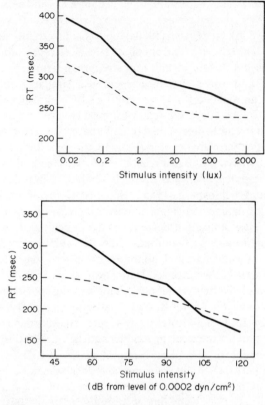

Figure 5. RT as a function of intensity of the visual and auditory stimulus for strong (continuous lines) and weak (dash lines) groups; strength determined by the photochemical method (from Nebylitsyn, 1960a).

Nebylitsyn suggests that, theoretically, the lag in the curve of strong Ss in its movement towards its functional limit should be equal to the difference between the absolute thresholds of the two groups. He tested this assumption by measuring RTs in weak and strong Ss, differentiated on the basis of extinction with reinforcement of the PCR, to a range of signal intensities differing not in absolute physical units, but in deviations from individual thresholds. Thus at each point in the intensity range, the inducing stimulus should have the same physiological effect, irrespective of inter-S differences in sensitivity (Nebylitsyn, 1960b). The mean RT curves for both groups coincide almost perfectly (Figure 7). From these results, Nebylitsyn infers a constant relationship between upper and lower thresholds.

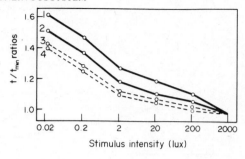

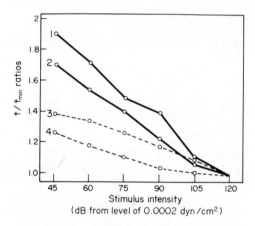

Figure 6. Curves of t/t_min ratios as a function of the intensity of the visual and the auditory stimulus for strong (continuous lines) and weak (dash lines) groups; caffeine trials are curves 1 and 4 for vision, 2 and 4 for audition, non-caffeine trials curves 2 and 3 for vision, 1 and 3 for audition (from Nebylitsyn, 1960a).

In the RT experiments described, transmarginal inhibition (TI) should be indicated by an uptrend in the curves of response to intense stimuli. Nothing of this sort, however, appears in Nebylitsyn's data. He considered TI to be indicated by the asymptote of the curve relating RT to signal intensity. No significant response decrement in fact occurs.

The transmarginal effect, however, has been demonstrated using RT and other methodologies. For example, Lovchikov (1975) reports data showing the effects of different doses of caffeine on conditioned salivation in dogs. As illustrated in Figure 8, a dose of 50 mg caffeine increases saliva production well above asymptotic level. As the dose is increased beyond 600 mg, the transmarginal effect is clearly shown.

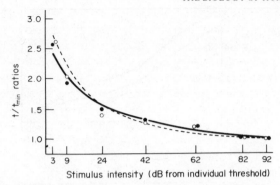

Figure 7. Curves of t/t$_{min}$ ratios as a function of intensity of the auditory stimulus measured in units from individual threshold for strong (continuous lines) and weak (dash lines) groups (from Nebylitsyn, 1960b).

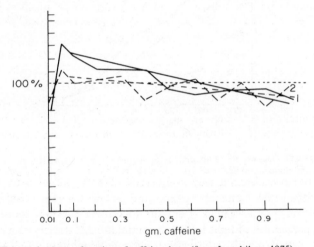

Figure 8. CR magnitude as a function of caffeine dose (from Lovchikov, 1975).

A similar effect has been reported in RT experiments. Venables and Tizard (1956, 1958) have reported response decrement to intense stimuli with groups of schizophrenic patients, as have Mangan and Seeley (1974) with similar patient groups following administration of caffeine. With normal Ss, Keuss and Orlebeke (1977), and Fowles, Roberts and Nagie (1977) report RT latency increase to the most intense stimuli (105 and 103 dB). Keuss and Orlebeke, however, report this effect only in the 3000, and not in the 1000 Hz band.

An interesting variation is suggested in a series of experiments reported by Vasil'ev (1960). He points out that Nebylitsyn's technique precludes the possibility of TI, since stimulus onset at the intensities employed does not expose S to prolonged or intense enough stimulation. Since the theory of strength involves a temporal endurance as well as a stimulus intensity aspect, in that not only ultra-strong stimuli of short duration, but also moderately strong stimuli of longer duration should provoke TI, Vasil'ev suggested that RT to the offset, rather than to the onset signal, is a more effective technique. He argues that temporal summation of excitation, at certain intensities, would lead to such a strong excitatory process that TI would occur before stimulus offset, and hence decrement RT.

Vasil'ev (1960) reports that RT/off to a 2 second auditory stimulus is faster at low intensities for all Ss, due to summation of excitation, but with increasing signal intensities, the advantage passes to RT/on, due to the appearance to TI in the offset case, as a consequence of prolonged, intense stimulation. Vasil'ev also asserts that the signal intensity at which the transition from offset to onset advantage occurs is an index of strength — the higher the intensity at which this occurs, the higher the TTI, and thus the stronger the nervous system.

There is, of course, the possibility of temporal summation of excitation from trial to trial, as occurs in the various extinction with reinforcement methods (battering technique). There is no information on the ITIs Vasil'ev employed in his experiments, which could obviously be a critical variable in determining the point at which RT/off latencies surpassed those of RT/on, since long ITIs would allow dissipation of residual excitation between trials, and thus lead to slower development of TI.

Similar results, i.e. showing differences between strong and weak Ss in the steepness of curves relating response magnitude to signal intensity, have also been demonstrated using phosphene and photic driving techniques. The phosphene technique, which is similar to critical flicker fusion, involves threshold perception of light following stimulation of the eye with an electric current. Since the neural substrate of phosphene appears to be the second retinal neuron, consisting of bipolar, horizontal and amacrine cells (Motokawa, Yamashita and Ogawa, 1957), this technique avoids the photochemical apparatus of the eye, and permits direct measurement of properties of the underlying neural elements. CFP — the critical frequency of phosphene – records the disappearance of perception of light in general. This depends on the intensity of the electric current; individual differences in CFP curves, therefore, should depend on S's threshold, i.e., on the strength of nervous system, as in the case of RT curves.

Nebylitsyn (1960c) reports curves covering a range of stimulus intensties from 3 to 21 volts for strong and weak Ss which strongly support this prediction

(Figure 9). He reports correlations between strength in the visual system, determined by four methods, and CFP at four intensities of stimulus, 7, 9, 11 and 13 volts, ranging from +0.52 to +0.84 (Table 20). Similar results have been reported by Turovskaya (1963b). Nebylitsyn (1964b) has also reported similar results for the photic driving reaction, although the correlations with strength measures are considerably lower.

### Neurophysiological Basis of Strength

Of concern here are the neurophysiological and physicochemical mechanisms and processes which mediate the organism's reaction to the range of stimulus intensities from extremely weak to ultra-strong.

Three preliminary questions need to be briefly considered: the first is whether all forms of inhibition or only the transmarginal form serve a protective function; the second whether transmarginal inhibition (TI) is essentially different from external inhibition; the third whether transmarginal inhibition is centrally or peripherally mediated, or both.

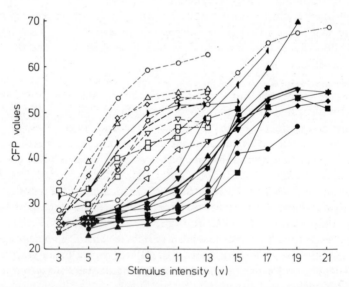

Figure 9. Critical frequency of flashing phosphene (CFP) as a function of the intensity of the stimulating electric current for strong (continuous lines), weak (dash lines) and intermediate (dash-dot lines) groups: thick continuous lines represent mean values (from Nebylitsyn, 1960c).

TABLE 20. *Rank-order correlations between strength of nervous system determined by four methods and CFP at four levels of stimulus intensity (from Nebylitsyn, 1960c)*

| Strength method | CFP | | | |
|---|---|---|---|---|
| | 7 | 9 | 11 | 13 |
| Extinction with reinforcement | .81‡ | .80‡ | .84‡ | .74‡ |
| "Exhaustion" | .83‡ | .81‡ | .82‡ | .79‡ |
| "Repetition" | .68† | .69† | .71† | .57* |
| "Form of curve" | .63† | .60† | .61† | .52* |

\* $p < 0.05$; † $p < 0.01$; ‡ $p < 0.001$.

### (a) Protective Role

Pavlov appeared at times to be uncertain about the precise relationship between excitation and inhibition.

> The question ... still baffles solution. Is it the same process of interchanging under different conditions, or two processes, strongly knit together, developing under certain conditions, on one occasion showing more or less, on others, fully, both their aspects? (1951–2, pp. 207–8).

No such doubts, however, were expressed about the protective role of inhibition when the cortical cells were fatigued or over-stressed. A cortical cell, Pavlov wrote

> being, so to speak, a sentry-post of the organism, is highly reactive, and, therefore, very rapidly functionally fatigued and destroyed. The inhibition which arises, while not a phenomenon of fatigue in itself, appears in the role of a protector of the cell; it prevents further excessive and dangerous destruction of the cell. During the inhibitory period the cell, released from any activity, recovers its normal composition (1951–2, p. 263).

However, since all inhibition, whether unconditioned or conditioned, was considered by him to be cortical in origin, this protective role should characterise "normal" sleep and the various types of internal inhibition, which, when irradiated over the cortex and into the subcortical structures — through, for example, continued application of a CS, or prolongation of the CS–US interval — produce hypnotic and drowsy states. Modern Soviet authors, with some notable exceptions, do in fact claim that all forms of cortical inhibition have a protective function, and maintain that this has been substantiated many times. They note, for example, that following injection of toxins, drug-induced sleep can remove certain pathological disorders, which previously had been considered almost irreversible. They also point to the reported efficacy of sleep therapy in the treatment of certain psychotic disorders, for example, schizophrenia, and in the treatment of traumatic brain injury and shock. Clearly the protective role does not differentiate transmarginal from other types of inhibition.

### (b) Relationship of Transmarginal to External Inhibition

Although Pavlov's view that conditioned or active (i.e. internal) inhibition is largely cortically mediated is generally discounted, the accepted version being that such inhibition is cortically triggered, but subcortically mediated, there is still the problem of the relationship between the two forms of unconditioned or passive inhibition, external and transmarginal.

Recent evidence suggests that external inhibition, i.e. the depression of ongoing reflexive activity by any external stimulus intense enough to elicit on OR, is not entirely a cortical phenomenon, as Pavlov had assumed. He suggested that when any CNS centre is activated by internal or external stimuli, there is an immediate decrease or complete cessation of excitability in other centres, due to attraction of the excitatory process by the newly activated centre, in line with Ukhtomskii's theory of the dominant. Subsequently, he described external inhibition in terms of negative induction — the new focus of excitation inhibits all other foci of cortical excitation. The inhibiting action of the extraneous stimulus, therefore, always occurs in the cortex.

It has been noted, however, that external stimuli, if sufficiently intense, can cause widespread inhibition or reflex activity in the CNS. For example, Beritov (1928, 1930) reports that in both intact and decorticate animals, pinching the skin of puppies' heads produces inhibition of the whole musculature, pinching of the tail depresses feeding, and that in both cases there is depression of phasic as well as tonic reflexes. This suggests that such inhibition is mediated, via the spinal cord and brainstem, by the RF and the substantia gelatinosa. Recent studies generally support this. Hagbarth and Kerr (1954), Roitbak (1958a) and Gershuni (1958) report that during feeding or strong mechanical stimulation the stream of impulses at different levels of the cat's auditory system is depressed. Hernández-Péon, Scherrer and Jouvet (1956) report that evoked potentials elicited by visual stimuli in the lateral geniculate body and the mesencephalic RF disappear partially or completely during olfactory and auditory stimulation which elicits ORs (described by the authors as "reactions of attention"). These and other data suggest that external inhibition of CRs is due not to cortical inhibition, but to the blockade of afferent volleys in the brainstem nuclei, i.e. to diffuse inhibition of the whole CNS from the spinal cord to the cortex. This type of inhibition, therefore, appears to have more in common with internal than transmarginal inhibition.

## (c) Central versus Peripheral Mediation

Evidence on this point involves visual and auditory stimulation, since the phenomena of adaptation, recovery and after-images in receptors such as vestibular and gustatory have been poorly researched, and provide little in the way of acceptable evidence.

It could be argued that TI in the visual system involves the same chemical processes known to underlie adaptation, viz. the speed with which rhodopsin is bleached in the presence of light and regenerated in the absence of light. This is reflected in the intensity and persistence of negative after-images, since these are a direct function of the extent to which receptive elements or chemical processes in the retina are adapted. When a stimulus is terminated, the retinal processes are capable of responding only to the extent that they are not adapted, so that the receptors fire at different rates, depending on their states of adaption. This means, according to the Helmholtz theory of colour perception, that S will "see" the complement of the original colour.

This was the rationale underlying the use of duration of after-image under a massed-trials condition as a measure of visual strength (White et al., 1969; White and Mangan, 1972). Note, however, that duration of after-image is now regarded by Soviet typologists as an index of lability, rather than strength of nervous processes (Nebylitsyn, 1973). White (1968) has also reported that strength in the visual system appears to relate to characteristic features of the flight of colours, a little known phenomenon describing the successive series of colours following an intense flash of light, which is known to vary from S to S, and within S, depending on the intensity of the original flash (Berry and Imus, 1935).

These two methods were thought to contrast the repeated presentations and the ultra-strong methods of measuring strength, which have been referred to previously. However, although results suggested that both these procedures were measuring rather similar processes, they provide little real information on the question of peripheral as opposed to central mediation of transmarginal inhibition.

Similarly, it could be argued that the phenomenon of temporary threshold shift (TTS), which has been reported in audiological research, measures transmarginal inhibition in the auditory system. TTS is the difference in audibility threshold produced by strong stimuli to which S is exposed for a long period. Most of the early studies in this field employed animal Ss (usually chinchillas), although in the last 10 years a considerable number of human studies have been reported. TTS is distinguished from PTS (permanent threshold shift) which is assumed to occur when TTS is greater than 40 dB. Probably at this point, some damage in the conductive mechanism — tympanic membrane and ossicular chain — has occurred, producing elevation of threshold by as much as 50 to 60 dB. Some protection against high intensity sound is provided by the aural reflex, which can reduce the intensity of sound transmitted to the inner ear by as much as 15 dB. The aural reflex involves the contraction of the tensor tympani and stapedius muscles of the inner ear, with a resulting loss in the amplitude of sound transmitted by the ossicular mechanism.

With human Ss, conditions are so arranged that threshold shifts do not exceed 30 dB, and complete recovery is ensured. Exposures have been limited to 24–48 hours, with noise levels around 80–95 dB SPL, and frequency usually in the octave band centred round 4 kHz. Under these conditions, asymptotic threshold shift occurs at between 8 and 12 hours. Illustrative data are drawn from Ward's (1975) graphs (Figure 10). The variables determining TTS appear to be stimulus intensity and duration, stimulus qualities normally determining TI, and the frequency band utilised (Ward, Glorig and Sklar, 1955; Ward, 1975; Melnick, 1976). Rate of TTS growth is exponential, the slope of the function, which at low levels of stimulation appears to be tri-phasic, and at high levels linear (Figure 10), increasing with the SPL level of the fatiguing stimulus. The frequency band involved has been thought to play an important role. For example, with 1 kHz noise, there is no evidence of TTS for approximately 15 minutes of exposure, while in the 3–6 kHz range resistance to TTS lasts approximately 2 minutes only. TTS appears to be significantly greater at 6 kHz than at any other frequency, and recovery slower (Jirsa, 1974). Note, however, the claim of Mills and Talo (1972) that amount of TTS does not vary with frequency band, as generally reported, if noise levels are equated for the acoustic properties of the external and inner ears.

Recovery from TTS appears to be a linear function of log of time following cessation of stimulation (Melnick, 1976), although recovery from asymptotic threshold shift (ATS) induced by long-term exposure to moderately intense noise is prolonged compared with recovery time from similar magnitudes of TTS produced by short-term, high-level exposure.

The mechanisms involved in recovery are unclear. Hirsh and Bilger (1955) have postulated two different processes associated with different phases of recovery from TTS produced by a tone of 1 kHz. The first process, R-1, is operative for the first minute or two of recovery, after which the second process, R-2, intervenes. They speculate that the R-1 process is related to the excitability of the auditory nerve fibres, and the R-2 process to the chemical properties of nerve cells.

The neurological locus of TTS is uncertain. Rawnsley and Harris (1952) suggest that it is unlikely to be the middle ear, since ossiculectomised patients show normal curves of TTS recovery. CNS involvement is counter-indicated by the Lüscher and Zwislocki (1949) report that threshold in one ear is not raised

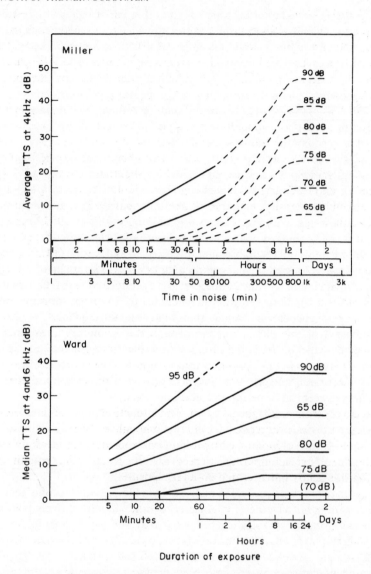

Figure 10. Proposed patterns of development of temporary threshold shift as a function of exposure level and duration. The top graph is an adaptation of curves proposed by Miller (1971) for $TTS_2$ at 4 kHz when the noise is an octave band centred at 4 kHz. The bottom graph is an adaptation of similar growth curves for TTS averaged 4 and 6 kHz proposed by Ward (1975) (from Melnick, 1976).

by providing an adaptation tone for the other ear. Evidence suggests that adaptation of this sort is a peripheral process which occurs at the cochlea, but it is not known whether neural or non-neural structures are responsible. Harris and Rawnsley (1953) report that recruitment — an accelerated growth of loudness — occurs in an ear already exhibiting adaptation due to a preceding tonal stimulus. Since recruitment is a non-neural phenomenon confined to the hair cells of the organ of Corti, and since recruitment was present in the ear exhibiting adaptation, adaptation is assumed to be a function of the peripheral organ rather than the auditory nervous system.

This inference is strongly supported in a number of later studies suggesting that long-term exposures affect the cochlea (e.g. Loeb and Smith, 1967; Benitez, Eldredge and Templer, 1972), losses in sensory cells being confined almost exclusively to the outer hair cells (Blakeslee et al., 1978). There is, however, some conflicting evidence. For example, Hunter-Duvan and Elliot (1972) report no clear signs of anatomical damage to the organ of Corti, even in the case of substantial PTS. Babighian, Moushegian and Rupert (1975) conclude, on the basis of their data, that central auditory processes are involved in TTS, while Salvi, Henderson and Hamernik, (1975) and Salvi (1976) claim that low-level (80–95 dB), short-duration (15 minutes to 3 hours) exposures fatigue primarily retrocochlear rather than cochlear structures. The authors' explanation of this latter, somewhat paradoxical finding, however, is not entirely convincing. As in the case of vision, therefore, the question remains open. There is as yet no unequivocal evidence that the effects of ultra-strong auditory stimuli, and the time taken to recover from such stimulation, are mediated by central or peripheral mechanisms, or both.

In the present context, possibly the most interesting finding is of large intra- and inter-S differences reported in many studies for short-term TTS (usually in human Ss), when compared with prolonged noise exposure (usually in animal Ss). Melnick (1976), for example, reports that in a group of Ss exposed to 85 dB noise in the octave band centred at 4 kHz, some Ss showed no TTS, others TTS of less than 5 dB and one S TTS of 35 dB, over the 24-hour exposure time. The question arises of whether TTS differences (and differences in recovery time, which are equally variable), can be related to Ss' auditory thresholds, and thus nervous system strength, in line with Nebylitsyn's $R/r = K$ criterion. Although there are no obvious methodological or ethical problems impeding such research, no data of this type have been recorded.

### Mechanisms of Excitatory Strength, Inhibitory Strength and Sensitivity
#### Excitatory Strength

Pavlov never speculated about possible transmarginal mechanisms, although at times he did suggest that excitation and inhibition were dependent on chemical substances in the brain. This, of course, considerably preceded the discovery of acetylcholine or other biochemical agencies which are thought to be concerned in these processes, and which might have provided a factual basis for his speculations.

Subsequently a number of possibilities have been considered.

1. The first is suggested by ionic theory of excitation. Nebylitsyn (1966a) postulates that the intra-cellular mechanism of strength is the system maintaining the ionic gradient during inter-stimulus intervals at a level fairly close to its resting gradient. In these intervals, strong nerve cells should be able to re-establish the initial values of the ionic gradient for a sustained period, i.e. exhibit a high working capacity, while weak cells should show a progressively slower and weaker recovery. Possible physicochemical bases for the functional exhaustion of cells are

(a) simultaneous lowering of the potassium and sodium gradients through a gradual, uncompensated flow of potassium ions from the cell, and of sodium ions into the cell, so that the cell suffers a lack of potassium and excess of sodium, thus preventing cell firing. This could be due to a depletion of immediately accessible energy stores (e.g. HTP) necessary for the Na/K pump.

(b) reduced functioning of synaptic transmission through the gradual depletion of transmitter substances such as ACH. More recent evidence, of course, would suggest that we should now refer to calcium ion fluxes in addition to the sodium/potassium pump, and, under the rubric "carrier" substances, include intra-cellular messengers such as cAMP, in addition to the proliferating list of inter-cellular messengers described in the current literature (e.g. ACH, GABA, NA, DA, 5HT, aminoacids and neuropeptides).

(c) reduction in the metabolic energy source in the cell.

Rather similar inferences can be derived from phase or denaturation theory (e.g. Nasonov, 1959; Rosental and Troshin, 1963). Phase theory attaches considerable significance to the intracellular protoplasm, consisting of protein polymeric molecules, rather than the cell membrane. Excitation is thought to be localised in the cell mass, and to produce structural changes in the large molecules and alteration of the spatial configurations characteristic of the resting state. These transformations, reversible processes of disintegration of protein macromolecules on the monomeric links, are denoted "denaturing", i.e. a loss by the proteins of the original physicochemical and physiological properties.

It has been suggested that the mechanism underlying transmarginal inhibition is the stability of these protein molecules — the longer the cells retain their original, highly regulated polymeric structure of protein molecules, the higher the threshold of transmarginal inhibition.

There have been a number of attempts to integrate ionic and phase theories of excitation. Ungar (1959), for example, attaches significance to changes in protein molecules, but also suggests that such changes can be related to changes in the penetrability of the cell to sodium and potassium ions, or to changes in the affinity of the cytoplasm to these ions. The weakening of links inside the molecular structure leads to the redistribution of potassium and sodium ions, and gives rise to the electrical phenomenon of excitation. Inferences about nervous system strength from this theoretical formulation, of course, parallel those derived independently from ionic and phase theory.

2. Wedenskii's theory of parabiosis, which Pavlov at times referred to in his speculations about nervous system strength, suggests some possibilities. The theory can be briefly summarised as follows. Because of the refractory phase which follows every excitatory impulse, excitable tissue can produce only a limited number of impulses per unit time. Thus, if the absolute refractory phase is 2 milliseconds, the tissue cannot produce more than 500 impulses per second. This maximum Wedenskii termed functional lability. In studying the flow of impulses through a section of nerve modified by various agents — e.g. narcotics, salt solution, strong electric current — Wedenskii observed that decrease in lability of the modified section follows a characteristic pattern. Initially, in the so-called equalisation stage, the difference between the action of weak and strong rhythmic stimulations disappears; as a result of continued stimulation, a strong stimulus either produces no response, or initially only a weak response, while a weak stimulus continues to produce considerable excitation — the paradoxical phase; finally, the nerve loses its ability to react to both strong and weak stimuli — the inhibitory phase.

Wedenskii suggested that certain agents acting on a nerve as a stimulus could create, by their protracted and uninterrupted action, a highly localised focus of stable, non-fluctuating (i.e. non-spreading) excitation. This deepening excitation Wedenskii termed parabiosis. When this state is fully developed, the tissue loses its functional properties of excitability and conductivity, since, itself being strongly excited, it becomes refractory to new stimulation. Since parabiotic excitation deepens under the influence of incoming excitatory impulses, the stronger or more frequent the latter, the stronger the local excitation in the parabiotic area, and the more impeded the following conduction. The parabiotic area, which is characterised by extremely low lability, is thus unable to reproduce strong and frequent excitations. This accounts for both the equalisation and paradoxical phases. Inhibition parabiosis, however, is not due to fatigue, since the nerve recovers its functional lability immediately stimulation becomes weaker or less frequent.

Wedenskii maintained that inhibition parabiosis is a fundamental property of nervous tissue, and depends solely on the strength and frequency of the stimulus, and on the characteristics of the reacting system. For him, inhibition was simply a modification of the excitatory process.

At times, Pavlov considered inhibition parabiosis and transmarginal inhibition to be similar, if not identical processes, possibly a necessary inference to account for the frequent observations that during extinction with reinforcement, a classic strength measure, the same pattern of nervous action characteristic of parabiosis occurred — equalisation, paradoxical, ultra-paradoxical and inhibitory phases. We should note, however, that this concept of functional lability is now regarded as the theoretical basis for the property of lability, which has recently been postulated as an independent nervous system property (Nebylitsyn, 1973), rather than nervous system strength.

3. More recent evidence than that available to Pavlov indicates quite clearly that transmission of excitation and inhibitory action are not solely electrical phenomena. It is now generally accepted that excitatory and inhibitory information is transmitted from one neurone to another by the release of chemical substances by one cell which will cause a target cell to fire, or which will inhibit it from so doing. Where such chemical substances are 'systemic', that is, released into the general circulation (e.g. adrenaline, ACTH), they are referred to as hormones. These are relatively slow acting, at least in terms of the time required to physically travel from the releasing to the target cell. By contrast, where the releasing cell is in close physical proximity to the target cell, synaptic transmission of information is relatively quick, and the substances involved – such as ACH, GABA — are referred to as "neurotransmitters". Sometimes these substances may fulfill both neurotransmitter and humoral roles, as, for example, in the case of noradrenaline. From iontopheric application of transmitters, it appears that some are excitatory (e.g., glutamate), some inhibitory (e.g., GABA, glycine), while others again have either an excitatory or an inhibitory action, depending on rate of release and type of receptor activated (e.g., ACH, neuropeptides, catecholamines).

It is obvious that neurotransmitters are an indespensible link in the process of neural transmission. ACH, for example, reproduces the action of almost all preganglionic fibres on the cells of the ganglia of the sympathetic system, and the excitatory effect of all postganglionic fibres of the parasympathetic system. The level of ACH, according to most authorities (cf. Cooper, Bloom and Roth, 1978) appears to be correlated with the electrical activity of the brain. Evidence suggests that acetylcholine formed by each neural impulse must be fully broken down into choline and acetic acid components by the enzyme cholinesterase during the refractory phase, otherwise the subsequent impulse will be unable to produce excitation, because of a longlasting depolarising blockade. Both acetylcholine and cholinesterase show highest concentrations at synaptic junctions and motor nerve endings, and could provide a possible chemical basis for individual differences in the work capacity of cells[1]. Of interest also in this connection is the well established finding that the physiological action of adrenaline, a highly similar compound, is to increase arousal and enhance the working capacity of muscles.

However, we should not ignore the possibilities suggested by other transmitters when considering the neurochemical basis of nervous system strength. For example, there is evidence that individual differences in pain threshold, which we would regard as reflecting nervous system strength-sensitivity, are related to individual differences in encephalin and endorphin levels in the brain, as indirectly assessed by the analgesic antagonist naloxone (Buchsbaum, Davis and Bunney, 1977).

4. According to Bykov (1952), inhibition in the cortex and in the nervous system generally is always connected with a change in blood circulation, or, in a broader sense, in the "supply" to the inhibited nerve cells. "Supply" denotes all the conditions under which the cells are supplied with, and assimilate compounds, including oxygen consumed during activity, and eliminate unused metabolites. He suggests that many or all groups of nerve cells or individual cells contain structures which function as receptors. Thus he assumes that excitation of one group of cortical cells can reflexively evoke changes in blood circulation and supply of other substances functionally connected with them. Reflex changes may arise in the trophic function of the cortical cells, in their supply with nutritive substances, and in the conditions under which these substances are assimilated. At the same time the state of each group of nerve cells probably influences its own blood supply. Changes in the supply of oxygen and nutritive substances to the cortical cells, and changes in the elimination of metabolites alter the functional state of these cells and their activity. Modification of blood supply, changes in the permeability of their membranes, in the endothelium of their capillaries, and in the properties of the glia, influence the activity of the cortical cells and the conditions of their transition to a state of inhibition or excitation. Bykov, however, also notes that this is not the only variable, and refers to the biochemical state of the tissues.

5. Of interest are the views of Robinson (1980), who has been concerned with the neurophysiological basis of Pavlovian strength of excitation and inhibition. He claims that strength of nervous system is reflected in the physicochemical properties of the diffuse thalamocortical projection system and associated cortical cell populations. These are represented in his model by proportionality or time constants. Variation in the proportionality constants of the diffuse thalamocortical projection system relate to behavioural "types", and to a

---

[1]Similar physicochemical processes might be postulated to underlie differences in lability and in irradiation of excitation, nervous system properties which are discussed in Chapter 8.

number of personality dimensions which are claimed to reflect strength of nervous system.

6. Finally, we should note the views of the Warsaw school on the nature of mechanisms underlying reactivity, a concept rather similar to Pavlovian strength, although reactivity implies responsivity to emotional as well as to sensory stimuli.

In line with their reactivity/activity model, Strelau and his colleagues suggest that low-reactive Ss (strong in Pavlovian terms), or subjects under conditions of perceptual isolation, stimulation seek by daydreaming or through irrelevant motor behaviour, and that this is accompanied by hormonal changes — in adrenaline and noradrenaline secretion, increased secretion of thyroid hormone — which increase sensitivity to stimuli. Under long-term deprivation, however, other compensatory mechanisms come into play. Overall sensitivity is reduced, there is increased tolerance for intense stimuli — the law of strength is negated. The mechanisms involved in such reactivity control can only be guessed at, but various agents have been suggested — GABA, encephalin levels, induction of enzymes, for example. Insofar as over-stimulation is concerned, a similar, but reversed process seems to occur. Thus, although Strelau does not describe in any detail the neurophysiological or physicochemical basis of reactivity, we might infer that this involves hormonal "re-tuning" mechanisms to equate stimulation level with individual stimulation requirements, which are genetically determined.

### Inhibitory Strength

Insofar as inhibitory strength is concerned, there are few suggestions in the typological literature about possible mechanisms. This probably reflects the general state of uncertainty in physiology about the nature of inhibitory processes. The basic problem is that inhibitory electrical impulses have not been demonstrated, so that we cannot conceive of inhibition spreading along a nerve fibre in the way that excitation irradiates. Nevertheless, irradiation of inhibition in the cortex, encompassing entire neuronal complexes, has been demonstrated, but this movement appears to be produced, inductively, by excitation.

It is possible that inhibitory or excitatory cell reactions are due to the cells being stimulated by different excitatory and inhibitory mechanisms, e.g. by different synaptic transmitter substances, one of which has an inhibitory, the other an excitatory, effect (Eccles, 1959), due to hyperpolarisation or depolarisation of the membrane, with consequent displacement of the membrane potential in opposite directions. Data on this point, however, are equivocal. While it is clear that certain substances exert a specific inhibiting action on some sections of the nervous system — e.g. atropine paralyses impulse transmission from the postganglionic parasympathetic fibres to the effectors – and while the inhibitory effects of brain extracts such as GABA and Florey's Factor 1 are indisputable, there is as yet no direct evidence of active inhibitory agents at the synaptic junctions which might underlie differences in inhibitory strength.

Beritov (1961) has suggested that the inhibition of pyramidal neurons is produced by activation of the dendritic branches so that the resulting excitation suppresses activity in the neuronal cell wall. As in the previous cases, however, the data are by no means compelling. It is generally conceded that although phenomena of inhibition have been observed and described in some detail, the nature of the chemical and physicochemical processes in the nervous tissue which determine inhibition are unknown.

### Nervous System Sensitivity

It has been suggested (Gray, 1964b; Nebylitsyn, 1966a,b; Eysenck, 1967) that nervous sensitivity-strength is similar to the western concept of arousability. Nebylitsyn (1966a) has reported highly significant correlations between upper and lower thresholds of response — LAT and TTI — in a number of modalities, and Gray (1964b), from an extensive review of the literature, has drawn an analogy between the upper point of the inverted U curve of arousal and the threshold of transmarginal inhibition. On this basis, the mechanisms underlying sensitivity are those mediating arousal.

Theories of arousal date from Duffy's (1934) views on the characteristics of emotional states, mainly their intensive and directive aspects, the former relating to differences in level of activation, the latter to the type of energetic action occurring in response to changed activation, which distinguishes one emotion from the other. We shall postpone consideration of the directive aspect of heightened activation, which is concerned with functional characteristics – learned and unlearned — of areas in the lower part of the brain concerned with biologically indispensible activity such as reproduction, attack and so on, to the next section, which is concerned with conditioning generally, and specifically with problems such as individual differences in sensitivity to different classes of reinforcement. For the moment, we shall concern ourselves with the energising aspects of emotion or motivation, which gives rise to the psychophysiological concept of arousal.

At any given moment, arousal level or activation describes S's position along a dimension of alertness. Arousal changes can be measured centrally — through frequency and amplitude of EEG waves (high frequency, low amplitude waves indicating increased arousal) DC shifts, evoked potentials and so on, through motor and sensory effects (greater restlessness, increased receptor sensitivity) and through autonomic effects — sympathetic mobilisation of increased blood pressure, HR and so on. These autonomic changes, which are normally regarded as arousal responses, depend on a group of structures — collectively the arousal or ergotropic system, consisting of the BSRF and centres in the hypothalamus, thalamus and cortex. The RF controls the electrical phenomena that characterise an alert cortex, resulting in increased sensitivity to external stimuli and facilitation of muscular activity; the hypothalamus controls the processes of the skin and internal organs which depend on the sympathetic nervous system. Although, as we shall note later, there is only a moderate tendency for the various indices of arousal to correlate, when animals are immobilised and isolated from extraneous influences, thus excluding competing and idiosyncratic influences, there is a much higher coincidence between indices (Block, 1965). Nevertheless, there are situations in which the electrocortical and behavioural indices appear to be contrasted — e.g., in situations of sensory deprivation or sensory bombardment, following administration of certain drugs, as a result of extirpation.

Contrasting with this arousal system is a "de-arousal" or "trophotrophic" system, which, when activated, produces signs of lowered arousal, including changes in the internal organs mediated by the parasympathetic division of the autonomic nervous system. These structures include centres in the cortex, thalamus and hypothalamus, as well as an inhibitory structure at the base of the RF. Some parts of the brain, e.g., the non-specific nuclei in the thalamus, and the caudate nucleus, seem to have both arousing and de-arousing functions, depending on the frequency and intensity of stimulation.

There are three ways, basically, in which these structures of the arousal and de-arousal systems can be activated — through hormonal secretions, through transmission of impulses from receptors along sensory nerves to the brain and through the afferent collaterals to the RF (the first providing specific stimulus information, the second crude information about sensory qualities such as volume, intensity and duration of stimulation, and some matching information) and finally, through fibres which convey information from the cortex to brainstem centres, a mechanism of particular importance when arousal or de-arousal depends on learning, or highly sophisticated analysis of complex perceptual patterns, or on thought processes (including imagery).

The most important determinants of arousal increase are cyclical variations such as sleep and waking, alteration in drive or emotional states — both unlearned (such as hunger) and learned (such as fear) — the psychophysical properties of stimuli (their intensity and duration, and what Berlyne (1960) describes as their collative properties — their novelty, ambiguity and so on) and in some cases an innate component, either arousing (sights and sounds of predators) or de-arousing (the "contact comfort" which Harlow (1958) suggests as the original source of the bond between mother and child).

It is obvious that the arousal potential, "arousability" or psychological strength of any stimulus will depend on a number of psychophysiological qualities of the stimulus. Gray's (1964b) model of arousability implies that the physiological effectiveness of the stimulus — its arousal potential — is an interactive function of stimulus intensity, drive, and individual differences.

Of some interest in this context is an application of the arousal concept suggested by Eysenck (1967) and Berlyne (1967, 1971a,b). Judging from considerable evidence (Berlyne, 1967) that a moderate rise in arousal is pleasant, that extremely high arousal is aversive, and that decrease in extremely high arousal is rewarding, these authors have speculated that the "hedonic" value of a stimulus — its pleasantness, reward value, or unpleasantness, aversiveness or punishment value — may depend on how arousing or de-arousing the stimulus is. Berlyne (1971b), in noting the Olds and Olds (1965) evidence of three hedonic centres in the brain — the primary reward system, the aversion system, and the secondary reward system — has suggested two distinct reward mechanisms, one concerned with the reward value of moderate arousal increase, the other, which depends on the secondary reward system, producing reward through inhibiting the aversion system, and thus reducing arousal from an uncomfortably high level. The wider implications of this theoretical formulation for conditioning and complex learning processes need not concern us here. At present, it is sufficient to note that reactivity in both primary and secondary systems should be an important factor in determining the levels of sensory stimulation experienced as both rewarding and aversive, which leads to the inference that sensitive Ss judge weaker levels of stimulation to have more positive hedonic tone, and that they tolerate sensory isolation more equably than do strong Ss.

## Strength-sensitivity and Personality

There have been a number of attempts to relate strength-sensitivity, particularly sensitivity, measured by the inverse of lower absolute threshold (LAT), to extroversion and neuroticism.

Gray and Lynn have suggested that "strength of the nervous system corresponds to anxiety, Ss with weak nervous systems being anxious" (Lynn, 1966, p. 103) or "more arousable" (Gray, 1964a), a suggestion which had previously been made by Eysenck (1957). Lynn, however, comments that "there is little evidence on the question of how far anxiety is related to the various threshold measures devised by Teplov and his associates". In fact, the only reported study found no significant relationship (Granger, 1957). On the other hand, since it has been generally recognised that N indicates predisposition to defensive arousal (A-trait), which Nebylitsyn (1964) and Berlyne (1968) suggest may be due to relatively ineffective constraint by the cortex on the brain stem structures which govern arousal, it could be argued that when stimulation is intense enough to be aversive, N rather than I reflects sensitivity in the sub-cortical structures mediating aversive stimulation.

More substantial evidence indicates some relationship between LAT and extraversion. This hypothesis was derived from Eysenck's observation of a close relationship between reticular thresholds and introversion, reflected in the lower thresholds of arousability expressed by introverts (Eysenck, 1967), which is in line with earlier suggestions that the E-I dimension might reflect arousal (Claridge, 1960; Eysenck, 1953; Corcoran, 1965), and on Gray's (1964a) suggestion that different arousal levels in the reticular formation could account for most of the experimentally determined differences between "weak" and "strong" nervous systems. These considerations prompted Eysenck (1966) to suggest that

> the Pavlovian notion of "strong" and "weak" nervous systems, which has formed the basis of most of Teplov's experimental work, bears a striking resemblance to the notions of extraverted and introverted personality types ... the "weak" personality type appears to resemble the introvert, the "strong" personality type the extravert (p. 33).

Subsequently, Eysenck and Eysenck (1967a) suggested that the link might be the association of sensitivity with a high level of cortical arousal.

There is considerable empirical support for this proposition. Significant correlations have been reported between introversion and thresholds for critical flicker fusion (Simonson and Brozek, 1952), for auditory (Smith, 1966), visual (Siddle et al., 1969), electrical vestibular (Dunstone, Dzendolet and Henckeruth, 1964) and gustatory (Fischer, Griffin and Rockey, 1966, with quinine) stimuli. Where weak to moderate stimulus intensities have been employed, which should elicit greater response magnitude in Is on the basis of the I = sensitivity hypothesis, significant correlations between I and responses to gustatory (lemon juice) stimuli have been reported (Corcoran, 1964; Eysenck and Eysenck, 1967b; Casey and McManis, 1971) and partial replications by Medeisos and McManis (1974), Wardell (1974) and Horne and Ostberg (1975). The latter report a significant relationship in the morning, not in the afternoon. We might also note the Sweeny and Fine (1965) study, which reported high pain reactivity (to cold) in field independent Ss, field independence and introversion showing some degree of correlation (Evans et al., 1967; Fine, 1972;

Bone and Eysenck, 1972; Sell and Duckworth, 1974; Fine and Danforth, 1975; Loo, 1976), although Joshi (1974) with 12-year-olds, and Lester (1976) report no relationship.

It is possible, however, that this I-sensitivity relationship might be confounded by N. Siddle *et al.* (1969) noted that when high N Ss were included in their samples, correlations between I and sensitivity, while still positive, were non-significant. A similar effect is apparent in the EEG data.

On the other hand, Mangan and Farmer (1967) and Zhorov and Yermolayeva-Tomina (1972) report significant correlations between E and sensitivity. In both these studies, however, the sensitivity measure was the slope of the RT curve relating signal intensity to latency, a measure which, as noted earlier, correlates highly with classic strength measures (Nebylitsyn, 1966a).

Commenting on this contradictory relationship, Zhorov and Yermolayeva-Tomina suggest that either the hypothesis relating introversion to weakness is wrong, or that the method employed for measuring strength in these experiments is inappropriate. The latter, they suggest, is closer to the truth, and that this question will only be resolved when adequate measures for measuring strength have been devised.

Some recent studies throw light on this issue. It is now clear that RT latency may relate to a number of nervous system properties, depending to some extent on methodology. For example, where a warning signal is employed, negative or positive induction effects may be expected, depending on the intensity of the warning signal, and ISI. Borisova (1969) reports that, in the case of choice RT, concentration of excitation and negative induction are correlated with short latencies, irradiation of excitation with long latencies. In a later study (Borisova, 1972) she reports a significant correlation between RT latencies and discrimination thresholds. Since the latter are thought to be determined by processes of irradiation and concentration, these are the processes underlying RT latency.

Suzdaleva and Chuprikova (1974) measured RT latencies in 17 tasks, and correlated these with measures of strength, lability and mobility. On the basis of a factor analysis, they report that simple RT latency reflects lability of nervous processes, but that choice RT, involving as it does additional information processing and decision making, also involves mobility. Note also the study by Ol'Shannikova and Aleksandrova (1969) reporting that RTs to visual and auditory signals are uncorrelated, and that a considerable practice effect, particularly to weak signals, obscures typological differences.

There are, therefore, some grounds for suggesting that RT latency reflects irradiation/concentration and lability (which, as we shall see later, have proved difficult to disentangle) rather than strength of nervous processes. We might also recall that Nebylitsyn, in his RT studies, employed extinction with reinforcement of the PCR as his strength measure. Although this technique is a standard procedure for measuring strength, it is possible that the PCR variant also measures irradiation/concentration. This could account for the strength/ RT latency correlations reported, and also for the reversed correlation with E, since there is some evidence that E-I correlates with indices of lability and irradiation/concentration.

At the strong end of the dimension, approaching TTI, a considerable amount of data support the prediction that the weaker, more arousable I should show earlier onset of TI than the stronger, less arousable extravert. This is a logical inference from Nebylitsyn's (1956, 1959) data suggesting that the system possessing high sensitivity, i.e. low LAT, also has a low TTI, so that the distance between the upper and lower thresholds of response is a constant.

A problem here is that a good deal of the reported data refer to pain and tolerance thresholds, an area which has produced a good deal of debate and controversy in recent years. Attempts to identify pain receptors, and the specific sensory pathways involved have been only partially successful. The most widely, but no means universally accepted theory of pain, which appears to account well for both the psychological and physiological facts, is the Melzack and Wall (1965) gate theory. Response to an initial non-noxious stimulus — for example, the tingling sensation to a threshold electric shock — appears to be mediated by large, rapidly conducting myelinated A fibres, which carry precise tactile information into the dorsal columns, and also send collaterals to impinge on the first cells of central transmission, the T-cells. At noxious levels, small high threshold fibres — the smallest A fibres and the very slow conducting C fibres — become excited. These small unmyelinated fibres, which subserve the perception of pain, are the main form of input into T-cells. Pain is experienced when the output of T-cells reaches or exceeds a critical level. Both small and large fibres enter the spinal cord, then branch. Some proceed to brain areas, others to efferent structures such as muscles. There is as yet no unequivocal evidence of a pain centre, as such, both the brain and the spinal cord acting to refine data from the periphery, although the intralaminar nuclei of the diffuse thalamocortical system are regarded as the major terminus for the paleo-spinothalamic pathway for pain (Guyton, 1976).

While the direct synaptic influence of both forms of T-cell input is excitatory, data reported by Wall show that sustained activity in these afferents quickly gives rise to opposing feedback effects. These are thought to be mediated by small "gating" cells in the substantia gelatinosa, which exert presynaptic inhibition on both the large and small fibre endings. Thus, according to theory, cells in the substantia gelatinosa act as a gate control system which modulates the synaptic transmission of nerve impulses from peripheral fibres to central cells. Further, low level stimulation which excites large fibre activity shuts the gate, thus inhibiting transmission along the small fibres, and thus transmission of pain information through the T-cells.

There is some anecdotal and clinical evidence to support this theory. Large fibre activity produced by mild tactile stimulation seems to increase tolerance for nociceptive stimulation. Wall and Sweet (1967) report that low intensity shock delivered to the skin at a painful site reduces neuralgic pain in arm and hand. Shealy, Mortimer and Hagfors (1970) report some relief from intractable pain in patients receiving stimulation from electrodes implanted on the surface of the dorsal column. Higgins, Tursky and Schwartz (1971), however, report data suggesting that the gating mechanism operates selectively on the reactive component of the pain sensation, but does not block details of the sensory intensity of the stimulus. Clearly something more complex than the negative feedback mechanism postulated by gate theory is involved here. Precisely what this is, however, is uncertain.

For our purposes, this is of no great consequence. Since it is generally conceded that the large A fibres are intimately concerned in sensory discrimination (aesthesiometric index, tactile threshold) we might equate thermal and tactile sensitivity with reactivity in the large A fibres, and pain and tolerance thresholds — the latter being regarded as TTI — with reactivity in the small A and C fibres. If there is a general factor of reactivity from potentially to actually noxious stimuli embracing both these receptor systems, it follows, on the basis of Nebylitsyn's theorem, that introverts should exhibit lower tactile/thermal pain and tolerance thresholds.

Despite gaps, the available evidence is generally supportive. Clark and Bindra (1954) report a high positive correlation between thermal sensitivity and tolerance thresholds, which is in line with Nebylitsyn's expectations. On the personality side, Barnes (1975) has reviewed most of the available data on the relationship of E to pain and tolerance thresholds for ischemic, thermal and auditory stimuli. His tabulated results are presented in Table 21. Combining probabilities by standard methods gave figures of $p < 0.05$ and $p < 0.001$ in testing predictions that introverts have lower pain thresholds, and are less tolerant of pain than extraverts. While Loo (1976) failed to confirm this relationship, data reported by Bartol and Costello (1976) are in agreement, although note the likelihood that pain and tolerance thresholds bear some relationship to N (e.g. Bond, Glynn and Thomas, 1976).

Evidence from studies in which non-noxious stimuli (arguably) have been employed are also in general agreement. Eysenck and Eysenck (1967) report that while Is salivate more than Es to lemon juice on the tongue, Es salivate more when the lemon juice is swallowed, i.e. when the gustatory stimulus becomes more intense. White et al. (1969) report that rate of inhibitory buildup in the visual system, measured by reduction in after-image duration to a moderately

TABLE 21. Summary of studies relating extraversion to pain and tolerance thresholds (from Barnes, 1975)

| Study | Subjects | Extraversion measure | Pain or sensation stimulus | Pain or sensation measure | Results |
|---|---|---|---|---|---|
| Petrie et al. (1960) | 42 patients | MPI | Clinical pain | Clinical assessment | Extraverts greater pain tolerance ($p < 0.05$) |
| Poser (1960) | 19 ex'l. pain 18 female students | MPI | Radiant heat Ischemic pain | Pain tolerance Pain tolerance | Significant correlation (0.53) E and pain tolerance |
| Lynn & Eysenck (1961) | 30 female students | MPI | Radiant heat | Pain tolerance | Correlation E and pain tolerance (0.69, $p < 0.01$) |
| Schalling & Lavander (1964) | 20 male delinquents | MPI and clinical assessment | Electric current | Sensation and pain threshold, pain tolerance | Psychopaths less sensitive to pain. Results E and pain n.s. but in right direction. |
| Martin & Inglis (1965) | 24 female ex-addicts 24 female non-addicts | MPI | Cold-pressor test | Pain tolerance | Addicts tolerate more pain. Correlation E and pain tolerance 0.12 (n.s.) |
| Levine et al. (1966) | 52 housewives 29 male students | MPI | Electrical stimulation Discrete administration | Sensation threshold, pain tolerance | No significant results E and pain or sensation for either group |
| Haslam (1967) | 19 male students 16 female students | MPI | Radiant heat | Pain threshold | Introverts had a significantly lower pain threshold ($p < 0.002$) |
| Davidson & McDougal (1969) | 60 female students | MPI | Cold pressor and radiant heat | Pain threshold Pain tolerance | No significant results for E and pain |
| Vando (1969) | 80 female students | EPI | Pressure | Pain tolerance | Introverts low on pain tolerance ($p < 0.01$) |
| Schalling (1971) | 8 male students 18 female students | MNT | Electric current continuous and discrete administration | Pain threshold Pain tolerance | Significant corr. solidity (extraversion) pain tolerance (0.40, $p < 0.05$) |
| Brown et al. (1973) | 52 female students | EPI | Cold stimulus Pressure stimulus | Pain threshold, tolerance, intensity | No significant relationship, pain tolerance and personality variables |

intense stimulus under conditions of decreasing inter-trial intervals, which they took as a measure of transmarginal inhibition, is significantly related to both E and N, neurotic extraverts showing the more rapid inhibitory growth. In line with Nebylitsyn's prediction, they also report that LAT measures correlate significantly with TTI measures. In their sample, Ss with high sensitivity scores, and therefore classed as weak, show a more rapid and greater inhibitory buildup. In a subsequent study, employing the same procedure, White and Mangan (1972) report that under caffeine treatment, N rather than E relates to inhibitory growth. The authors suggest that under non-arousing conditions, both E and N, which interactively determine excitation-inhibition balance, may fix S's position on the inverted U curve, but that under strongly arousing (caffeine) conditions S's displacement up the U curve, and the behavioural consequences of this — e.g. the extent to which the previously moderate stimulus becomes transmarginal — is a function of N.

In the auditory modality, similar relationships of E–I to onset of transmarginal inhibition have been reported. Both Keuss and Orlebeke (1977) and Fowles, Roberts and Nagie (1977) report earlier onset of TI to intense auditory stimuli (105 and 103 dB) in introverts than in extraverts.

Insofar as EEG studies are concerned, Eysenck's prediction that introverts are more cortically aroused than extraverts has been generally supported in studies employing low frequency analysis (Savage, 1964; Marton and Urban, 1966; Hume, 1968; Gale, Coles and Blaydon, 1969). Only two studies, those of Fenton and Scotton (1967) and Gale et al. (1971) report that Ss high on N do in fact show high EEG arousal, but report no correlation between EEG variables and E. However, some data reporting higher cortical arousal in extraverts have been reported (Glass and Broadhurst, 1966; Broadhurst and Glass, 1969).

Eysenck (1967) has suggested that both I and N may exert some effect on cortical arousal, I by means of reticular arousal, and N through the visceral brain activation system. There is some evidence that N is associated with low EEG amplitude or greater EEG abundance, i.e., with increased cortical arousal (Broadhurst and Glass, 1969; Winter, Broadhurst and Glass, 1972; Gale et al., 1971). In theory, therefore, we might expect higher cortical arousal in the neurotic introvert and lower cortical arousal in the stable extravert. Winter, Broadhurst and Glass (1972) and Gale et al. (1971) report no differences between Es and Is. However, when considering only those Ss low on neuroticism, Gale, Coles and Blaydon, (1969) and Winter, Broadhurst and Glass (1972) report that the relationship between E and cortical arousal is in the direction predicted by Eysenck (1967). E appears to be related to low cortical arousal in low N groups, but to high cortical arousal in high N groups.

From these EEG data, roughly the same picture emerges as that described by Siddle et al. (1969) in their study of the relationship between LAT sensitivity and

E — that when high N Ss are excluded from the sample, introversion is positively related to sensitivity. Similar trends have been reported in studies, described later, relating E and N to OR habituation rate (Mangan and O'Gorman, 1969; Scott and Wilkinson, 1962; Marton and Urban, 1966). From these studies, I seems to be associated with high cortical arousal in low N groups, and E with strong internal inhibition.

In this connection, of interest are two recent studies in which introversion-extraversion has been related to measures of extinction with reinforcement, the classic "standard" index of excitatory strength. Eysenck and Levy (1972), in their conditioning study, report earlier onset of transmarginal inhibition in Is than in Es. Frigon (1976), using the EEG variant of extinction with reinforcement, reports that the EEG CR remains stable for Es, but reduces for Is, which again suggests earlier onset of transmarginal inhibition. These results add to the body of data from other sources, already described — the pain studies, the "lemon juice" studies, and the Fowles, Roberts and Nagie, (1977) study — suggesting strongly that in Is there is an earlier downturn in response amplitude as stimulus intensity increases.

Finally, we might note a study relating extraversion to RT induction effects, which, according to Nebylitsyn (1972), measure nervous system strength. Initial amplitude of orienting response to a warning signal can "induce" RT, as a function of readiness, or can inhibit second response (TIR), depending on the temporal relationships involved. Both these phenomena have been extensively investigated in the West, interest dating back to the early work of Wundt (1911) and Woodworth (1938). This question will be more fully discussed in Chapter 7. At this point, it is sufficient to note that the extent and direction of induction effects following a warning signal appear to depend on intensity of the warning and the actual signal, strength-sensitivity in the reacting system, and the lengths of the inter-trial and inter-stimulus intervals. Under "normal" conditions, positive induction seems to occur with ISIs up to 2 seconds (Boiko, 1957; Chuprikova, 1952). As yet, however, exact relationships between all the critical variables have not been worked out.

Mangan (1967a) has reported an RT induction study (induction being thought to reflect mobility rather than strength of nervous system), in which ISIs of 1 and 1.5 seconds were employed. S responded to both signals. Second response was significantly facilitated at all signal intensities (0.02, 0.2, 2, 20, 200 and 2000 lux) for both ISIs, which accords with the Soviet evidence, although the stronger the stimulus intensity, the smaller the induction effect. Induction effects for the upper and lower thirds of the E–I distribution are presented in Figure 11. From these data, it is clear that while at the weakest stimulus intensity (0.02 lux) differences in the amount of positive induction are attributable to ISI (1.5 sec ISI producing greater facilitation), at 2000 lux intensity, differences are

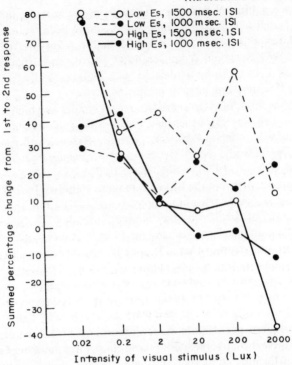

Figure 11. Positive and negative induction in the two ISI conditions for the upper and lower thirds of the E-I distribution (from Mangan, 1967a).

a function of introversion-extraversion. High Es show negative induction, high Is positive induction, with both ISIs. It was suggested that high Es, since they possess weaker nervous systems, and thus a lower working capacity, should express greater TIR following summation of two intense, successive stimuli.

## The Relationship of Nervous System Strength to Monotony and Fatigue

The extent to which individual differences in nervous system strength, measured by a variety of techniques — photic driving, alpha index, for example — influence performance in monotonous and fatiguing tasks has been reported in a number of studies. It seems that strong Ss show faster and more pronounced inhibitory buildup, shown in lower output and higher error scores, than weak Ss under monotonous conditions (Rozhdestvenskaya and Levochkina, 1972). Weak nervous systems, however, show earlier onset of fatigue (Rozhdestvenskaya, Golubeva and Yermolayeva-Tomina, 1969a), fatigue being measured by photic driving and threshold for critical fusion frequency for auditory stimuli.

There is, however, some evidence of an interaction between nervous system strength and initial level of arousal in monitoring performance under monotonous conditions. Rozhdestvenskaya (1973) reports that while Ss with weak nervous system generally perform better under monotonous conditions, this is not the case if their initial levels of arousal are high. She reports an inverted U function between performance and arousal level, but only in Ss with weak nervous systems. The highest level of performance was shown by Ss with weak nervous systems expressing moderate initial levels of arousal. Similar relationships have also been reported by Aminov (1974).

The Warsaw group has reported relationships between reactivity (roughly equivalent to strength of nervous system) and performance. Reactivity differences appear to be related to preference for particular styles of action (Klonowicz, 1974a; Strelau, 1975a). However, where Ss are not permitted to choose their own individual work styles, reactive Ss (weak nervous systems) perform better under monotonous conditions, low reactive Ss (strong nervous systems) better under stimulating conditions (Klonowicz, 1974b).

## Summary

From the research, particularly where EEG and LAT measures of arousal are employed, it is clear that I is related to arousability in a number of modalities, particularly in groups of Ss scoring low on N, and thus to the typological property of sensitivity. The methodologies employed by Teplov and Nebylitsyn suggest that they were measuring arousability in receptor and cortical projection structures, i.e. tissue excitability, most accurately measured, physiologically, by chronaxie or rheobase, measures which in fact Nebylitsyn (1966a) and Turovskaya (1963b) have at times employed in their experiments. There are also the considerations that Is appear to tolerate sensory isolation better than Es, and that they judge weaker levels of stimulation to have greater positive hedonic tone, and stronger levels more negative hedonic tone than do Es, both observations being consistent with the proposition that Is are more sensitive, that Es exhibit greater "stimulus hunger". It would be interesting to establish whether Es consistently show a higher level of "pacer stimulus", a concept employed by Dember and Earle (1957) to describe differences in preferred level of stimulation, i.e. the level maximally effective in tuning the organism and thus promoting the most effective conditions for learning and development.

At the strength pole the pain tolerance and lemon juice data fit Nebylitsyn's $R/r = K$ requirement very well, in that Is show greater response to moderately intense gustatory and pain threshold stimuli, and earlier response decrement and lower tolerance to very strong stimuli. At this end of the dimension, however, there are indications that while both E and N are related to speed of inhibitory buildup under "normal" experimental conditions, when S is "over-aroused", anxiety — A-State or A-Trait or both — may be the critical variable. As noted previously, if a stimulus is strong enough to be aversive, reactivity in the subcortical systems could be a confounding variable, and this may be what N is reflecting. Western data on this point are few and equivocal, since arguably stimuli which many experimenters describe as "intense" or aversive in reality belong in the moderate intensity range, and the Soviet data with human Ss record few, if any, instances in which ultra-strong stimuli have been employed to measure strength. Both have preferred the repeated presentations method, which avoids the problem of the aversiveness of intense, as compared with fatiguing stimuli. This may in fact constitute the real difference between the two methods, the repeated measures involving largely the receptor and cortical projection areas, the ultra-strong method involving additionally certain sub-cortical structures.

On the whole, the bulk of evidence suggests that introverts express both lower LATs and higher responsiveness to intense stimuli, and that, therefore, the introversion-extraversion dimension is similar to the strength-sensitivity property in most essential respects. Some exceptions have been noted, but a number of considerations suggest that these contradictions may be more apparent than real.

1. Insofar as the reversed relationship between RT latency and E is concerned, it could be that RT is measuring irradiation/concentration rather than strength of nervous processes. Alternatively, Es may be more sensitive in their efferent systems, particularly in respect to feedback from the striate musculature, while introverts are more sensitive in exteroceptive (analyser) and interoceptive systems, particularly those requiring information from the viscera.

There is, however, only indirect support for this proposition, from studies concerned with the concept of barrier (Fisher and Cleveland, 1958; Fisher, 1963, 1964), which describes a generalised response style reflecting S's relative awareness of his exterior body layers and body interior, and thus appears to be conceptually and descriptively similar to extraversion. Light (1972) reports that the two dimensions are related.

There is evidence to suggest that high barrier Ss respond maximally to stress in the musculature, while low barrier Ss respond maximally at interior sites. Barrier scores are positively correlated with level of physiological reactivity, both phasic (Cassell and Fisher, 1963; Zimny, 1965) and tonic (Davis, 1960) at exterior or interior body sites, with "conditionability" in exterior and interior systems — GSR compared with cardiac, for example (Armstrong, 1964) — with efficacy of muscular relaxation compared with muscle activity in systematic desensitisation (Farmer and Wright, 1971), with the occurrence of psychosomatic symptoms at exterior or interior body sites (Cleveland, Reitman and Brewer, 1965; Malev, 1966). In view of the assumed overlap between extraversion and barrier, the latter observation fits well with the classic psychiatric view that muscular conversions characterise hysterics — in Eysenck's terms, neurotic extraverts.

2. In many of the studies, I-sensitivity relationships have been recorded only in low N samples. Comments by Nebylitsyn, Gray and Lynn seem to implicate an element of manifest anxiety in strength-sensitivity, and since E and N are considered to be orthogonal, there is some conflict here. However, it is possible that both E and N are critical at different points along the strength-sensitivity continuum, the I factor being associated with specific analyser sensitivity, the N factor with a generalised sensitising influence of the mesencephalic reticular system. Thus in non-stressful threshold experiments, degree of introversion should largely determine sensitivity, except in highly anxious Ss, whose high arousal level might be expected to interfere with search and discrimination behaviour. Under strongly arousing conditions, however — through the use of caffeine or stimuli intense enough to induce defensive reflexes, for example — S's displacement up the U curve of arousal, and the behavioural consequences of this, may be an interactive function of both E and N.

This is an extension of Claridge's (1960, 1961, 1967) view. There have been indications from a number of studies concerned, for example with the spiral after-effect (Knowles and Krasner, 1965; Claridge, 1967), eyeblink conditioning (Franks, 1964) the orienting reaction (Mangan and O'Gorman, 1969), adaptation to intermittent light (Ginsburg, 1969), that N may be directly related to measures of excitation-inhibition balance. Claridge suggests that arousal or drive level interacts with excitation-inhibition balance, reflected in N and E respectively, in such a way that a "high arousal level actively facilitates the occurrence or continuance of a positive excitatory process, at the same time preventing the occurrence of the opposite inhibitory ones" (Claridge, 1961, p.62). Additionally, it is suggested here that such facilitation has a limit, so that at extreme levels of N, we might expect a performance decrement, i.e., earlier rather than later onset of TI.

3. Nebylitsyn's R/r theorem implies that if introversion is associated with high sensitivity, it must also be associated with earlier onset of transmarginal inhibition. Introverts have been shown to exhibit a lower pain tolerance, which might be taken as a measure of TI, and greater tolerance of sensory isolation, which seems a reasonable inference if introverts are "weak". On the other hand, a considerable body of evidence suggests that Es develop reactive inhibition more rapidly than Is (Eysenck, 1967), and if reactive inhibition is considered to

be similar to transmarginal inhibition, as both Gray (1964a) and Eysenck (1967) imply, it is the extravert who is weak at the strength pole.

This, however, rests on the assumption that TI is similar to reactive inhibition, which is akin to tissue injury, fatigue or pain. Mateyev (1961) has argued that fatigue in the neuromuscular apparatus, measured by ergographic strength measures, is due to transmarginal inhibition in the motor analyser. Despite Eysenck's (1967) view that reactive inhibition is a general cortical state, it may be that, when measured by involuntary rest pauses in muscular tasks such as pursuit rotor or tapping, it is similar to transmarginal inhibition in the motor analyser, since both processes result in work decrement in muscular activity following repeated stimulation of moderate load. If so, reactive inhibition is probably unrelated to TI in the afferent systems, in view of Rozhdestvenskaya *et al.'s* (1960) report that ergographic strength measures fail to load a strength factor defined by visual and auditory tests. This relates back to the point made previously concerning the relation of E to strength, using an RT — i.e. motor — response. On the other hand, it is difficult to see how the finding of greater inhibitory buildup in satiation experiments — such as spiral after-effect — fits into the schematum, although again it might be argued that there is a motor component of this response.

# CHAPTER 7

# *The Orientation Reaction*

*The biological significance of this (i.e. orienting) reflex is obvious. If the animal were not provided with such a reflex its life would hang at every moment by a thread. In man, this reflex has been greatly developed with far reaching results, being represented in its highest form by inquisitiveness – the parent of that scientific method through which we may hope one day to come to a true orientation in knowledge of the world around us.*
I. P. Pavlov (1927, p. 12)

## Introduction

PAVLOV in 1910 identified the orienting-exploratory reaction, a gross organismic response involving multiple skeletal-motor and autonomic components, which can be initiated by any environmental change (e.g. visual, auditory, tactile) as an external inhibitor of conditional reflex or ongoing activity, and in 1922 incorporated this concept into his theory of inhibition and sleep.

Pavlov's original speculations, and a considerable amount of subsequent experimental work, notably by Anokhin (1958) and Sokolov (1963b), which has been reviewed by Lynn (1966), have disclosed certain characteristic features and mechanisms involved in OR evocation and extinction (habituation).

Pavlov emphasised the dual nature of the OR, which consists of a positive orienting reflex, and an inhibitory reflex of "biological caution", which can change to an investigatory reaction as the animal explores the novel stimulus, giving rise to the orienting reaction. Both these reflexes are important for survival. During the course of the OR, all other acts may be excluded through complementary or external inhibition.

> ... the recognition by the nervous system of a difference between external agents ... is revealed by the excitatory process in the form of an OR, an investigatory reflex, which only secondarily has an inhibiting or disinhibiting effect on conditioned reflexes. The latter is expressed by the development of an inhibitory process, which is the result, so to speak, of a struggle between excitation and inhibition (Pavlov, 1951-2, p. 116).

In line with Ukhtomskii's theory of the dominant, in certain circumstances external inhibition is followed by assimilation of OR energy into the preceding, previously dominant activity of the organism (Yermolayeva-Tomina, 1959; Siddle and Mangan, 1971).

The unconditioned OR appears to be innate, appearing shortly after birth (Wertheimer, 1962; Berg, 1974; Pomerlau-Malcuit, 1974; Dormann and Hoffmann, 1973; Kearsley, 1974; Friedman, Bruno and Vietz, 1974; Van der Maelen, Strauss and Starr, 1974; De Loache, 1976; Moreau, 1976), as does habituation of OR (McCall *et al.*, 1973; Berg, 1974). The OR is claimed to be non-specific with regard to stimulus modality (Anokhin, 1958; Sokolov, 1958a). Initial amplitude of OR appears to be a function of stimulus intensity and duration (Sokolov, 1958a; Nebylitsyn, 1966a; Jackson, 1974; Edwards, 1974; Spinks and Siddle, 1976), magnitude (SCR component) increasing monotonically with stimulus intensity (Jackson, 1974), even in the very weak intensity range (20–50 dB, for example) (Barry, 1975). Jackson (1974), however, reports that with the heart rate deceleration component of OR the intensity/amplitude relationship approximates an inverted U function, large OR amplitude being expressed to both threshold and strong stimuli. Stimulus variability seems to have little effect on magnitude (Gatchel and Lang, 1974; McLean, Ohman and Lader, 1975).

The OR can be readily transformed into a CR. Biryukov (1958) cites as an example Klimov's observation that fox cubs, after extinguishing the motor components of OR to mouse squeaks, develop inextinguishable ORs to these stimuli after killing and eating a mouse. Inextinguishable ORs are claimed to characterise "weak" nervous systems, decorticate animals and certain groups of schizophrenics, all of whom are assumed to exhibit weak cortical inhibition.

The OR is differentiated from defensive and adaptive reflexes. It is characterized by cephalic vasodilation and peripheral vasoconstriction — an observation first recorded by Pillsbury (1908) in Ss "paying attention" — while the normal adaptive response to warmth is vasodilation in both head and extremities, and the defensive response vasoconstriction in both. Other OR components are pupillary dilation, alpha-blocking, increased skin conductance (SCR) and heart rate (HR) deceleration. The latter is somewhat paradoxical, since activity is usually accompanied by cardiac acceleration. Nevertheless, HR deceleration when S is required to pay attention is well documented (Davis, 1957; Lacey, 1959). Davis reports that this is an element of the P pattern of reaction recorded in purest form when male college students are observing pictures of nude females. Startle reactions may precede the OR, depending on S's set, his level of arousal and stimulus intensity, all of which determine the vigour of the OR. The characteristics of stimuli evoking the OR, according to Berlyne (1960), are novelty, intensity, colour, signal value, surprise, complexity (uncertainty, incongruity) and conflict. Lynn (1966) reduces these categories to three — novelty, conflict and signal value.

The OR may be generalised or localised. The generalised OR is characterised by higher frequency EEG rhythms over the whole cortex, which habituate relatively quickly, in 10–15 trials. Following tonic OR habituation, there remains the localised or phasic OR (Sharpless and Jasper, 1956), although Barry (1976) failed to detect local EEG OR to low level (up to 50 dB) auditory stimulation. EEG desynchronisation is confined to the particular projection area being stimulated, the reaction subsides relatively quickly, and is more resistant to extinction, surviving for about 30–40 trials.

While most authors generally agree on the stimulus characteristics initiating OR, the subsequent course of the reaction is differently understood by different theorists. The most commonly held view is that expressed by Pavlov, and formulated by Orbeli, that the OR starts as an unconditioned reflex, and develops as a conditioned inhibitory reflex — i.e. extinguishes with repeated presentation — and that the processes underlying the extinction of OR and CR are similar, both leading to the development of drowsy and sleep states through the generalisation of internal inhibition in the cortex and subcortex. Biryukov (1958) maintains that the OR is a complex unconditioned-conditioned two-phase reaction, the first phase being the reflex of novelty which can progress independently and end in extinction; the second, exploratory reflex, however, may be transformed into a CS–OR, as a result of which the original unconditioned OR becomes almost inextinguishable.

Following Pavlov, subsequent theorists (Vinogradova, 1966; Sokolov, 1958a,b, 1963b; Stein, 1966; Nebylitsyn, 1966a) have proposed that OR extinction is a gradually elaborated inhibitory conditioned reflex process, in which the CS is the onset of the to-be-habituated stimulus. OR habituation is attenuated when stimuli are intense or of long duration (Sokolov, 1963b; Bradley, 1957; Gastaut and Bert, 1961; Jackson, 1974; Edwards, 1974; Spinks and Siddle, 1976) possibly because such stimuli elicit defence reflexes, which are highly resistant to extinction. Habituation is accelerated when a constant ITI is maintained, the shorter the ITI, the faster the habituation, both in waking (Davis, 1934; Coombs, 1938; Winokur et al. 1962; Geer, 1967; Gatchel and Lang, 1974; Gatchel, 1975) and in sleeping (Frith, 1973) states. This is consistent with the finding that CR extinction occurs more rapidly under massed than under spaced CS+ trials (Reynolds, 1945), and that habituation generalises (Appelbaum et al., 1960; Sokolov, 1960), which might be expected if OR habituation is a measure of rate of growth of internal inhibition. It is also clear that there are large individual (Mangan and O'Gorman, 1969) and sex differences (Berry and Martin, 1957; Kimmel and Kimmel, 1965; Fisher and Kotses, 1974) in OR habituation rate.

The extinguished or habituated OR may recover spontaneously (dis-habituation) following repeated presentations of the habituated stimulus — the "over-extinction" effect — the number of trials required for over-extinction being determined by factors such as extent of irradiated inhibition and the characteristics of the nervous model. Recovery may also occur following any change in stimulus characteristics; habituation is thus considered to be selective with respect to the characteristics of the stimulus producing it (Sokolov, 1963a). Any change in stimulus characteristics re-evokes the OR, due to the discrepancy between the incoming stimulus and the neuronal model of the habituated stimulus.

A problem which has been debated at some length is that of the unitary nature of OR, i.e., whether the different electrocortical, autonomic and somatic (EEG, SCR, cardiac, respiratory, etc.) OR components reflect a central arousal state. From activation theory one might suppose that an increase in one autonomic measure might be accompanied by increases in others, if arousal is a general phenomenon. However, while it is true that under conditions meant to be arousing, all measures tend to rise (Lacey, Bateman and Van Lehn, 1953; Schnore, 1959), not all measures increase equally. Rather, a subject responds in an idiosyncratic way, more intensely in some response modes than in others. Although there appear to be some individual patterns which are trans-situational, there is evidence that the nature of stimuli can affect such patterns (Davis, Buchwald and Frankmann, 1955; Davis and Buchwald, 1957).

Evidence on this point from the OR literature is inconclusive. Anokhin (1958), Biryukov (1958) and Nebylitsyn (1966a) have summarised a large body of data involving EEG, SCR and vascular OR measures, and report little evidence of intra-S correlations between the various components. Nonetheless, they all suggest that the various components should not be regarded as independent reflexes. Robinson and Gantt (1947) arrive at a similar conclusion, based on significant positive correlations between motor components of OR and heart rates recorded during these movements, and some concordance between salivary, respiratory and cardiac component measures. However, their observation that "the more measures we take the nearer we come to the truth" strikes a cautionary note. In a later study Gantt (1958) suggests that the motor and the cardiovascular and respiratory reflexes are fundamentally distinct, and sometimes contrasted, and that where this occurs, the discrepancy between surface and depth reactions may become so great that the functional harmony of the organism is disrupted, leading to neurosis (schizokinesis).

In this context, we might note that inter-component correlations would demand systemic unity of arousal reactions, a concept which has been strongly challenged. Lacey (1967) suggests that there are three phases of arousal — electrocortical, autonomic and behavioural — each complex in itself, and that the well-accepted principles of intra-stressor and inter-stressor sterotypy, which state that Ss characteristically respond to stress in one particular physiological system, and that this preference is maintained across stressor episodes, would imply some variance between the electrocortical and the autonomic responses, and between these and the behavioural responses. It is clear that not all Ss respond in the same systems to stimulus change. For example, Voronin and Sokolov (1960) report that of 100 Ss, 85 showed occipital alpha-block, 53 Rolandic rhythm blockage, 95 GSR, 83 respiratory changes, and 11 Ss changes in all components to a tone of 1000 Hz and 50 dB. It seems clear that whatever pattern of excitation occurs within the brain, it may be modified at the periphery, probably due to differences in the reactivity of the mechanisms involved. Some Ss, for example, have active and responsive sweat glands, others have not. The extent to which these peripheral effects modulate the responses taken, however, is unknown.

A further problem is the difficulty, sometimes reported, of reliably reproducing certain OR phenomena in particular response modalities. For example, although habituation of the electrodermal and heart rate components of OR has been demonstrated in a large number of studies, this is not the case with the vasomotor component. Thus, Koepke and Pribram (1967), Berg (1970) and O'Gorman (1971) report vasomotor habituation; however, Furedy (1974) failed to establish habituation of this component, although his samples were large. To further complicate matters, Ginsberg and Furedy (1974) report habituation of the pulse volume (PV) but not the blood volume (BV) component of vasomotor responding, although the two measures were highly and significantly correlated, and both showed reliable increases to stimulus change. Lidberg, Levander and Schalling (1974), on the other hand, report habituation of both these responses, PV habituating faster than BV, with the two measures again being highly correlated. The obvious explanation is that the vasomotor system is less sensitive to central events than the electrodermal system, as Maltzman and Mandel (1968) and Stern and Plapp (1969) suggest, and that the blood volume index is less sensitive than the pulse volume index. Unger's (1964) report of increased vasomotor responding when numbers are presented out of sequence, however, calls this into question.

On the stimulus side, Sokolov (1958a) and Anokhin (1949, 1958) have maintained that the generalised OR is modality non-specific, and what evidence there is seems to support this. Nebylitsyn (1966a), from an extensive series of studies, reports highly significant correlations (+ 0.6–+ 0.8) between ORs to visual and auditory stimuli, using vascular, GSR and EEG OR indices. He notes, however, special problems in the measurement of the EEG component of OR, since in the case of auditory stimulation, duration of desynchronisation may be less than stimulus duration from about the second trial on. On the other hand, desynchronisation to a visual stimulus persists for a considerable period of time. According to some authors (Sharpless and Jasper, 1956; Vinogradova, 1961), this indicates transfer of activating mechanisms from the mesencephalic to the thalamic level. The first ensures a prolonged, but speedily extinguished tonic reaction — the generalised OR — the second, a shorter but more slowly extinguished phasic reaction. Thus, with auditory stimuli the transfer from tonic to phasic activation occurs from about the second presentation of the stimulus, while with visual stimulation the transfer is much slower. Nebylitsyn (1966a) suggests that there may be large individual differences in this transfer, and that it may be important to differentiate Ss with a predominantly thalamic level of activation from those whose nervous systems tend towards a more generalised activation of predominantly mesencephalic origin.

## Models of OR Elicitation and Habituation

There are a number of models of the evocation and habituation of the OR, many of which have been briefly but adequately summarised by Lynn (1966). Subsequently, a number of modifications have been suggested, notably Claridge's (1967) model, Routenberg's (1968) two-stage interaction theory of arousal, which claims to account for both general arousal phenomena and those occurring under incentive conditions, and the dual-process theory of habituation of Thompson and Spencer (1966) and Groves and Thompson (1970), and some recent variants of this. However, Sokolov's theory (1966, 1970, 1976, 1977, 1978) is still the most comprehensive.

### i) OR Elicitation

Sokolov proposes that incoming stimuli are compared with coded information preserved in cortical traces (polyvalent nervous models) concerning the characteristics of previous stimuli of the same general class, by an analysing mechanism in the cortex. The model is similar to the mechanism thought to underlie the dynamic sterotype (Pavlov, 1949), Kruskinskii's (1949) concept of the extrapolating properties of the nervous system, and Anokhin's (1949, 1958) "acceptor of effect", all of which refer to processes concerned with the matching of incoming stimuli with traces of previous stimulation remaining in the nervous system. If a mismatch occurs, i.e. if the stimulus is novel, or if it is significant, the non-specific excitation into the reticular formation (RF) via the afferent collaterals is amplified by excitatory impulses from the cortex, i.e., the OR occurs. As a consequence, the excitability of the sense organs increases, i.e., "attention" is increased, and stimulus reception is facilitated. If, however, the stimulus is a familiar one, the non-specific excitatory effects are blocked by inhibitory impulses from the cortex. Facilitation or inhibition is mediated by positive and negative cortico-reticular feedback loops from the cortex to the RF. If the inhibition or facilitation occurs at the level of the afferent collaterals or the synaptic connections, for example, through hyperpolarisation, rather than in the RF itself, as appears likely, time relationships are critical.

There is evidence that specific and non-specific activation is mediated by different types of impulse. For the specific system, a primary response action potential (ER) quickly appears in the appropriate cortical projection area; in the case of light stimulus, for example, the latency is around 67.5 milliseconds. For the non-specific system, however, there is a secondary response, which reaches its maximum relatively slowly — around 117.5 milliseconds for light stimulus (Monnier, 1956) — and a sustained change or desynchronisation in the background rhythmical activity of the cortex, which irradiates over wide cortical areas, with a latency of about 300 milliseconds. The latency of the secondary and the generalised responses, in theory, would allow stimulation to pass up the classical tracts to the cortex and down again in time to block the non-specific input through the collaterals because of the slower conduction rate in the latter, which is assumed to be due to short axons and the large number of synapses.

Obviously, there are a number of assumptions underlying this model, particularly with regard to the role of the RF. Evidence from a number of sources, however, is generally supportive. It is clear, for example, that the RF is normally activated through the afferent collaterals. Gross behavioural signs of arousal and alerting, as well as the autonomic and attentional aspects of OR, have been shown to follow RF stimulation (e.g. Moruzzi and Magoun, 1949; Grastyan, 1959). There is evidence that cortico-reticular connections of the type postulated by Sokolov do exist, and that cortical stimulation can elicit the OR via these pathways (French, 1957; Lagutina, 1958). Feedback pathways to the receptors from the cortex (Polyakov, 1959; Shkolmik-Yarros, 1958) and from the specific and non-specific RF (Dodt, 1956; Granit, 1955) have been traced; Granit reports that excitation of the RF increases the excitability of the sense organs, an effect which has been shown to occur during OR (Sokolov, 1960; Chang, 1959). In turn, experiments on de-afferentation reveal that sense organs help maintain a level of activity in the organism; destruction of the RF and complete de-afferentation produce the same effects — slow waves typical of the inhibitory state (Roger, Voronin and Sokolov, 1959). A number of studies have pointed to the increased discriminatory power of the cortex in the sensory system under reticular stimulation, such as occurs during the OR (Lindsley, 1958; Dumont and Dell, 1958; Bremer and Stoupel, 1959).

The neurophysiology of the nervous model has been the subject of some debate. Sokolov initially assumed that it involves three types of neurones — afferent, extrapolatory and comparator. Afferent neurones always respond to a stimulus (Jung, 1961; Vardepetyan, 1967). Extrapolatory neurones, however, begin to respond only after repeated stimulus presentations. A record of the stimulus sequence is fixed by a molecular mechanism in the neurones, so that they generate a sequence of nervous impulses which anticipates the future impulse (Lettvin et al., 1961), i.e., the nervous system elaborates a forecast of future stimuli and compares this forecast with the stimulus being registered. Extrapolatory neurones thus form the basis of an information storage system which reflects the most probable sequence of future actions (Haider, 1967); the mould, however, is not static, but constantly undergoes revision to accommodate changing characteristics of current stimulus input (Sokolov, 1969). Finally, comparator neurones, which have been likened to the "attention" neurones identified by Heubel et al. (1959) and Lettvin et al. (1961), compare the output from the afferent and extrapolatory neurones. If there is a mismatch, the comparator neurones stimulate the amplification system and initiate the OR; if there is a match, the cortex inhibits input to the non-specific recticular system from the collaterals. The model comparison, therefore, can serve both an excitatory or an inhibitory function.

### ii) OR Habituation

OR habituation is assumed to follow a predictable course. The generalised OR, according to both Sokolov and Sharpless and Jasper (1956), is comparatively lengthy, has a latency of up to 30 seconds, habituates rapidly and recovers slowly. Continued action of a stimulus results in inhibition of the non-specific RF responsible for the generalised OR, due to adaptation at the periphery (e.g. pupil contraction, reduction of concentration of visual purple) which reduces the physical strength of the stimulus acting on the receptor. In addition, there is blocking of the impulses travelling over the collaterals to the RF, which affects mainly the BSRF.

The thalamic system connected with the local OR is inhibited more slowly. The localised or phasic OR, which remains after habituation of the tonic or generalised OR, has a short latency, is resistant to extinction, and recovers within a few minutes. The change from generalised to localised OR is shown behaviourally by a drowsy state, and physiologically by the replacement of EEG alpha-rhythm by slow, large amplitude waves. With repeated stimulation, the generalised OR reappears — the over-extinction effect reported by Sokolov (1960), Oswald (1962) and O'Gorman (1972) — then rehabituates, following the general pattern of primary habituation, although taking longer. The latter observation, however, has been challenged by O'Gorman (1972). Following secondary habituation, S falls asleep, due to irradiation of inhibition over the cortex, in line with classic Pavlovian theory. Although the notion that stimulus repetition provokes sleep has been questioned by Konorski (1948b), the bulk of evidence supports Pavlov's original view (Moruzzi, 1960; Oswald, 1962; Gastaut and Bert, 1961; Bohlin, 1972).

One-stage models of habituation, which are in most respects varients of Pavlov's original "fatigue" model, have been suggested by Sharpless and Jasper (1956), Gastaut (1957) and Roitbak (1958a). They have in common the assumption that a particular body of neurones is continuously stimulated until the cells become fatigued, and that the resultant inhibition raises the threshold of response until it is eliminated entirely — i.e., the OR is habituated. According to Pavlov, the inhibition is initially generated in the cortical analyser, and subsequently spreads over the neighbouring neurons, over the whole of the cortex, and into the subcortex. On the other hand, Sharpless and Jasper (1956) and Gastaut (1957) attach somewhat less significance to cortical mechanisms; they suggest that the inhibitory sites are located in the BSRF for the generalised OR, and in the thalamic RF for the localised OR. Roitbak (1958a) limits the inhibitory site to the thalamo-cortical inhibitory system.

Weight of evidence and commonsense suggest that one-stage models of habituation are untenable. They fail to account for one or more OR phenomena — the return of OR to a stimulus change, to stimulus omission or to changed signal value, for habituation to sequences or patterns of stimuli and to conceptual categories, and for the fact that habituated stimuli continue to elicit evoked potentials in the cortex.

Two-stage models are obviously more robust. However, they throw up a number of problems, two of which, in particular, have created a good deal of controversy, and are still unresolved. These are the nature of the mechanisms involved in cortical stimulus analysis, and the site of inhibitory blocking at reticular level.

*(a) Cortical stimulus analysis*

There is, as yet, no clear indication of the cortical site for stimulus analysis. However, judging from Luria's (1966a,b) evidence that normal frontal lobe functioning is necessary for complex selective organisation, and orienting activity, it is probable that stimulus analysis occurs somewhere in this region.

Following the suggestions of a number of authors that the event which gives rise to an OR or the return of OR to an already habituated stimulus (dishabituation) might not be the stimulus itself, but the unexpectedness of aspects of the stimulus, or the sequence in which it occurs, an inference which can be derived from the processes thought to occur in the extrapolatory neurones, Sokolov (1966) has suggested an information theory approach to the problem of OR evocation and habituation.

He describes habituation as a "dynamic" process, and briefly refers to a number of experiments in which habituation has been studied to a continually changing stimulus. He suggests that here there is an ongoing process of neural encoding in which stimulus novelty, which is a necessary and sufficient condition for OR evocation, is determined with reference to the "statistical" properties of the stimulus, i.e., the OR is evoked whenever a stimulus creates uncertainty, the latter being described in information theory terms as the probability of stimulus occurrence. On this basis, where habituation occurs to a series of stimuli varying, for example, in pitch, the process would tend to be "normal", but attenuated, the amount of attenuation varying with uncertainty, which itself would be a function of the number of stimulus changes in the effective pitch range. There is some evidence that this appears to be so (Allen, Hill and Wickens, 1963; Fried, Korn & Welch, 1966). One might also expect that in such cases habituation would be more pronounced to a stimulus value represented by Helson's (1964) AL value — the log mean value of the stimulus series — which has not been actually experienced by S, than to any other stimuli experienced within the stimulus range. Relevant data on this point, however, have not been reported.

There is some support for the uncertainty hypothesis in Lovibond's (1969) report that GSR–OR habituation rate is a function of uncertainty of reinforcement. On the other hand, Or and Stern (1960) failed to find a relationship between the information value of the stimulus and resistance to extinction of the GSR and EEG components of OR. However, the fact that in both these cases signal or reinforced stimuli were used in the habituation series makes interpretation of results difficult. In one of the few studies in which non-signal stimuli were employed, O'Gorman (1972) reports a significant positive linear relationship between information value of the orienting stimulus and resistance to GSR–OR habituation. However, he failed to find this effect with the finger pulse volume (FPV) OR component, but suggests that this may be because the vascular system is less responsive to central events than the electrodermal system. Spinks and Siddle (1976) also suggest that habituation is a process of information extraction.

While this simple information theory approach could account for the fact that altered stimulus sequence and stimulus omission re-evoke ORs, and possibly for the "normal" but attenuated habituation to patterns of sensory stimuli and conceptual categories, it nevertheless fails to account for the fact that familiar but significant stimuli continue to elicit ORs. Obviously stimulus analysis involves evaluation of stimulus significance in terms of the organism's past learning and present needs. To account for this, rather than the simple, mechanistic nervous model proposed by Sokolov, we probably need to invoke something like the filtering processes which some perception theorists suggest are involved in perceptual scanning and vigilance behaviour.

Sokolov (1963a) has, in fact, mentioned that the nervous model might function as a selective filter, and there is some indirect evidence of this from relationships reported between certain OR parameters and psychopathological states such as schizophrenia, which is assumed to reflect attentional deficits (Bernstein, 1967), and typical ways in which normal Ss take in information, reflected in differences in "cognitive style". These data will be discussed later.

### (b) Site of inhibitory blocking at reticular level

Apart from uncertainty about the nature of the cortical mechanisms of stimulus analysis, there is also some doubt about the exact nature of the cortical inhibitory control mechanisms, and the site of blocking at reticular level. The fact of cortical control over habituation is well established. Although habituation can occur at spinal level, as has been demonstrated by Ksavov with decorticate rabbits, there is extensive evidence that sensory habituation is generally abolished in decorticate animals, and that there is a temporal sequence of habituation. The autonomic components habituate first, followed by EEG hypersynchronisation in the analyser being stimulated. With repetition of the stimulus the cortex itself becomes habituated, and slow waves characteristic of low arousal begin to appear. This inhibition weakens the control exercised by the cortex on the RF: the RF is released from cortical control and the OR is reinstated (the over-extinction effect). Finally the inhibition irradiates and S goes to sleep. Even then, however, the habituated stimulus continues to generate evoked potentials in the analyser, i.e., stimuli are reaching the cortex for analysis even if the OR does not occur, which suggests that the cortex continues to be active in initiating downward inhibitory impulses to the RF.

It is generally accepted that specific information about the qualities of the stimulus are mediated via the classic sensory pathways, which, for vision, for example, begins in the retinal photoreceptors, passes through the retinal system of bipolar and ganglion cells into the lateral geniculate body, thence to the fourth layer of the occipital region (Brodman 17). Non-specific activation, on the other hand, is mediated via the afferent collaterals from this system to the reticular system, the complex cell structure which begins in the spinal cord and ends in the non-specific nuclei of the thalamus, and reaches all layers of the cortex, transmitting toning or activating impulses through a system of non-specific fibre synapses in the cortex (Lorente de No, 1943). The brainstem reticular formation (BSRF) influences the entire cortex, producing widespread desynchronisation of slow cortical rhythms (the generalised OR), while the thalamic reticular system (TRF), which mediates the local OR, has a more selective action. Some parts produce local effects on the anterior sensori-motor region, others influence the posterior cortical regions concerned with the processing of combined auditory and visual stimulation.

It has long been recognised that Pavlovian internal inhibition, which is indexed by OR habituation rate, is mediated by the diffuse thalamocortical system. Magoun (1963) comments

> Many contributions point to the existence of a non specific thalamocortical system, the low frequency of which evokes large slow waves as well as recruiting responses and spindle bursts in the EEG. These characteristically bear a close relation to internal inhibition, behavioural drowsiness and sleep .... When activated from the basal ganglia and cerebral cortex, this system appears to manage all the Pavlovian categories of internal inhibition of higher nervous activity ... the consequences of the action of this mechanism are the opposite of those of the ascending reticular activating system for internal excitation.

Winocur et al. (1962), on the basis of the Hernandez-Péon and Scherrer (1955) report that habituation is abolished following lesions of the mid-brain tegmentum, suggest that the BSRF is the site of inhibitory control; this is also suggested by the enhanced and dishabituated phasic reactions reported by Jus and Jus (1960) following chlorpromazine. Sokolov assumes that blocking occurs at the level of the afferent collaterals, first in the BSRF, later in the TRF, which seems a reasonable inference, judging from the fact that in the early stages of habituation the animal is alert to other stimuli, so that there obviously can be no dampening of the RF itself (although this fails to account for the onset of sleep with repeated stimulation). Sokolov and his group have identified comparator neurones in the auditory cortex of cats and in the non-specific thalamic nuclei of rabbits. They point out that the hippocampus is evidently responsive to multi-modal stimuli in a predominantly inhibitory fashion — neurones become silent or at least decrease in response rate — so that this is a structure capable of mediating habituation. In other structures — e.g. the lateral midline areas of the RF — signs of habituation fail to appear. They interpret the evidence as suggesting that a number of properties of an object, represented by outputs of neocortical neural nets, converge on hippocampal pyramidal neurones which are responsive to a variety of stimuli. During stimulus repetition, these neurones are selectively habituated following the general principles of the OR.

Moruzzi (1958) has suggested an inhibitory centre in the pons, with the habituated stimulus, either via the afferent collaterals or the cortex, activating the mid-pontine system, which then blocks the activating system and induces sleep. His explanation, however, fails to account for the selective habituation of patterns. Grastyan (1959) proposes that the hippocampus is the inhibitory mechanism linking the cortex and the RF arousal system. The hippocampus normally exerts a tonic inhibitory effect on the RF: with habituated stimuli, hippocampal desynchronisation represents an increase in the inhibitory effects on the RF. It is known that slow theta activity occurs to novel or to signal stimuli; this reflects a decrease in the tonic inhibitory function of the hippocampus, followed by the release of the reticular arousal system.

Electrophysiological studies over the past 20 years, which have provided the basis for a number of attentional models of hippocampal functioning, strongly support this view. These data suggest that although the integrity of the medial septal nucleus and its cholinergic projection to the hippocampus is not essential for normal OR habituation (Kohler, 1976), the septal-hippocampal pathway is a necessary link in regulation of hippocampal theta rhythm. Fibres projecting from the septal area terminate in laminae lying on, or near, the large hippocampal pyramidal or granule neurons. Septal influences on the hippocampus appear to be primarily inhibitory, owing in part to septal terminals among the small interneurons which inhibit the areas surrounding the large hippocampal neurons. Recordings of the activity of single hippocampal units suggest that around 60% of these neurons habituate relatively quickly, but are reinstated by presentation of novel stimuli (cf. Mays, 1973).

On this basis, the hippocampus must be intimately involved in the encoding of incoming stimuli, and in comparing these to previous stimuli. According to the Douglas-Pribram model (Douglas and Pribram, 1966), the hippocampus acts as an "error-evaluate" system by (a) eliminating non-reinforced stimuli from awareness through facilitation of recurrent inhibition in the sensory systems, and (b) filtering out irrelevant stimuli during concentration. Kimble (1961), employing a traditional Pavlovian framework of internal inhibition, argues that the hippocampus directs attentional shifts, a view which receives some support from Micco and Schwartz (1971). Micco (1973) suggests that the hippocampus acts as a "polysensory multiplexer" which serves both to facilitate the formation of a neuronal model, and to perform the basic match/mismatch evaluation of sensory input. He also suggests that a change in the external environment either in terms of stimulus configuration (novelty) or changed contingencies involving reinforcement (extinction) produces a mismatch which results in disruption or inhibition of the most probable response sequence.

In their most recent statements, Sokolov and his collaborators (Sokolov, 1969, 1970, 1975, 1976, 1977, 1978; Vinogradova, 1975) strongly support the view that the site of the neuronal model of the stimulus, and thus the structure mediating selective habituation of OR, is the hippocampus. Judging from data reporting habituation characteristics in rabbit retina, the optic nerve, the superior tubera of the quadrigeminal lamina, the external geniculate body, and the visual cortex, Sokolov contends that the neuronal model is not sited peripherally, nor in rearrangements of specific pathways, nor in the neocortex. However, there is clear evidence of spatial, intensity and time-interval detectors in the cortical projection areas, neurons which respond only to specific stimulus characteristics. When a particular intensity detector is maximally excited, excitation in other intensity detectors is an inverse function of their distance from the active detector neuron, so that a profile of excitation is created in the whole set of detectors. Any change in stimulus intensity, stimulus duration or ISI causes excitation to shift from one channel to another within groups of intensity and time-interval detectors, such stimulus characteristics being coded by channel number. For spatial detectors, on the other hand, any change in stimulus location in the visual field causes a shift in excitation from one group of channels to another.

It follows from this, argues Sokolov, since an OR filter is self-aligning and suppressive, and since filters represented by detector neurons are transmitting filters — response rates are stable even after multiple stimulus presentation — that the cortical areas themselves cannot be the site of the neuronal model, or of the selective habituation, although they are obviously critical in stimulus analysis.

What of the hippocampus, the caudate nucleus, the mesencephalic reticular system, and the non-specific thalamus? Sokolov (1977, 1978) reports that while all these structures show extinction effects, neurons in field $CA_2$ of the hippocampus show closest correlation with the dynamics of OR extinction (Vinogradova, 1975). All such neurons, of which there are two types — A or novelty neurons, which respond only when the stimulus is new, and T or identity neurons, which respond only when the stimulus is familiar — show similar patterns. Following repeated stimulus presentations, stimulus change provokes increased spike activity in A neurons, and inhibition of such activity in T neurons. Since coding is by line number, when detectors are activated, it follows, according to Sokolov, that the entire set of detectors converges on each neuron in the dorsal hippocampus. This creates a universal receptive field in a particular neuron in field $CA_3$. And since detector responses are stable, extinction therefore occurs at the detector terminal, i.e., in the postsynaptic membrane of the hippocampal neuron, through afferent collateral inhibition, whereby excitation is transmitted in parallel along an afferent collateral pathway to an interneuron, which exerts an inhibitory action on an integrative neuron. Thus the parallel inhibitory action mediated by the interneuron and the direct excitatory action of the detector terminal converge at the integrative neuron. On repetition of a stimulus exciting a particular group of detectors, the synapses at the interneuron are potentiated, thereby producing an increasingly stronger inhibitory effect.

What structures and/or processes mediate parallel inhibition? A number of possibilities have been suggested, although critical data are lacking. One is the dentate fascia, since reduced reactivity of the pyramidal neurons of field $CA_3$ to afferent stimuli follows stimulation of this structure. Another suggestion points to reduced availability of transmitter substances in the endings of axons of detectors converging on integrative neurons following repeated stimulation. Again, it could be due to decreased sensitivity of the postsynaptic membrane of the integrative neurons, such desensitisation involving a selective transformation of membrane loci.

Hippocampal neurons are obviously linked to the reticular system, type A neurons being connected, presumably, with the activating system, type T neurons to the inhibitory system. When a stimulus is repeated, its activating influence will attenuate, and its inhibitory influence increase. If hippocampal neurons are interconnected, via the reticular system, with various OR components, selective extinction of response in the hippocampal neurons is probably responsible for selective habituation of the multicomponent OR.

Thus, the neuronal model of the stimulus appears to be constructed as follows. Sets of detectors converge on integrative neurons, transforming individual synaptic contacts formed by detector terminals. On stimulus repetition, detector excitation remains constant, but the influence of these detectors on responses of hippocampal neurons attenuates, such attenuation being selectively restricted to those detectors which are activated by the stimulus, but affecting the entire population of A and T neurons. The characteristics of selective extinction of hippocampal integrative neurons reproduce the selectivity of detector reactions produced by the stimulus. When stimulus change occurs, all detectors not previously activated are recruited into the response, reaching A and T neurons without attenuation, producing excitatory responses in the former, inhibitory responses in the latter. Thus, stimulus change generates a shift in active loci on the neuronal membrane in synchrony with the detectors activated by the stimulus. The greater the number of newly recruited loci, the stronger the neuronal response, and the more pronounced the OR. The neuronal model, therefore, is a configuration of postsynaptic areas which reflects external conditions. A precondition for selective habituation is local modification of areas of the postsynaptic membrane in accordance with signal characteristics which have been discriminated by a system of detectors.

This rather elegant model proposed by Sokolov, however, leaves a number of important questions unanswered. Perhaps most critical is the likelihood that the extent to which the hippocampus actually participates in the "decision" to make an OR depends very much on the stimulus parameters. In the case of non-signal, sensory stimuli, Sokolov's simple mechanistic model is probably adequate. However, where signal or "conceptual" stimuli are involved, the most plausible assumption, as Grastyan (1959) suggests, is that the decision to release hippocampal inhibitory control over the RF is exercised by the cortex. It is difficult to argue otherwise.

Again, despite Sokolov's claim to the contrary, there is some evidence for inhibition at peripheral sites. The study by Hernández-Péon and Scherrer (1955) reporting that habituation of auditory stimuli occurs in the cochlear nucleus and the auditory cortex, while none was observed in the inferior colliculus or the medial geniculate, suggests that habituation may be semi-independent at each station in the auditory pathway. Note also claims that the OR is modality specific rather than non-specific, from some data suggesting that the nervous model is formed at the level of analyser systems, rather than the hippocampus. Riley (1974), for example, reports findings that the habituated OR is re-evoked to a cross transfer of "compatible" conceptual information between modes, but not to mild physical change within mode. His stimuli, however, were conceptual, and it is difficult to evaluate his findings. Another interesting report is that of Carroll and Surtees (1976) that blind and deaf Ss show faster habituation, and fewer SFs, to auditory and visual stimuli respectively, suggesting that loss of modality encourages a more efficient development of a neuronal model of salient stimulus features by intact modalities. Hammerman, Fogel and Stein (1972) also propose different modelling systems for different modalities.

It is also worth pointing out that habituation at cortical sites is not solely a consequence of successive filtering at reticular level. There is some evidence of cortical cell "learning", in that habituation is paralleled by changes in the electroexcitability of cortical cell membranes, and by post-synaptic changes in input resistance (Pivovarov and Guselnikov, 1979; Guselnikov and Pivovarov, 1979). Clearly, it is the neurone itself which has become less reactive.

A final comment concerns the question of extrapolating from rabbit data to human functioning. Studies of brain-damaged humans suggest that the hippocampus plays a significant "gating" function in recall, and probably in encoding processes, particularly with respect to semantically encoded stimuli. As there is ample evidence (Posner, 1973) to suggest that even sensory material is rapidly converted to verbal, and hence to abstract "semantic" forms of representation in human information processing, we should exercise caution in drawing parallels between human and sub-human information processing system dynamics. If the form of encoding and representation of a stimulus differs between human and sub-human species, it is at least a strong possibility that different neural structures are involved. While there are bound to be features in common between man and rabbit in this respect, the level of semantic representation of the object world achieved by the former suggests that simple mechanistic models of hippocampal functioning derived from the latter are likely to be of limited value in understanding representational processes involving cortical areas beyond those serving mere sensory projection.

For the reasons suggested, it is likely that none of the explanations advanced fully account for all the phenomena of OR evocation and habituation.

## c) Dual process theory

Some attempts have been made to devise a model of OR habituation without recourse to the concept of a nervous model. An example is the dual process theory of Thompson and Spencer (1966), which has been further developed by Groves and Thompson (1970).

These authors suggest that two independent processes — inhibition in the classical afferent-efferent pathways, and sensitisation in the non-specific arousal system — interactively produce habituation. A sensitisation process seems necessary to account for two effects in particular. The first is the enhanced responsivity following repeated stimulus presentations (Groves, Lee and Thompson, 1969), an effect which has also been demonstrated in conditioning, where responsivity to CS initially increases following US presentations, even when CS—US contingencies are not maintained. The second is dishabituation, i.e. the reinstatement of the habituated OR, following application of a high intensity stimulus, without further stimulus presentations (Groves and Thompson, 1970). Sensitisation decays over time, since it is clear that the response gradually returns to the habituated level without further presentation of the (dis)habituating stimulus. It is also assumed that repeated stimulus presentations reduce sensitisation, i.e. that sensitisation habituates, seemingly a necessary inference to explain the finding that repeated presentation of a high intensity stimulus produces slower habituation than presentation of a range of stimuli of increasing intensity (Davis and Wagner, 1967; Groves and Thompson, 1970). Since little or no sensitisation occurs at low stimulus intensities, and since spontaneous decay and habituation of sensitisation have been shown to occur, Groves and Thompson (1970) propose that decrement in sensitisation over trials and summation of inhibition in the specific pathways is more pronounced, and habituation thus greater, in the case of increasingly intense stimuli than in the case of constant intense stimulation, which they claim produces a persisting sensitisation and small amounts of inhibition.

There are difficulties with this conceptualisation, not the least of which is uncertainty about the inferred processes underlying sensitisation. However, the theory does account for dishabituation, suggesting that this is an independent process rather than a disruption of habituation, a point also made by Edwards and Siddle (1976), and for the fact that habituation appears to occur more rapidly to stimuli of increasing intensity than to constantly intense stimuli, which is opposite to the prediction derived using a nervous model construct. On the other hand, it could be argued that predictable increases in stimulus intensity could lead to rapid habituation in terms of the known functional properties of the nervous model, if we employ an expectancy mechanism such as Lykken and Tellegen's (1974) negative preception. There is also the problem of accounting for dishabituation to a stimulus change of decreased intensity, which, although not found by O'Gorman, Mangan and Gowen (1970), has some recent support (Edwards, 1975a,b; Siddle and Heron, 1976; Rust, 1976; O'Gorman and Jamieson, 1975), and for dishabituation to stimulus omission. Groves and Thompson's (1970) attempt to acount for dishabituation in terms of temporal conditioning is not wholly convincing.

## Functional Characteristics of the OR

### (a) Induction Effects

Soviet investigators have stated that the main functional property of the OR is that it facilitates stimulus reception, producing a phasic increase in the "sensitivity of the analysers" (Sokolov, 1958a, p. 13). OR elicitation is accompanied by increased receptivity in the sense organs, specifically the receptors, and the cortical projection areas. Depending primarily on the characteristics of the evoked OR and the duration of the inter-stimulus interval (ISI), this may result in increased receptivity ("Bahnung" or positive induction) or decreased receptivity ("Hemmung" or negative induction) to immediately following stimuli, reflected in lowered or heightened sensory thresholds, or improved or decremented sensorimotor performance, for example, reaction time (RT).

Facilitation is most clearly shown in studies reporting that OR elicitation is accompanied or followed by lowered threshold for a variety of sensory stimuli — visual (Sokolov, 1960), auditory (Gershuni et al., 1960), olfactory (Sokolov, 1960), for example. A good deal of the Soviet evidence in this area has been reviewed by London (1954) and Sokolov (1960). A typical demonstration is reported by Sokolov (1960). A visual stimulus, of intensity 80% of threshold, and thus not "detectable" to S, is however "detected" (alpha-block measure) immediately following the presentation of an auditory stimulus which elicits an OR. It is assumed that the effect of the first stimulus is to lower the threshold for the second, due to increased excitability of the cortex, which is a component of the generalised OR.

Essentially the same explanation is advanced to account for facilitation of RT as a function of "readiness", which has been reported in a number of Western studies. Interest in this problem dates back to Wundt's (1911) study of RT to auditory stimuli of increasing intensity, and to Woodworth's (1938) discussion of the factor of temporal readiness as a facilitating or inhibiting condition. Woodworth suggests that readiness depends on the length of the foreperiod or warning period, and cites studies by Woodrow (1914) demonstrating the maximum readiness is attained in about 2 seconds, and is not maintained much beyond 4 seconds, and by Telford (1931) reporting that RT is reliably shorter with 1 and 2 second than with 0.5 and 4 second warning periods.

The findings of Lansing, Schwartz and Lindsley (1958) have suggested temporal zones of maximal facilitation. They report that a warning signal facilitates second response only if it is presented in time to produce alpha-block co-terminously with the second signal. Thus signals presented 100 milliseconds or less before the test stimulus are too late to produce alpha-block, and thus do not facilitate RT. A warning signal of 100–400 milliseconds duration produces some alpha-block and facilitation. A 400 millisecond warning period, however, is necessary to produce the full amount of alpha-block and maximum RT facilitation. Lindsley (1962) also reports that RTs are facilitated when the warning signal precedes the test stimulus by at least 300 milliseconds, and suggests that the auditory warning signal has an arousing orienting function which facilitates the visual reaction time. In view of the fact that the latency of the generalised EEG desynchronisation to stimuli is around 300 milliseconds, these findings support Berlyne's (1960) suggestion that the function of desynchronisation is to ensure that the stimulus reaches a group of nerve cells whose cycle is at its optimum. Under these conditions RT is facilitated.

Recent work on the related question of the temporary inhibition of (second) response (TIR), using both double stimulation RT and tracking procedures, points to the same general conclusions. Time and event uncertainty and modality presentation have been systematically varied (Adams, 1961; Helson, 1964: Reynolds, 1966). It appears that event uncertainty, usually measured in terms of the spatial location or intensity of the signal, is important, and that the two most relevant temporal variables are the inter-trial interval (ITI) — its predictability and extent (Hardesty and Bevan, 1965), and whether a warning cue is utilised — and the length of the inter-stimulus interval (ISI). In most of the reported studies, ISIs are less than 0.5 second, and the two signals are projected from different points in the visual field. Results suggest that with these ISIs, TIR occurs, while with ISIs greater than 0.5 second, no delay occurs (Telford, 1931; Vince, 1948; Adams, 1961). In some studies, facilitation of second response with ISIs greater than 0.5 second has been reported (Reynolds, 1966; Mangan, 1967a).

When the preceding or supplementary stimulus and the test stimulus excite the same or closely adjacent cortical cells, however, positive or negative induction may occur, depending on the intensity of the inducing stimulus, time and event uncertainty, and the strength-sensitivity of the responding system.

Evidence from Soviet sources suggests that when the same cortical points are successively stimulated, or closely adjacent points simultaneously excited, successive or simultaneous negative induction occurs. ISIs have usually been longer than 0.5 second. Bronstein (1927) for example, employing a simple motor method, i.e. pressing a rubber ball to a visual stimulus, elicited reactions in pairs with a range of ISIs. He reported increased latencies of second reaction, i.e. negative induction, compared with control responses. He comments "by stimulating a given point in the cortex, we induce a lowering of its excitability which occurs after 0.5 second, but disappears after 2.55 seconds. This phenomenon is fully analogous to 'negative induction' which is observed in the same cortical elements". He reports, with both children and adult Ss, increases in latency ranging from 65% with 0.5 second ISI to 20% with 1 second ISI. Similar results with children have also been reported by Poznanskaya (1930) and Blokh (1940). They report that with ISIs of 0.5–2 sec, there was increased RT latency to the second stimulus, due to the development of negative induction.

Subsequently, however, a series of studies by Boiko (1957), Chuprikova (1954, 1955), Kostomarova (1953) and Mangan (1967a) report different results. Chuprikova's (1954) study is typical. She employed preliminary verbal instructions and a warning signal "attention" introduced 2 seconds before the onset of the first stimulus of the pair. ISIs were 15, 8, 6, 4, 2, 1 and 0.5 seconds, with ITIs greater than 18 seconds. For all ISIs greater than 0.5 seconds she reports facilitation of second response, which she considers due to the summation of excitation from the two stimuli. Boiko (1957) suggests that the negative induction reported in the Bronstein (1927), Poznanskaya (1930) and Blokh (1940) studies was due to lack of a warning signal, so that the first stimulus of the pair elicited the unconditioned orienting reflex, which, with the ISIs employed, resulted in increased latency of second response. Presumably the 2 second warning signal employed by Chuprikova (1954) evoked the generalised OR, and any negative induction effect had terminated before the onset of the second stimulus, particularly in those cases where ISIs were longer than 1 second, i.e. where the interval between warning signal and eliciting stimulus was 3 seconds or greater. Note Bronstein's (1927) comment that negative induction disappears after 2.55 seconds.

The direction of the induction effect is also determined by the intensity of the inducing stimulus (Teplov, 1937, 1941; Nebylitsyn, 1956; Rozhdestvenskaya, 1959b; Rozhdestvenskaya et al., 1960). Teplov has reported that a supplementary light source located at a small distance from the (visual) test spot (45 seconds) effects the perception threshold of the test stimulus, the amount and direction of effect depending on the intensity of the additional stimulus. When the brightness is up to 5 times threshold intensity, sensitivity is enhanced. However, when brightness is 9–15 times threshold intensity, the positive effect weakens and disappears. With further increase in the intensity of the additional stimulus, facilitation recurs (Teplov, 1937, 1941; Rozhdestvenskaya, 1959b; Rozhdestvenskaya et al., 1960). Nebylitsyn (1956) suggests that with low intensities of the additional stimulus, sensitivity to the test stimulus is enhanced through irradiation of excitation from the point in the immediately adjacent cortical area on which the radiating energy from the additional stimulus falls. When the latter enters the intermediate intensity range, and a zone of negative induction forms around the excitatory focus, however, sensitivity decreases. With further increase in the intensity of the additional stimulus, irradiation recurs, with a consequent rise in sensitivity.

It is possible, of course, that the effect noted above applies only at threshold intensities of the stimulus. Mangan (1967a), using ISIs of 1 and 1.5 seconds between two auditory stimuli, to both of which S responded, reports increasing positive induction throughout a range of stimulus intensities (0.02–2000 lux), but no reversal of effect such as that reported by Teplov. However, the methodologies in the two cases were very different, and results are probably not comparable. It might be noted, in addition, that, according to Nebylitsyn (1966a), the extent and direction of induction is a function of a complex interaction between intensity of the inducing stimulus and the strength-sensitivity of the nervous system.

The effect of an immediately preceding or coincident supplementary stimulus on response to a test stimulus (threshold or RT), therefore, appears to be a function of time and event uncertainty, and the modality of the additional stimulus. A warning signal which evokes a generalised OR, and thus increases general cortical excitation, facilitates both detection of threshold stimuli and reaction time, providing the ISI is sufficiently long (0.5 to 3 seconds) to allow the generalised OR to become effective. The same applies in the double stimulation RT situation, where the inducing and the test stimuli are in different modalities. When the inducing and test stimuli are in the same modality, however, so that they stimulate the same or adjacent cortical cells, negative induction seems to occur with all ISIs up to 2.5 to 3 seconds. When a warning signal of about 2 seconds precedes the inducing stimulus, and presumably evokes the generalised OR, positive induction occurs with ISIs greater than 0.5 second. Whether the excitation from the inducing stimulus irradiates or concentrates also determines the type of induction. With weak and strong intensities, irradiation occurs, with facilitation of response to the test stimulus; with moderate intensities, on the other hand, concentration occurs, with negative induction of the following response.


### (b) Basic OR Parameters

Although in some OR studies, electroencephalographic (EEG), heart rate (HR), and occasionally, vasomotor responses such as pulse volume (PV) and blood volume (BV) have been recorded, in the majority of cases, both Western and Soviet, electrodermal reactivity (EDR) has been employed as response measure. The reasons for this are obvious enough. EDR instrumentation and methodology are simple, at least superficially. Approximately 90–95% of Ss show electrodermal reactivity to stimulus onset (Voronin and Sokolov, 1960; Venables, 1977) percentages being somewhat lower in other response modes. EDR offers a wide range of easily derivable measures, which are thought to relate to an equally wide range of behavioural dimensions. In addition, there is little need for complicated recording devices which often are not readily available in most psychological laboratories. While heart rate recording has similar advantages, and has proved particularly useful in animal studies employing telemetry in free moving Ss, the measure is relatively insensitive. An added difficulty is that in the middle to upper stimulus intensity range, heart rate responses across Ss vary from attentional (OR) responses (HR deceleration) to defence responses (HR acceleration) depending on factors not easily controllable within the experimental session — strength-sensitivity of nervous system, interacting with stimulus intensity, A-trait levels, for example. On the other hand, a continuous arousal measure such as electrodermal base level (SCL) avoids measurement problems of this sort. However, a possible consequence of this choice of electrodermal response, in view of Lacey's (1956, 1967) claim of semi-independent electrocortical, autonomic and behavioural arousal systems, is that the majority of OR research may refer only to features of the electrodermal, not necessarily to characteristics of the electrocortical and behavioural arousal systems.

A number of measures of tonic and phasic EDR have been described in the literature. The most frequently employed are rate of spontaneous fluctuation (SF), the number of above criterion excursions from skin conductance base level (SCL), both of which are obtained from Ss at rest, prior to first stimulus presentation. Three temporal measures can be obtained from first response — latency, i.e. time between stimulus onset and response peak, rise time and recovery time ($p/2$), the time elapse between response peak and a defined fall in response amplitude. This latter response, usually referred to as SCRec or EDRec, although first described by Darrow (1927, 1933) has only recently assumed importance. The most extensive series of investigations employing this measure has been reported by Edelberg (1964, 1970, 1972a,b). The most frequently used measures are half recovery time, p/2, the time taken for the response to decay to 50% of its peak value (Edelberg, 1970), and half recovery rate, t/2, calculated by dividing half the peak response amplitude by half p/2 (Mednick, 1974).

One magnitude measure is normally taken, change in skin conductance (SCR) between response onset and response peak.[1] On repeated stimulus presentations, habituation rate can be measured, i.e. the number of trials before response extinction, or the slope of the regression of SCR onto number of trials, and, less often, the number of trials to spontaneous recovery of the habituated response (over-extinction). In addition, there are a number of independent variables which affect dishabituation (the re-evocation of the habituated OR to a change in stimulus parameters), for example, the nature and extent of stimulus change necessary to produce dishabituation, and the extent to which repetition of the habituating stimulus "strengthens" the inhibitory process, thus making dishabituation more difficult (the "sub-zero" effect).

Although investigators have usually assumed that electrodermal activity simply reflects sweat secretion, recent evidence suggests that electrodermal activity in general, and in particular the recovery limb, is more complex than this, and probably reflects a number of peripheral and central factors.

Possible peripheral mechanisms have been reviewed by Edelberg (1972a, 1973), Fowles (1973, 1974), Venables and Christy (1973) and Venables (1974). All these authors propose a two-component theory of electrodermal phasic activity, identifying sweat duct filling and the passage of current through an epidermal membrane (the reabsorption mechanism), which, according to Edelberg (1972a), are independently innervated, as critical factors in SCR. Slow recovery SCRs are claimed to reflect the activity of the duct filling component, and rapid recovery SCRs the activity of the epidermal membrane. Edelberg (1972a) suggests that if the reabsorption process is active, SCR recovery times are shorter — i.e. SCRec reflects reabsorption activity. Fowles (1974), on the other hand, maintains that SCRec is a function of the fullness of

[1]There are as yet some unresolved difficulties in measuring SCR, and SCRec, probably the most critical of which is that the electrolyte medium employed may affect these measures to the extent that it is effective in absorbing water from the previously hydrated epidermis. An aqueous medium, for example, might be expected to produce longer SCRecs than other mediums which do not hydrate the skin to the same degree (Venables, 1974). The extent to which variables of this sort account for inconsistencies and lack of replicability in many studies is a matter of conjecture. The fact that the physiology of sweat gland activity is still imperfectly understood, however, should encourage a more conservative interpretation of research data.

duct and the hydration of the corneum. Bundy and Fitzgerald (1975) have further suggested that SCRec is an inverse function of preceding electrodermal activity, so that SCRec is in part determined by ITI, in that if the stimulus is repeated while the duct is still relatively full, and reabsorption not yet completed (which is more likely when ITIs are short), SCRec is attenuated, and the return to baseline slower. Finally, Venables (1974) has indicated that a third critical factor may be the momentary capacity of the epidermal ductal reabsorption mechanisms, which is under hormonal control.

However, while there is clearly some controversy about the peripheral factors underlying SCRec, it is generally accepted that the primary determinant of tonic SCR (i.e. SCL) is the amount of sweat in the ducts (Edelberg, 1972a; Fowles, 1974). At the psychological level, although there is still some disagreement as to whether SCR is primarily related to arousal or attentional processes (Raskin, 1973), there is some consensus that SCL is simply an index of arousal (Edelberg, 1972a; Raskin, 1973), or specifically electrodermal arousal (Stern and Janes, 1973).

Insofar as central factors are concerned, Mednick (1970) and Venables (1973), judging from animal studies which report that ablation of parts of the limbic system known to have major effects on orienting and avoidance behaviour produces marked changes in the recovery limb (Bagshaw, Kimble and Pribram, 1965; Bagshaw and Kimble, 1972), have interpreted the well-established finding of faster recovery of SCR in schizophrenics as indicating hippocampal damage. Mednick (1974) further hypothesises that this may be due to anoxia produced in pregnancy and birth complications (PCBs), and that such damage, via the inhibitory influence the hippocampus exerts on RF control of ACTH, the adrenocorticotrophic hormone, may in turn lead to schizophrenic breakdown in predisposed individuals. The case, however, is arguable, if only because hippocampal control of ACTH is not necessarily inhibitory, ACTH facilitation or inhibition depending on the type of stress involved (Kesler and Weale, 1974). In any event, some recent evidence (Mirdal et al., 1977) suggests that in high risk samples there is no greater incidence of PCBs than in normal samples.

A problem in this area is the question of the non-responder versus the minimal responder. Venables (1977), from a review of the literature, states that approximately 50% of schizophrenics give no response whatsoever to stimulation, usually SCR to auditory stimuli. Similar figures have been reported by Bernstein (1964) for visual stimuli. This compares with the figure of about 8% for normals. Gruzelier and Venables (1972, 1974) have proposed a dichotomy of responders/non-responders, the responder showing non-habituating orienting responses. Patterson (1976b), however, has identified a further sub-group, approximately 17% of sample, who respond only to first and second stimuli, then habituate quickly. Clearly, for this group, we can derive a recovery measure, which is not possible with non-responders. In many studies, however, the quickly habituating responder is lumped together with the non-responder, although the underlying psychophysiological characteristics might be quite different. The problem in part involves differences in amplitude and habituation criteria employed, and is exacerbated by stimulus intensity considerations. Bernstein (1970), for example, reports that while around 50% of his confused schizophrenic Ss can be classed as non-responders when the stimulus is 60 dB, the figure falls to 12.5% when the stimulus is 75 dB, and to 4% when intensity is increased to 90 dB. On the other hand, Venables (1977) reports data indicating that responsiveness does not increase with increase in stimulus intensity even in the region of 100 dB.

Inconsistency in the data can be due either to recognised but uncontrolled factors, or alternatively to unrecognised factors which enter as important variables affecting the dependent variable. For example, data concerning effects of medication (Teece and Cole, 1972; Venables, 1975) suggest that while medication may have an effect on SCL, effects on phasic responding are minimal (Zahn, 1975). In addition, it is clear that the relevance or significance of stimuli is an important determinant of responsivity (Gruzelier and Venables, 1973; Bernstein, 1967, 1970). This variable may be difficult to control with certain psychiatric groups — it is hard to imagine, for example, how any experimental situation or stimuli can be "neutral" for paranoids.

In this context, a problem is posed by the law of initial value (LIV) (Lacey, 1956; Wilder, 1958), which is assumed to reflect a homeostatic mechanism producing inhibition of phasic response when the response system is already tonically highly aroused. With normal neonates, Bridger and Reiser (1959) report a negative relationship between pre-stimulus heart rate and change in rate following the stimulus. They also report a "paradoxical" effect, one previously reported by Lacey (1956), which amounts to a change in direction of response following very high initial levels. Thus, while there is an increase in heart rate to stimulation when initial heart rate is low or moderate, when initial level is very high, the stimulus produces a decrease in heart rate. There is also an intermediate point where stimulation produces no change at all. The implications of this for responsivity levels in schizophrenic groups — or any other highly aroused sample, for that matter — is obvious enough.

Finally, a question which has commanded some attention in the recent literature is the extent of genetic determination of individual differences in electrodermal responding. Most authors have adopted some variant of twin methodology. There seems to be some agreement that there are strong genetic effects for SCL and SF (Lader and Wing, 1966; Hume, 1973; Zahn, 1977) and for latency (Lader and Wing, 1966; Hume, 1973) though note the unpublished study by Bell, cited by Mednick (1974), suggesting no significant genetic effects for SCL, SF, latency or rise time. Concerning habituation rate, some reports indicate genetic effects (Lader and Wing, 1966; Hume, 1973), others not (Zahn, 1977).

Recovery limb data present a confusing picture. Zahn (1977) states that half recovery rate shows strong genetic influences, but not half recovery time, a surprising result in view of Mednick's (1976) report that half recovery time differentiates high risk Ss who have a schizophrenic spectrum diagnosis on most recent assessment, and Bell's unpublished data, reported by Mednick (1974), that recovery time, but not recovery rate, showed significant genetic effects. Overall, SCL and SF appear to have the strongest support for a genetic basis, although there is some evidence that latency, habituation and tonic response to stress may be genetically determined in part. Significant genetic effects for electrodermal amplitude (SCR or EDR) are doubtful.

### (c) Interrelationships of Basic Parameters

Since the publication of Sokolov's (1958a) monograph, considerable interest has been shown in the West in individual differences in OR characteristics, and in relating these to peronality measures such as Eysenck and Eysenck's (1964) dimensions of extraversion (E) and neuroticism (N), and to conditioning. This research, however, has been unsystematic and uncoordinated, and for a variety of reasons, largely methodological, many of the studies are difficult to compare.

An initial problem is that of the relationship between the frequently used OR indices. Although no systematic investigation of OR parameters was attempted in Pavlov's laboratories, it was generally accepted that the weak nervous system is characterised by an almost inextinguishable OR to any adequate stimulus. Usually, OR was measured by GSR, which is considered to be one of the most satisfactory indices (Voronin, Sokolov and Bao-Khua, 1959). Rapid OR extinction was thought to indicate a predominance of the inhibitory processes, and slow extinction a predominance of the excitatory processes. Thus OR extinction rate indexed balance of excitatory and inhibitory processes, according to strength.

From considerable evidence, however, which has been reviewed by Nebylitsyn (1966a), OR habituation rate was subsequently regarded as an index of dynamism of inhibition, the nervous system property concerned with speed of growth of internal inhibition. Habituation rate has been shown to correlate significantly (+ 0.68, N = 24) with speed of forming a differentiation, and with speed of CR extinction, in a variety of response modes — GSR, EEG and vascular.

Initial OR amplitude, however, appears to be dependent on a complex set of relationships. Yermolayeva-Tomina (1963), using a GSR measure, and Rozhdestvenskaya *et al.* (1960), employing a vascular measure, report significant correlations between initial OR amplitude and rate of OR habituation, i.e. the larger the initial amplitude, the greater the number of trials to habituation. Nebylitsyn (1966a) also reports correlations between initial OR amplitude and speed of development of positive CRs. However, he suggests that this relationship is found only in Ss unbalanced on the side of excitation. In such Ss, who might be expected to condition quickly, there is a tendency both for high amplitude of first reaction and for slower OR and CR extinction. He considers that dynamism of excitation determines the range, amplitude and duration of OR, and that inhibitory dynamism acts as an arresting device, so that the balance between the properties serves an autostabilising function.

Nebylitsyn (1966a) also maintains that initial OR amplitude cannot be completely independent of excitatory strength. In the event that the strong nervous system is less sensitive than the weak system, there should be an inverse relationship between initial OR amplitude and strength-sensitivity, since Ss with weak nervous systems should have more expressive ORs, particularly to stimuli in the weak to moderate range of intensity. There is some empirical support for this proposition (Fowles, Roberts and Nagie, 1977; Mangan, 1974, 1978a).

Precisely what rate of spontaneous fluctuations (SF) is reflecting is unclear. A number of views have been expressed in the literature. Lacey (1956) suggests that the source of spontaneous fluctuation, or autonomic oscillation, should be sought not in adventitious stimuli, nor in fleeting, disturbing ideation, but in physiochemical processes at the level of cell aggregates. On the other hand, Stern, Stewart and Winocur, (1961) suggest that SF is stimulus induced, citing a study by Burch and Griener (1960) reporting that pentothal, a sedative, lowers SF, which, however, is increased by epinephrine and "anxiety". The fact that "anxiety" is associated with heightened SF had also been observed by Lacey (1956). On these grounds, Stern, Stewart and Winocur (1961) equate SF with activation or generalised drive state, as conceptualised by Malmo (1955). Much the same view has been adopted by a number of authors who have employed SF to measure individual differences in arousal (Mundy-Castle and McKiever, 1953; Wilson and Dykman, 1960; Katkin and McCubbin, 1969; Crider and Lunn, 1971; Bohlin, 1972). We might note also that this procedure is in line with Gray's (1964a) suggestions about appropriate arousal measures, and in view of his assumption of similarity between the concepts of arousability and excitatory strength-sensitivity (Gray, 1964a), there is the obvious inference that SF differences reflect variability in nervous system strength and sensitivity.

A quite different interpretation, however, has been suggested by a number of neuroanatomical studies (e.g. Block and Bonvallet, 1960; Wang, 1964) reporting that level of spontaneous activity is governed by hindbrain inhibitory centres. On this basis, it is probable that level of nonspecific responding is one of a complex of variables — including OR and CR extinction rates — defining inhibitory dynamism, a high SF level characterising Ss with low inhibitory dynamism relative to level of excitatory dynamism, i.e. unbalanced Ss. Such Ss would be expected to show a tendency towards slow habituation and extinction rates.

Available evidence seems to support this assumption. Although Martin (1960) reports a significant correlation between level of spontaneous fluctuation and number of CRs emitted, her CR measure appears to be a conditioned orientation reaction rather than a true CR. Stern, Stewart and Winocur (1961) report a correlation of + 0.84 between conditioning rate and level of spontaneous fluctuation measured between conditioning trials, but no correlation between conditioning rate and resting SF level. The latter, however, correlated significantly with extinction rate, high SF being associated with a large number of extinction trials — a finding also reported by Geer (1967). O'Gorman (1972) reports a strong relationship between level of non-specific electrodermal responding at rest (fluctuation rate) and the amount of OR return to a change in stimulus characteristics following habituation — Ss with high SF levels showing large response amplitudes — which has been shown to be related to rate of initial habituation (O'Gorman, Mangan and Gowen, 1970).

Significant positive relationships between spontaneous fluctuation rate and number of trials to OR habituation have been reported in a number of studies (Johnson, 1963; Koepke and Pribram, 1966; Katkin and McCubbin, 1969; Crider and Lunn, 1971; Bohlin, 1972, 1976; Verbaten, 1972). Nebylitsyn *et al.* (1965) report positive correlations, approaching significance, between number of spontaneous fluctuations in resting GSR and OR habituation rate and number of trials to the development of differentiation. Nebylitsyn (1963b) also reports that high resting alpha-index and large amplitude and low frequency of alpha-rhythm, which have been associated with low levels of cortical arousal (Beckman and Stein, 1961), and with traits such as passivity, stability, slowness (Gastaut *et al.,* 1951; Mundy-Castle, 1957; De Lange *et al.,* 1962), which might be taken as behavioural indices of inhibitory control, correlate significantly with fast OR habituation and CR extinction. Groups of Ss selected on the basis of dynamism of inhibition and dynamism of excitation scores were compared on these EEG measures (Nebylitsyn, 1963b). Although the group showing high dynamism of inhibition expressed significantly higher alpha-index and alpha-amplitude and lower frequency of alpha rhythm, as predicted, the groups high on excitatory dynamism failed to show the expected levels. Nebylitsyn suggested that at that point in time too little was known about resting EEG variables for them to be used as critical measures of nervous system properties. Recent studies, however, have been somewhat more optimistic.

The relationship of recovery limb to other SCR components is unclear. Edelberg (1972b) reports that lower SF rate is associated with lower SCLs and longer SCRecs for a number of stimulus conditions. The one exception was a cold pressor task, where high SF rate and high SCL were associated with longer recovery times. On the basis of these results, Edelberg (1972b) concluded that recovery limb is a measure of goal orientation, since all highly activating experimental tasks, except the cold pressor task, reflected goal oriented activities. Insofar as SCRec and SCR are concerned, Edelberg (1970) reports a range of correlations between 0.0 and + 0.74 for 6 Ss. On the other hand, Lockhart (1972) reports that SCR is unrelated to any of the temporal SCR measures, though the latter are significantly related, the correlation between SCRec and rise time being + 0.62. Ax and Bamford (1970) report no correlation between SCR and $p/2$ for both normal and schizophrenic groups, while Gruzelier (1973) reports a significant negative correlation between these variables for his schizophrenic group, with no significant correlation for normal Ss.

Venables (1974) has argued that since small amplitude, non-duct filling SCRs have long recoveries, no correlation can be expected between amplitude and $t/2$ when S is resting and low stimulus intensities are employed, nor can other than minimal correlations be expected when highly arousing conditions and intense stimuli are employed, since all responses would be of the high amplitude, short recovery type. Only when a range of SCR activity bridges secretory duct filling and membrane aspects of SCR might one expect intra-individual correlations between the two measures.

Overall, while some consistant relationships have been reported between SCRec and other temporal components of SCR, correlations between SCR and SCRec seem to depend on task and subject groupings.

It appears that fast SCR recovery may reflect the stressfulness of the situation, fast recovery from stress, or both.

Few data of any consequence have been reported on latency and rise time aspects of SCR.

## Dishabituation of OR

Dishabituation refers to the re-evocation of the habituated OR. Synonymous terms are dehabituation and disinhibition. Dishabituation can occur spontaneously following repetition of the unchanged habituating stimulus (the over-extinction effect), or to some detectable change (in intensity, quality, etc.) in stimulus parameters, prior to over-extinction. Stimulus change can be executed immediately after habituation (we shall refer to this as primary dishabituation), or following a specified number of repetitions of the habituating stimulus, described in the literature as sub-zero habituation. We might note that in a few studies dishabituation to an external stimulus in another modality has been examined, a procedure similar to the probe technique used in measuring strength of internal inhibition when an inhibition of delay paradigm is employed.

Since in Pavlovian theory common mechanisms are thought to underlie both CR and OR extinction, principles applying to intensification (concentration) and irradiation of extinctive inhibition should apply equally to OR habituation. These are obviously highly relevant to problems of dishabituation. Insofar as concentration is concerned, a good deal of evidence suggests that sheer repetition of the inhibitory stimulus intensifies the inhibitory process — for example, continued application of CS, following CR extinction, strengthens inhibition, as does the development of a "delicate" compared with a gross diferentiation (Bykov, 1953). Such inhibition irradiates, spreading to neighbouring cell complexes, the strength of the irradiated inhibition being proportional to the proximity (spatially or in some other sense, e.g. semantic) of the inducing stimulus to that used in extinction. The rate at which inhibition intensifies and irradiates is claimed to be dependent on type of nervous system and the intensity of the inhibitory stimulus.

On this basis, and ignoring for the moment the role of cortical factors in disinhibition, we might expect that the stronger the inhibition, measured by number of trials to primary habituation, and the greater the intensification or concentration of inhibition as a function of repeated presentations of the habituating stimulus following primary habituation (i.e. greater sub-zero habituation), the greater is the discrepancy required in the changed stimulus to produce dishabituation. Relevant data, however, are equivocal, although to what extent this is due to uncontrolled differences in nervous system type and intensity of the eliciting stimulus is unknown.

### (a) Primary Dishabituation

Although Sokolov's (1960) contention that any detectable variation in stimulus input — in duration, intensity, frequency, quality — that is, any mismatch between current and previous input stored in memory in "neuronal models" — will evoke an OR, and that the magnitude of the re-evoked OR will be proportional to the amount of stimulus discrepancy, has been supported in a number of studies (e.g. Voronin and Sokolov, 1960; Sokolov, 1960; Grim and

White 1965; Corman, 1967) many attempts to replicate Sokolov's findings have proved only partly successful.

A number of recent studies of OR recovery following change in the habituating stimulus suggest that not all Ss manifest OR to change, even when they are aware of such a change (Bernstein, 1969; Koepke and Pribram, 1966; Corman, 1967; O'Gorman, Mangan and Gowen, 1970; O'Gorman, 1972). O'Gorman, Mangan and Gowen (1970) report that only an increase in stimulus intensity disinhibited the habituated OR, and then only with certain Ss, and that decrease in stimulus intensity, contrary to Sokolov's (1960) observation, did not re-evoke OR. Bernstein (1968, 1969) reports similar results, increase in stimulus intensity producing greater OR return than decrease. Both Edwards (1975a) and Rust (1976), however, report dishabituation to a decrease in stimulus intensity. Change in stimulus duration following habituation appears to re-evoke OR (Koepke and Pribram, 1966), as does altering a compound stimulus by omitting one or more elements (Allen, Hill and Wickens, 1963; Badia and Defran, 1970). However, omission of the stimulus rather than deletion of elements in a compound stimulus, contrary to Sokolov's (1963b) claim, does not result in dishabituation (Fried et al., 1967) nor does change in the order of a sequence of stimuli by adding an additional stimulus (Fried, Welch and Friedman, 1966; Fried, Korn and Welch, 1966; Zimny, Pawlick and Saur, 1969; Furedy, 1968). Nutritional factors may also be important. Lester (1975) reports greater dishabituation in well nourished than in poorly nourished children. These studies suggest that there is no simple answer to the question of type of stimulus variation likely to re-evoke OR. What is clear, however, is that the OR is less sensitive to variation in stimulus conditions than originally implied by Sokolov.

Essentially the same judgment applies to Sokolov's (1960) claim that the magnitude of the reappearing OR is proportional to the discrepancy between the habituated and the new stimuli. Although Grim and White (1965), employing visual stimuli, Williams (1963) and Corman (1967), employing auditory stimuli, and Yaremko, Blair and Leckhart (1970) using "conceptual" stimuli (number series) all report larger OR associated with a greater change in the test stimuli, Zimny and Schwabe (1966), Geer (1969), O'Gorman, Mangan and Gowen (1970) and McCubbin and Katkin (1971) failed to demonstrate such a relationship.

A number of possibilities have been suggested to account for these discrepancies. Two in particular are worth consideration. The first is the functional significance hypothesis formulated by Bernstein (1969), which is in line with suggestions previously advanced by Dykman (1965), Lewis and Horwitz (1969) and Maltzman and Mandell (1968). Bernstein suggests that in addition to a matching process, Sokolov's OR mechanism must include a process for evaluating the significance of the mismatch for S. There is some support for this contention in the Bernstein *et al.* (1971) report that apparent movement in the visual field towards S results in greater OR than movement away from S. On the other hand, the findings of Leitenberg, Agras and Barlow (1969) that some stimuli judged by S as anxiety-eliciting failed to elicit OR, suggest that stimulus significance, like stimulus discrepancy, is not a sufficient condition for OR elicitation.

The alternative suggestion involves the inhibitory postulate which Sokolov (1960) considered relevant to the process of OR habituation, but was of less significance, compared with the modelling process, in OR return. It is possible that strength of inhibition within the particular response system may be the critical factor, judging from the fact that failure to respond to stimulus change is shown by Ss exhibiting more rapid primary habituation (O'Gorman, Mangan and Gowen, 1970; Siddle, Foggitt and Nicol, 1973) even at an early age (De Loach, 1976), and by Ss showing low levels of spontaneous fluctuation during the period preceding stimulation (O'Gorman, 1972; Siddle, Foggitt and Nicol, 1973). Data supporting the relationship between amount of sub-zero habituation and amount of dishabituation are also relevant here. Habituation rate, intensification of inhibition and level of spontaneous activity are considered to be measures of rate of growth of internal inhibition (Nebylitsyn, 1966a). We could argue, therefore, that Ss showing high dynamism of inhibition might be aware of stimulus change, but not dishabituate because of strong inhibitory control, except perhaps in those cases where the change stimulus is substantially more intense, or becomes significant. There is some support for this in the O'Gorman, Mangan and Gowen, (1970) report that within the group of Ss showing dishabituation to a more intense stimulus, amplitude of returned OR and number of trials to primary habituation correlate +0.78. Siddle, Foggitt and Nicol (1973) also report a positive relationship between speed of response return and SF rate, and a significant relationship between fast speed of response return and long latency of SCR — the latter suggesting strong inhibitory control — during primary habituation.

### (b) Sub-zero Habituation

Sub-zero habituation, which, until recently, has attracted relatively little interest in the literature (cf. Thompson and Spencer, 1966), the few studies reported involving mainly animal Ss (Appelbaum *et al.,* 1960; Prosser and Hunter, 1936; Gardner, 1968) poses the question of whether increase in the number of presentations of the habituating stimulus, before stimulus change, increases or decreases the probability of OR return. There are essentially two approaches to this problem. The first, the expectancy hypothesis, states that the greater S's experience with the habituating stimulus, the greater his expectancy that the next stimulus will match the nervous model, thus the greater the stimulation by the cortex when a mismatch occurs, and the greater the amount of OR return. Sokolov incorporates this prediction in his habituation model. Supporting evidence is offered by Waters and McDonald (1974) and Edwards (1974), although in the latter case much lower than normal intensity auditory stimuli were employed. Failures of prediction are reported by James, Daniels and Hanson (1974), Siddle and Heron (1976), Stephenson and Siddle (1976) and Waters and McDonald (1975).

The alternative hypothesis proposes that as the inhibition produced by habituation irradiates, up to the point of over-extinction, an increasingly greater discrepancy is required to re-evoke the OR to stimulus change. This is consistent with the well-known facts about irradiation of inhibition, which follows the principles applying to CR generalisation and extinction. Induced inhibition spreads to neighbouring cell complexes, and the strength of the irradiated inhibition is directly proportional to the proximity of the particular stimulus to that used in extinction. Thus, for example, after OR extinction to stimulation on the palm of the hand, no OR occurs to stimulation of the fingers. OR increases as a function of remoteness of the stimulated point from the point originally stimulated (Sokolov, 1958a).

Empirical support for this proposition, insofar as orienting responses are concerned, has been reported by Williams (1963), Corman (1967), James and Hughes (1969) and Geer (1969). In line with this, it also appears that inhibition dissipates as an increasing negatively accelerated function of recovery interval (James, Daniels and Hanson, 1974). The fact that return of OR to the change stimulus reduces as a function of the number of sub-zero stimulus presentations is explained in terms of incomplete generalisation of the inhibitory process induced by repeated stimulus presentations.

The data, however, are by no means conclusive. It is possible, as Graham (1973) suggests, that there is an interaction, as yet undisclosed, between expectancy and inhibitory variables, which reflects the operation of both the cortical and the subcortical mechanisms involved in habituation.

### (c) Over-extinction

Over-extinction, according to Sokolov (1958a) is the paradoxical return of the habituated OR following protracted stimulation beyond the point of primary habituation. The effect has been reported for the vascular, GSR and EEG components of OR to auditory, visual and proprioceptive stimuli (cf. Gray, 1964a). The most detailed account of over-extinction is provided by Sokolov and Paromonova (1961), who report studies of over-extinction of the

EEG, respiratory, GSR, muscle tension and eye movement components of OR to an auditory stimulus. According to Sokolov (1958a), the OR returns during an uninterrupted series of stimuli after the onset of drowsy states or sleep; the response is stronger than that originally recorded, the threshold for the reaction is lowered, it habituates more slowly than the original OR, the vasomotor component of the re-evoked reaction is similar to that associated with the defence reflex, and appears to be almost inextinguishable, and it is subject to external inhibition, as the original OR.

Sokolov (1958a) suggests that the over-extinction process is due to a functional cortical inhibition, as distinct from the active cortical inhibition characteristic of habituation. Functional inhibition is manifested behaviourally in drowsiness or sleep, which Sokolov considers to be critical for the phenomenon. The OR returns to the stimulus in over-extinction because of loss of cortical control over the lower brain structures which mediate the OR components, i.e. there is a reduction in tonic arousal. Since the local OR appears to habituate in 30–50 trials (Sokolov, 1963a), which is approximately the stage in the habituation series at which over-extinction occurs (O'Gorman, 1972; Siddle, 1974) it is possible that local OR habituation signals loss of cortical control. Data on this point, however, are lacking.

Although OR habituation is well documented in the Western literature (Thompson and Spencer, 1966), Johnson and Lubin's (1967) review has indicated that there has been some difficulty in replicating the over-extinction effect, particularly the GSR–OR component. In the first place, the Pavlovian view that OR habituation leads to sleep — which Sokolov (1958a) considers to be a necessary condition for over-extinction — is arguable (Konorski, 1948b; Tizard, 1966). On the other hand, Marton and Urban (1966) report the occurrence of EEG waves characteristic of sleep in their group of extraverts, and a number of Western authors have reported effects which appear similar to over-extinction.

Oswald (1962) found a return of habituated GSR during "spindle", sleep and Broughton, Poiret and Tassinari (1965) report increased frequency of evoked response during stage 2 sleep, as well as a lowered threshold for response evocation during this period. There are a number of reports (e.g. McDonald, Johnson and Hord, 1964; Tizard, 1966) concerned with characteristics of autonomic components of OR during drowsiness or sleep, but in most cases a changing stimulus, or an interrupted series of stimulus presentations was employed, and it is difficult to evaluate these results, as Sokolov and Paramonova (1961) maintain than an extended habituation series without variation is required before OR return can be classified as over-extinction. Johnson and Lubin (1967), while reporting GSR–OR return following sleep onset, found no evidence of habituation of the returned OR, contrary to the findings of Broughton, Poiret and Tassinari (1965) and Sokolov and Paramonova (1961). Certain methodological differences, however, could account for this discrepancy.

In a number of more recent studies, in which the conditions considered necessary for over-extinction have been more nearly met, the effect has been demonstrated. O'Gorman (1972) and Siddle (1974) report an over-extinction effect in their Ss. O'Gorman (1972) notes a significant rise in SCL preceding over-extinction, an effect which was not reported by Siddle, Foggitt and Nicol, (1973). Contrary to Sokolov's (1958a) observations, however, in O'Gorman's (1972) study, the returned OR was less stable, and did not differ either in magnitude or in habituation rate from the original OR. Siddle (1974) reports an interesting finding that although some of his Ss showed OR return in 40–50 trials, when measured by SCR, there was no apparent change in cortical alertness, measured by EEG.

O'Gorman (1972) reports that Ss habituating slowly showed earlier over-extinction ($r = -0.67, p < 0.05$), a finding also reported by Siddle, Foggitt and Nicol (1973) and Siddle (1974). O'Gorman (1972) and Siddle, Foggitt and Nicol (1973) also record higher SF rate in these Ss. This latter relationship is well attested (Stern, 1966), both habituation rate and SF level being assumed to reflect level of cortical inhibition (Davidson, Payne and Sloan, 1966). Siddle (1974) also reports a negative relationship between latency of returned SCR, and both SF rate and number of trials to primary habituation.

O'Gorman (1968) has reported a significant correlation between speed of over-extinction and EPI N, suggesting that high N Ss, because of their slower decline in arousal, might be expected to take longer to show over-extinction. This is in line with Sokolov's (1958a) suggestion of a relationship between slowness of OR habituation in neurotic Ss and speed of over-extinction in normal Ss, arguing that both effects are due to "weakness of inhibition", and with the observation that neurotics show almost inextinguishable ORs. To Sokolov, habituation rate and over-extinction are instances of response suppression which reflect level of (internal) inhibitory strength-weakness.

### (d) Vigilance

A particular problem in the area of dishabituation involves the phenomenon of vigilance, which describes the maintenance of attention over relatively long periods, the readiness to detect and respond to a specified change in the signal occurring at random intervals (Mackworth, 1957). A vigilance task requires S to respond to a wanted signal occurring randomly against a background of unwanted events. It appears that vigilance decrement is a function of the task used, the stimulus conditions, and certain organismic states.

It is generally acknowledged that if a stimulus is given special significance, such as requiring S to count the number of times it occurs, or requiring him to react to it in some manner such as pressing a key, the OR habituates to all other stimuli other than that which requires the specified response. However, even here one might expect individual differences in habituation rate, reflecting differential rate of growth of internal inhibition, to influence detection of and response to the wanted signal. This is the general conclusion of Mackworth (1969, 1970) from a review of vigilance studies; she suggests that decrement is due, in part, to habituation of the arousal or orienting response produced by the repetitive background events. On this basis, fast habituators should show a faster vigilance decrement than slow habituators.

Relevant data are generally supportive. Siddle (1970) predicted that since OR habituation is followed by a state of drowsiness or low tonic arousal in a number of response modalities — SCR (Stern, 1966), EEG (Daniel, 1967), blood concentration of adrenalin (O'Hanlon, 1965) — which have been shown to be associated with vigilance decrement, habituation rate in the modality of the vigilance task should be correlated with vigilance decrement. He reports a significant regression of SCR habituation rate in the modality of the vigilance task on vigilance decrement. Crider and Augenbaum (1975) also report that slow auditory habituation is associated with a high and sustained rate of signal detection, and fast habituation with lower overall rate and a time-on-task decrement. Indirect evidence is offered by reports that extraversion — which is claimed to be related to habituation rate — and vigilance are correlated (Bakand, 1959, Eysenck, 1967), high extraverts showing greater vigilance decrement.

On the other hand, Pushkin (1972) reports a number of experiments indicating a strong relationship ($r = 0.72-0.76$) between vigilance and strength of the nervous system, the weak system being less vigilant. Since in Soviet typological theory, strength and dynamism are orthogonal properties, it is difficult to envisage how both these can be highly correlated with vigilance performance.

## Individual Differences in OR Functioning

Most research in this area has focussed on the relationship of OR variables to "anxiety", extraversion, psychopathology and mental defectiveness.

### (a) "Anxiety"

A number of problems are encountered in reviewing relevant studies in this area.

The first is whether the anxiety measured is trait (A-trait) or state (A-state), the latter being regarded as a transitional emotional state which is to a degree situationally specific, the former as a relatively permanent personality characteristic (Spielberger, 1972). Spielberger (1972) has suggested that high A-trait Ss experience greater A-state arousal than low A-trait Ss under threatening conditions, but that under "neutral" conditions, no gross arousal differences are observed between the two groups. Differences on A-trait dependent variables, therefore, can be anticipated only when Ss are threatened.

However, while in many of the reported studies threat (e.g. of shock) is explicit, in other, supposedly neutral situations, it may be that "incidental" features of the experimental situation are experienced by some Ss, possibly those high on A-trait, as threatening or stressful. For example, susceptibility to apparatus stress, a tendency for some Ss to become agitated when they encounter experimental or electrical apparatus with which they are unfamiliar can markedly increase A-state (Kamin, 1955). Again experimenters select from a wide range of stimulus intensities, some of which are obviously aversive. Reported intensities range from the "weak" auditory stimulus employed by Marton and Urban (1966), to the 100 dB stimulus employed by Martin (1960) and Lader and Wing (1966), the 94 dB stimulus used by Koepke and Pribram (1966), and the "harsh" auditory stimulus selected by Mundy-Castle and McKiever (1953), which might be expected to evoke defensive rather than orienting reactions. There is the added problem that experienced intensity of stimulus is in part a function of nervous sensitivity, which varies between Ss, and possibly between groups. To the writer's knowledge, there are few, if any, experiments reported in the Western literature in which inter-S differences in sensitivity have been partialled out.

A further difficuty is that A-trait anxiety may not be as broad a personality dimension as was first assumed. Some recent evidence suggests that A-trait is multi-dimensional, subsuming a number of orthogonal factors, primarily inter-personal ego threat and threat of physical danger (Endler et al. 1976). These authors report that correlations across A-trait and A-state measures are generally higher than those between any two A-state measures, indicating A-trait as well as A-state specificity. Factor analyses of A-trait and A-state measures failed to yield separate A-trait and A-state factors. Taken together, these findings imply that A-state may be thematically related to A-trait anxiety; for example, A-trait fear of physical danger may produce high A-state only when S is threatened with electric shock — not when he is subjected to ego threat — and that when high A-trait is reflecting feelings of personal inadequacy, ego threat, but not threat of physical danger, is likely to evoke high A-state arousal. Only where A-trait has generalised over a wide range of behaviours can we refer to A-trait as a general personality dimension.

A second major question is that anxious psychiatric and normal samples are probably drawn from different areas under the normal distribution curve. The distribution of A-trait anxiety in normal samples covers a relatively narrow band, and it is likely that only when highly anxious normal Ss experience very severe threat that they approach the debilitating A-state levels experienced by anxious psychiatric Ss under neutral conditions. For this reason, it seems advisable to consider research findings for these groups under separate headings. Consideration of anxious psychiatric groups will be reserved for a later section.

## SCR

Results from studies are highly contradictory. Many have reported no relationship between SCR and A-trait, when the eliciting stimulus has been auditory (Dykman *et al.* 1959; Raskin, 1963; Belloni, 1964; Maltzman and Raskin, 1965; Koepke and Pribram, 1966; Roessler, Burch and Childers, 1966; Zuckerman, Persky and Curtis, 1968; Katkin and McCubbin, 1969; Raskin, 1969; Epstein and Fenz, 1970; Koriat, Averill and Malmstrom, 1973), or visual (Lovibond, 1963). On the other hand, Dykman *et al.* (1959) report that Ss high on self-rated, rather than manifest, anxiety gave larger GSRs to the first presentation of an auditory stimulus. Again, Galbrecht *et al.* (1965) report that throughout a habituation series Ss with highest MAS scores gave the smallest GSRs, a finding consistent with Lader and Wing's (1966) conclusion that anxiety, clinically defined (thus A-state?), results in smaller GSRs, both on initial presentation of the stimulus, and throughout the habituation series. O'Gorman (1968) and Mangan and O'Gorman (1969) report similar results, using the EPI N score. Mangan (1974, 1978a) reports that EPI N scores are significantly and negatively related to initial OR amplitude to tactual and visual stimuli, but not to auditory stimuli.

## SF

No differences between high and low A-trait Ss in SF rate have been reported by Katkin (1965a,b), Koepke and Pribram (1966), Katkin and McCubbin (1969) and Neva and Hicks (1970) during the pre-experimental rest period, even when Ss were under threat of future shock (Katkin, 1965b). On the other hand, a consistent positive relationship has been reported between the two measures (Burch and Griener, 1960; Stern, Stewart and Winocur, 1961). Nielsen and Petersen (1976) report a similar relationship for Ss high on both A-trait and A-state, when test conditions were stressful, as do Rapaport and Katkin (cited by Katkin and McCubbin, 1969) who describe the experimental procedure as "moderately stressing".

*SCL*

The bulk of evidence suggests that high and low anxious Ss do not differ on this measure, whether anxiety is A-trait (Bitterman and Holtzman, 1952; Zuckerman, Persky and Curtis, 1968; Koepke and Pribram, 1966; Epstein and Fenz, 1970) or A-state (Katkin, 1965b). An interesting observation is the McDonnell and Carpenter (1959, 1960) report of an inverted U relationship between SCL and A-trait, the latter being measured by the Mandler–Sarason general anxiety scale. If such a relationship holds, there are no grounds for expecting differences between high and low anxious groups when tested by usual significance tests. On the other hand, Nielsen and Petersen (1976) report that under stressful conditions, Ss high on A-trait, but not A-state, record higher SCL levels.

*Habituation*

A number of studies report no differences between Ss high and low on A-trait in habituation rates (Bitterman and Holtzman, 1952; Martin, 1960; Koepke and Pribram, 1966; Katkin and McCubbin, 1969; Galbrecht *et al.*, 1965; Koriat, Averill and Malmstrom, 1973; Mangan, 1974). On the other hand, slow habituation rate has been reported from high A-trait Ss (Stewart *et al.*, 1959; Lader and Wing, 1966; Lader, 1967; Lader and Sartorious, 1968; Fried, Friedman and Welch, 1967; McGinnies, 1973; Hart, 1974; Raskin, 1975; Hirschman and Brumbaugh-Beuhler, 1975), and Ss high on A-state, usually induced by threat of electric shock (Bohlin, 1976; Gatchel and Gaas, 1976; Carroll and Pokara, 1976) or by examination stress (Maltzman *et al.*, 1971). A relevant finding is that high level of arousal, whether tonic (Bohlin, 1972, 1976; Verbaten, 1972), usually measured by SF rate, or phasic, i.e. stimulus induced (Maltzman *et al.*, 1971; Verbaten, 1972) or drug induced (Van der Maelen, Strauss and Starr, 1974), is associated with slow habituation rate. Others again have reported curvilinear relationships (e.g. Epstein and Fenz, 1970).

*SCRec*

Edelberg (1970, 1972b) reports that SCRec is slower under defence conditions and faster when S is goal oriented. Furedy (1972) has also reported that slow SCRec ia a good predictor of S's anticipation of electric shock.

*(b) Extraversion-Introversion*

*SCR*

O'Gorman (1968) and Mangan and O'Gorman (1969) report that initial amplitude of OR (SCR) is related to extraversion, but only when N is partialled out. Under the constraint of low N scores, extraverts showed significantly larger SCRs that introverts. Mangan (1974) reports that E is significantly and positively related to SCR to a tactual stimulus, but not to visual or auditory stimuli. Nielsen and Petersen (1976), on the other hand, report that under stressful conditions, Es showed fewer and smaller electrodermal responses to a moderately intense stimulus, a finding similar to that reported by Orlebeke (1972). Koriat, Averill and Malmstrom (1973), however, report no relationship between E and SCR.

*SF*

Comparatively little research has been reported on the relationship between these variables. Eysenck (1967) has argued that E is a measure of low reactivity in the reticular activating system. On this basis, SF rate should be lower in extraverts. Results reported by Coles, Gale and Kline (1971), Crider and Lunn (1971) and Nielsen and Petersen (1976) are in agreement, although Bohlin (1972) reports no relationship.

*SCL*

Few data have been reported on the relationship between E and SCL.

There appears to be limited agreement that Es and Is do not differ in SCL (Coles, Gale and Kline, 1971; Nielsen and Petersen, 1976). Fowles, Roberts and Nagie (1977), however, report that SCL is higher for Es at higher levels of arousal, but that the reverse is true at lower levels (75–85 dB stimulus compared with 100–103 dB stimulus). These authors suggest that this finding is consistent with the notion that introverts have "weak" nervous systems which develop transmarginal inhibition under stress.

*Habituation rate*

Much of the reported research has focused on this variable in attempts to validate Eysenck's (1957) typological postulate which states that the extravert is the inhibitory type, showing more rapid and stronger development of reactive inhibition than the introvert. On these grounds, we might anticipate faster habituation rate from Es.

There is minimal support for this proposition. Crider and Lunn (1971) report that Es show EEG and SCR habituation in significantly fewer trials than Is. Small (1974) reports similar results for SCR habituation, when Ss were subjected to threat. On the other hand, a number of studies have reported that habituation rate is unrelated to E or "secondary process" (Martin, 1960; Mundy-Castle and McKiever, 1953; Lader, 1967; Coles, Gale and Kline, 1971;

Bohlin, 1972; Koriat, Averill and Malmstrom, 1973; Marchman, 1973; Mangan, 1974).

A resolution of this conflict is suggested in the Mangan and O'Gorman (1969) report that Es habituate SCR more rapidly than Is only when both groups are low on N, which supports the earlier findings of Scott and Wilkinson (1962) and Marton and Urban (1966). When E and N were allowed to vary independently, high N/low E and low N/high E groups habituated quickly, suggesting a complex interaction between the personality variables and habituation rate (Mangan and O'Gorman, 1969).

## (c) Psychopathology and Mental Deficiency

Under this rubric we shall include material concerned with OR characteristics of highly anxious psychiatric samples, schizophrenics and defectives. In passing, we shall touch on the limited data pertaining to different cognitive "styles".

### i) "Anxious" psychiatric groups

SCR

No differences between highly anxious psychiatric groups and normals have been reported (Goldstein, 1964; Lader and Wing, 1964; Lader, 1967; Hart, 1974).

SF

There seems to be some unanimity that highly anxious psychiatric Ss show a higher SF rate than normals (Malmo et al., 1948; Lader and Wing, 1964, 1966; Hart, 1974), both during the pre-stimulus rest period (Lader and Wing, 1964, 1966) and during habituation (Malmo et al. 1948; Lader and Wing, 1964, 1966; Lader, 1967). The only study reporting no differences between groups is that of Kelly, Brown and Shaffer (1970).

SCL

Although there have been reports that highly anxious psychiatric Ss show higher SCL levels than normals (Howe, 1958; Lader and Wing, 1964, 1966), in some studies no differences have been reported (Goldstein, 1964; Kelly, Brown and Shaffer, 1970). In both these latter studies, however, Ss were permitted to relax for about an hour before SCL measures were taken, which might have substantially reduced any existing A-state anxiety.

HABITUATION

Most studies report slower habituation in highly anxious psychiatric groups (Stewart et al., 1959; Lader and Wing, 1964, 1966; Lader, 1967; Raskin, 1975), although Hart (1974) reports no differences. In some studies, researchers have used slope of regression line as a measure of habituation, allocating Ss to habituating and non-habituating groups using steepness of slope as a criterion. Typical studies are those by Lader and Wing (1964, 1966) who report 6 habituators from 20 in the high anxious psychiatric group, and 20 habituators from a group of 20 normals, and by Lader (1967), who reports 7 habituators from a group of 16 highly anxious psychiatric Ss, and 64 habituators from a group of 75 normals.

### ii) Schizophrenic groups

Since schizophrenia, behaviourally, is shown in impairment of the individual's relationship with the environment, of his capacity to receive and assimilate information (McReynolds, 1960; Bernstein, 1967), psychophysiologically, schizophrenics might be expected to be hyporesponsive in reacting systems.

Evidence for this proposition, which is generally supportive, derives from two sources. A number of early Western studies report slowness and variability of reaction time with schizophrenics (Shakow, 1950; Zahn, Rosenthal and Shakow, 1963 e.g.), due to the intrusion of "minor sets" during the preparatory interval, that is, to greater distractibility (Zahn, Rosenthal and Shakow, 1963). The bulk of evidence, however, derives from OR studies. Summaries by Razran (1961b) and Lynn (1963) of early Soviet studies, and a considerable body of Western research (cf. Bernstein, 1964, 1967, 1969; Pishkin and Hershier, 1963) are in general agreement that schizophrenics, compared with normals, show depressed phasic responsivity.

The reasons for this are unclear, but two possibilities suggest themselves. Attentional deficits of this sort can be due to limbic system malfunctioning, to hippocampal damage, or to any one of a number of organic syndromes, as some authors (e.g. Venables, 1974) have suggested. Data on this issue, however, are equivocal. On the other hand, there is a body of opinion suggesting that these deficits are functional, that schizophrenics control anxiety by filtering and restricting intake of various classes of information, and that this generalises, producing depressed levels of phasic orienting activity. This is an inference from data — though these are by no means compelling — that tonic arousal levels in schizophrenics are little different from, or higher than normals in a variety of response modes (Bernstein, 1964; Zahn, 1964; cf. reviews by Teece and Cole, 1972; Depue and Fowles, 1973), and that phasic hyporesponsivity is abolished by caffeine. This latter might be expected in view of the fact that caffeine, in certain doses, increases arousal, and that increased arousal narrows the attentional focus (Calloway, 1959; Wachtel, 1967; Teichner, 1968). This could be due simply to reinstatement of the autonomic components of OR (Streltsova, 1955), possibly through the recovery of the enhancement effect which occurs in specific cortical projection areas following instructions to expect a particular sensory signal (Nauta, 1971). A further possibility is suggested by Gray's (1975) behavioural inhibition model, according to which increased ARAS arousal initiates septo-hippocampal inhibition of sensory input — such inhibition being functionally part of the selective attention mechanism — which in turn leads to the exclusion of irrelevant stimuli and thus increased attention to focal stimuli. Alternatively, or additionally, it could involve facilitation of voluntary motor behaviour (Stanley and Schlosberg, 1953; Pomonarev, 1955). There is evidence that patients under long-term treatment with major tranquillizers such as chlorpromazine develop akinesia, due to the side-effects of such drugs on the dopaminergic system of the nigro-striatal pathways (Greengard, 1974). Since caffeine has been shown to facilitate, post-synaptically, higher-order motor integration in adrenergic systems (Goodman and Gilman, 1971), this may account for some of the improvement noted. A critical test of this hypothesis, however, would require investigation of the effects of L-Dopa with such Ss.

A functional thesis is also proposed by Maltzman and Mandell (1968), who suggest that the unresponsiveness of schizophrenics to environmental change continues until their ORs are augmented in some way, for example, by therapeutic intervention. They propose that lack of ORs may be due to inhibition produced by excessive orientation to internal stimuli. External stimuli tend to elicit defense reflexes (DRs), which are incompatible with ORs. Thus the schizophrenic S expressing strong DRs does not discriminate amongst stimuli since his ORs are inhibited by his DRs.

Recent data concerning responsivity levels of schizophrenic groups generally support the functional hypothesis.

TONIC RESPONSIVITY

Reviews by Depue and Fowles (1973) and Teece and Cole (1972) report higher tonic arousal levels (SCL) in schizophrenic Ss, as do Mednick and Schulsinger (1968) in high risk samples, although Van Dyke, Rosenthal and Rasmussen (1974) report no difference between adoptees with one schizophrenic parent. Higher levels have been also reported when a heart rate measure is employed (Berger, 1964; Goldstein and Acker, 1967; A. L. Gray, 1975; Gruzelier and Venables, 1975b) or blood pressure (Malmo and Shagass, 1949). An interesting finding is that tonic heart rate decreases with increase in stimulus intensity (A. L. Gray, 1975). These high tonic levels of autonomic responding, which are claimed to contribute to the impaired attention and performance of schizophrenics (Lang and Buss, 1965), are considered by Buss

(1966) to result in the low phasic responsivity of schizophrenics reported by Lynn (1963) and Venables (1966).

PHASIC RESPONSIVITY

There is evidence of reduced SCR in schizophrenic Ss (Pishkin and Hershier, 1963; Bernstein, 1964, 1967). However, it has been reported that SCR is restored to parity with normals when stimulus intensity is increased — from 60 dB to 90 dB, for example (Bernstein, 1967). There is also some support for the reduced responsivity hypothesis from Goldstein and Acker (1967), using a heart rate measure, although they report no difference between schizophrenics and normals in phasic electrodermal responding.

An interesting report is that of Patterson (1976a), who measured pupil area under a variety of conditions in groups of long and short recovery limb schizophrenics. He reports that time to maximum pupil constriction following exposure to light, after dark adaptation, significantly differentiates the groups. Although precise interpretation of his results is difficult, Patterson (1976b) argues along lines previously suggested by Douglas (1972), that since slow time to maximum pupil constriction can result from cholinergic depletion, which is one consequence of hippocampal lesions, fast recovery may reflect effects of hippocampal damage.

Zahn (1964), however, reports that schizophrenics are more reactive — both heart rate and SCR — than normals to low intensity tones, a finding which has been replicated for SCR by Dykman *et al.* (1968), by Mednick (1974) and Anthony, cited by Garmezy (1974) with high risk samples, and by Van Dyke, Rosenthal and Rasmussen, (1974) with an adoptee sample, and for heart rate by A. L. Gray (1975). Schizophrenics appear to show a decrease in phasic SCR as well as stronger heart rate response to high intensity stimuli (A. L. Gray, 1975). There is also evidence that schizophrenic Ss show reducing behaviour, i.e. a reduction in averaged evoked response to stimuli of increasing intensity, to both visual (Buchsbaum, 1975) and auditory (Shagass, 1976) stimuli. On the other hand, a bimodal distribution of reactivity has been reported by Zahn, Rosenthal and Lawlor (1968) with drug-free schizophrenic patients, the stimuli being 72 dB tones or light flashes of moderate intensity, and by Gruzelier and Venables (1972, 1973, 1974, 1975a,b), who derived a mutually exclusive responder/non-responder category, using moderately intense stimuli and an SCR measure. Of some interest is that non-responders responded to tones having signal value, a finding which had previously been reported by Bernstein (1964, 1967).

SF

Szpiler and Epstein (1976) report that schizophrenic Ss in an active avoidance task showed lower SF rate than Ss encountering unavoidable shock, and rated their anxiety lower. Fowles *et al* (1970) report higher SF rates amongst poor premorbid schizophrenics. Gruzelier and Venables (1975b) report that SF rates in their samples parallel their responder/non-responder distinction. Van Dyke, Rosenthal and Rasmussen, (1974), on the other hand, report no differences in SF rate between their adoptee samples.

## HABITUATION

A bimodal distribution similar to that suggested by the responsivity data (SCR and heart rate) seems to apply also in the case of habituation. Bernstein (1964, 1967) reports faster habituation in schizophrenics than in normals, as does Venables (1960) in withdrawn compared with active schizophrenics. However, Zahn, Rosenthal and Lawlor (1968), Depue and Fowles (1973), Van Dyke, Rosenthal and Rasmussen (1974), and Anthony, cited by Garmezy (1974) report slower habituation, as do Fowles *et al.* (1970) with poor premorbid patients. The Gruzelier and Venables (1972) and Zahn, Rosenthal and Lawlor (1968) findings seem to support the assumption that responders, i.e. those who are autonomically reactive, habituate more slowly than normals or non-responders, which agrees with the general finding that high levels of arousal (i.e. high reactivity) are associated with slower habituation.

## EDRec

Perhaps the most interesting body of data involves the relationship of this variable to asocial behaviour and to schizophrenia.

A good deal of data suggests that psychopaths and criminals are characterised by hyporeactive autonomic nervous systems, and that this may account for the reported deficit in avoidance learning (Lykken, 1957; Quay, 1965; Hare, 1968; Schmauk, 1970). Mednick (1970) has added an additional variable to those normally postulated in learning to inhibit asocial acts — viz., fast dissipation of the anticipatory fear elicited, so that the inhibitory response will be promptly rewarded with fear reduction, and is thus highly reinforcing. On this basis, Mednick (1970) hypothesised that since dissipation of anticipatory fear is measured by EDRec, slow EDRecs should characterise those who commit asocial acts.

What evidence there is tends to support this view (Hare, 1968b; a number of unpublished papers cited by Mednick, 1974; Mednick's re-analysis of Siddle, Foggitt and Nicol's (1973) data, reported in Mednick, 1974).

In line with what might be loosely described as learning theory of schizophrenia, which suggests that some types of schizophrenia constitute an evasion of life, and that this evasion is learned, i.e., that some schizophrenics are efficient at avoidance learning, Ax and Bamford (1970), Mednick and Schulsinger (1968), Gruzelier and Venables (1972), Gruzelier (1973), Zahn, Carpenter and McGlashan (1975) and Mednick (1976) report that recovery times or ratios in their schizophrenic groups were substantially faster than those of normals. Venables (1974) has suggested that fast recovery indicates openness to the environment and inability to filter. An interesting report is that of Stevens (1973), who suggests that delusional and hallucinatory behaviour follows from defective filtering.

Consistent with this general view, it has been reported that schizophrenics learn an avoidance response faster than normals (Spain, 1966), that, in active avoidance, schizophrenics learn to avoid more quickly (Cavanaugh, 1958; Johannsen, 1964; Losen, 1961), and that schizophrenics learn faster in active avoidance learning when their reponse produces reward (Atkinson and Robinson, 1961). An interesting addendum is that in the Spain (1966) study, schizophrenics who exhibit the most withdrawn, avoidant ward behaviour show the fastest avoidance learning.

Some conflicting data, however, have been reported. Maricq and Edelberg (1975) report longer rather than shorter recovery times from schizophrenic groups with non-aversive stimuli. Of interest is their finding of no differences between schizophrenics and normals in recovery times when aversive stimuli are employed.

From the data, there appears to be a paradoxical effect with schizophrenic groups. With normals, a linear relationship exists between stimulus intensity and response amplitude (the law of strength) while with schizophrenic Ss there is evidence of increased responsivity to stimuli in the weak to moderate intensity range, and reduced responsivity to more intense stimuli (A. L. Gray, 1975; Buchsbaum, 1975; Shagass, 1976). However, these data can be accommodated within the Pavlovian law of strength, since they indicate an effective range of responding which is consistent with very "weak" nervous system characteristics. A question at issue is whether the inhibition is active or passive. However, the fact that an active-withdrawn dichotomy seems of importance (Venables, 1960; Gruzelier, Lykken and Venables, 1972; Silverman, 1972; Depue, 1976), with the active group showing response levels approximating more closely to normal levels, suggests tentatively that the response suppression is an active process, although this might be an artefact of high pre-stimulus tonic levels.

In view of these findings, a number of authors have reinterpreted the responsivity characteristics of schizophrenics in terms of the Pavlovian construct of transmarginal and protective inhibition (Venables, 1971; Depue, Dubicki and McCarthy, 1975; Depue and Fowles, 1976; Depue, 1976). They suggest that schizophrenia involves the pathological lowering of the threshold of transmarginal inhibition, which results in enhanced responsivity to stimuli in the weak to moderate intensity band, and reduced responsivity to moderately intense or intense stimuli.

Critical data, however, are lacking, although there are no compelling reasons why this should be the case. There are, of course, obvious methodological and theoretical issues, perhaps the most important of which, on the stimulus side, is Venable's (1971) observation of a modality effect, with transmarginal inhibition seemingly more pronounced in the auditory than in the visual modality, and, on the response side, Zahn's (1977) report of the inconsistency between the heart rate and the electrodermal data, which he suggests might be attributable to differences in amount of genetic contribution. LIV considerations, which have only recently been taken into account when testing normal samples, are also of particular significance.

### iii) Cognitive style and defense mechanisms

With normal Ss, there is also the suggestion of selective filtering, which may perform a general defensive function. Luborsky, Blinder and Schimek (1965) report that the eye-movement component of OR is related to type of cognitive control, i.e., to S's typical way of taking in information. Defense of isolation is associated with greater eye-movements (more looking around) and defence of repression with restriction of eye-movements (less looking around), and with preference for differentiated response, high repressors showing low reactivity, as indicated in Rorschach responses. In a subsequent study, Luborsky (1967) reports that level of autonomic reactivity, measured by initial amplitude of OR (GSR, finger vasoconstriction, FPV and heart rate components) is also related to S's cognitive style. Ss showing high levels of differentiated response, as measured by Rorschach responses and field dependence measures of embedded figures and rod-and-frame test, also express small initial OR amplitudes, i.e. low levels of autonomic reactivity.

Of some interest in this general context is the "preception" hypothesis of Lykken and Tellegen (1974), which the authors propose to account for the well-established finding that predictable, compared with unpredictable shock, produces reduced OR amplitudes, whether measured by GSR (Grings, 1973), cardiac acceleration (Lykken, Macindoe and Tellegen, 1972; Epstein, 1973), or the P300 component of the vertex evoked cortical response (Lykken, Macindoe and Tellegen, 1972; Roth, 1973), as do fixed, compared with variable warning periods (Peeke and Grings, 1968). They suggest a "preception" mechanism, by means of which Ss selectively "tune" afferent systems either to augment the intensity of pleasant, interesting or signal stimuli (positive preception), which should enhance the detectibility of weak signals, or to attenuate the subjective intensity of noxious or distracting stimuli (negative preception) (cf. Lykken, 1962; Lykken, Mackindoe and Tellegen, 1972). Although the existence of a detuning mechanism of this sort has been questioned by Furedy and Klajner

(1974), largely on the grounds that signalled shock is not rated by Ss as less aversive, and that the smaller GSR is due to effector fatigue following the anticipatory GSR (i.e. negative induction), there is considerable behavioural evidence that while signalled shock *per se* is judged as being no less aversive than unsignalled shock, the subjective impact of the latter is greater and thus more aversive. In addition, during a series of signalled shock, S can relax during the entire ITI, i.e., shock offset becomes in effect a safety signal, indicating zero probability of another shock until the next CS occurs (Lykken and Tellegen, 1974). This could explain S's preference for signalled over unsignalled shock.

### iv) Mental retardation

Most of the early Soviet (cf. Luria, 1963a) and Western data (Lindsley, 1957; cf. review by Berkson, 1961; Ellis, 1963) suggest that retardates are less responsive to stimuli than normals. Luria (1963a) also reports that retardates produce fewer ORs to weak stimuli, and that when such ORs do occur, they habituate quickly. Lindsley (1957) suggests that this hyporesponsivity is due to deficit in the functioning of the ARAS.

More recent evidence, however, while in general agreement, has raised a number of questions which are as yet unanswered.

RESTING LEVELS

There seems to be general agreement that retardates show higher resting levels (usually measured by GSR) than normals (O'Connor and Venables, 1956; Ellis and Sloan, 1958; Berkson, Hermelin and O'Connor, 1961). With children, however, the opposite has been reported (Collmann, 1931, 1959; Hermelin and O'Connor, 1968). The reason for this is unclear.

PHASIC RESPONSIVITY

With simple sensory stimuli, there is some consensus that retardates are less reactive, whether the measure is heart rate (Vogel, 1961), vascular (Vinogradova, cited by Razran, 1961b), GSR (Berkson, Hermelin and O'Connor, 1961; Paramonova, cited by Razran, 1961b; Baumeister, Spain and Ellis, 1963; Luria, 1963a; Clausen and Karrer, 1968) or alpha-block (Baumeister, Spain and Ellis, 1963). A similar result is reported by Collmann (1959) with children.

A number of authors, however, have reported no difference between groups, the measure employed being GSR (Bower and Das, 1972) and heart rate (Powazek and Johnson, 1973). Ball, Barber and Kohler (1975) also report no differences between groups when they used SCR as a measure of tactile discrimination. On the other hand, Wolfensberger and O'Connor (1965) report larger GSRs from retardates than from normal Ss.

In this context interesting findings are reported by Das and Bower (1971). In a vigilance task, normals express more GSRs to the warning than to the imperative signals, while retardates showed the opposite effect. Powazek and Johnson (1975) report that, although there were no differences between groups in OR responses to simple stimuli, retardates showed smaller responses to signal stimuli. This latter finding is in agreement with the earlier report of Carrier, Malpass and Orton (1961) that "primitive" responses in retardates are less affected than more complex processes. It might be inferred from these results that retardates suffer a deficit in attaching signal value to stimuli.

## HABITUATION

Evidence here is conflicting.

Hozima *et al.* (1973) report a much greater range of habituation scores in retardates.

Luria (1963a) and Lobb, Moffitt and Gamblin, (1966), employing a GSR measure, report that OR habituates more rapidly in retardates. On the other hand, Baumeister, Spain and Ellis, (1963) and Tizard (1966), employing GSR and EEG measures, report slower habituation in retardates than in normals. Siddle and Glen (1974) also report slower SCR habituation in retardates to complex compared to simple stimuli, while normal Ss showed no difference in habituation rates.

Finally, Das and Bower (1971), Bower and Das (1972), and Clausen & Karrer (1968) using a GSR measure, Wolfensberger and O'Connor (1965), employing GSR and alpha-block measures, and Vogel (1961), using FPV measure, found no differences between groups.

## The Relationship of CR Acquisition and Extinction to OR Variables

Anokhin (1958) has given the clearest account of the Pavlovian view concerning the role of OR in conditioning. He suggests that in conditioning, there is a natural sequence of stimuli — A, B, C, D, E — linking the signal A with the US E — the sound of the feeding apparatus, the sight of food, the effect of the food on the gustatory apparatus of the tongue. Each of the successive stimuli which link the signal with the food evoke specific ORs, b, c, d. The first US reinstates and augments the general somatic components of OR, but not the specific motor orientation to signals. The early positive CR seems to be an amalgamation of the CS–OR and certain non-specific US reactions (e.g. looking at electrodes, general restlessness). After a few pairings, the cortex unites all these separate excitations into an unbroken sequence abcde. Thus as soon as stimulus A becomes effective, excitation propagates rapidly over the afferent or cortical elements of the previously effective stimuli, and precedes the effects of the actual stimuli B, C and D. When the final CR emerges, all the ORs evoked during the intermediate stages disappear, and the conditioned excitation proceeds unobstructed to the cortical representation of the US. The function of the OR is thus to connect these links; it is a process of automatisation, or "narrowing of the afferent flux". After the CR has been formed, the afferent or cortical representation of the US is activated before the actual US begins to produce any effect. The conditioned excitation based on previous experience with the particular CS (i.e. expectancy) must coincide with the excitation produced by the US; any discrepancy re-evokes an OR (see later discussion on the concept of the acceptor of effect, pp. 356 ff.). Thus the role of the OR in the formation of the CR is the linkage of the cortical representation of the analysers which participate in the series of stimulations between the CS and the terminal reinforcement. The OR initially enters into this process, establishes connections, and then disappears. Its function is thus to arrange temporal sequences. Clearly, however, the OR is not solely a cortical phenomenon, for if the activating influence of the RF is lacking, the separate afferent stimulations remain isolated. Again, cortical extirpation leads to the abolition of OR and CR extinction (Jouvet, 1961). Thus the OR is an entity combining both cortical and subcortical elements.

Considerable interest has been shown in the relationship of different parameters of phasic and tonic OR to classical conditioning and extinction (e.g. Grings, 1960; Hartman, 1963; Kimmel, 1973; Mangan, 1974). In many of the studies, sensory CSs have been employed (e.g. Stewart *et al.,* 1959; Reese and Dykman, 1960; Stern, Stewart and Winocur, 1961; studies from Teplov's laboratory, reviewed by Nebylitsyn, 1966a; Mangan, 1974), in others, verbal CSs, and the related problem of semantic generalisation or transfer has been investigated (e.g. Schwartz, 1948, 1949; Luria and Vinogradova, 1959; evidence from Soviet sources reviewed by both Razran, 1961b, and Hartman, 1963; Maltzman and Raskin, 1965; Maltzman, 1967; Maltzman and Langdon, 1969, Freeman, Johnson and Long, 1972). Although methodological differences between many of these studies make comparisons difficult, the findings overall point to a number of conclusions.

### OR Habituation Rate and SF

Although Reese and Dykman (1960) report an inverse relationship between habituation rate and CR acquisition rate, in that slow habituators condition more rapidly, the weight of evidence fails to support this. Nebylitsyn (1966a), in a re-analysis of Rozhdestvenskaya's (1963b) data, reports only a small, non-significant relationship in the vascular system. Nebylitsyn *et al.* (1965) failed to find evidence of this relationship using EEG indices, and Nebylitsyn *et al.*

(1965), Stern, Stewart and Winocur (1961), and Mangan (1974) report similar results using a GSR response. These findings are in general agreement with Nebylitsyn's typological theory; dynamism of excitation, measured by speed of development of CRs, is considered to be orthogonal with dynamism of inhibition, which is indexed by rate of CR extinction and OR habituation.

Insofar as CR extinction is concerned, although Stern *et al.* (1961) report no evidence of correlation between habituation rate and rate of CR extinction, significant correlations have been reported between habituation rate and speed of development of GSR differentiation (Nebylitsyn *et al.*, 1965) and between habituation rate and rate of EEG (Nebylitsyn *et al.*, 1965) and GSR (Stewart *et al.*, 1959) extinction. Voiku (1964) reports a correlation of +0.75 between number of trials to habituation and CR extinction rate with children. Mangan (1974) reports that habituation to visual, tactual and auditory stimuli index an aversive-appetitive extinction factor.

Much the same position applies insofar as SF is concerned. There are no indications in the literature that rate of spontaneous fluctuation in resting Ss predicts rate of CR acquisition. However, there is substantial evidence that SF does relate to OR habituation rate (Johnson, 1963; Nebylitsyn *et al.*, 1965; Koepke and Pribram, 1966; Katkin and McCubbin, 1969; Crider and Lunn, 1971; Bohlin, 1972), to CR extinction rate (Stern, Stewart and Winocur, 1961; Geer, 1967), and to amount of OR return to stimulus change following habituation (O'Gorman, 1972; Siddle, Foggitt and Nicol, 1973). The latter, in turn, appears to be related to rate of initial habituation (O'Gorman, Mangan and Gowen, 1970; Siddle, Foggitt and Nicol, 1973).

### Initial Amplitude (IA) of OR

Unlike OR habituation, which appears to be a unitary variable, IA seems to reflect a number of nervous system properties, and thus presents a complex, and at times, apparently contradictory, set of relationships with CR acquisition and extinction data.

Nebylitsyn *et al.* (1965) and Yermolayeva-Tomina (1965) report significant negative correlations between IA and speed of differentiation and habituation rate using a GSR response, and Voiku (1964) a significant correlation between alpha-block IA and habituation rate with children, the stimulus in both cases being auditory. These findings suggest that initial OR amplitude reflects, negatively, dynamism of inhibition. On the other hand, there is equally strong evidence relating IA to dynamism of excitation. Although Rozhdestvenskaya (1963a) reports no correlation between IA and speed of formation of vascular CRs, Nebylitsyn *et al.* (1965) report a positive correlation, approaching significance, between IA and speed of GSR conditioning, and Yermolayeva-Tomina (1965) a significant correlation. Putnam, Ross and Graham, (1974) report increased cardiac orienting during classical eyeblink CR acquisition and extinction. Nebylitsyn, in a series of EEG studies (Nebylitsyn, 1963b, 1964; Nebylitsyn et al., 1965), reports that mean duration of alpha-block to first presentation of an auditory stimulus correlates significantly (r = +0.71) with the mean conditioned reflex effect, a relationship which has also been reported by Voiku with children (Voiku, 1964) and by Ingram and Fitzgerald (1974) using a GSR measure. Mangan (1978a), in a factor analysis, reports significant loadings of initial amplitude in tactual and auditory, and to a lesser extent, visual modalities, on a factor defining aversive and appetitive GSR acquisition.

Maltzman and his colleagues (Raskin, 1963; Maltzman and Raskin, 1965; Belloni, 1964; Nies, 1964; Smith, 1966; Maltzman, 1968; Maltzman and Mandell, 1968; Maltzman and Langdon, 1969) have reported an extensive series of studies concerned with semantic conditioning and transfer. They suggest that the OR is a fundamental determinant of learning, functioning as a reinforcer which does not necessarily involve drive or drive reduction. Individual differences in the size of the OR to the initial presentation of a stimulus — either the first in a habituating list or the first US — predicts differences in the amount of semantic conditioning of autonomic responses (Raskin, 1963; Maltzman and Raskin, 1965; Maltzman and Langdon, 1969), in the ability to verbalise experimental contingencies — "awareness" (Raskin, 1963; Maltzman and Raskin, 1965; Smith, 1966) — and in paired-associate learning in male Ss (Belloni, 1964; Nies, 1964). Cousins (1976) reports that faster learners (9–11 years old) in a tactile discrimination task showed larger ORs and slower habituation rates. Maltzman suggests that OR corresponds to what has in the past been called attention, rather than drive, and that elicitation of an OR constitutes a reinforcing state of affairs.

Morgenson and Martin (1968), however, argue that OR–CR relationships of the sort reported might simply reflect high levels of responsivity in the particular response systems employed, rather than a general arousal factor, since in most of the relevant studies the same response was employed to measure both orienting and conditioning – for example, Nebylitsyn (1963b) employed duration of alpha-block to visual and auditory stimuli as his initial OR measure, and duration of conditioned alpha-block as his measure of EEG conditioning, while Raskin (1963) and Maltzman and Raskin (1965) used the skin resistance response to measure orienting and conditioning. Morgenson and Martin (1968) report significant correlations within but not across response systems. Maltzman and Mandell (1968), however, report studies in which OR differences predicted conditioning across certain response systems. For example, individual differences in GSR–OR, but not vasomotor OR, predicted semantic conditioning of alpha-block, and differentiated "aware" from "unaware" Ss. They suggest, therefore, that certain OR components, such as GSR, for example, do possess generality. GSR and alpha-block more directly reflect attentional processes, and may serve as indices of the reinforcement value of stimuli. In a response system such as GSR, they suggest that CS–OR, CR and UR are all manifestations of OR type phenomena — biologically significant USs elicit ORs which are highly resistant to extinction. The UR, and thus the CR, seem to be simply strong ORs.

This interpretation, however, is debatable. At this point in time, it is impossible to say whether the relationships reported reflect individual differences in responsivity, or more general characteristics of nervous system activity corresponding to what might be considered an aspect of attention, or "sensitisation".

The well-established phenomena of semantic generalisation and transfer, usually demonstrated in classical conditioning experiments in which words are employed as CSs — studies which have demonstrated dynamic transfer of CRs, "elective generalisation", and transfer within larger verbal units — have already been discussed in Chapter 3. In that discussion we noted that most learning theorists interpret these results in terms of Osgood's (1953) theory of mediated generalisation. Ss form a conceptual model of the semantic category of the original CS, and verbal (test) stimuli produce mediators which come to elicit responses as a result of conditioning. Responsiveness to test stimuli is thus the degree to which stimuli elicit the mediating responses.

In a sense, this model is the semantic analogue of sensory stimulus generalisation. In Pavlovian theory, stimulus generalisation is a function of irradiation of excitation. Semantic generalisation follows the same general pattern, irradiation varying as a function of the connotative distance between CS word and test word, the latter normally being a member of the same conceptual category. It has been suggested that extent of irradiation is expressed through certain OR parameters, initial amplitude being the obvious candidate. Thus initial amplitude to the test word should indicate the extent to which it activates a system of connections and links of a highly selective nature, and, for this reason, might be expected to measure connotative distance, taking into account individual differences in irradiation, in the OR parameters involved, and in cognitive capacity. As we noted previously, intellectually retarded Ss are capable of little semantic generalisation, although exhibiting relatively high levels of phenotographic generalisation, which follows the principles applying to simple sensory generalisation.

Maltzman and Langdon (1969), however, dissent from this view. From their studies, they report no evidence of semantic generalisation as a function of connotative similarity, and suggest that the critical element is the size of OR evoked by the change from conditioning to generalisation test words. Nothing more. They reject Osgood's mediational theory, his concept of the critical role of connotative distance. Amount of generalisation simply reflects differential responsivity to signals, expressed as OR amplitude.

## Summary

1. It is clear that Sokolov's two-stage model, involving mechanisms of stimulus analysis in the cortex, and arousal amplification in the RF, accounts reasonably well for the facts of OR evocation and habituation to simple sensory stimuli, and for related phenomena such as dishabituation and over-extinction. His subsequent information theory model of stimulus analysis also appears to accommodate OR phenomena to more complex stimulus presentations — to sensory patterns, conceptual categories, for example. It is equally obvious, however, that the simple mechanistic nervous model of afferent, extrapolatory and comparator neurones, although offering a compelling parsimony, fails to explain why the OR continues to be evoked by familiar but significant stimuli. A more "dynamic" mechanism is required.

2. From evidence to date, it seems likely that the RF inhibitory site is initially at the level of the afferent collaterals, and subsequently in the hippocampal areas.

3. In general, the OR serves a general facilitatory function, energising the organism for stimulus reception. The neurophysiological evidence is impressive. In addition, there have been suggestions that suppression of OR activity to produce "conditioned inattention" is typical of certain pathological and normal states as a defensive stratagem.

4. There are large individual differences in certain OR parameters. Evidence — mainly electrodermal responsivity measures — suggests that rate of spontaneous fluctuation, latency, habituation rate and over-extinction (and to a lesser extent dishabituation) are expressions of inhibitory dynamism, or internal inhibition, and that rise time and initial amplitude of OR are measures of excitatory strength-sensitivity, "arousability" or predominance of excitation over inhibition. Precisely what recovery limb is measuring is problematical. There have been suggestions that this indicates limbic system dysfunctioning or hippocampal damage, and that therefore the latter underlies certain forms of schizophrenia. However, direct evidence on this point, from both animal and human studies, is equivocal, and to suggest that schizophrenia involves limbic system or hippocampal damage simply because these structures are attentional mechanisms, and because schizophrenics show attentional deficits of one form or another is theorising at the crudest level.

5. Research relating OR parameters to personality measures, mainly

extraversion (E) and neuroticism (N) is extensive. While it may be tempting to summarise the reported findings as indicating a relationship between extraversion and speed and ease of generation of inhibition, and between N and arousability to aversive stimuli, the data do not justify this conclusion.

We should note a number of studies suggesting a complex interaction between E and N and OR variables. Eysenck's (1967) theory of extraversion-introversion postulates that introversion is related to high reactivity in the reticular activating system, with N reflecting reactivity in the more centrally located, probably limbic system, emotion arousing mechanism, the former being activated by any supra-threshold external stimulus, the latter only when S is subjected to stress, as in states of pain or fear, or when stimulation is very intense. Note that this differs from Eysenck's earlier typological postulate, which emphasises more the rapid development of inhibition in extraverts than the greater arousability of introverts. It is possible that some of the negative findings reported between high and low anxious groups, and between extravert and introvert groups for that matter, could be confounded by lack of control over stress factors in the experimental situation, which could trigger off, or fail to trigger off, the emotion-arousing mechanism.

Taking the view that extraversion-introversion is a dimension of reticular arousal, we might expect that when N is held constant, in the middle range, high Es should show fewer SFs, smaller initial amplitude, and faster habituation, under conditions of moderately intense stimulation. Supporting data have been reported. On the other hand, it seems clear that Es are more tonically aroused than Is. We thus have the confusing situation that Es are less aroused phasically, but more aroused tonically, than Is.

6. Habituation rate is related to rate of CR extinction, and initial amplitude, and, less clearly, to rate of CR acquisition and semantic generalisation and transfer. There is the suggestion in the literature that size of OR to both CS and US — which is considered to be an attentional variable — is the best predictor of CR acquisition rate, and that the concept of reinforcement is superfluous in accounting for acquisition of classically conditioned CRs.

7. In most of the research reviewed, technical and measurement problems abound, and it is difficult to establish to what extent these factors are responsible for the many failures of prediction. The most critical of these appear to be individual response specificity, and the related problem of whether we can assume a general arousal state, or different electro-cortical, somatic and autonomic arousal systems, which are not necessarily interrelated, LIV considerations, and technical problems such as the appropriateness of the electrolyte medium, which is only now being seriously debated.

CHAPTER 8

# Mobility, Concentration and Lability

*Since the organism's external environment is constantly – and often powerfully and abruptly – fluctuating, both processes (excitation and inhibition) must, so to speak, keep pace with these fluctuatings, i.e. they must possess great mobility and be able, in compliance with the demands of the external conditions, rapidly to recede, to give preference to one stimulus, to excitation before inhibition and vice-versa.*

I. P. Pavlov (1955, p. 316)

## Introduction

MOST typological research in Soviet laboratories over the past 30 years has centred round the properties of strength-sensitivity of excitation and dynamism of nervous processes, and although mobility has been extensively discussed, until the reformulation of the Pavlovian typology by Teplov and Nebylitsyn, little critical work on this aspect of higher nervous functioning has been reported.

First mention of mobility was made early in 1932, describing differences in work capacity of phlegmatics and sanguines. The property was designated "lability" or "excitation", but it is clear that the construct is identical with that subsequently described as mobility, a term which was actually introduced in 1933.

As we previously noted, Pavlov originally ascribed three meanings to the term[1] — the speed with which the nervous processes arise and concentrate, after the initial irradiation phase, the persistence of the after-effects of stimulation, and the speed with which one process is replaced by the opposite process. Subsequently, however, Pavlov referred to mobility as "the speed with which the organism, on external demand, yields, gives preference to one stimulation over another, substitutes stimulation for inhibition and vice versa (Pavlov, 1951–2, p. 268).

---

[1]Four processes are, in fact, referred to, if we distinguish speed of arousal from speed and extent of irradiation and concentration of nervous processes.

Nevertheless, uncertainty about the content of the property persisted. Pavlov's students and colleagues emphasised now one, now another of these different aspects, and, as a consequence, a large number of experimental indices of "mobility" were suggested —speed of formation of CRs, measures of alteration, association, delay, of changes in the stereotype, of chronaxy, of sensory after-effects, of RT latency, for example. Differences in methodologies and response modes employed introduced further uncertainty in an already confused area.

Teplov (1956), in attempting to introduce some order into the field, listed a number of possible indices of mobility;[2]

1. speed of arousal and termination of nervous processes;
2. speed of irradiation and concentration of excitation and inhibition;
3. speed of development of positive and inhibitory CRs;
4. speed of alteration;
5. speed of response change following changes in external conditions, involving (a) alteration of the stereotype; (b) development of a delayed reflex using the short-trace method.

This categorisation, as in the case of Pavlov's original description, refers to a number of different processes. The common denominator, according to Teplov (1956), is that the list embraces "all the temporal characteristics of nervous system functioning . . . to which the description 'speed' may be applied" (pp. 61–2). This, of course, is arguable. It depends on what is meant by speed, whether speed of entry of nervous processes into some aspect of nervous system functioning on a particular trial, or the number of trials required for a particular response to be stabilised at some criterion level. Speed, in this latter sense, may have quite different typological connotations. For example, number of trials to form a differentiation has always been, and still is, regarded as the referent index of strength of inhibitory processes, which is orthogonal to the mobility property.

At this point in time — the middle 1950s — it was becoming clear that speed of formation of positive and inhibitory CRs (category 3 above), which had earlier been identified by Asratyan (1937) and Davidenkov (1947) as mobility measures, measures dynamism of nervous processes. This index, therefore, had to be omitted from Teplov's list. In addition, a good deal of evidence indicated that some of the remaining indices did not intercorrelate, that some correlated with well validated indices of other properties, and that some again clustered to form dimensions outside the recognised typological model. For example, Ravich-Shcherbo (1956) reports no significant correlations between speed of

---

[2]Teplov's original list suggests slightly different categories; some obvious redundancies and ambiguities have been omitted.

development of photochemical trace reflexes and visual after-image duration, which was thought to measure speed of termination of nervous processes. A number of other studies pointed to the same general conclusion — that at least three properties are required to account satisfactorily for the sets of relationships observed — lability, describing speed of arousal and termination of nervous processes, concentration, the speed of irradiation and concentration of excitation and inhibition, and mobility of excitation and of inhibition, the number of trials required to reverse the signal value of positive and inhibitory CRs.

Let us briefly review some of the critical studies which led to this revision of the typological model.

## 1. Lability, or Speed of Arousal and Termination of Nervous Processes

As previously noted, Wedenskii and Ukhtomskii (cf. Golikov, 1950), regarded lability — sometimes referred to as "functional mobility" — as the maximum number of impulses nervous tissues can reproduce per second in phase with the rhythm of maximum stimulation. For a considerable period, researchers in the Wedenskii—Ukhtomskii school of physiology regarded the photic driving reaction as the most valid index of lability, although substantial evidence that caffeine, which is often used to "sensitise" the nervous system, induces more efficient photic driving at high frequencies of stimulation (Kopylov, 1956, 1957, 1960; Zislina, 1957; Melnichuk, 1958), implies that nervous system strength is also involved.

Mechanisms underlying the photic driving reaction, which was first identified by Adrian and Matthews (1934), are not yet fully understood. Photic driving describes the synchronisation of bio-electric brain waves with the frequency of intermittent, photic stimuli, and is thus a type of evoked potential (EP). Components of photic driving vary with the frequency and the duration of the stimuli. While at relatively low frequencies, the normal components of evoked potential predominate, at higher frequencies apparently additional elements are involved (Meshchevskii and Smirnov, 1961), although precisely what these are has proved difficult to establish. The visual cortex plays an important role in the photic driving reaction, although activation of cortical cells by the reticular formation extends the range of assimilated frequencies (Volokov and Shilyagina, 1968). In general agreement with this, a number of studies have emphasised the dependence of the photic driving reaction on functional states (Kopylov, 1956, 1957; Melnichuk, 1958; Rozhdestvenskaya, Golubeva and Yermolayeva-Tomina, 1972). There is also a temperamental factor involved, judging from the fact that more excitable, impulsive Ss show more efficient photic driving at relatively high frequencies of stimulation

(Mundy-Castle, 1953). In recent years, Soviet typologists have preferred photic driving as a response measure to other bio-electric measures, since this reaction is shown by all Ss, whereas other commonly used indices, such as the alpha index, are absent in about 15% of adults (Walter, 1966).

Working along more or less independent lines, a number of researchers in Teplov's laboratory in the 1950s and 1960s reported that measures of critical flicker fusion (CFF), adequate optical chronaxie (AOC), size of the interval of uncertainty in visual threshold measurement, and speed of restoration of visual sensitivity after "flooding" with bright light, intercorrelate highly to form a homogeneous cluster. Ravich-Shcherbo and Schwartz (1959) report a correlation of 0.64 ($p < 0.001$) between AOC and CFF, Schwartz (1963) a highly significant correlation between CFF and speed of threshold restoration ($0.87, p < 0.001$), and between CFF and size of the interval of uncertainty ($0.82, p < 0.001$); Turovskaya (1963b) reports significant correlations between AOC and CFF ($0.57, p < 0.01$) and between CFF and interval of uncertainty ($0.51, p < 0.01$). Borisova et al. (1963), in a large study, report replications of these findings.

Adequate optical chronaxie (AOC) has been extensively used in Soviet laboratories to measure the electro-excitability of the visual system.[3] At the strength end of the dimension, the index is the critical frequency of phosphene (CFP). The neural substrate of phosphene is the second retinal neuron, consisting of bipolar, horizontal and amacrine cells, distributed to a depth of several score microns under a layer of receptors (Motakawa, Yamashita and Ogawa, 1957). Measurement of the electro-excitability of the eye bypasses the photochemical apparatus of the retina, and reveals more clearly the functional state of the neural elements. Optical chronaxie is thus the threshold for light perception; as the electrical impulses are increased in frequency and strength, perception of flicker and eventually of light in general disappears. This is CFP. It is similar to critical flicker fusion, except that the disappearance of light marks the threshold of transmarginal inhibition or Wedenskii pessimum. Nebylitsyn (1966a; 1972) has employed CFP curves, as well as photic driving and RT curves, to measure strength of nervous system, the different curves for weak and strong Ss under increasing stimulus intensity reflecting differences in absolute sensitivity between strong and weak systems.

AOC, CFF and the two visual threshold measurements, which correlate poorly with measures of alteration of photochemical reflexes, were regarded by Teplov as measuring speed of initiation and termination of nervous processes,

---

[3]The minimum stimulus intensity of "sufficient duration" producing excitation in the tissue is the rheobase; the threshold voltage is doubled, and the shortest duration at which such a current must act upon the tissue to produce excitation is termed the chronaxie.

and thus defining a separate property which "may be conditionally called lability of the nervous system, without defining beforehand how this property is related to lability as understood by N. E. Wedenskii" (Teplov, 1963).

The clustering of these indices has been confirmed in a number of subsequent studies. Golubeva and Schwartz (1965), for example, report significant correlations between CFF and threshold re-establishment. Lability, as defined, appears to be an independent property. It also appears to have similar content to Wedenskii lability, judging from evidence that these indices correlate highly with photic driving measures. Golubeva and Schwartz (1965) report highly significant correlations between photic driving indices and speed of restoration of sensitivity after flooding, and between AOC indices and efficiency of photic driving in the highest frequency bands. These data, plus additional data relating CFF indices to photic driving measures, are reported by Golubeva in a later review (Golubeva, 1972a,c). Results are reported in Table 22.

TABLE 22. *Correlations between photic driving indices and indices of lability of nervous system (from Golubeva, 1972a)*

| Photic driving indices | CFF | AOC | Sensitivity restoration |
|---|---|---|---|
| Total driving (1.5–80 Hz) | 0.53** | | 0.54** |
| Driving in alpha band (8–14 Hz) | | | 0.45* |
| Driving in gamma band | 0.54** | −0.43* | 0.58* |

  \* $p < 0.05$
\*\* $p < 0.01$

Clearly all three lability indices correlate with photic driving efficiency at the highest (gamma) frequencies (35–80 Hz). Only speed of sensitivity restoration, however, correlates with photic driving in the alpha band (8–14 Hz). Note that the negative correlation of AOC with photic driving indicates that Ss with shorter optical chronaxies show more efficient high frequency driving. Golubeva thus describes lability in terms of efficiency of photic driving at high frequencies of stimulation, low frequency driving being considered to reflect nervous system strength.

These data replicate some earlier findings. Jasper (1957), Toman (1941) and Kopylov (1960), for example, have also reported significant correlations between CFF and photic driving to high frequency stimuli. Nebylitsyn *et al.* (1965) report correlations of the same general order when low frequency (3–4 Hz) stimulation is employed, although in this case stimulus intensity was not equated across subjects.

There are, however, clear indications that the photic driving reaction, and, for that matter, the other three lability measures, especially AOC (Nebylitsyn, 1966a), are not "pure" measures of lability. Weak nervous systems show more efficient photic driving in theta, alpha and beta frequencies (Nebylitsyn, 1966a; Golubeva, 1972a). AOC measures both lability and strength of nervous system (Nebylitsyn, 1966a), while CFF is determined in part by level of reticular arousal (Lindsley, 1962; Gray, 1964a). Because the weak nervous system is more sensitive, more efficient photic driving or CFF in weak systems is a special case of the law of strength, since stimuli of objectively equal intensity generate higher levels of arousal in weak than in strong systems. At some point on the stimulus intensity continuum, of course, such differences disappear. Presumably it is for this reason that the differences between weak and strong systems in efficiency of photic driving observable at low stimulation frequencies are not readily detectable in the higher frequency bands.

There is also limited evidence that photic driving efficiency reflects balance of nervous processes according to dynamism. Both "unbalanced" and weak nervous systems show similar photic driving characteristics — more efficient driving in the low, particularly theta bands (Nebylitsyn, 1966a; Golubeva, 1972a). The reason for this, however, is unclear.

Despite these unresolved theoretical and methodological difficulties, there is clear evidence that the speed with which excitation arises in the nervous system describes an independent nervous system property. In addition, labile Ss not only show more rapid recruitment, but also faster recovery to the initial resting state, judging from the fact that labile Ss show faster restoration of alpha (resting) rhythm following the action of photic stimuli (Golubeva and Schwartz, 1965), and strenuous mental activity (Golubeva and Rozhdestvenskaya, 1969). The lability property thus appears to measure both speed of arousal and termination of nervous processes.

It has also been suggested in the literature that sensory after-effects, which were originally regarded as measures of mobility, do, in fact, reflect lability of nervous processes. Nebylitsyn (1973), for example, claims that the speed with which after-effects from excitatory stimuli are extinguished, and hence the speed with which one cycle of excitation can be followed by another when a series of stimuli is applied, is a direct measure of lability, or the rapidity of nervous system activity.

Data on this point, however, are equivocal. Leites (1956) maintains that duration of after-effect is dependent on strength of the inhibitory process — as does Turovskaya (1963a) — or mobility of nervous processes. Ravich-Shcherbo (1959), with a group of mentally defective Ss, presents evidence to show that this measure describes mobility. On the other hand, Gurevich (1963) claims that two factors are involved in duration and intensity of after-effect; the excitatory after-effect is dependent on strength of nervous system, and on the speed of irradiation and concentration, which are "probably not connected closely with other indices of irradiation and concentration, or with mobility". On the other hand, inhibitory after-effects, measured by the "collision" technique, are determined either by balance of nervous processes or their mobility. Schwartz (1959, 1963) reports that strong Ss demonstrate shorter after-imagery latency, and faster extinction. Gurevich (1963) points out that the intensity of the eliciting stimulus significantly affects both intensity and duration of after-effect.

In summarising the available evidence, Nebylitsyn (1972) comments that excitatory strength significantly influences both intensity and duration of the after-effects of both positive and inhibitory stimuli — the stronger the nervous system, the weaker and more short-term the after-effect, although this relationship is apparent only when the eliciting stimuli are physiologically unequal, when measured in units of individual threshold, since a standard intensity stimulus induces a more intense excitatory focus in systems with lower absolute thresholds, i.e. more sensitive or weak systems. However, when stimulus intensities are equated across Ss, individual differences in after-effect intensity and duration remain. Another factor is obviously involved, and, in view of the fact that after-effect indices correlate with CFF (Schwartz, 1959), this is probably lability of nervous processes. It is possible, of course, that other factors might be involved, such as dynamism of inhibition in the case of extinction of after-effect, as Ravich-Shcherbo (1956) claims.

## 2. Concentration: Irradiation and Concentration of Nervous Processes and their Mutual Induction

A second aspect of speed of nervous processes, their "speed of movement ... their irradiation and concentration" was identified at an early stage of typological research. In his 1911 paper "The main operational characteristics of the cerebral hemispheres" Pavlov notes "stimulation, once it has arisen in the cerebral hemispheres ... irradiates ... but diffuse stimulation gathers, as it were, and gradually concentrates in a certain channel" (Pavlov, 1951–2, p. 161). Irradiation and concentration were regarded as critical features of higher nervous activity, being "one of the central laws of the entire central nervous system" (1941, p. 174). In a very precise sense, they describe the mechanism underlying generalisation and the development of differentiations. Individual differences in the capacity to concentrate must therefore influence the manner in which experience is physically represented and organised in the nervous system.

The importance Pavlov attached to this property is clearly indicated in the following passage from Teplov

In his last talk with his associates, Pavlov discussed aspects of various kinds of differentiation, and, with great insight, proposed the hypothesis that differentiation "is based on the process of concentration of the positive or negative, the excitatory or inhibitory process". In the higher nervous activity of man, the property of concentration of the nervous processes plays an exceptionally important role: all finely adjusted human habits demand above all a high concentration of the nervous processes. There is evidence from studies conducted in Ivanov-Smolenskii's laboratory that an increase in the ability of the nervous processes to concentrate is an important aspect of the ontogenetic development of higher nervous activity in children. In experiments with human beings, Kvasov has suggested that "speed of concentration can be used in defining type of higher nervous activity in Man".... But it will not be easy to demonstrate that concentration is independent of the three basic Pavlovian properties . . . At one of the "Wednesdays", Pavlov observed that "concentration is to be understood as a result or product of strength". Secondly, concentration is frequently regarded as an effect of equilibrium between the opposing processes. Thirdly and finally, "concentration in time" is indissolubly connected with certain aspects of mobility: the speed of movement of the nervous processes and the speed with which it comes to an end. In the phenomenon of concentration, all three basic properties of the nervous system come together, as it were, at a point of focus (1964, p. 120).

At the present time, the neurophysiological processes and structures mediating these hypothetical constructs are unknown. However, in view of evidence that structures in the brain stem miniature cortical events, so that, arguably, the latter are topographically represented in the former, it may be that initially we have to look for these effects in the reticular structures. Field effects, insofar as excitation is concerned, can be postulated in the diffuse thalamic projection system, where cells are very densely packed and reticulated. If field effects of this sort are reflected in background activity of cortical cell populations, this would be the phenomenon Pavlov described as irradiation. But what about concentration? The effect is well described in the typological literature, and may be the mechanism underlying the progressive localisation of background cortical activity as conditioning proceeds which has been described by authors such as Gastaut (1957). If this is the case, we might suggest that concentration is evoked by inhibitory influences from the diffuse thalamic system, which, on stimulus repetition, localises, i.e. "concentrates" that excitation diffusely irradiated over the cortex, via the ARAS, following stimulus presentation.[4]

Arguing from a somewhat different standpoint, we might argue that the recent emphasis in Soviet conditioning theory on the integrative and co-ordinating role of the whole nervous system, particularly the cortex, in CR acquisition (e.g. Asratyan's views, pp. 345 f.), necessitates a process something like irradiation and concentration. In this connection, interesting data have been reported by Livanov (1969), who recorded EEG amplitude changes, simultaneously, from 50–100 cortical points during the formation of a

[4]For a fuller discussion of this and other possible neurophysiological mechanisms underlying irradiation and concentration, see Robinson (1980).

conditioned defensive reflex in rabbit. Results are presented in Figure 12. Each square demarcates an electrode site. The hatched squares indicate equivalent changes in EEG amplitude during 70–100% of the 1.5 second segments recorded throughout the conditioning period, hatched areas thus reflecting synchrony of EEG activity between different cortical structures, i.e. the global integration of cortical activity. High synchrony may be restricted to adjacent sites, or ramify through relatively discrete sites. Areas of high synchrony are denoted synchronised systems, which change and fluctuate during the course of conditioning. Two systems may correlate in a given interval, in another, show little or no relationship.

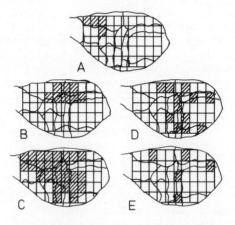

Figure 12. Changes in synchronisation of cortical activity during the formation of a conditioned defensive reflex in rabbit. A — first trial; B — after 6 pairings; C — after 12 pairings; D — after 66 pairings; E — after 99 pairings. The CR is formed, i.e. stabilised, at stage C (after Livanov, 1962).

A similar interpretation might be given data reported by Nelsen, Pelley and Goldstein (1973). They recorded highly correlated increases in EEG activity at both reticular and cortical sites during CR acquisition. During the post-acquisition phase, however, when control shifts from general reticular to limbic structures, increasingly more localised cortical activity is observed.

From Livanov's data, it is clear that maximum synchronisation occurs when the CR is established. Up to this point, increasingly more cortical and subcortical areas are recruited. Beyond this stage, synchronisation diminishes. Livanov and his collaboratories have also demonstrated that synchrony is facilitated by electrical stimulation of subcortical structures; that maximum synchrony values between cortical and subcortical areas occur at that point in time when the CR is actually stabilised; that synchrony increases during human mental activity, being particularly prominent in the frontal areas of the cortex. All these findings are consistent with the proposition that while behaviour is being shaped, cortical activity increasingly generalises, and that when the behaviour is finally programmed, such activity retreats to more localised sites. Whether we label this process irradiation and concentration seems of little consequence. Certainly the phenomena described by Livanov and by Nelsen, Pelley and Goldstein (1973) are similar in essential respects to those included under that rubric by Pavlov and later Soviet theorists.

Insofar as irradiation and concentration of inhibition are concerned, it could be argued that these are simply mirror images of irradiation and concentration of excitation. When similar CSs evoke a CR early in conditioning, we refer to irradiation of excitation — when this ceases to occur, to concentration. Clearly, inhibition is critically involved in this process, but precisely how the excitatory and inhibitory processes interact to produce the observed effects, is unclear.

Despite the theoretical difficulties and uncertainties touched on briefly in the preceding discussion, effects which might be described in terms of irradiation and concentration have been extensively reported.

Irradiation of protective inhibition was thought to account for some early data indicating that, following cortical extirpation, large numbers of CRs are abolished. Only when this inhibition concentrates around the site of the injury are specific pathological symptoms expressed. Functional compensation, mediated by "reserve mechanisms" (the less specialised cells in the outlying cortical zones) then occurs, leading to recovery of CRs. This is derivable from Pavlov's theory of nervism, the view that the nervous system, specifically the cortex, maintains a dynamic equilibrium between external conditions and internal processes, a theory which has been extended and elaborated by Asratyan and Bykov.

A considerable amount of experimental data from normal subjects gathered in Pavlov's laboratories in the twenties and thirties (e.g. Podkopaev, 1924; Skipin, 1932) pointed to some fairly clear-cut conclusions. Irradiation and concentration are not specific to a particular analyser, acting in all areas and zones of the cortex, and, for that matter, in the lower divisions of the central nervous system. They have critical significance in the development of temporary connections, both because irradiated excitation from activated cortical centres of both CS and US effect the actual coupling, and because concentration transforms the initial generalised CR into a specific, adaptive reflex act. Data also suggested that weak and intense stimuli tend to irradiate, and moderately intense stimuli to concentrate — one of the Pavlovian laws of irradiation and concentration — and that irradiation of excitation and inhibition exhibit an oscillatory pattern. The exact significance of this latter finding, however, remains unclear.

It is obvious that irradiation of excitation is a basic functional characteristic of nervous tissue, observable in early stages of embryonic development, and in early neonatal life. During the first 2 or 3 weeks of life, for example, stimulation of the chin and neck of the neonate, as well as the lips, produces the sucking reflex. Adaptive reflex acts in the maturing organism, however, are only possible when the irradiating excitation is circumscribed by inhibition. In the early stages of CR formation, all stimuli similar to the CS evoke a generalised CR, while in the concentration stage, only the specific energy of the CS possesses this power. If the animal is conditioned to a tone of, say, 500 Hz, it will initially express a CR to a tone of almost any pitch, and, indeed, to many other musical sounds. The generalised CR has not yet been subjected to cortical analysis, so that the CR irradiates to other outlying areas of the cortex, until checked by inhibition, usually evoked by contrast or differentiation. Finer and finer discriminations can be produced, up to the limit of the individual animal's DL. This is analysis through inhibition, the concentration of excitation into increasingly narrower zones. We should note that, according to Pavlov, laws of irradiation and concentration apply equally to the second and to the first signal system.

Pavlov (1960, pp. 153 ff) cites a considerable amount of data demonstrating irradiation and concentration of inhibition from experiments reported by Krasnogorsky (differential inhibition), Kogan (extinctive inhibition) and Anrep (conditioned inhibition), all of whom employed tactile CSs, and by Ivanov-Smolenskii, who employed auditory CSs. Differential, extinctive and conditioned inhibition are considered to be forms of internal inhibition.

Krasnogorskii's experiment is typical. He developed an inhibitory CR to tactile stimulation of the dog's paw, and positive CRs to tactile stimulation at four points on the upper part of the dog's leg. CR amplitude following presentation of the positive CS 1 minute after three successive presentations of the inhibitory CS was a positive function of the physical distance between the inhibitory and positive sites. The shorter the distance, the smaller the positive CR amplitude, due to the greater irradiation of inhibition. Varying the time interval between the applications of the inhibitory and the positive CSs produced similar results. The inhibitory after-effect following four rather than three applications of the inhibitory CS produced almost complete lack of response 15 seconds later at the most distant positive site, which, 1 minute after three successive applications of the inhibitory CS, has produced an almost full reflex. The additional fact that with increasing experience, the more distant excitatory sites are freed from the inhibitory after-effects suggests that concentration of inhibition follows initial irradiation.

Data concerning irradiation of excitation point to the same general conclusions. Typical experiments are reported by Pavlov (1927 pp. 178 ff.).

Anrep, for example, developed a salivary CR, using a short-trace method, to tactile stimulation of the thigh (place 0). Stimulation of six alternative (non-reinforced) sites gave the following results (Table 23). Spontaneous CR amplitude varies with distance between the stimulated sites and the original CS site.

TABLE 23. *Generalised CR (number drops of saliva) (after Anrep)*

| Number of place stimulated | 1 | 0 | 2 | 3 | 4 | 5 | 6 |
|---|---|---|---|---|---|---|---|
| Secretion (in drops) | 33 | 53 | 45 | 39 | 23 | 21 | 19 |

Pavlova's data are also of interest. Following the development of one positive and four inhibitory sites, using a 30-second CS in all cases, the positive site was stimulated for 15 seconds, followed by presentation of one of the inhibitory CSs for 15 seconds. Salivation to the inhibitory CSs in the second 15-second intervals was measured. Stimulation of the nearest inhibitory site produced almost the same secretory rate as continuation of the positive CS, the rate diminishing as the sites further away were stimulated. Such effects are assumed to be due to irradiation of excitation.

Pavlov (1927) reports no data concerning concentration of excitation.

A related phenomenon is that of induction, a term introduced by Hering and Sherrington. When certain groups of central neurons become excited, other neurons in the central nervous system show inhibition or lowered excitability. Similarly, when a group of neurons become inhibited, a state of heightened excitability may arise in other neurons. If inhibition emerges around excited cells while these are still in a state of excitation, the induction is "simultaneous" — negative where excitation results in an inhibitory process, positive where inhibition results in an excitatory process. Successive induction occurs where an excitatory process in one group of cells is followed by lessened excitation in the same structures when the excitation is discontinued, while, in inhibited neurons, discontinuance of inhibition results in heightened excitability which may manifest itself in excitation. These induction phenomena are particularly pronounced in the cortex, although also found in the lower divisions of the central nervous system, as in the case of simultaneous and successive induction involving the centres of antagonistic muscles.

Induction data cited by Pavlov (1941, p. 189) are illustrative. Foursikov conditioned an alimentary CR to a CS of 76 metronome beats per minute, and differentiation to 186 beats per minute. When the positive CS is presented immediately following the inhibitory CS, however, salivation is increased by 30%. Kalmykov reports a similar positive induction effect of approximately

40%. Additional data from these two authors are presented in Figure 13 (from Bykov, 1952).

From the data, it is clear that positive induction[5] does not suppress the development of successive inhibition. The next presentation of the positive CS, which, immediately following the differentiation, produced an enhanced CR, now shows a diminished effect.

Negative induction circumscribes the irradiation of excitation over the cortex. For example, if a differential stimulus of 72 metronome beats per minute is positively reinforced by food, it is quickly transformed into a positive CS. But if the differentiation reinforced by food alternates with the action of a positive

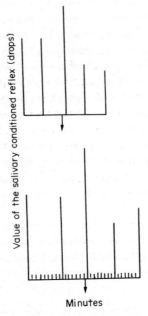

Figure 13. Phenomena of positive induction. Height of each line indicates value of conditioned salivary reflex; bottom, to mechanical stimulation of foreleg; top, to bright light. Inhibitory stimulus is indicated by arrow; bottom, to stimulation of hind leg; top, to weak light. Time indicated along the abscissa. (Taken from Pavlov's *Lectures on the Work of the Large Hempishperes of the Brain* and from experiments performed by D. Fursikov and L. Kalmykov.)

---

[5]Note that positive induction should be differentiated from disinhibition: the former occurs only when the differential stimulus is immediately replaced by the positive CS. Positive induction is a temporary, phasic phenomenon associated with the development of new relationships in the nervous system: it appears only with the maximum development of cortical inhibition, and disappears after inhibition has finally concentrated.

stimulus (e.g. 144 beats per minute) transformation of the differential stimulus may be difficult. According to Pavlov, this occurs when the differential stimulus falls in the phase of negative induction from the positive CS. Despite the reinforcement of the differential stimulus, the latter maintains its inhibitory action.

It is clear that irradiation and concentration of both excitation and inhibition, and their mutual induction, are not independent processes. They interrelate in complex ways which are not yet fully understood. There are, however, some data which demonstrate certain important mutual induction effects. For example, Kreps (Pavlov, 1941, p. 205) stabilised positive CRs to tactile CSs at five sites, and an inhibitory CR to tactile stimulation at one site on the foreleg. The inhibitory CS was presented, followed by one or other of the positive CSs, immediately, and at different time intervals from inhibitory CS offset. CR magnitudes to the positive CSs are shown in Table 24. While the effects of irradiated inhibition are clearly expressed after a 15-second interval, the immediate effect (0′ interval) is enhancement of the positive CR at all sites, i.e. the initial positive induction is succeeded by irradiation of inhibition, which gradually disappears, so that the effect of the positive CS returns to normal. Thus the inhibitory after-effect exhibits a rhythmical undulation. This is illustrated graphically by Andreev's data (Figure 14). There are clearly two waves of inhibition, with crests at 60 seconds and 5 minutes. Note also that at site 1, closest to the inhibitory site, positive induction occurs at 0′ interval, while in the remoter sites irradiated inhibition is practically unimpeded.

Other data suggest that this wave form is a spatial as well as a temporal phenomenon.

From the very earliest experiments, it was clear that there are large individual differences in speed of irradiation and concentration and in mutual induction effects (Rozhansky, 1913; Petrova, 1914). These were considered important features of the dog's individuality (Pavlov, 1927, p. 212). The point is

TABLE 24. *Positive CR amplitudes, in percentages of normal value, following presentation of inhibitory CS (from Kreps)*

| | 0 | 5 Sec | 15 Sec | 30 Sec | 1 min | 2 min | 3 min | 5 min |
|---|---|---|---|---|---|---|---|---|
| Place | | | | | | | | |
| 1 | 138 | 123 | 92 | 53 | 71 | 100 | 85 | 100 |
| 2 | 141 | 117 | 92 | 64 | 67 | 110 | — | — |
| 3 | 127 | — | 97 | 68 | 98 | 112 | 108 | 98 |
| 4 | 145 | 123 | 100 | 77 | 88 | 95 | 81 | — |
| 5 | 127 | — | 90 | 80 | 100 | 105 | 106 | 110 |
| Mean | 136 | 121 | 94 | 68 | 85 | 108 | 94 | 102 |

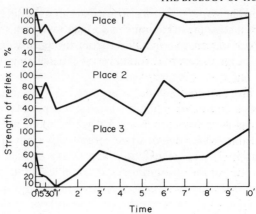

Figure 14. Rhythmical undulation of the inhibitory after-effect (from Andreev, cited by Pavlov, *Conditioned Reflexes*, p. 211).

underlined in Kogan's data (Pavlov, 1927, p. 160). In one of his dogs, the irradiation of inhibition phase lasted 20 seconds, and the concentration phase about 75 seconds, while in another dog, the corresponding figures were 4–5 minutes and 20 minutes. Sources of variance are unknown, but it seems likely that amount of induction is in part a function of intensity of excitation and inhibition, which, in turn, are predicated on stimulus intensity and nervous system type (nervous system strength). Of interest is the observation that older, coarser differentiations lose their power of positive induction more quickly and easily than finer differentiations. Over and above this, however, are there consistent individual features of speed of movement of these processes which allow us to postulate an independent nervous system property?

It is only recently that this possibility has been seriously considered. Despite earlier comments by Nebylitsyn (1972) that "the induction method . . . appears to be one of the most promising referent methods of testing this nervous system property (strength)" (p. 153), and Teplov's (1937, 1941) demonstrations, previously described, that individual differences in simultaneous induction in RT experiments are attributable to differences in nervous system strength, consideration of irradiation and concentration data reported by Borisova (1959, 1972) and Avakyan (1961) — the only induction studies reported in which the effect of nervous system strength has been partialled out — led Nebylitsyn (1973) to suggest that speed of concentration is an independent nervous system property, one of the basic determinants of speed of central processing of information, or speed of the decision-making process. Borisova (1972) hypothesised that a high degree of concentration should result in smaller differential thresholds, and greater irradiation in larger thresholds. Ss was presented with a standard tone, immediately followed by a louder tone, the intensity of which was decreased in 1 dB steps, the subject noting, by pressing a button, when the intensity of the second sound equalled that of the first. Tones were of 1000 Hz at six intensity levels — 1, 5, 20, 40, 60 and 80 dB above individual auditory thresholds.

Discrimination thresholds for the twelve Ss are shown in Table 25. Intercorrelations of discrimination thresholds at the different intensity levels are shown in Table 26. The highly significant correlations in Table 26 indicate both reliability of measurement and stability of the functions underlying discrimination threshold. Although the absolute values are different (Table

TABLE 25. *Discrimination thresholds for the 12 Ss (from Borisova, 1972)*

| Ss | | | | | | |
|---|---|---|---|---|---|---|
| | Levels above threshold, in dB | | | | | |
| | 1 | 5 | 20 | 40 | 60 | 80 |
| 1 | 1 | 3 | 3.6 | 5 | 4.4 | 2.3 |
| 2 | 3 | 5.5 | 9.5 | 9.4 | 4.4 | 2 |
| 3 | 3.7 | 5.4 | 10 | 10 | 7 | 5 |
| 4 | 3.7 | 6 | 8.5 | 8.7 | 8.4 | 6 |
| 5 | 4 | 7 | 7.3 | 8.5 | 7.3 | 8 |
| 6 | 4.5 | 6.4 | 8.3 | 8 | 8 | 5.4 |
| 7 | 5.2 | 6.4 | 9.3 | 10 | 8.1 | 5 |
| 8 | 5.7 | 6.7 | 8.5 | 9 | 8.5 | 6.8 |
| 9 | 5.7 | 6 | 9.7 | 10 | 8.2 | 5 |
| 10 | 6 | 5 | 10 | 11 | 10 | 9 |
| 11 | 6.3 | 7 | 12 | 9.6 | 7.5 | 6.2 |
| 12 | 8.3 | 10.5 | 14 | 13 | 10.4 | 10.9 |
| Mean | 4.7 | 6.2 | 9.2 | 9.4 | 7.7 | 6.0 |

TABLE 26. *Inter-correlations of discrimination thresholds (from Borisova, 1972)*

| Intensity levels in dB | 1 | 5 | 20 | 40 | 60 | 80 |
|---|---|---|---|---|---|---|
| 1 | | | | | | |
| 5 | .81** | | | | | |
| 20 | .88** | .77** | | | | |
| 40 | .86** | .73** | .93** | | | |
| 60 | .85** | .64* | .61* | .72* | | |
| 80 | .79** | .72* | .68* | .88** | | |

** $p < 0.01$
* $p < 0.05$

25), the relative positions of Ss throughout the stimulus intensity continuum are highly stable.

It is clear from the data reported that at both high and low intensity levels discrimination thresholds are smaller than at medium intensity levels. As Borisova comments, this U function is opposite to the inverted U function expected on the basis of the Pavlovian laws of irradiation and concentration. However, her data agree with those reported by Avakyan (1961), describing discrimination thresholds measured at intervals of 10, 40, 60 and 80 dB from auditory threshold.

Borisova reports a correlation of– 0.05 between absolute auditory thresholds and discrimination thresholds, which suggests that the latter are not influenced by strength of nervous system.

The reason why discrimination thresholds do not obey the laws of irradiation and concentration is somewhat puzzling. Borisova's procedure, however, may have fatigued Ss, and there are data suggesting, paradoxically, that fatigue reduces DLs (Elliot, Riach and Silbiger, 1962). The data reported by Borisova and Avakyan are highly similar, and lead to almost identical conclusions, viz., that there are large individual differences in discrimination thresholds, that these differences are maintained throughout a range of stimulus intensities, and that at moderate stimulus intensities discrimination thresholds are substantially larger than at either very weak or very strong stimulus intensities.

Borisova (1972) reports two further experiments in which she attempted to measure irradiation and concentration using RT induction procedures. In the first experiment, she presented pairs of 8000 Hz stimuli at 50 dB above individual thresholds, with intervals of 400 milliseconds, 600 milliseconds, 1 second, 3 seconds and 5 seconds between members of each pair. ITI was 12 seconds, and response was a key press to each member of the pair. In interpreting her results, Borisova accepts Gurevich's (1963) suggestion that increased latency of second reaction is due to negative induction, as a result of concentration of excitation evoked by the prior stimulus, and decreased latency the result of irradiation of excitation from the first stimulus of the pair, and its summation with excitation from the second stimulus.

In the second RT series, a choice reaction time method was employed, Ss being presented with three tone stimuli, two of which demand a response, the third not (Khilchenko's (1958) method). For example, a tone of 400 Hz is responded to by pressing a key with the right hand, a tone of 1200 Hz by pressing with the left hand, while a tone of 3000 Hz is not responded to. Tones were presented randomly, with intervals of 2,600, 2,000, 1,800, 1,600, 1,400, 1,200, 1,000, 800, 600, and 400 milliseconds, the different ISIs being administered in successive 60 to 80 stimuli blocks. Borisova asserts that under the choice RT regime, the mechanism of discrimination is concentration, and that the task of discriminating three stimuli under conditions of accelerating speed makes the discrimination more complex, thus maximising the significance of concentration of nervous processes.

Correlation data showing relationships between after-effects in the first RT induction experiment, and RT latencies at the various intervals in the second series are presented in Table 27. The results are difficult to interpret, but the pattern of significant correlations, all of which are negative, indicates that decreased RT latency in the first experiment is associated with long RT latencies in the second experiment, and vice versa. Reduction in RT latency in experiment 1 is due to irradiation of excitation, i.e. a reduced tendency to concentrate, while longer latencies in the choice RT experiment (experiment 2) appear to reflect the same weaker tendency of the nervous processes to

TABLE 27. *Correlations of positive after-effects with choice RT latencies (from Borisova, 1972)*

| RT Intervals of | Positive after-effects at | | | | | Overall value |
|---|---|---|---|---|---|---|
| | 400 msec | 600 msec | 1 sec | 3 sec | 5 sec | |
| 600 msec | .09 | −.04 | −.14 | −.30 | −.12 | −.10 |
| 800 | .03 | −.22 | −.33* | −.34* | −.24 | −.23 |
| 1000 | −.08 | −.29 | −.40* | −.43** | −.43** | −.33* |
| 1200 | −.22 | −.24 | −.36* | −.45** | −.31 | −.30 |
| 1400 | −.13 | −.27 | −.33* | −.49** | −.15 | −.35* |
| 1600 | −.22 | −.33* | −.43** | −.53** | −.19 | −.39* |
| 1800 | −.26 | −.27 | −.32 | −.48** | −.18 | −.35* |
| 2000 | −.14 | −.19 | −.25 | −.27 | −.01 | −.19 |
| 2200 | −.19 | −.22 | −.26 | −.38* | −.06 | −.27 |
| 2600 | −.10 | −.08 | −.29 | −.39* | −.02 | −.21 |

\* $p < 0.05$
\*\* $p < 0.01$

concentrate. Thus negative correlations of the sort reported are to be expected. In other words, increased RT latency in experiment 1 and reduced RT latency in experiment 2 are both due to negative induction as a result of a strong tendency of the nervous processes to concentrate, and RT facilitation in experiment 1, and increased RT latencies in experiment 2 a result of a strong tendency of the nervous processes to irradiate, or a weak tendency to concentrate. In either case, the outcome is a negative correlation. An interesting feature of the table is that the blocks of correlations between 1 and 3-second ISI intervals in experiment 1 and 1000- and 1800-millisecond intervals in experiment 2 show the highest negative correlations. These are presumably the conditions under which the highest cumulative effects of both irradiation and concentration occur.

Overall, the data reported by Borisova (1972) and Avakyan (1961) suggest that irradiation and concentration of excitation affect both discrimination thresholds and RT induction effects. Since the effects appear to be consistent within-Ss across experimental treatments, Borisova (1972) suggests that these processes define an independent nervous system property. Such a claim, however, is probably premature. The empirical evidence is weak, and there remain a number of important, unanswered questions.

One of the most difficult problems is the effect of nervous system strength on induction. If, as Pavlov originally claimed, weak and intense excitatory stimuli tend to irradiate, and moderately intense stimuli to concentrate (Pavlov, 1951-2, p. 239), we would expect the latter, other things being equal, to lead to smaller discrimination thresholds, the former to larger differential thresholds. However, what is a moderately intense stimulus for a strong system may be an intense stimulus for the weak system, thus producing different levels of discrimination. Where nervous system strength has been partialled out (experiments of Borisova and Avakyan), the inverted U function is reversed. No explanation immediately suggests itself. In experiments using a standard methodology, a critical factor could be ISI, since RT induction experiments suggest that short ISIs (less than 0.8 second) produce negative induction, and longer ISIs positive induction (Boiko, 1957). Thus both strength-sensitivity of the nervous system and ISI could interact to produce irradiation and concentration effects on both perceptual judgments and sensori-motor behaviour. Such relationships, however, have not yet been worked out.

In addition, we should make a distinction between induction effects where the first of the pair of stimuli has significance — e.g. as a warning signal in RT experiments — and induction from sensory after-effects, as, for example, reported by Teplov in his experiments on the effects of supplementary light stimuli on threshold discrimination. Some of his supplementary stimuli were, in fact, sub-threshold; in addition, the induction was simultaneous rather than successive, which could introduce an additional source of variance.

In summary, excitation and inhibition appear to irradiate and concentrate, and can evoke the opposite process by reciprocal inhibition or mutual induction. When excitation or inhibition concentrate, the relevant foci are surrounded by zones of opposite process. The stronger the processes, the deeper and more lasting the inductive effects. Nervous system strength of excitation and of inhibition are clearly involved here. Over and above this, however, there are suggestions that speed and extent of irradiation and concentration are an independent dimension of nervous system functioning, which Nebylitsyn (1973) has termed concentration.

The psychological correlates of this property are uncertain. Pavlov initially suggested that the phenomenon of mutual induction provides a physiological basis for the large group of contrast phenomena described in connection with the physiology of the sense organs. Borisova (1972) claims that induction effects are important in perceptual discrimination and RT facilitation. Nebylitsyn (1973) has suggested that individual differences in this property underlie individual differences in speed of decision making. More precise information about the functional significance of concentration awaits critical experimental studies.

### 3. Alteration

The earliest test of alteration was the collision test — well-known from Pavlov's classic demonstration of experimental neurosis — which involved alternate presentation of maximally effective inhibitory and positive stimuli (Razenkov, 1924), thus producing a collision between excitatory and inhibitory processes. This procedure, however, was subsequently considered too radical and/or dangerous, and it was replaced by the transformation or alteration method (Mayorov, 1938). This involves alteration of signs of positive and inhibitory stimuli after the formation of the appropriate CR. The more quickly both stimuli acquire new signal value, and the more quickly the criterion CR is attained, the higher the mobility. Most typological theorists now view alteration as the sole mobility index "It may be said that in practice mobility is that property of the nervous system which is characterised by alteration of stimulus signs" (Teplov, 1963, p. 37). Alteration is considered the basic index of mobility in the laboratories of Krasuskii (1964) and Fedorov (Alekseeva, Elkin and Fedorov, 1964; Malyugina et al., 1963; Fedorov, 1964). We might note, however, that Fedorov has used the alteration of two positive CSs rather than the more usual alteration between an inhibitory and positive CS in measuring mobility.

Clearly, however, alteration is not completely independent of other nervous system properties. For example, Fedorov (1951) reports that with mice alteration occurs more easily in strong than in weak animals, a result also reported by Kolesnikov (1953) who notes that alteration "presents insurmountable difficulties for all dogs of the weak type (whose behaviour verged) on the breakdown of higher nervous activity". Krasuskii reports that mobile and inert types occurred with about equal frequency in strong dogs, but in weak groups inert outnumbered mobile types by two or to one. Melikhova (1964), Ravich-Shcherbo (1956) and Moldovskaya (1964) all report marginal or significant relationships between CR alteration and different measures of strength, Baronenko et al. (1979) a negative relationship with strength of internal inhibition. It may be, however, that a critical factor is the intensity of the stimuli used in alteration. To partial out strength of nervous system, these should be physiologically of equal intensity for all Ss, taking into account individual thresholds. Under these conditions, it may be that mobility is orthogonal to other nervous system properties such as strength and dynamism.

Finally, we should consider the possibility that mobility relates to irradiation and concentration. Kolosova and Formicheva (1979) report that dogs with low and medium levels of irradiation of excitation show good mobility, while dogs with high co-efficients of irradiation, derived from salivary responses to different sites on the tongue, have inert nervous processes.

## 4. Delayed and Trace Conditioned Reflexes

The original standard had suggested that speed of transforming from short trace to delayed CRs involves inertia in the nervous system, while ease of transformation suggests high level of mobility. However, a number of studies suggested that nervous strength, rather than mobility, is the critical factor in this process (Kharchenko, 1960; Kreps, 1924; Timofeeva, 1947; Nikolaeva, 1957; Melikhova, 1964). These studies reported that delay can be produced in dogs of the weak type only through a gradual lengthening of the non-active or delay period, and that the delay interval is significantly smaller than in dogs of the strong type. Clearly, maintenance of inhibition in the delay period involves inhibitory strength.

However, other data suggest that formation of delay is also related to dynamism of the nervous processes, and balance according to dynamism (Petrova, 1929; Nikolaeva, 1957). Rozhdestvenskaya (1963b) reports that speed of development of delay is determined by balance of the nervous processes according to dyamism. Ss showing high dynamism of excitation, but not of inhibition, record a highly significant frequency of positive responding during the delay period. Rozhdestvenskaya's data are presented in Table 28.

TABLE 28. *Relationship between speed of development of delay and CR formation (from Rozhdestvenskaya, 1963b)*

|  | N anticipatory CRs as % of conditioned effect during formation of delayed reflex | | | |
|---|---|---|---|---|
| Ss | Excit. Type | Inhib.Type | N trials to CR formation | N trials to differentiation |
| D | 71 | 29 | 5 | 10 |
| P | 60 | 17 | 7 | 18 |
| A | 57 | 14 | 3 | 12 |
| I | 56 | 33 | 7 | 12 |
| V | 28 | 48 | 12 | 9 |
| Z | 14 | 58 | 10 | 2 |
| G | 5 | 67 | 10 | 3 |
| L | 0 | 100 | 26 | 2 |

Nebylitsyn (1963b) reports similar results with EEG conditioned responses. However, he makes the distinction between primary and final development of delay. While dynamism of excitation plays an important role in primary development of delay, final development of delay, i.e. CR inhibition until the end of the delay period, is determined by mobility of nervous processes (Teplov and Nebylitsyn, 1963). These authors cite a number of studies reporting significant relationships between speed of final development of delay and mobility measures such as chronaxie and CFF (which are now regarded as measures of lability) (Rozhdestvenskaya, 1963b), and alteration mobility (Melikhova, 1964). It is obvious that development of delay is a complex process. At different stages, different properties appear to be involved, dynamism of excitation at the initial stage, and lability and mobility in the final stages.

Speed of development of trace conditioning, a "very special and most precise method" of measuring mobility, was first referred to by Pavlov in "General Types of Higher Nervous Activity in Animals and Man" (1955, pp. 315–46). Subsequent research, however, indicates clearly that there is no reliable relationship between this measure and other (assumed) mobility measures. Ravich-Shcherbo (1956) reports no relationship between speed of formation of trace photochemical CRs and both alteration mobility and duration of visual after-images. Adamovich-Gerasimov (1959) reports greater dependence of this measure on nervous system strength. The adequate trace is 4 to 5 times shorter in weak than in strong dogs.

## Summary

The conclusion from the empirical work reported from Teplov's laboratory on indices of mobility is that the three processes originally identified by Pavlov — the speed with which excitation and inhibition arise and subside, the speed of irradiation and concentration of both excitation and inhibition, and the speed of alteration of stimulus signs — are independent processes. This was acknowledged by Nebylitsyn in his last (1973) publication, in which he identifies two additional nervous system properties — concentration, i.e. the speed of irradiation and concentration of nervous processes, and lability, which reflects rate of initiation and termination of nervous processes. The exact boundaries of these properties, and their interrelationships, however, have not yet been established.

We should note that a good deal of the confusion encountered in attempting to validate these independent properties has been due to methodological problems. In many of the studies reported, little attempt has been made to partial out the effect of nervous system strength, which clearly is a confounding variable. For example, it is clear that irradiation and concentration, as measured by induction methods, depend to a considerable degree on the strength-sensitivity of the reacting system. The same is undoubtedly true of lability, where sensory after-effects and photic driving indices are contaminated by intensity of the eliciting stimulus. There is the additional problem that whereas alteration mobility and irradiation and concentration have been demonstrated in at least two stimulus modalities — visual and auditory — lability has been measured using only visual stimulation, the indices involved being critical flicker fusion (CFF), optical chronaxie (AOC), duration of visual after-image, and the speed of re-establishment of visual threshold after flooding. The question arises, therefore, of whether lability is a general property of all cortical activity, or is characteristic only of the visual cortex, involving specific long-term activity of photochemical after-effects. There is also the problem, as yet unresolved, of whether lability is expressed as photic driving only in the high frequency bands, as Golubeva (1972a,c) asserts, while photic driving in the lower frequency bands does not correlate with other lability indices, or is represented through all frequency bands, as Nebylitsyn et al. (1965) suggest. It is obvious that critical studies of the parameters of concentration and lability are necessary before these questions can be answered.

### Relationships of Mobility, Concentration and Lability to Personality Dimensions and to other Psychological Phenomena

Since comparatively little experimental work has been reported from Soviet laboratories detailing the exact boundaries of the properties in question, it is hardly surprising that there are few data relating these to personality functioning and to other psychological phenomena. An exception is data on the relationship of lability and concentration, particularly the former, to memory, which have recently been published in the Soviet typological literature. These will be referred to briefly in the following sections. In addition, some information on the questions at issue can be gleaned indirectly from a variety of sources. For example, some studies have reported relationships between a range of psychological variables and evoked potential (EP), and we might infer similar relationships with photic driving indices, and thus lability. On the whole, however, review data tend to be sketchy and attenuated.

### (a) Alteration Mobility and Personality

There is an obvious behavioural analogue to alteration mobility in the Western concept of flexibility, or the ability to change set rapidly. Although a good deal of research has been reported in this area, particularly by Witkin et al. (1962), the basic parameters of flexibility remain unclear. Witkin's original concept of field dependence/independence, defined as the ready ability to overcome an embedding perceptual context (perceptual flexibility), is now regarded as overly narrow. Witkin subsequently employed a more general differentiation concept, an analytical-global dimension, of which field dependence/independence represents only the perceptual component. This latter shows loadings of rod and frame test (RFT), concealed or embedded figures test (EFT) and a number of sub-tests of the Wechsler scale. Performance on reversible figures has also been shown to be related to perceptual flexibility (Newbigging, 1954; Jackson, 1958).

The origin of differences in level of differentiation is problematical. Witkin *et al.* (1962), while recognising the possible role of both constitutional and experiential factors, and favouring an interaction approach, attach more weight to the latter; Witkin does, however, concede the possible significance of genetic, neurophysiological variables. He cites the twin study of Vandenburg (1967) showing greater similarity in RFT performance from identical than fraternal pairs, and the study by Block (1957) reporting that GSR-labile or responsive Ss are more field independent, showing greater freedom from disruptive impulse expression. There is, in addition, the study of Courter, Wattenmaker and Ax (1965) suggesting that lack of differentiation by field dependent Ss is a function of less well differentiated autonomic nervous systems.

Mangan, in a series of studies (1967a,b; 1978c) has attempted to relate alteration mobility and lability, measured by after-image duration,[6] to measures of thinking flexibility (creativity), derived from Guilford and Merrifield's (1960) structure-of-intellect battery, perceptual flexibility, indexed by measures defining the perceptual component of Witkin's analytic-global dimension, and to speed-accuracy.

For measuring mobility, Mangan employed an RT method, S+ and S– being auditory and visual stimuli of 1000/360 Hz and blue/yellow patches respectively. Number of trials to asymptotic RT, following the transformation, was taken as a measure of alteration mobility. This is, in fact, a measure of mobility of inhibition, i.e. the speed with which inhibition is replaced by excitation, and not mobility of excitation, the speed with which excitation is replaced by inhibition.

In the first of the mobility studies (Mangan, 1967b), significant correlations were reported between the alteration measure and measures of creativity and fluency (associational flow). More fluent Ss showed a larger response decrement, following the transformation, than more flexible, "original" Ss. Data are shown in Figure 15. Suggestive correlations were reported between

[6]At time of publication, the author considered after-image duration to be a measure of mobility, rather than lability.

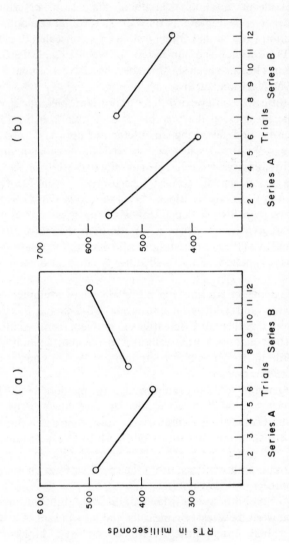

Figure 15. Lines of best fit for 2 Ss (a) scoring high on originality, (b) scoring high on fluency (adapted from Mangan, 1967b).

extraversion and mobility, and significant correlations between a measure of sensitivity and alteration mobility, which supports the suggestion that alteration mobility includes a strength-sensitivity component.

A factor analysis of these data (a dubious procedure in view of very small N) suggested that both flexibility and mobility load what was tentatively described as an inhibitory control factor (Mangan, 1967c). Mobile Ss, because of stronger inhibitory control, seem able to change set more efficiently, and thus test out as more "original", less fluent and/or perseverative. But note, however, the Barr and McConaghy (1972b) study reporting that allusive (flexible?) thinkers show weak internal inhibition.

In the third study (Mangan, 1978c), thinking and perceptual flexibility and alteration mobility measures were intercorrelated, and correlated with scores derived from standard speed-accuracy tests (sensori-motor flexibility). Although the content validity of speed-accuracy tests is questionable, there seems little doubt that speed in error-free tests of this sort correlates with verbal fluency (Mangan, 1959), and that there exists a careful/accurate–speedy/inaccurate dichotomy, which is temperamentally biased (Himmelweit, 1945; Mangan, 1959). Himmelweit (1945) reports a trend towards speed preference in hysterics and accuracy preference in dysthymics. Data from a number of sources are weak, but generally supportive — extraverts and hysterics tend to be quick and inaccurate, dysthymics and introverts slow and careful (Eysenck, 1967).

Rotated factor loadings from Mangan's (1978c) study are shown in Table 29.

TABLE 29. *Rotated factor loadings (from Mangan, 1978c)*

| | | Factor | | | |
|---|---|---|---|---|---|
| | Variable | I | II | III | IV |
| 1. | E | -.60 | .40 | | |
| 2. | N | | | | .38 |
| 3. | Sensori-motor flexibility | .80 | | | |
| 4. | Audit. Transf. | | .63 | .36 | |
| 5. | Visual Transf. | | .69 | | .44 |
| 6. | SAE decline | .30 | .66 | -.51 | |
| 7. | Auditory OR ⎱Hab. rate | .72 | | | |
| 8. | Visual OR ⎰ | .35 | | -.31 | |
| 9. | After-image duration | | | | .77 |
| 10. | Appet. Spont. Recovery | .75 | | | |
| 11. | Avers. Spont. Recovery | .40 | | -.61 | |
| 12. | Originality | | .86 | | |
| 13. | Fluency | -.40 | -.54 | | |
| 14. | NC | | | -.48 | -.65 |
| 15. | CFT | | .40 | | -.63 |

Some of the data replicate earlier findings (Mangan, 1967c). Auditory and visual alteration mobility tests load the same factor, which also positively loads the originality tests, and extraversion, and negatively loads fluency. Extraverts are thus more mobile than introverts, less fluent and more original.

From Mangan's (1978c) study, there is no evidence of a general factor of flexibility. The factor contents of the various flexibility tests — sensori-motor, perceptual and thinking — are quite different. Each occupies its own vector. Of importance is the fact that the different flexibility tests are underpinned by different "types" of inhibition and psychophysiological typological dimensions — sensori-motor flexibility by dynamism of inhibition, reflected in speed of OR habituation, thinking flexibility by satiation-type inhibition, measured by speed of development of reactive inhibition (SAE), which also relates to mobility, and perceptual flexibility by transmarginal inhibition, reflected in after-image duration under massing conditions.[7] This structure strongly supports Nebylitsyn's (1966a, 1972) claim that dynamism of inhibition, mobility of inhibition, nervous system strength and lability are independent nervous system properties.

Finally, it is clear from these data that extraverts show low dynamism of inhibition, as measured by OR habituation rate, which also replicates an earlier finding (Mangan and O'Gorman, 1969), but poor sensori-motor flexibility. They appear to have difficulty in changing set in a speed-accuracy task. Thus, while extraverts are more mobile, and more original, introverts show greater adaptability to changing sensori-motor task conditions. The reasons for this are not obvious.

Some data have been reported showing significant positive relationships between STI measured mobility scores and extraversion (Strelau, 1970a) and Guilford's flexibility and fluency dimensions (Strelau, 1977). Kozcielak (1979) reports that her "inventors" are more flexible in their thinking, and more mobile. However, Klonowicz (1979) suggests that transformation "ability" is subject to training, while Yermolayeva-Tomina (1977) reports that ideational fluency and flexibility are independent dimensions which produce "creativity" only in certain combinations. She also reports a negative correlation between creativity and lability, measured by photic driving in high frequency bands.

*(b) The Relationship of Irradiation and Concentration to Personality Variables*

To the writer's knowledge, few studies have been reported on the relationship of differences in irradiation and concentration to personality. Dependent

---

[7]As noted previously, the after-image duration score probably is a confounded measure, reflecting both strength-sensitivity and lability.

variables employed by Borisova — changes in discrimination thresholds and RT induction effects — have not appealed to personality theorists as important sources of personality variance.

This being said, considerable interest has been shown in the West in RT induction effects, dating back to Wundt's (1911) experiments, and to Woodworth's (1938) discussion of temporal readiness as the most important condition inhibiting or facilitating RT. Generally speaking, it is clear that readiness depends on the length of the warning period,[8] maximum readiness being attained in about 2 seconds (Woodrow, 1914; Telford, 1931), and is not maintained much beyond 4 seconds, a temporal range which fits well enough with the Soviet findings (Boiko, 1957). Recently there has been considerable interest in the related question of the temporary inhibition of (second) response, using both double stimulation RT and tracking procedures. In this latter case, critical variables are event uncertainty and the length and consistency (predictability) of the inter-trial and the inter-stimulus intervals.

The only study in the Western literature relating induction effects to personality is Mangan's (1967a) study. He reports a double stimulation RT experiment in which ISIs were 1.0 and 1.5 seconds. The intensities of the warning and eliciting stimuli ranged from 0.02 to 2000 lux. Data for the upper and lower 33% of the extraversion-intraversion distribution (N of 5 in each case) have already been presented in a previous figure (Figure 11, p. 216).

From the graph, it is clear that whereas at 0.02 lux positive induction effects can be attributed to ISI differences, at 2000 lux intensity, differences appear to be a function of E–I. At this intensity, high Es show negative induction in both series, the greatest amount at 1.5 seconds ISI, while high Is show positive induction in both series. These results were interpreted in the light of a previous RT experiment with the same Ss (Mangan and Farmer, 1967). Data indicated that Es possess more sensitive, weaker nervous systems, which should be expressed in a greater decrement of second response to the more intense stimulus, i.e. summation of two intense, successive stimuli should produce a greater decrement of second response (greater TIR) in high E than in high I Ss.

We should note, therefore, that Mangan's (1967a) results are probably contaminated by nervous system strength, as are most of the TIR studies. Negative induction in Es at higher stimulus intensities could be reflecting differences in irradiation and concentration, nervous system strength, or both.

---

[8]The studies mentioned briefly in this section have been more fully discussed in Chapter 6: Strength of the Nervous System; the reader is reminded that there has been some debate in the literature as to whether induction effects relate to strength or irradiation and concentration of nervous processes.

*(c) The Relationship of Lability Indices to Personality and to*
*Pscyhological Phenomena, particularly to Memory Functioning*

Over the past 20 years, a considerable amount of data has been reported in the Western literature on the relationships of what would now be regarded as lability indices — sensory after-effects (visual after-image duration, visual and kinaesthetic figural after-effects), critical flicker fusion (CFF), two-flash threshold, photic driving and evoked potential (EP) measures — to personality, and in the Soviet literature on the relationships between lability indices such as photic driving and psychological phenomena such as memory functioning. For convenience, we shall deal with these areas separately.

*1. Sensory after-effects and personality*

Visual after-image duration has been accorded comparatively little interest in the West, a good deal more attention being paid to figural and kinaesthetic after-effects. The relationship of the latter to a variety of psychological phenomena has been demonstrated — to perceptual rigidity (Wertheimer and Aronson, 1958), to hysteria/dysthymia (Nicholls, 1955) for example, and since figural and kinaesthetic after-effects appear to correlate significantly (Wertheimer, 1955), figural after-effects should be similarly related to these phenomena.

Precise relationships between visual figural after-effects (VFAE) and visual after-image (VAI) duration are unclear, although Terwilliger (1963) claims that since both are subject to inter-ocular transfer, they are probably closely related. In any event, current theory proposes that VAI is biochemically produced in the retina, and that VAI duration varies as a function of the intensity (Brindley, 1959; Berry and Imus, 1935) and duration (Franz, 1899; Brownfield, 1965) of the eliciting stimulus, developmental stages (Morsch and Abbot, 1945) and sex (Brownfield, 1965). In addition, there is evidence that accompanying loud auditory stimulation (Narikashvili, 1944, 1946) and stimulus changes in the visual field (Hall and Wilsoncroft, 1964) lengthen VAI duration.

Some work has been reported on the relationship of VFAE and VAI duration to E and N.

Eysenck (1960) suggests that failure to find supporting evidence for his 1955 prediction that Es will show greater VFAEs than introverts may be due to the operation of two competing factors, both of which can be derived from reactive inhibition theory, (a) that satiation is quicker and stronger in Es, a suggestion which has strong empirical support (cf. Eysenck, 1967), (b) that Es have greater difficulty in maintaining visual fixation (Franks, 1964). The former consideration would predispose Es to exhibit greater VFAEs, the latter to express smaller VFAEs. Eysenck (1962) has argued that since satiation is in part a function of the total sum of sensory input, and since inhibition reduces this sum to a degree dependent on S's position on the E–I continuum, inhibition and satiation work against each other. As a result, Es have less total input under identical objective conditions, and generate more satiation for equal sensory input.

The length of the inspection period clearly is of critical importance, in that Es should show greater satiation effects at short inspection times (ITs), and Is greater satiation effects at long ITs. At intermediate ITs, we might predict no difference between groups. Data to hand, however, are contradictory. Rechtschaffen (1958) reports a suggestive correlation between VFAE and E with a 40-second IT, Holland (1960) a similar result with a 90-second IT. Generally speaking, however, most studies have failed to report significant relationships between E and VFAE measures with intermediate/long ITs (e.g. Wertheimer, 1955; Gardner, 1961; Spitz and Lipman, 1960). Insofar as short ITs — less than 30 seconds — are concerned, few relevant studies have been reported. Holland and Gomez (1963) employed ITs ranging from 5 seconds to 1/16th second, and depressant and stimulant drug treatments, which might be expected to increase and decrease VFAEs, due to the "extraverting" effect of the former, and the "introverting" effect of the latter. These authors report significant VFAEs, and were able to confirm the drug hypothesis at the 1% significance level.

We should also note the contradictory evidence about sex differences in VFAE. While some studies report smaller VFAEs in females (McEwan and Roger, 1960; Satinder, 1965; Koffman and Pressey, 1967), Pressey (1970) reports no significant differences between male and female Ss.

A few studies are reported in which attempts have been made to relate visual after-image duration to personality dimensions. Mangan (1967a, 1978c) has reported significant correlations between VAI duration and two measures of perceptual flexibility, Thurstone's (1951) concealed figures test and Necker cube alternation. These tests are claimed to measure the perceptual component of Witkin's analytic-global dimension, which in turn, has been shown to be related to a variety of psychological phenomena. For example, Ss who respond in a field dependent way on the concealed figures test are more apt to show open anxiety, reflecting less effective controls (Gump, 1955; Cohen, Silverman and Shmavonian, 1959), to show authoritarian tendencies (Pollack et al., 1960), "social rigidity" (Fenchel, 1958), and suggestibility (Sangiuliano, 1951). To the extent that VAI duration is an index of nervous system lability, highly labile Ss thus show high levels of perceptual flexibility, and presumably, field independence.

White et al. (1969) report a study relating extraversion and neuroticism to decrement in VAI duration, using the method of repeated presentations of a moderate to strong stimulus (2000 lux) at decreasing inter-stimulus intervals, which they regarded as a measure of strength in the visual system. The regression of after-image duration on inter-stimulus intervals (four observations at each of four intervals) generated two scores, slope and intercept of the regression line. Intercept scores were considered to be an index of the amount of inhibitory build-up, and the slope score, the rate of growth. While in this study there is no reported correlation between VAI duration and E, it is clear from the figure presented (Figure 16) that extraverts and high N Ss show longer durations in the first four trials (ITIs of 6 minutes), i.e. before the massing effect operates to any significant degree. It is also clear from the data reported that non-sensitive Ss (in terms of lower absolute threshold, independently determined) or "strong" Ss, show both longer VAI durations at all ITIs, and a less rapid inhibitory buildup. However, since in this study no attempt was made to control for individual differences in sensitivity, in that one stimulus intensity was employed throughout for all Ss, the VAI duration measure is clearly a compound of both nervous system strength and lability in the visual system. In a second study, White and Mangan (1972) report the effects of depressant (sodium amatyl) and stimulant (caffeine) drugs on VAI duration under similar

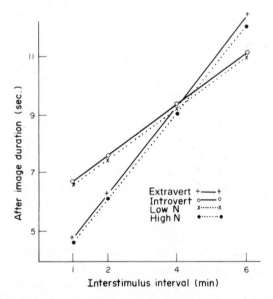

Figure 16. After-image duration at each of the four interstimulus intervals for the eight Ss scoring above and below the mean on the extraversion and neuroticism scales (from White *et al.*, 1969).

massing conditions. Although results are not directly relevant to the present issue except that N, rather than E, is associated with longer VAI durations under these conditions, one observation in particular is of interest. The depressant drug had an "extraverting" effect, prolonging VAI duration, and the stimulant drug an "introverting" effect, reducing VAI duration (Figure 17), an effect similar to that reported by Holland and Gomez (1962) in the case of VFAE. This accords well with Pavlovian and later Eysenckian (1967) theorising. Under the influence of caffeine, cortical cells may become over-stimulated, and the onset of transmarginal inhibition (as a consequence of massing) prevents the full development of subsequent excitation. Under the sodium amytal condition, decreased arousal presumably allows the excitatory process to run a fuller course within the central nervous system. In the study under consideration, both the massing of trials and the stimulant drug probably pushed Ss over the top of the inverted U-curve, resulting in greater performance decrement, i.e. decreased VAI duration.

In the Mangan (1978c) study, high N is associated with longer VAI duration, which replicates two earlier findings (White et al., 1969; White and Mangan, 1972). Both high N and high E Ss, therefore, show longer VAI durations. To this extent, these personality sub-groups show the lowest lability of nervous processes, although in most of the studies reviewed no attempt has been made to partial out the effects of nervous system strength-sensitivity, which is obviously a confounding variable.

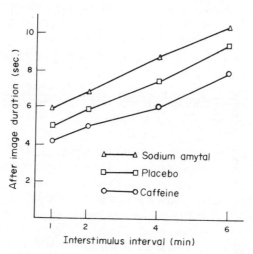

Figure 17. After-image duration for the three treatment conditions ($n=16$ in each case) (from White and Mangan, 1972).

## 2. The relationship of electro-cortical indices of lability and their perceptional correlates to personality

As mentioned previously, the Wedenskii-Ukhtomskii school of physiology regarded photic driving as the basic index of lability. This appears to be related to a cluster of measures — CFP, AOC, sensitivity recovery, and area of the interval of uncertainty in threshold measurement — investigated by researchers in Teplov's laboratory. However, optical chronaxie and the related measure of critical phosphene flicker have not been favoured by Western psychophysiologists for measuring electro-cortical activity. Nor for that matter has photic driving, which Soviet typologists have adopted as a measure of strength (Nebylitsyn, 1972) and lability (Golubeva, 1972a,c) in the visual system, with CFF the perceptual correlate. In Western research, evoked potential (EP) and contingent negative variation (CNV) have proved more popular as bioelectric measures, and two-flash threshold and CFF the perceptual measures.

Some studies relating photic driving to personality dimensions, however, have been reported. Shagass (1955), for example, reports that patients showing anxiety symptoms express more efficient photic driving at faster frequencies, while depressed patients showed superior driving at slower frequencies, suggesting that day-to-day fluctuations in affective state are correlated with photic driving. Ulett et al., (1953) also report relationships between photic driving indices and anxiety proneness. In both cases, however, there were failures of replication (Shagass, 1972). Vogel et al. (1969) report that Ss with strong automatising cognitive style — i.e. who are able to perform efficiently on simple repetitive tasks — are less responsive to photic driving than weak automatisers. These authors used flash frequencies of 10, 15, 20, 25 and 30 impulses/second at four stimulus intensities.

There are difficulties with photic driving in measuring phasic reactivity, and sensory evoked potentials have been preferred. These, however, are not easily recorded from the scalp, as is EEG, since they can be almost totally obscured by the larger spontaneous rhythms. It was only with the development of special techniques and instruments such as averagers that real advances in this area became possible.

EP is the peak-to-peak or peak-to-trough amplitude of the bi-phasic response to a flash or auditory stimulus. The inter-flash interval usually varies between 0.5 and 1 second, with individual averaging sequences lasting approximately 2 minutes — involving around 120 flashes.

There is sound evidence that EP amplitude relates to stimulus intensity and to ISI. The intensity-response curves (Figure 18) resemble growth functions. Note, however, Shagass, Schwartz and Krishnamoorti's (1965) comment that there are exceptions to this rule. Some Ss (reducers) showed smaller rather than greater (augmenters) response to brighter flashes. Buchsbaum and Silverman

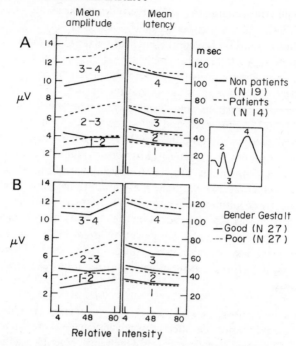

Figure 18. *A*, intensity-response curves for amplitude and latency of visual responses in patient and nonpatient groups. *B*, curves for 54 subjects (including 43 patients) divided with respect to Bender Gestalt performance. Note similarity between patient-nonpatient differences and those related to Bender performance. Amplitudes tend to increase and latencies to decrease with increasing intensity of light flash (from Shagass *et al.*, 1965).

(1969) have noted that personality factors related to stimulus-intensity control affect the intensity-response curve, a possibility also suggested by the Spilker and Calloway (1969) report that there are personality correlates of visual A (averaged) EP. In the present context, these findings are of particular interest.

A further observation of interest is that EP characteristics are correlated with stable background EEG activity (Rodin *et al.*, 1965; Shagass *et al.*, 1968; Cigánek, 1961). Generally speaking, EP amplitude is positively correlated with resting EEG amplitude, and it has been suggested that such concordance is a measure of "tightness" of inhibitory control exercised by RF structures. "Unbalanced" Ss have poorer control, shown behaviourally in poorer performance in simple perceptual tasks, which involve stimulus processing.

The second measure which has been used extensively is contingent negative variation (CNV). Kohler *et al.* (1952) were the first to observe steady potential shifts occurring during prolonged auditory and visual stimulation. The phenomenon in this general area which has received the greatest attention is the expectancy-E wave (CNV), first described by Walter (1964). CNV is the sum of a variety of slow potentials. It is contingent in that it develops in the 1- to 2-second interval between a warning and an imperative signal (as in RT), to which S must make a response. A minimum of 0.5 second is required for development of CNV (Walter, 1969). A slow potential deviation of the CNV commences 200 milliseconds after warning signal onset, and continues to rise until the imperative signal is presented and responded to, at which point there is a precipitous shift towards baseline. CNV thus occurs under conditions of "readiness", expectancy, conation (Low et al., 1966), arousal/motivation (Irwin et al., 1966), and is subject to diurnal variation, as are other EP characteristics (Heninger et al., 1969). CNV amplitude is thus greater when S is concentrating (McCallum and Walter, 1969), attentive (Hillyard, 1969). CNV amplitude is probably also dependent on the intensity of the warning signal.

An early negative wave has recently been distinguished from a later negative wave which precedes the imperative stimulus (Loveless and Sanford, 1974). CNV appears, therefore, to be composed of functionally separable early and late components.

(a) THE RELATIONSHIP OF EP AND CNV CHARACTERISTICS TO PERSONALITY

Initially, we might note parallels between very general mental processes and event-related brain electrical processes which have recently excited comment. There have been suggestions (Ornstein, 1972) that activity in gross cortical areas can be associated with the four personality types suggested by Jung — logical, intuitive, feeling and sensation — which he postulated in addition to extravert and introvert types. Some evidence indicates an association between logical operations and the left hemisphere, and between intuitive operations and the right hemisphere. There are also suggestions that the posterior half of the brain is concerned with feeling, and the anterior half with sensation.

We might also refer to evidence relating shorter visual EP latencies to high intelligence (Ertl and Schafer, 1967; Ertl, 1969, 1971). By contrast, auditory AEP latencies are occasionally longer in brighter Ss (Hendrickson, 1974). There is also evidence that brighter children have more asymmetrical visual AEPs than have dull Ss of the same age (Rhodes, Dustman and Beck, 1969; Richlin, Weisinger and Weinstein, 1971; Giannitropani, 1969; Calloway, 1975), although there have been failures of replication (Shucard, 1969; Plum, 1969).

1. Field dependence

Buchsbaum and Silverman (1969) have described an EP analogue of field dependence. EP differences are more pronounced in Ss with low error scores in rod-and-frame test (RFT) and smaller in those Ss showing high errors. These authors claim that RFT discrimination is parallelled by EP discrimination.

Insofar as CNV is concerned, Timsit-Berthier, Delaunoy and Rousseau (1973) cite Knott and Irwin's (1968) finding that field dependent Ss have a characteristic, abrupt and sharp development of CNV with some delay before the imperative stimulus. This CNV characteristic was found more frequently in hysteric than in obsessive patients.

### 2. Repressiveness

Repressiveness, measured by Rorschach variables, has been shown to relate to EP and CNV variables. Shevrin, Smith and Fritzler (1969) and Shevrin (1973) have claimed that EP amplitude can be used as a measure of repressiveness. Repressive Ss show reduced amplitude of early EP (less than 250 milliseconds) components to subliminally (1 millisecond) presented meaningful stimuli. Repressive Ss tend to show earlier EP components to both meaningful and non-meaningful stimuli, and large late components. They also give fewer responses which are associated with the meaningful stimulus, in free recall. By contrast, when stimuli are presented supraliminally, repressive Ss give larger AEPs than non-repressive Ss.

### 3. Augmenting/reducing

The augmenter-reducer (A/R) dichotomy, as a cognitive stimulus control mechanism, was first postulated by Petrie (1967). She related the dimension to pain threshold and ability to tolerate sensory isolation — reducers tolerate pain well, but sensory isolation poorly. The reverse is true for augmenters. Clearly, however, this description has a much wider application. Buchsbaum and Silverman (1969) and Spilker and Calloway (1969), for example, report that AEP A/R correlates highly with A/R measured by kinaesthetic figural after-effects, which was Petrie's original criterion measure. Studies by Buchsbaum and Pfefferbaum (1971), Vaughan and Hull (1965) and Henry and Teas (1968) point to the same general conclusion. The consensus seems to be that A/R describes habitual strategies of attention deployment. Silverman (1967) has employed the concept in relation to schizophrenia, emphasising the important defensive role of stimulus reduction.

Thus, although it is generally true that response amplitude is a positive growth function of stimulus intensity across Ss (law of strength) some Ss fail to show regular increase in EP amplitude as stimulus intensity increases, so that at very high levels of stimulation their EP amplitudes may be lower than those expressed to weaker stimuli (reducers), while others express larger EP amplitudes to weak stimuli than would be expected on the basis of their typical responses to more intense stimuli (augmenters). VEP measures of augmenting/reducing appear to be highly reliable (Soskis and Shagass, 1974; Birchall and Claridge, 1979), suggesting that A/R variations are stable individual characteristics.

The underlying dynamics of augmenting-reducing are unclear, although a number of possibilities come to mind. One such is suggested by hedonic theory of arousal (cf. pp. 373 ff.), which postulates an individual, genetically determined and ontogenetically invariant preferred level of arousal — sometimes referred to as the pacer stimulus (Dember and Earle, 1957) or "optimal arousal flux" (Berlyne, 1971b) — which ensures maximum psychological comfort and optimal conditions for learning and adaptation. In regressing to this preferred mean, Ss who are chronically under-aroused stimulation-seek, while those chronically over-aroused seek to restore homeostasis by damping down stimulation. The former would presumably be the augmenters, the latter, reducers.

This is a possible interpretation of the Birchall and Claridge (1979) finding that the amount of A/R shown by S is dependent on the psychophysiological state of Ss at time of testing. Within the one session, amount of A/R systematically varies with S's ongoing arousal state. Some Ss changed from augmenters to reducers during the session, and vice versa. These authors suggest that the range of shift may be relatively fixed, but that the direction and amount of shift varies with S's arousal state, and with the intensity of the stimulation to which he is exposed.

Insofar as the personality correlates of A/R are concerned, there seems to be a clear relationship between augmenting (using a flash procedure) and a generally outgoing, distractable, manic-like, stimulus-seeking temperament. Augmenters score highly on the MPI E scale (Soskis and Shagass, 1974), and on Zuckerman's SSS (Buchsbaum et al., 1971; Zuckerman, Murtaugh and Siegal, 1974). Patients with bipolar affective disorders tend to be augmenters, and lithium converts them to reducers (Borge, Buchsbaum and Goodwin, 1971; Buchsbaum et al., 1971). Silverman, Buchsbaum and Henkin (1969) report that male reducers are more sensitive to threshold stimuli than male augmenters.

Insofar as perceptual efficiency is concerned, Shagass et al. (1968) and Shagass (1972) report larger AEP/EEG amplitude correlations in good than in poor perceivers — the categorisation based on above and below median scores on two-flash threshold (Shagass et al., 1968) and letter recognition and weight discrimination (Shagass, 1972). Shagass (1972) suggests that high correlations reflect tightness of inhibitory RF control, which leads to good performance on simple perceptual tasks, and poor performance on complex tasks.

**4. Extraversion and neuroticism**

On the relationship of extraversion and neuroticism to AEP and CNV, Shagass (1972) reports a significantly shorter latency of first positive peak in VEP (about 45 milliseconds) in low E/high N Ss (as assessed by MPI). High N Ss also showed significantly greater amplitude of initial negative-positive component. In general, however, the MPI data reported by Shagass contribute little more than a confirmation of EP differences in relation to psychopathology. It has generally been reported that psychopaths, criminals and psychotics have much smaller AEPs than normals, although the reason for this is not known.

With non-patients, Shagass and Schwartz (1965) report significant EP interactions with E score and age. In Ss aged 15 to 19 years, high AEP amplitude of initial response is associated with high E; the reverse is true for Ss aged 40 and over. Shagass suggests that this could be reflecting a personality-related neurophysiological manifestation of aging, EP amplitude being greatest in children, and after the age of 40, and smallest in the third and fourth decades of life. Additional data in this study suggest greater "excitability" in more introverted Ss, judging from the initial EP component, less so for the later components.

Shagass's study (1972) of EP recovery function in 131 patients employing a number of Minnesota multiphasic personality inventory variables reports few significant relationships. Patients who were less dysphoric, less introverted, and displayed greater ego strength, as measured by MMPI, tended to show larger EP amplitude and slower latency recovery.

A number of studies have attempted to relate CNV characteristics to anxiety scores. McCallum and Walter (1969) report significant negative correlations between CNV amplitude and Middlesex Hospital Questionnaire scores of anxiety, obsessionalism and depression. These results contradict those reported by Dongier and Bostem (1967) although the methodology was different. Knott and Irwin (1968) report no differences in CNV amplitude between high and low Taylor MAS groups under conditions where a motor response was required, where none was required, and where the imperative stimulus was a low intensity shock. Where the latter was a high intensity shock, however, CNV amplitude was lower for highly anxious Ss. Available evidence suggests that CNV may be diminished in amplitude under stressful or anxiety-making conditions in Ss prone to such reactions.

(b) PERSONALITY CORRELATES OF CRITICAL FLICKER FUSION (CFF) AND TWO-FLASH THRESHOLD

Critical flicker fusion (CFF), which appears to have a genetic component (Murawski, 1960), is the "rate of successive light flashes from a stationary light source at which the sensation of flicker disappears and light becomes steady" (Shagass and Lipowski, 1958). Two-flash threshold, which might be regarded as a special case of CFF, is the threshold for fusion of brief, paired light flashes. CFF is thought to be a peripheral phenomenon (Levinson, 1968; Granger and Ikeda, 1968), two-flash threshold being more centrally mediated (Venables, 1963). For this reason, many researchers have preferred two-flash threshold to CFF as a measure of central arousal.

Both variables show similar stimulus intensity-response amplitude curves, threshold being related to flash intensity. In the case of two-flash threshold, however, there is an additional factor involved, since it is possible that the second flash cannot be detected until the noise from the first flash has dissipated (Venables and Warwick-Evans, 1968). This is the rationale for Venables' (1968) two-factor theory of two-flash threshold, according to which threshold is a function of both an arousal component determining the minimal detectable inter-flash interval, and speed of dissipation of the noise generated by the first stimulus.

In general, increased arousal improves both two-flash threshold (Hieatt and Tong, 1968) and CFF (Granger, 1960) in normal Ss, and decreases sensitivity in schizophrenics (Venables, 1963; cf. review by Granger, 1953). This latter finding is consistent with Venables (1966, 1969) over-arousal theory of schizophrenia. In the general context that high as well as low levels of arousal are detrimental to performance, there being an optimal level of arousal for any particular task (Yerkes and Dodson, 1908; Broadhurst, 1959), there is substantial evidence to support an inverted U function relating cortical resolution of stimuli (measured by two-flash threshold, and presumably also by CFF) and arousal level (measured, for example, by skin potential) a relationship, which, however, appears to be reversed in schizophrenic groups (Venables, 1963; Gruzelier and Venables, 1975a; Birchall and Claridge, 1979).

A similar inversion has been reported for Ss scoring high on Eysenck and Eysenck's psychoticism (P) scale (Claridge and Chappa, 1973; Birchall and Claridge, 1979). Claridge interprets these data in line with his dissociation model of schizophrenia (Claridge, 1967), according to which schizophrenia is a homeostatic anomaly, a malfunctioning of the feedback loops normally regulating and harmonising sensory feedback and internal arousal, which produces a dissociation between perceptual responsiveness and tonic arousal. As a consequence, schizophrenics express levels of perceptual sensitivity inappropriate to their level of ongoing arousal.   We should note, however, that these effects may be modality-specific. Venables (1966), in a comparison of two-flash and two-click thresholds, which we might assume to be closely related, reports that schizophrenics show relatively higher two-click thresholds than normals, indicating that auditory temporal discrimination is more impaired in the schizophrenic group. This agrees with the Hermelin and O'Connor (1968) findings of a similar modality effect with autistic children.

Insofar as the relationships of two-flash threshold and CFF to personality are concerned, a considerable amount of early data are in good agreement with Eysenck's (1957) hypothesis that Es and hysterics will have lower CFF than introverts and dysthymics, i.e. lower levels of cortical excitation (Washburn *et al.*, 1930; Madlung, 1935; Simonson and Brozek, 1952). Subsequent findings have, on the whole, been supportive. Frith (1967), for example, reports that when arousal is increased by presentation of auditory noise, sensitivity to flicker increases in Es, but not in Is, which is consistent with Eysenck's (1967) proposition that Is are consistently more highly aroused than Es. Increased arousal takes Is beyond the optimal level for CFF performance.

N also appears to be related to CFF (cf. review by Eysenck, 1957). Recent work by Waggoner (1960) and others support the finding that high Ns have lower CFF thresholds, i.e. poorer resolution of stimuli. We might note Waggoner's (1960) comment that highly anxious Ss show high response latency near CFF, indicating that the decision-making process probably plays an important part in threshold determination. This is in line with the Clark, Brown and Rutschmaan (1967) suggestion that with psychiatric patients — and probably also highly anxious Ss — what appears to be threshold change may be due to change in response criterion rather than to change in sensitivity.

A question which has excited comparatively little interest amongst psychophysiologists, but which is of considerable importance in the present context, is the nature of the recovery function in two-flash threshold. The problem is referred to by Shagass (1972), who presents some data on various aspects of this problem, and by Venables (1968) in his identification of speed of noise dissipation from the first stimulus as a critical element in two-flash threshold. Shagass (1972) takes the ratio of second to first response ($R_2/R_1$) as recovery index, this ratio varying with ISI and stimulus intensity. Schwartz and Shagass (1964) report recovery function curves for 21 Ss using standard stimulus intensities over a range of ISIs. They report that most Ss display peaks with ratios of 1.0 or greater with ISIs less than 20 milliseconds, followed by a period of suppression between 25 and 40 milliseconds, then a second recovery period with ISI greater than 40 milliseconds. This finding is supported by visual masking data reported in the Western literature indicating that with ISIs of around 20–40 milliseconds, a second stimulus is not responded to.

Insofar as intensity is concerned, Shagass *et al.* (1968) report suppression of $R_2$ when stimulus intensity is 10 milliamps above threshold, and that $R_2$ is greater than $R_1$ when stimulus intensity is 1.5 ma above threshold. Generally speaking, $R_2$ amplitude is greater following weaker, compared with stronger conditioning stimuli.

These phenomena are obviously similar to induction effects reported in the Soviet literature, although there is no information from this source about induction effects with ISIs as small as 20–80 milliseconds. Note, however, what appears to be a similar rhythmicity in after-effect reported by Kreps and Andreev, in one case involving an ISI of 0 seconds, and in RT experiments where ISIs are varied between 400 milliseconds and 2 minutes. While it would be unwise to draw an analogy between such effects and the biphasic recovery curve reported by Shagass *et al.* (1968), it is possible that a waveform of this sort characterises irradiation and concentration of both excitation and inhibition throughout a wide range of ISIs. If so, the effects on flicker phenomena and on CNV characteristics could be substantial.

In summary, the relationships between individual features of electrocortical responding, personality variables and nervous system properties are uncertain. One source of confusion is uncertainty about the interrelationships of photic driving, CFP, EP and CNV on the one hand, and between these and CFF and two-flash threshold on the other. Photic driving, CFP and EP vary positively with stimulus intensity — as does CFF — and to this extent probably reflect nervous system strength, fitting the pattern of weak nervous systems reacting more strongly to a standard intensity stimulus than strong systems. CFP and photic driving have been shown to relate to other strength measures over a wide range of voltages and frequencies (Nebylitsyn, 1973). CFF and two-flash thresholds, however, have never been employed as strength measures.

CFF, on the other hand, has been shown to correlate with a number of measures thought to define lability of nervous processes (Golubeva, 1972a,c; Nebylitsyn, 1972), one of which is photic driving in the high frequency bands. The fact that CFF is higher in introverts than in extraverts, is higher in weak nervous systems and in labile systems when strength-sensitivity is partialled out, leads to the conclusion that introverts are both weak and labile. There is, in fact, some direct evidence that high weakness is correlated with high lability (Golubeva, 1973).

Available data, however, are scarcely adequate to answer these and other relevant questions. More definite conclusions are unlikely until the ongoing debate in the Soviet literature about the typological significance of sensory after-effects and electro-cortical responsivity, and their interrelationships, has been resolved, and until more data are available of the relationships of these variables to personality dimensions.

(c) THE RELATIONSHIP OF LABILITY TO MEMORY
There are a number of well-documented reports that human intellectual activity is accompanied by changes in EEG activity. However, while some authors have reported increased amplitude of fast waves (Chainova, 1971;

Becker-Carus, 1971), others have reported changes in low frequency components (e.g. Rozhdestvenskaya, 1975). It seems clear, however, that some of the discrepancies noted may be due to differences in typological characteristics. In strong systems, intellectual activity results in increase in total alpha and beta activity, such changes being much less pronounced in weak Ss (Rozhdestvenskaya *et al.*, 1967). On the other hand, there is equally good evidence that overall increase in EEG activity is more marked in labile than in inert Ss (Golubeva and Rozhdestvenskaya, 1969) in simple (2-digit multiplication) speeded tasks.

Gorbunov, Sirotskii and Maravenko (1978) report that in a choice RT task, the signals being conceptual stimuli presented at different rates (60, 80, 100 and 120 stimuli per minute), the higher the performance rating, measured as number of errors, the higher the amplitude of theta and delta rhythms. No effects were shown in the alpha and beta bands. The authors conclude that the greater the speed of processing of visual material, the more pronounced the delta rhythm. Similar results have been reported by Rozhdestvenskaya (1975), although the typological status of S was a significant element. She reported that strong Ss showed a unidirectional increase in "energy" in the delta band during monotonous mental work. Weak Ss, on the whole, showed little change.

Thus, speed of processing information seems to be related to typological characteristics, although exact relationships have yet to be worked out. It seems that during intellectual effort, there is a tendency for EEG activity in all bands to increase. It is only in the delta range, however, that between-group typological differences approach significance.

A rather similar outcome has been reported from research investigating the relationship of nervous system properties, particularly strength-sensitivity and lability, to memory functioning. A good deal of evidence suggests that, depending on experimental conditions and on task demand, complex interactions emerge. One major problem is the effect of monotony and fatigue, one or both of which probably intrudes in most memory experiments, and which differentially affect weak and strong nervous systems. Weak systems fatigue earlier, but are also less susceptible to monotony. Of interest in this connection are the findings of Golubeva and Vasilenko (1965), of Rozhdestvenskaya, Golubeva and Shibarovskaya (1965) and Rozhdestvenskaya, Golubeva and Yermolayeva-Tomina (1972) that functional changes in the efficiency of photic driving in the low frequency bands, which is a measure of nervous system strength, occurs to monotonous as well as to fatiguing stimuli, fatigue being shown specifically by a rise in phosphene threshold.

Probably monotony and/or fatigue accounts in part for Paley's (1968) finding that both weakness and lability are factors reducing efficiency of short term memory, indicated by greater number of errors and larger number of trials to error-free reproduction. Undoubtedly this is an important factor in Golubeva and Rozhdestvenskaya's (1969) demonstration of a negative correlation between recall and efficiency of photic driving in the 5–10 cps band when Ss were required to recall 3-digit numbers during a 4-hour period of mental work. Poorer recall is clearly associated with more efficient driving. The authors suggest that weak Ss show earlier fatigue, and thus changed efficiency of low frequency driving, and poorer recall.

Golubeva (1972b) reports a study relating incidental and intentional recall in short- and long-term memory to nervous system type. High levels of excitation and lability of nervous system, measured by alpha frequency and summed energy in EEG bands, and photic driving to high frequency stimulation, relate to efficiency in incidental recall. On the other hand, Ss with more pronounced inhibitory processes and more inert nervous systems were superior in intentional recall. Golubeva also reports that strong nervous system types retain meaningless material better than weak types, especially if the amount of material is large. Golubeva and Guseva (1972) report that Ss with strong nervous systems, as determined by photic driving in low frequency bands, are superior in both incidental and intentional recall. High lability, assessed by photic driving in high frequency bands, and CFF, is related only to incidental recall of visual material. These authors observe that Ss superior in intentional recall show lower alpha rhythm frequencies and lower energy indices in the beta band of background EEG, suggesting some connection between memory and balance of nervous processes.

An interesting study is reported by Guseva (1975) who compared groups of adolescents and adults on a number of tonic and phasic EEG indices, short- and long-term memory for pictorial material, under conditions of incidental and intentional recall. She reports that while recall was roughly similar in both groups, differences were suggested in the underlying physiological mechanisms. In the adolescent group, there was a positive correlation between intentional recall and indices of both tonic and phasic arousal. In the adult group, however, greater efficiency in incidental recall was associated with strength of inhibitory processes.

Golubeva (1973) has reported a series of studies in collaboration with Rozhdestvenskaya, Ippolitov, Guseva, Izyumova ad Trubnikova relating lability and strength-sensitivity to recall under a variety of conditions. Test material covered a range from 2-digit numbers to pictorial material, letter-number codes, syllables and prose passages. Parameters investigated were intentional versus incidental recall, short- (2 minutes) and long-term (1 week) memory, and conditions under which initial learning occurred — speeded versus non-speeded conditions, for example.

Concerning the relationship of lability, assessed by efficiency of photic driving in high frequency bands, to intentional and incidental recall of verbal and numerical material, Golubeva (1973) reports results from a number of relevant studies. Data are presented in Tables 30 and 31. For both short-term and long-term memory, excitable (unbalanced, with predominance of excitation) and labile Ss perform better in incidental learning, inhibitory and inert Ss being superior in intentional learning, although these relationships do not hold for all types of material.

While it seems reasonable to account for the balance relationship to incidental and intentional recall in terms of attention deployment, the inertness/intentional recall link poses a problem. If lability involves both the speed of arousal and termination of excitatory processes, then this property might be expected to underlie capacity for differential perception of the environment, as Ukhtomskii (1937) and Golubeva and Trubnikova (1970) have suggested, and, as a consequence, rate of information processing per unit time, which, in turn, should relate to storage capacity. While this might be true for incidental learning, however, it is certainly not the case with intentional learning.

TABLE 30. *Recall of different types of material under different conditions by labile/inert types; labile denotes superiority of Ss showing efficient photic driving in the high frequency bands, inert superiority of those Ss showing poor driving in these bands (from Golubeva, 1973)*

| Stimulus Material | Incidental | | Intentional | |
|---|---|---|---|---|
| | Short-term | Long-term | Short-term | Long-term |
| Nonsense figures | No data | No data | Inert | Inert |
| Objects | Labile | Labile | Inert | Inert |
| 2-digit numbers | equiv. | Labile | No data | No data |
| Prose | No data | No data | Inert | Inert |

TABLE 31. *Recall of different types of material under different conditions by "unbalanced" Ss; inhibitory denotes superiority of Ss unbalanced with predominance of inhibition, excitable, superiority of Ss unbalanced with predominance of excitation (from Golubeva, 1973)*

| Stimulus Material | Incidental | | Intentional | |
|---|---|---|---|---|
| | Short-term | Long-term | Short-term | Long-term |
| Nonsense figures | No data | No data | Inhibitory | Equiv. |
| Objects | Equiv. | Equiv. | Inhibitory | Inhibitory |
| 3-digit numbers | Excitable | Excitable | Equiv. | Equiv. |
| 2-digit numbers | Equiv. | Equiv. | Equiv. | Equiv. |

A partial explanation might be found in the Bokharova and Laktionov (1972) finding that, while, under normal conditions, the inertness/intentional recall relationship is retained, under speeded conditions, it is reversed, with labile Ss now gaining the advantage. The authors suggest a possible mechanism, that of proactive interference. This is claimed to be highest in inert Ss when ISIs are short, i.e. under speeded conditions, interfering with information processing even in the initial stages. In labile Ss however, proactive interference is considerably lower, so that the relative advantage now accrues to these Ss. Presumably, in order to account for the original finding on this basis, we would have to assume that proactive interference is greater in labile Ss under non-speeded conditions. The reason for this, however, is obscure.

Another variable of interest is meaningfulness of the task material. Smirnov (1966) postulated that strong nervous systems perform better with rote material; confirmatory results are reported by Trubnikova (1971a,b). Golubeva, Guseva and Trubnikova (1970), Golubeva and Trubnikova (1970) and Trubnikova (1971a,b), however, report that Ss with strong nervous systems, measured by photic driving indices, while showing superior recall of rote material as the volume of stimulus material increases — presumably due to their greater capacity to resist fatigue and monotony — show poorer recall of meaningful material under the same conditions. Golubeva comments that continued presentation of nonsense material leads to the development of "preventive" inhibition, i.e. restriction of information flow, indicated by high frequency of alpha and delta waves in the EEG record. EEG records of weak Ss show these characteristics. Golubeva (1973) also suggests that better recall of meaningful material by weak Ss indicates a greater capacity for conceptual re-coding of information.

Golubeva (1973) postulates that incidental and intentional recall probably involve different brain systems, the former primarily the arousal and the afferent/processing brain systems, the latter the regulatory system. Golubeva, Guseva and Trubnikova (1970) report EP data which they claim support this contention. Efficiency of incidental recall correlates with characteristics of EP vertex components, which record the activity of the non-specific thalamo-cortical system, and efficiency of intentional recall with characteristics of the occipital EP.

From this admittedly rather sketchy account, it seems that we have a three-way interaction between strength-weakness of nervous system, length of task, and meaningfulness of the material. Insofar as lability is concerned, the critical variable seems to be incidental versus intentional recall. In neither case does short-term versus long-term memory emerge as a significant factor. It would be of interest to establish the relationship, if any, of CFF to recall under similar conditions. No relevant data, however, have been reported.

## Summary

Overall, the research reviewed in this chapter clearly pinpoints some of the difficulties encountered in relating typological properties to Western psychophysiological and personality dimensions. In some cases (e.g. concerning lability and concentration) theoretical postulates are imprecise, and typological boundaries inexact; in almost all cases, the methodologies employed in critical experiments are so different that comparisons are difficult. Add to this the dearth of research relating personality variables to electro-cortical phenomena such as EP, CNV and flicker phenomena, and the fact that the data are in any event somewhat equivocal, and comparisons become even more questionable. Nevertheless, with these difficulties and reservations in mind, the following points seem worth making.

1. Although much of the research exploring relationships between mobility, concentration and lability is confounded by lack of control over strength-sensitivity of nervous system, orthogonal factors have been identified in a few recent studies in which stimulus intensities have been equated across Ss in terms of individual thresholds. More extensive investigations are required, however, before typological boundaries can be plotted with any accuracy.

2. There are some replicated, but limited, data relating alteration mobility of inhibition to thinking and perceptual flexibility, and to extraversion. No data are available on the relationship of these or other variables to mobility of excitation.

3. While it is obvious enough that irradiation and concentration of excitation and of inhibition, and their mutual induction, which are regarded by Soviet typologists as important characteristics of nervous system functioning, bear similarities to what in the West are referred to as "readiness" factors in RT, to CNV, and to sensory after-effects which are shown in a variety of contexts such as visual masking, two-flash recovery function, for example, too little is known about laws of irradiation and concentration to draw exact parallels, and to relate these variables to personality and sensory/perceptual functioning. However, some analogies are nonetheless impressive, as for example, the time course of CNV and induction effects in RT experiments — both occur at around 200 milliseconds following the warning signal, both are maximal at approximately 0.5 seconds, and do not continue much beyond 2–4 seconds. The functional significance of both processes appears to be much the same.

4. Insofar as lability is concerned, the similarity between photic driving and EP could provide a bridge — admittedly shaky — between Soviet and Western research. The same is true for CNV and induction effects, and for two-flash threshold, which, although never attracting much interest from Soviet typologists, correlates with CFF, which has been extensively investigated in both Soviet and Western laboratories.

These relationships permit some very tentative extrapolations, which we should regard simply as pointers to future enquiry.

EP seems to be positively related to anxiety. So does photic driving in the higher frequencies, judging from the (non-replicated) findings of Shagass (1955) and Ulett *et al.* (1953). We might suggest, therefore, that highly anxious Ss are more labile. EP amplitude also appears to be related to extraversion. Since introverts show greater EP amplitude, Is are therefore more labile. We might recall that CFF data also suggest that Is are both weak and labile.

As in the case of induction effects, however, there is little, if any, research reported in which EP has been measured independently of nervous system strength. Inferences based on correlations between E and N, and lability (and concentration, for that matter), therefore, should be viewed with caution.

Finally, an argument could be made that it is facile to consider lability and concentration of nervous processes independently of nervous system strength, since a stimulus always has an intensity, and since S's "arousability" is a biologically determined component of responsivity. From this angle, lability and concentration are secondary properties, which can never be measured independently of nervous system strength. However, in the moderate stimulus intensity range, which, arguably, embraces most behaviour sequences, weak and strong nervous systems respond with approximately similar amplitudes, i.e., strength-sensitivity is in effect partialled out, in which case individual differences in concentration and lability could be major sources of variance. It may be that only under conditions of psychological stress, sensory overload, and sensory isolation is strength-sensitivity of critical importance. Possible implications of this will be discussed in a later section.

# CHAPTER 9

# *The Structure of Nervous System Properties*

IN THIS section we have attempted to describe the substantive content of most of the nervous system properties included in the typological model, and, from the available correlational data, have made some inferences about the extent to which these biological dispositions direct personality development. In this connection, an interesting question is whether any one property is more distinctive or pervasive than any other in shaping development. If we cover a broad enough spectrum of psychophysiological functioning to permit comparative assessment, does excitatory strength, or inhibitory strength, or mobility, or lability, for example, contribute more to typological status, and thus to personality structure?

To the writer's knowledge, this question has not been seriously considered in the Soviet or the Western literature. Nebylitsyn (1966a) has consistently objected to the attachment of evaluative labels to one or other typological attribute — for example, regarding sensitivity, the inverse of strength, as weakness, and thus biologically maladaptive — but this is a somewhat different issue. We might also note that there has always been the suggestion in the typological literature that strength-sensitivity is the most critical property. This is reflected in greater research involvement in this area, and the comparative neglect, until very recently, of properties such as mobility and lability, although these were identified at a very early stage of typological theorising. It may be, however, that this is the sort of temporary imbalance which sometimes occurs in the development of a new theoretical approach.

Over a period of years, the present author has employed a wide range of psychophysiological and psychological measures in relating personality dimensions of extraversion, neuroticism, originality and fluency, cognitive and perceptual flexibility, speed and accuracy, to Pavlovian typological properties of strength-sensitivity of excitation and inhibition, dynamism of excitation and inhibition, mobility of inhibition, and lability (e.g. Mangan and Farmer, 1967; Mangan, 1967a,b,c; Mangan and O'Gorman, 1969; White *et al.* 1969; Siddle *et al.*, 1969; Siddle and Mangan, 1971; White and Mangan, 1972; Mangan, 1974;

324 THE BIOLOGY OF HUMAN CONDUCT

1978a,b,c; Paisey and Mangan, 1980). In the most recent series (Mangan, 1974; 1978a,b,c), in which an attempt was made to identify general factors of appetitive and aversive CR acquisition and extinction, excitatory and inhibitory strength-weakness, and mobility of inhibition, and to assess the contribution of a number of psychophysiological and personality variables to these factors, it was possible to derive 40 independent measures from a sample of 20 Ss, and to perform a Q analysis on these data. Although a considerable amount of controversy has surrounded the use of Q analysis (Stephenson, 1953), which reduces correlations between persons rather than between tests to "types" rather than factors, this form of analysis appeals as a useful adjunct to more conventional R-type analysis, in that it could reveal biological dimensions more pervasive than R-type factors.

The list of variables (Table 32) includes primary indices of the typological properties and personality dimensions involved — for example, speed of development and extinction of appetitive and aversive CRs as measures of excitatory and inhibitory dynamism, speed of transformation as the measure of mobility of inhibition, measures of originality and fluency as indices of cognitive flexibility — and second-order variables which contribute to these primary properties, measures such as habituation rate, which relates to inhibitory dynamism and to mobility of inhibition, UR amplitudes, which predict both excitatory and inhibitory dynamism, initial OR amplitude measures, which contribute to excitatory dynamism, and so on. From the research reported, these forty variables appear to account for the major portion of the variance of the primary properties under discussion.

The sample consisted of 20 male undergraduate volunteers aged between 18 and 22 years, all of whom had completed an experimental programme of approximately 30 hours of individual testing. Subject scores were transformed to standard scores, the columns and rows transposed, and the correlation matrix analysed by the principal components method, with both Varimax and Oblimin rotations. The Oblimin loadings are shown in Table 33.

In determining subject "types", standard scores on the 40 measures for Ss showing the highest negative and positive loadings, in the case of bipolar factors, or the highest negative or positive loadings, were compared. Variables defining types were those showing mean standard score differences of ± 1.75.

Criterion differences for the seven types identified are shown in Table 34.

Type 1, which accounts for the largest proportion of the variance, is obviously a "mobile" type. However, since the measure is mobility of inhibition, and since the direction of differences on some of the other variables indexing the type — viz., weak generation and quick dissipation of SAE inhibition, slow CR extinction, and slow habituation of orienting response — suggests weak development of inhibition in a variety of situations, we could be

TABLE 32. *The battery of psychological and psychophysiological tests*

|  |  | Content |
|---|---|---|
| 1. | EPI E | Extraversion |
| 2. | EPI N | Neuroticism |
| 3. | Clerical speed I | Clerical speed |
| 4. | Clerical speed II |  |
| 5. | Transformation | Sensori-motor flexibility |
| 6. | Accuracy |  |
| 7. | Auditory mobility | Transformation mobility |
| 8. | Visual mobility |  |
| 9. | Tactual mobility |  |
| 10. | SAE decline | Reactive inhibition |
| 11. | SAE recovery |  |
| 12. | SAE duration |  |
| 13. | After-image duration | Lability |
| 14. | Habit. rate of auditory OR | Dynamism of inhibition |
| 15. | Habit. rate of visual OR |  |
| 16. | Habit. rate of tactual OR |  |
| 17. | Spon. recov. to auditory CS in extinction | Inhibitory strength |
| 18. | Spon. recov. to visual CS in extinction |  |
| 19. | Rate appetitive CR acquisition | Dynamism of excitation |
| 20. | Appetitive UR amplitude |  |
| 21. | Frequency sexual outlet |  |
| 22. | Rate appetitive extinction | Dynamism of inhibition |
| 23. | Auditory threshold | Excitatory strength |
| 24. | Visual threshold |  |
| 25. | Tactual threshold |  |
| 26. | Auditory imagery | Imagery vividness |
| 27. | Visual imagery |  |
| 28. | Tactual imagery |  |
| 29. | Init. amplit. auditory OR | Excitatory strength |
| 30. | Init. amplit. visual OR |  |
| 31. | Init. amplit. tactual OR |  |
| 32. | Rate aversive CR acquisition | Dynamism of excitation |
| 33. | Aversive UR amplitude |  |
| 34. | Rate aversive extinction | Dynamism of inhibition |
| 35. | NC alternation | Perceptual flexibility |
| 36. | Embedded figures test |  |
| 37. | Originality | Cognitive flexibility |
| 38. | Fluency |  |
| 39. | Trials to over-extinction | Dynamism of inhibition |
| 40. | Spontaneous OR fluctuations |  |

TABLE 33. *Oblimin rotated loadings (loadings less than .30 omitted)*

| | I | II | III | IV | V | VI | VII |
|---|---|---|---|---|---|---|---|
| | | | | Rotated factors | | | |
| S | | | | | | | |
| 1 | -.76 | | | | | | |
| 2 | | -.84 | | | | | |
| 3 | | | -.90 | | | | .35 |
| 4 | | | -.50 | | | | |
| 5 | | | | | -.81 | .74 | |
| 6 | .81 | | | | | .35 | |
| 7 | | | | .77 | | | |
| 8 | -.62 | | | | | | |
| 9 | | -.68 | | | | | |
| 10 | .73 | | | -.34 | | | .53 |
| 11 | | .45 | .36 | | | | |
| 12 | | | | | -.75 | | |
| 13 | | | | | | -.83 | |
| 14 | | | | -.57 | | | |
| 15 | | | | .43 | | | |
| 16 | | | | -.72 | | | |
| 17 | | | | | | | .83 |
| 18 | | .60 | | | | | |
| 19 | | .55 | | .34 | .34 | .44 | |
| 20 | | | .33 | | | | -.71 |

referring here to a more general "inhibitory" type, despite Nebylitsyn's (1966a) assertion that mobility of inhibition and inhibitory dynamism are independent nervous system properties, involving different forms of inhibition.

Type 2 is characterised by high levels of tactual reactivity, high unconditional responsivity to sexual stimuli, high frequency of sexual outlet, and high extraversion at the positive pole, and weak auditory imagery and slow generation of internal inhibition at the negative pole. Clearly sexual arousability is a highly significant biological characteristic. We might note that speed of CR acquisition to sexual USs does not identify the type — type characteristic refers to unconditional responsivity. Note also the weight for extraversion, which strongly supports suggestions by Eysenck and Cattell that extraversion has a strong sexuality component.

Type 3 is the stable introvert, who expresses short after-image duration, and high levels of visual, auditory and tactual imagery. It is worth recalling that although after-image duration was originally thought to be an index of mobility, subsequently it was regarded, with photic driving indices, as a measure of lability, i.e., speed of initiation and termination of nervous processes, which relates to speed of information processing (Nebylitsyn, 1973). Why this should be associated with high levels of imagery, however, is

TABLE 34. *Standard score differences indexing the seven types*

| | |
|---|---|
| **Type 1, contrasting Ss 6 and 10 with 1 and 8** | |
| Auditory mobility | +4.82 |
| Visual mobility | +4.61 |
| SAE recovery | +4.13 |
| SAE decline | −4.01 |
| Originality | +4.00 |
| Fluency | −3.52 |
| Appet. extinction | −3.11 |
| Hab. rate of visual OR | −3.06 |
| Hab. rate of tactual OR | −3.02 |
| | |
| **Type 2, contrasting Ss 2 and 9 with 18 and 19** | |
| Appet. UR amplitude | +3.05 |
| Init. amplitude tact OR | +3.04 |
| Freq. sexual outlet | +3.00 |
| Extraversion | +2.75 |
| SAE decline | −3.08 |
| Auditory imagery | −3.58 |
| | |
| **Type 3, contrasting Ss 3 and 4 with 20 and 11** | |
| Extraversion | −3.88 |
| Neuroticism | −3.71 |
| A-I duration | −3.70 |
| Auditory Imagery | +3.34 |
| Visual Imagery | +3.31 |
| Tactual Imagery | +3.28 |
| | |
| **Type 4, contrasting Ss 7 and 15 with 16 and 14** | |
| Init. Ampl. visual OR | +3.55 |
| Init. Ampl. tactual OR | +3.41 |
| Init. Ampl. audit. OR | +3.39 |
| Appet. CR acquisition | +3.27 |
| Avers. CR acquisition | +3.18 |
| Tactual mobility | +3.17 |
| Freq. sexual outlet | +3.09 |
| | |
| **Type 5, indexed by Ss 8 and 12** | |
| NC alternation | −2.42 |
| A-I duration | −2.14 |
| Introversion | +2.08 |
| Avers. UR amplitude | −2.07 |
| Visual mobility | −1.96 |
| Visual imagery | +1.77 |
| | |
| **Type 6, contrasting Ss 5 and 19 with 13** | |
| Clerical speed I | +3.72 |
| Clerical speed II | +3.66 |
| Auditory sensitivity | −3.51 |

(Cont.)

TABLE 34. (Cont.) *Standard score differences indexing the seven types*

| | |
|---|---|
| Type 7, contrasting Ss 17 and 11 with 20 | |
| Transformation | +4.42 |
| Accuracy | −3.69 |
| Hab. rate of audit. OR | +3.58 |
| Auditory sensitivity | +3.33 |
| Spon. rec. to avers CS | −3.05 |
| Hab. rate of visual OR | +3.02 |

uncertain. A further query involves the relationship of introversion with strength-sensitivity. Since introverts are more sensitive, we might expect these Ss to show longer after-image durations to standard intensity stimuli than strong, i.e., extraverted Ss. The influence of strength-sensitivity differences, of course, would be minimised where stimuli in the medium intensity range, rather than weak or very intense stimuli, are utilised, as in the present case. On the basis of present results, stable introverts appear to be more labile, which supports earlier findings (White *et al.* 1969; White and Mangan, 1972).

Type 4 differences offer a ready interpretation. These Ss show large differences in initial amplitude of orienting response in the three modalities, in acquisition of appetitive and aversive CRs, and in tactual mobility and frequency of sexual outlet. Since initial OR amplitude is a strength-sensitivity measure, and since sensitivities in the modalities of the appetitive CS are determinants of CR acquisition rates, the clustering of strength-sensitivity and conditioning variables to index a type is to be expected. This is an "excitable" or strong type which, under certain circumstances, may be the "conditionable" type.

Type 5 is a reflection of a factor identified in a previous analysis (Mangan, 1967a). Since most of the differences (except for extraversion) relate to visual functioning, this might be described as a "visual" type. Ss show fast inhibitory build-up in the visual system, poor NC alteration, high visual imagery, low visual mobility, small aversive UR amplitude and low extraversion. The contrast of after-image duration and NC alternation is not unexpected, since persistence of the visual trace, measured by after-image duration, would tend to resist figure-ground reversal, which is indexed by Necker Cube alternation rate.

Types 6 and 7 do not emerge as strong types. Type 6 is characterised by fast clerical speed, and type 7 Ss by high "cognitive" transformation, low accuracy, fast OR habituation rate, high auditory sensitivity, and slow rate of spontaneous CR recovery to the aversive CS in extinction. The latter differences are of some interest. In a previous study (Mangan, 1978c), it was suggested that the lack of correlation between the cognitive transformation and the alteration mobility scores might be due to differences in degree of task complexity.

However, the present finding, that transformation is associated with strong internal inhibition, and alteration with weak internal inhibition suggests that the former may be measuring mobility of excitation (the ease of replacing excitation by inhibition), and the latter mobility of inhibition (the ease of replacing inhibition by excitation). According to Nebylitsyn (1966a), these properties are uncorrelated.

Despite the fact that the R and Q analyses of this broad range of psychological and psychophysiological functions converge reasonably well, it seems that in some instances the types may be reflecting more general processes than the factors, and thus might represent more fundamental psychophysiological dimensions. For example, while CR acquisition and extinction factors emerged from the R analyses, the Q analysis identified "excitatory" and "inhibitory" rather than "conditionable" types.

An alternative interpretation of the Q analysis to that suggested by Nebylitsyn's model is one more in line with Strelau's reactivity-activity model. It could be that identification of type-individuals in whom certain combinations of nervous system properties are exaggerated allows a more comprehensive model of actual dimensions to be constructed than that produced by imposing continuously distributed variation on the sample. This suggests that there are two types (I and 4) which reflect predominance of a single, general nervous system type. Type 1 is the mobile versus inert type, type 4 the dynamic versus the non-reactive type, this being regarded as level of dynamism related to drive. Types 2 and 6 are also contrasted, the former expressing predominance of appetitive (sexual) drive, of reactivity to appropriate signals, and social activity, the latter weak reactivity (excitatory strength) and high levels of motor activity. Two types (3 and 5) reflect behavioural adaptation to constraints imposed by need for stimulation, type 3 expressing need for stimulation through generation of internal imagery — an effect clearly shown in the Gawecka and Posnaniak (1979) study — and type 5 decreased need for stimulation, primarily through the dampening of visual afferent input. Type 7 shows bias in one aspect of mobility — reactive inhibition (low perseveration), the other time parameter of mobility not sampled by appropriate measures.

A second source of data bearing on this general question — indirect but nonetheless relevant — is the number of conjoint factor analytic studies (Strelau and Terelak, 1974; Carlier, 1979; Paisey and Mangan, 1980; unpublished data from Strelau's laboratory) of items from the STI, the EPQ and a number of other scales. It will be recalled that Strelau's temperament model postulates differences along a dimension of energy level, which is claimed to subsume all those physiological processes responsible for the storage and release of energy. Energy level has two basic features, reactivity and activity, the former referring to both emotional and sensory reactivity, thus being similar, in certain respects, to Nebylitsyn's dimension of excitatory strength, the latter to the vigour of goal-directed activity. Strelau employs the STI — an observation chart assessing Pavlovian properties of excitatory and inhibitory strength and mobility — to measure individual differences along these dimensions. Importantly, in the present context, Strelau (1972a) claims that these scales have been validated against laboratory indices of the properties in question. The conjoint analyses therefore, should disclose both the order of appearance of Strelau's typological properties (and, by inference, Nebylitsyn's properties), and the extent to which these are related to personality dimensions. In this latter respect, such data are a valuable addendum to the body of studies relating personality measures to typological indices which we have reported in the three preceding chapters.

Strelau and Terelak (1974) tested two samples of 190 male Ss, aged between 20 and 40 years, the one group highly reactive, the other low reactive, reactivity being measured by alpha index, on twenty-four temperament dimensions, derived from Eysenck's MPI, Taylor's MAS, the Guilford-Zimmerman Temperament Survey, the Thurstone Temperament Schedule, and Strelau's Temperament Inventory.

Six temperament factors (seven for the highly reactive group) were identified. The authors report that between-group differences, which they regard, collectively, as indicating differences in energy level, were most clearly shown on the following dimensions — impulsivity, extraversion, sociability, mobility, dominance, ascendance, excitatory strength, and activity. Unfortunately, no higher-order analysis is reported, but these factors clearly form a fairly tight cluster, with extraversion and its subscales the central component. The relationship of mobility and excitatory strength to extraversion is well documented, and dominance and ascendance are source traits which contribute strongly to second-order exvia or extraversion. Impulsivity presumably reflects emotional sensitivity, the remaining factors referring to sensory reactivity.

Carlier (1979) reports an item analysis of the STI using a French translation of the Inventory with a sample of 202 Ss. Four factors were extracted and rotated to a Varimax solution. Factor 1 closely resembles extraversion, while Factors 2 and 3 are similar in content to the factors of strength of inhibition and strength of excitation, respectively, identified by Paisey and Mangan (1980). Although Carlier did not attempt conjoint factor analysis of STI and EPI items, she did report correlations between her factor scores and scale scores, including extraversion and neuroticism from the EPI. It is clear from this analysis that Carlier's first factor is very similar to Eysenck's extraversion factor, combining elements of strength of excitation and mobility. Factor 2 is highly related to strength of inhibition, and correlates negatively with N. Factor 3 reflects strength of excitation.

Paisey and Mangan (1980) report a series of analyses, at first, second and third order, of questionnaire data from various psychoticism scales, the EPQ, Zuckerman's sensation seeking scale (SSS) and the STI, administered to a sample of 277 Ss, 193 females, 84 males.

Analysis of EPQ data yielded thirteen obliquely rotated factors, of which the first four — neuroticism, extraversion, lie scale and psychoticism factors — satisfied the scree criterion. The 101 Strelau items generated first-order factors of adaptability, mood control, behavioural restraint, introversion, a sleep factor, and preference for vigorous behaviour, and higher-order analysis two factors, the first referring to both excitatory strength and mobility, the second to inhibitory strength. Second-order factoring of combined EPQ and Strelau items revealed factors of excitatory strength, extraversion, inhibitory strength, and neuroticism/psychoticism-stability, and third-order analysis two factors, the first loading extraversion, strength of excitation and stability, and the second loading conscientiousness, super-ego (negatively), and inhibitory strength. Factor analysis of items from the three scales, neglecting scree, tautologous and uninterpretable factors, disclosed five factors — extraversion, sensation-seeking, neuroticism, strength of excitation and of inhibition, in that order.

Although Strelau's scale was initially designed to measure mobility, as well as excitatory and inhibitory strength, the factor emerges at second-, rather than first-order level in this analysis, and then only in combination with excitatory strength. Item content, however, suggests that many items assumed to measure mobility could more appropriately refer to excitatory strength or extraversion. There is an interesting analogy here with the Q analysis, where it proved equally difficult to disentangle mobility of inhibition from inhibitory dynamism. In both cases, there is the suggestion that mobility is not an independent nervous system property.

Inappropriate item content may also be the explanation of why differentiation between excitatory and inhibitory strength is not well maintained at higher-order levels of analysis, except where the Strelau items are factored in combination with the EPQ, when it is obvious that E and N attract much of the variance of Strelau's items which refer to sociability and anxiety.

There is the additional point, made originally by Nebylitsyn (1973), that although strength is, to some extent, modality-specific, it is arguably the only nervous system property which can be reliably expressed in gross behaviour, and is thus the only property amenable to self-report as measured by questionnaire.

In addition to the results of studies reviewed above, there is now a sizeable body of data from Polish sources (Strelau, personal communication) suggesting substantial relationships between scales from the Strelau and the Eysenck questionnaires. These are summarised in Table 35. Clearly, strength of excitation and mobility are positively intercorrelated. Neuroticism appears to correlate negatively with strength of excitation, less so with strength of inhibition and with mobility. The correlation patterns reported suggest that the questionnaire items from the Eysenck and Strelau scales can be combined to produce major personality/temperament clusters along the following dimensions — extraversion/strength of excitation/mobility; stability/strength of excitation/strength of inhibition; strength of inhibition/impulse control.

Obviously, a good deal more work is required to refine Strelau's temperament inventory, particularly with regard to item content. Nevertheless, comparison of the Q and R analyses, keeping in mind that the former employed psychophysiological data (including CR acquisition and extinction), the latter only questionnaire data, points to the following conclusions.

1. The fact that mobility of inhibition and dynamism of inhibition in the Q analysis, and mobility of both excitation and inhibition and excitatory strength in the R analyses load one type of factor suggests that transformation mobility is not a primary property, a possibility which Nebylitsyn (1966a, 1973) has repeatedly stressed. On common-sense grounds, it seems obvious that dynamism of inhibition, for example, to some extent subsumes mobility of inhibition, since the latter involves both the capacity to inhibit response to the previous CS+, and to disinhibit response to the previously negative, now positive, CS. If similar inhibitory processes are involved in both cases, we would expect the "inhibitible" type to be more mobile, and to show faster CR extinction. On the other hand, in neither analysis was there any attempt to partial out the effects of excitatory or inhibitory strength or dynamism, so that some contamination is to be expected. It may be that transformation ability is a product of excitatory/inhibitory strength balance, which must be differentiated from lability, the primary property describing speed of nervous processing, and of irradiation/concentration of nervous processes, as we previously suggested. Not enough critical data are yet available, however, to answer this question. From the present vantage point, since the inhibitory/mobile type, and the excitatory strength-mobility factor emerged as primary components in the analyses described, we might conclude that, in terms of biological adaptation, the capacity to inhibit response to inappropriate CSs, and to respond positively to previously indifferent, but now significant sensory signals — however we like to refer to this in typological language — is at least as important a biological asset as arousability in the afferent systems, or in the subcortical structures mediating reinforcement.

2. From the conjoint studies, there is considerable commonality between

TABLE 35. Intercorrelations between scores of Strelau's and Eysenck's questionnaires

| | Strelau personal communication | | | Strelau (1970a) | | Carlier (1979) | | | Paisey (unpublished) | | |
|---|---|---|---|---|---|---|---|---|---|---|---|
| | E | N | MAS | E | N | E | N | L | E | N | P |
| | n = 171 | n = 169 | n = 148 | n = 78 | | | n = 202 | | | n = 174 | |
| SE | r = 0.44<br>n = 183 | r = -0.38<br>n = 178 | r = -0.48<br>n = 159 | r = 0.45<br>r = 0.48<br>n = 159 | r = -0.48<br>r = -0.56 | r = 0.38 | r = -0.49 | r = 0.17 | r = 0.37 | r = -0.53 | r = -0.14 |
| SI | r = 0.08<br>n = 178 | r = -0.25<br>n = 177 | r = -0.20<br>n = 157 | r = -0.01<br>r = 0.03 | r = -0.53<br>r = -0.45 | r = -0.21 | r = -0.48 | r = 0.43 | r = -0.07 | r = -0.14 | r = -0.54 |
| M | r = 0.69 | r = -0.17 | r = -0.18 | r = 0.67<br>r = 0.65 | r = -0.30<br>r = -0.21 | r = 0.54 | r = -0.21 | r = 0.00 | | | |

Koscielak (1979) n = 200, r SE and M = 0.54
Carlier (1979) n = 202, r SE and M = 0.45

major personality dimensions and Strelau's STI properties. The factor structures are robust, particularly when we remember the different populations sampled in the studies reviewed, and thus the possibility of contamination by cultural features, phraseological subtleties or infidelities of translation. Since there is some consensus regarding the hierarchical structure of personality dimensions (cf. discussion, Chapter 5) we can make some sort of case for assuming, however tentatively, a similar hierarchical structure for nervous system properties. Perhaps this approximates that of intellectual abilities and personality dimensions — general, higher-order or superordinate factors (reactivity/activity/transformation mobility in the present case, "g" in the case of intellectual abilities, E, N and P in the case of personality dimensions), with group factors (e.g. N, V, K) nervous system properties, and "source" traits such as those suggested by Cattell and Guilford having special relevance in specific experimental and behavioural contexts. How we can incorporate this structure in Nebylitsyn's final typological model, which suggested that the basic nervous system properties of strength, mobility, dynamism, lability and concentration refer only to functional properties of the sensory, afferent systems, temperamental characteristics of reactivity and activity being mediated by larger, more extensive brain systems, however, remains an intriguing question.

3. The relevance of this structure to the concept of "conditionability", which is the lynchpin of Eysenck's biological theory of personality, is of considerable importance. It may be, as Paisey and Mangan (in press) have suggested, that reactivity/activity levels in efferent, as well as afferent systems, have a considerable effect on speed of development of autonomic and motor CRs. Within these constraints, we might be able to identify broad "conditionability" factors, given a representative enough sampling of conditioning situations, involving a range of types and intensities of CS and US. On the other hand, it is entirely possible that different conditioning paradigms — "sensory" compared with "biologically significant" conditioning, for example — may reveal unique sets of relationships with the primary typological indices, nothing more. It may also eventuate that relationships of personality dimensions to conditioning performance fit this same general pattern.

# PART 3

# Personality and Conditioning

A PROBLEM which has excited considerable interest amongst personality theorists in recent years is the extent to which differences along personality dimensions such as extraversion and neuroticism are mediated by conditioning, and thus reflect biologically-based differences in nervous system characteristics. Some data suggest that introverts are more susceptible to threat, and thus condition more readily to a variety of aversive USs, and that extraverts condition more quickly under reward conditions. Overall, however, empirical support for these propositions is weak. In any event, it is a matter of conjecture whether such findings can be extrapolated to all social learning situations. On the other hand, the hypothesis has not been subjected to critical test, largely because we lack a sophisticated enough model of conditioning, and the appropriate methodology, to take into account all the complexities of social learning. In the following chapters, we shall attempt to identify important sources of variance in conditioning, to critically review the relationship of personality dimensions to these variables, and, in the concluding chapter, to specify some problems which we consider viable and important in the area of differential psychophysiology.

CHAPTER 10

# Sources of Variance in Conditioning

*I venture, though somewhat timorously, the prophecy that the phenomena of the pure*
*conditioned reflex will teach us more about excitability than about learning.*
E. L. Thorndike, as quoted by K. W. Spence in S. S. Stevens (1951)

## Introduction

AT THE simplest conceptual level, 'conditionability' implies within-S correlations between learning situations and across response systems in speed of acquisition and extinction of CRs, irrespective of the conditioning paradigm employed, of the nature of the reinforcement, of the sensory characteristics of the CS, or of the modality of response.

As yet, however, there is little evidence for factors of this sort, a not surprising outcome since few serious attempts have been made to test assumptions — implicit in most models of conditioning — about the nature of the relationships between psychophysiological parameters thought to underlie responsivity to CS and US, and UR characteristics, and the related question, one central to 'conditioning' theories of personality, of the extent to which such parameters reflect personality dimensions such as extraversion (E), neuroticism (N) or "emotionality".

Although a number of experiments have been reported describing crude comparisons between personality groups in speed of development of eyeblink and GSR CRs, critical studies have yet to be done. These need to be directed by a sophisticated model of conditioning which will allow identification of sources of variance at different points in the reflexive chain, which might then be related to personality variables. Currently, no such model(s) is available.

The problem stems partly from different views about the functional significance of the conditioned reflex. Soviet theorists tend to view it as a tool for studying higher nervous activity. On the other hand, Western theorists, because of their strong behaviourist tradition, regard the conditioned response more as a source of concepts useful in constructing theories to explain more complex behaviour. As we have observed in approaching other problem areas,

337

schisms of this sort can usually be traced to different scientific and philosophical traditions, in this case one attitude being dominated by the views of Sechenov, Pavlov and Asratyan, the other by the theories of Thorndike, Hull and Skinner. Thus, even if we employ the simplest possible afferent/central mediation/efferent model of conditioning, a very different range of interest and emphasis is evident in the two approaches. Soviet theorists come down more strongly on the afferent side — they are more concerned with cortical functioning — Western theorists on the unconditional and efferent sides — their interests centre round reward and punishment mechanisms, instrumental learning and complex processes. This difference is reflected in a number of important ways. One example is the type of "cognitive" mediational variable identified. Soviet theorists emphasise cortical representation of the US, the importance of "acceptor of effect", of return and sanctioning afferentation. On the other hand, for Western learning theorists a more important mediational variable is awareness of CS–US contingencies.

Before reviewing evidence for conditioning theories of personality, which we shall attempt in Chapter 11, we need to examine a number of broad questions in this area, about which some information can be gleaned from both Soviet and Western sources. However, there are a number of difficulties in evaluating such material. Available models of conditioning are fundamentally different. The methodologies employed are hardly comparable. There are infidelities of translation. For these, and other reasons, any subdivision of material for review purposes will inevitably be arbitrary, probably over-inclusive, and likely to have an awkward appearance.

Despite this, we feel that the material can be coherently presented. We shall begin by suggesting a general model of conditioning which is faithful to current neurophysiological theories about structures mediating associations and reinforcements, and one which encompasses learning processes such as sensitisation, habituation and conditioning, which can occur at primitive phyletic levels, involving, for example, simple biological systems such as molluscs. Next we shall briefly touch on one- versus two-process theory of conditioning, and then address ourselves to the real substance of the chapter — sources of variance in conditioning — using, as before, the convenient summary device of identifying separate CS, cortical representational, unconditional (US/UR) and cognitive mediational components. The cortical representational section refers largely to Soviet work, perhaps best represented by Anokhin, with his concept of "acceptor of effect". In discussing the unconditional component, however, we shall be dealing largely with Western theories of arousal, reward and punishment systems, and functional relationships between different arousal systems, a question which is now achieving some prominence in the Western clinical literature. In the section on cognitive mediational variables, problems under discussion will be awareness of CS—US contingencies, the role of imagery, and the contentious issue of "cognitive" control of "involuntary" behaviour.

We are aware, of course, of the dangers of sketching on such a wide canvas. Fine detail is often lost, the viewer may be overwhelmed. Nevertheless, in our opinion, consideration of all these factors is essential before we can begin to understand the dynamics of conditioning, and the ways in which conditioning might account for individual differences in human behaviour.

## Basic Models of Conditioning

A critical feature of any such model is the interaction between cortical and subcortical systems, which, even in the case of relatively simple reflexes, underlies the conditioning process. Consider, for example, limb withdrawal to a painful stimulus or reflex salivation to a food US. In the former, afferent and efferent aspects of the reflex arc occur largely at spinal level, in the latter via the projection from gustatory receptors to the salivary nuclei of the brain stem and thence directly to the salivary glands. However, the CS can only elicit such responses by exciting corticopetal fibres normally activated by the US, which, in turn, can activate cortifugal pathways which excite the motoneurons or salivary nuclei originally responding to the US.

One model which is broadly consistent with known anatomical, electro-physiological and neurophysiological facts is that proposed by Gastaut (1958). This is reproduced in Figure 19. Gastaut proposes that closure, i.e. the new connection, in conditional learning is not completed within the cortex, since considerable evidence indicates that sectioning between, or extirpation of, cortical analysers does not prevent closure. Closure is obtained at sites of convergence of signals within the reticular formation or the non-specifically projecting thalamic nuclei of the brain stem. The development of an excitatory focus in the reticular formation occurs via collaterals from the US afferent pathways, and this is then represented in the cortical projection area, the specificity of this projection mirroring that of the thalamo-cortical focus. The model proposes that ultimately the afferent projections normally activated by the neutral stimulus come to excite projections of the diffuse thalamic system which are activated by the paired CS. Thus the neutral stimulus becomes a CS because it can now excite not only its own cortical representation, but also that of the US.

A good deal of evidence suggests that the diffuse thalamocortical system is involved in selective attention. Samuels (1959) comments that production of selective and phasic alterations of cortical activation by this system might "permit it to control the continuum of consciousness and to serve as a selective

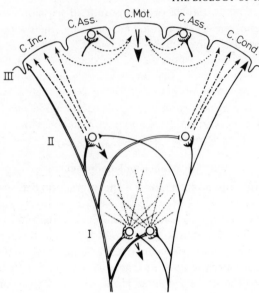

Figure 19. Diagram of the proposed subcortical and cortical levels of the brain involved in the formation of a conditioned reflex. Key: I — The midbrain reticular formation; II — thalamus; III — Cortex. The white pathway (left) is that of the unconditioned stimulus (S); the black pathway (right) that of the conditioned stimulus (s). The circles represent reticular neurons on which the heterogeneous stimuli converge. The unconditioned (C-Inc), the conditional (C-Cond), associational (C-Ass), motor (C-Mot) cortical areas are shown (from Gastaut, 1958).

mechanism for the facilitation of certain perceptions, sensations and memories as well as the inhibition of others" (p.5). Arguably, this system is the locus where CS-US links are formed, so that it might be expected to play an important role in memory. Memory is clearly involved in the re-activation, by the CS, of afferent projections originally excited by the US. Lesions of the dorso-medial nucleus of the diffuse thalamo-cortical system cause memory deficits; degeneration of this nucleus has been associated with Korsakov's syndrome (Barr, 1974).

The actual mechanisms determining the formation of new connections at the cellular level are obviously of considerable importance. These mediate transfer of response from US to CS, and, in simple organisms, probably account for a good deal of adaptive behaviour. One such cellular model, which is depicted in Figure 20, has been suggested by Matthies (1980). The central element is common to mollusc and man — those processes which mediate the making and breaking of associations. The input and output phenomena are the

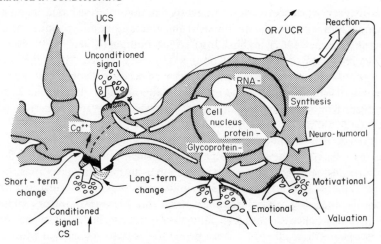

Figure 20. Cellular model of memory formation. Short-term changes of synaptic connectivity by a conditioned input to an integrating neuron; activation of RNA and protein synthesis by an unconditioned input and/or by the subsequent depolarization and action potential; modulation of protein synthesis by motivational neuronal and humoral influences, emotional valuation by dopaminergic input controls glycoprotein synthesis; dendritic transport of glycoproteins and incorporation into synaptic structures formerly facilitated by the conditioned signal; change from a transiently to a permanently efficient synaptic transmission (from Matthies, 1980. *Reproduced by permission of Elsevier/North-Holland Biomedical Press*).

evolutionary "add-ons", which, in some cases, are "hard-wired", as, for example, in certain cases of taste aversion.

## One-/two-process Theory of Conditioning?

We have to ask, of course, whether Gastaut's model is a model of conditioning generally, or simply a model of classical conditioning. Do we propose a one- or two-process theory of conditioning?

While there is little value in fully tracing the history of this controversy, we need to refer to a number of questions, some of which are still unresolved. Initially, a distinction was made between two types of conditioning by Konorski and Miller (1936) and Skinner (1938), who contrasted classical or respondent with instrumental or operant conditioning. Konorski (1948a) commented that instrumental conditioning has a completely different mechanism from that of ordinary (classical) conditioning, and suggested ways in which the two types of conditioning differ. The most fundamental difference — that classical CRs are autonomic, and instrumental CRs skeletal or somatic responses — maintained the earlier distinction between voluntary and involuntary responding.

More recent evidence, however, suggests that this criterion has little validity, judging from extensive data on instrumental autonomic conditioning in humans (Kimmel, 1967), and in curarised sub-humans (Miller, 1969). There is still the residual issue raised by Konorski (1967, 1973) that "the animal must know that the instrumental movement has been performed, or at least ordered, otherwise it will not continue to occur". In attempting to describe mediating variables, Konorski suggests that this "knowledge" need not derive from peripheral feedback, but requires only that appropriate kinaesthetic units be activated coincidentally with drive states. These units are located either in the basal ganglia or in the phyletically newer cortical-kinaesthetic fields. Since there is no neuroanatomical evidence that autonomic responses have appropriate analogous kinaesthetic units, Konorski has suggested that autonomic reactions can be instrumentalised only "if some stimuli provoking a definite autonomic response (e.g. salivation or change in heart rate) coincide with a certain drive (then) they are prone to form an association with it; in consequence, this drive, plus the situation in which coincidence repeatedly took place, will evoke, by association, that activation of the units representing that stimulus (giving rise to its image or hallucination), and this in turn will produce the given autonomic response" (Konorski, 1967).

Generally speaking, two arguments have been advanced in the American literature to support the conclusion that there are no basic differences between the two forms of conditioning. On the one hand, there is some consensus (Kimmel, 1973), that the differences are mainly procedural. While classical conditioning focuses on the relationship between CR and UR, instrumental conditioning focuses on the relationship of CR and US, the difference thus involving the network of connections formed between particular centres. In classical conditioning, since the CS regularly precedes the US, connections are formed between the CS and the US centres (or, more precisely, the cortical representation of the US) under the influence of drive which produces arousal in these centres. On the other hand, in instrumental conditioning, since the CS regularly precedes the appropriate movement, a direct connection is initially formed between the CS centre and the kinaesthetic of that movement (Wyrwicka, 1952); in addition, indirect connections are formed between these and the appropriate US centre (or its cortical representation), which is activated by the appropriate drive (alimentary or defensive, e.g.) (Soltysik, 1960). This is shown schematically in Figure 21.

Within this general framework, Kimmel (1973) has proposed a theory of "reflex habituability" to account for differences between operant and classical conditioning. He has noted the views of a number of authors that differentiation between respondents and operants is largely a matter of differences in degree of stimulus control (Turner and Solomon, 1962;

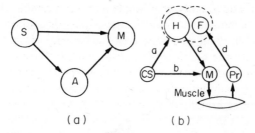

a: S, centre of CS; A, alimentary centre; M, motor centre.
b: CS, centre of CS; H, hunger centre; F, food centre; M, motor centre; Pr, proprioceptive centre.

Figure 21. Block models of alimentary instrumental CR according to Wyrwicka (a) and Soltysik (b).

Schoenfeld, 1966), and the Kozak and Westerman (1966) proposal that all reflexes can be dichotomised as positive or negative feedback reflexes. The former increase afferent input into the CNS (as in the case of OR), the latter reduce afferent input, as in the case of nociceptive reflexes (which also reduce noxious stimulation by withdrawal and escape, as well as by reduction in sensory input).

Kimmel (1973) notes that positive feedback reflexes are plastic, habituate easily, and are, therefore, not generally reinforcing in conditioning, while negative feedback reflexes are relatively non-habituable and reinforcing. Type of reflex interacts with antecedent events to generate different habituation rates. In the case of positive feedback reflexes, where antecedent events are fixed and stable, the reflex habituates very quickly. Since normally a classical CR involves the pairing of a plastic positive feedback reflex (tone reflex) with a negative feedback reflex (such as food reflex), and since habituation of the OR to the CS has long been recognised as an important variable in classical conditioning, it is obvious that, in the latter, fixed, repetitive CS presentation encourages habituation of the plastic reflex, and thus CR development. There is a good deal of supporting evidence on this point (Grings and Kimmel, 1959; Kimmel, Hill and Fowler, 1962; Kimble and Ray, 1965; Kimmel and Reynolds, 1971). Variability in antecedent stimulation clearly attenuates acquisition of classical CRs, since it interferes with habituation of the OR to the CS.

The obverse of this, that constant, antecedent stimulation may attenuate the acquisition of instrumental CRs by facilitating habituation of the original response to the CS, has also been demonstrated. Kimmel (1973) claims that this is the explanation for early failures to demonstrate instrumental conditioning of emotionally mediated responses by Mowrer (1938) and Skinner (1938). He also suggests that subsequent failures to demonstrate the effect (Kimmel and Terrant, 1968; Miller, 1972), after some initial highly encouraging results, may be due to more refined experimental controls, which, in fact, produce precisely those invariant antecedent conditions which impede instrumental learning.

A somewhat different view is the assertion that classical conditioning can be reduced to the same process of "effect" (in the original Thorndike sense) presumed to govern instrumental conditioning. In other words, a CR is acquired in classical conditioning because it is capable of so altering the stimulus consequences of US delivery that execution of a CR is rewarding. CR–US overlap is presumed to be the source of differential reinforcement of CR, through its attenuation of the noxiousness of the aversive US in classical defence conditioning, and by its enhancement of the "attractiveness" of the appetitive US in classical reward conditioning (Hebb, 1956).

This issue has never been unequivocally resolved, although some data make the assertion highly dubious. Gormezano and Coleman (1973), for example, have reported a number of experiments in which amount of CR correlated reinforcement has been manipulated, which suggest that "law of effect" interpretations are not applicable in the case of classical conditioning. Also relevant is Gantt's (1941) finding that the secretary CR and the UR do not summate. Onset of UR inhibits CR. While a reciprocal relationship between CR and UR might be, and often has been, assumed, in that CR secretion might be expected to summate with its following UR, like two allied, segmental motor reflexes (Sherrington), Gantt's data suggest that these are more like antagonistic reflexes struggling for the final common path.

This longstanding debate has recently been brought into sharp focus in a series of articles by Kimmel, Ray and Brown, Dykman, and Gormezano and Tait (*Pavlovian Journal of Biological Science* (1976)) to which the reader is referred. These authors suggest different approaches to the analysis of classical/instrumental differences, but all agree, in principle, that traditional distinctions do not stand the test of careful logical/empirical inspection. Of greatest interest for present purposes is the paper by Gormezano and Tait, who examine the power of the Beritov–Asratyan two-way conditioning theory in accounting for both classical and instrumental conditioning.

According to theory, bidirectional (i.e. forward and backward) connections are assumed to occur in all pairing operations — the pairing of two CSs (sensory preconditioning), of CS and US, of a US followed by a CS (backward conditioning), and of two USs (the paradigm usually chosen by Soviet investigators to demonstrate this effect). Since bidirectional connections occur alike in classical and instrumental conditioning, Pavlovian principles account for both forms. The empirical differences lie not in the mechanisms involved, but in the relative strengths of the forward and backward connections.

The bidirectional distinction can be traced originally to Beritov (1924). The concept of backward connection was subsequently adopted by Pavlov (1932), despite earlier (1927) rejection of such a possibility, to account for "voluntary action" (i.e. instrumental behaviour). The constructs were formally incorporated into a general model of conditioning by Asratyan (1970, 1981), and introduced to Western learning theorists by Razran (1971), and subsequently by Kimmel (1973), whose theory of reflex habituability we have already briefly described. Each of these theorists has addressed different aspects of the theory, two of which have particular significance — that of accounting for the greater strength of the forward, relative to the backward connections in classical conditioning (Beritov and Asratyan), and for the greater strength of the backward connections in instrumental than in classical conditioning (Razran).

Beritov identified characteristic features of bidirectional connections. Forward and backward connections are formed simultaneously, but independently. They obey different functional laws. Backward connections are weaker and more unstable than forward connections, and require many more trials to establish. The strength of the backward connection is inversely related, and the strength of the forward pairing directly related to US intensity. Backward connections are formed more readily when the US is relatively weak, since a strong US interferes with formation of backward connections by generating inhibition — the amount being directly related to US intensity — which blocks transmission of impulses from the CS to the US cortical sites.

Pavlov's account differs little from that of Beritov. He considered that an instrumental response occurs when bidirectional connections are formed between the cortical representations of an appetitive US, and preceding CS-related events, for example, kinaesthetic stimuli arising from leg movements. Subsequently, when the neural centre of the appetitive US is excited (e.g. by deprivation) and the situational (conditioning) cues are present, lifting of the paw is triggered via the reverse connection — "gustatory" US centre kinaesthetic CS centre.

It is Asratyan, the most strictly orthodox of Pavlov's pupils, who has been mainly responsible for consolidation of the concept of bidirectional reflexes within the Soviet theory of conditioning (Asratyan, 1967, 1970, 1972, 1981). He begins with the proposition that the UR/CR interaction is the basic unit of behaviour, being the result of the integrated activity of the whole nervous system in its various centres — the spinal cord, the medulla oblongata, the hypothalamus, the cerebral cortex (Figure 22). A critical element in this integrative process is the extraordinary plasticity of the cerebral cortex, reflected in the complexity of reflexive integration demonstrated by higher forms. He identifies three categories of reflex.

(a) Switching reflexes, where a neutral CS is reinforced with different USs in different situations, at different times of day, and so on, so that the one CS can provoke different CRs, depending on situational variables (see later, pp. 359–60).

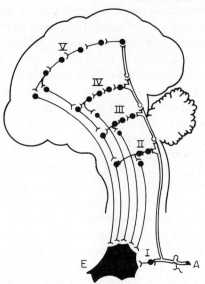

Figure 22. Levels of unconditioned reflex; the CR occurs through integration of levels I–IV with level V. (I) spinal cord; (II) medulla oblongata; (III) hypothalamus; (IV) thalamus; (V) cerebral cortex; A afferent neurons; E efferent neurons (from Asratyan, 1970).

(b) Binary reflexes, where a "dual" CR is developed by reinforcing the same CS simultaneously with two different USs (e.g. food and electric shock), so that the animal emits two CRs to the one CS — salivation and paw withdrawal.

(c) Bidirectional reflexes (following Beritov). When a "simple" CR is formed, both forward and backward connections occur; in the former (direct CR), the CS evokes the CR, in the latter (reverse CR), application of the US, alone, provokes a response "corresponding to the CS". For example, when a mild electric shock to the paw (CS) is reinforced with a food US, eventually the shock will produce conditioned salivation, i.e., a direct CR. However, when food is subsequently presented alone, it evokes a conditioned motor defence reaction (paw withdrawal), i.e. a reverse CR.

In emphasising the integrative capacity of the nervous system, particularly the cerebral cortex, Asratyan points out that even in the case of relatively straightforward, direct CR development, the processes involved are probably quite complex. Environmental factors, and experimental conditions, in combination, form "continuously active conditioned stimuli", or tonic reflexes, which create a functional background on which the phasic CS is superimposed, as figure. Thus, in most conditioning situations/experiments, the "simple" CR represents an integration of those tonic and phasic stimuli which delineate the total environmental situation in which the animal is behaving. It is always an interaction between the functional state of the animal, motivational variables, and the continuing kaleidoscope of environmental flux.

There are two other aspects of Asratyan's general theory which are germane to the present discussion. Firstly, he replaces Pavlov's single reflex pathway with a "neural net", a multitude of pathways passing through different cortical structures, the extent of such nets being proportional to the physical characteristics (e.g. intensity, duration) of the external stimulus. Secondly, he attaches great importance to the "biological significance" of stimuli, which Pavlov also emphasised but which he did not attempt to operationalise. Asratyan maintains that the biological significance of the stimuli determines the size of the neural net, and thus the amount of neural excitation. This greatly affects the strength of stimulus pairing — the connection will be strongest between two stimuli of intense biological significance ($US_1$–$US_2$), and weakest between two stimuli of slight biological significance (sensory preconditioning, $CS_1$–$CS_2$). It follows also that the forward connection in classical conditioning occurs because the US neural net is stronger than the CS neural net, "drainage" thus proceeding from CS to US. Where intensity of CS is increased, however, we may reach a stage where cortical drainage is equal in both directions, so that the strengths of the forward and backward connections are equivalent.

In his most recent statement, Asratyan (1981) continues to insist on the universality of two-way connections, which he regards as inherent in all known types of CR in higher animals, and cites extensive supporting data from his own and from Czech laboratories (Dostalek, 1964). Illustrative data for both classical and instrumental conditioning are presented in Figure 23. Asratyan claims that the bidirectional connection is not one CR conducting excitation in either direction, but rather two CRs, which may differ in strength and stability, moving in opposite directions, a view similar to that proposed by Ebbinghaus (1885) in accounting for two-way associative connections between meaningless syllables. Thus, for example, a BAV–ZOL link implies a ZOL–BAV connection. The direct CR is established following principles of Bahnung, dominance or sensitisation, and it is only with the emergence of the reverse connection that "true" conditioning occurs, since this allows excitation to "circulate" between the two activated cortical points, potentiating and enhancing their activity. The reverse connection, according to Asratyan, serves as a nucleus, a central element in the physiological mechanism of reinforcement. In extinction, omission of reinforcement leads to the blocking, through internal inhibition, initially of the reverse conditioned connection, and subsequently of the direct conditioned connection.

The two reflexes, however, are integrated into one functional system. This is

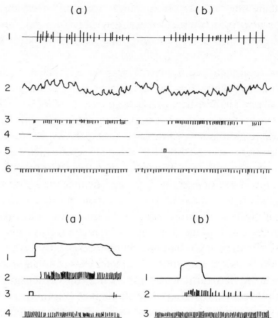

Figure 23. Upper trace: Eyeblink — alimentary bilateral CR. A: Air-puff (4) elicits eyblink UR (I) and CR salivation (3). B: Food (5) evokes UR salivation (3) and eyeblink CR (I); (2) is respiration, (6) time in seconds. (Rudenko's data, cited by Asratyan, 1981. Reproduced by permission of J. B. Lippincott Co.)
Lower trace: Alimentary instrumental CR. A: Appearance of food (3) evokes CR flexion of paw (I) and salivaion (2). B: Passive flexion of paw (I) evokes CR salivation (2); (4) and (3) indicate time in seconds. (Popova's data, cited by Asratyan, 1981. Reproduced by permission of J. B. Lippincott Co.)

suggested by evidence of sequential or chained responding. When a two-way CR is established between paw flexion and eyeblink reflex, for example, unconditional paw movement "causes" conditional blinking, followed by conditional paw movement, followed eventually by further conditioned blinking.

Asratyan also notes that insofar as reflex "correction" is concerned, his intra-neocortical model does not demand a fourth link in the reflexive chain, as required by some Soviet theorists, such as Anokhin, who postulates an "acceptor of action" to monitor the central-peripheral feedback loop in order to assess the appropriateness of the adaptational response.

Asratyan, therefore, in general agreement with Beritov and Pavlov, regards instrumental conditioning as a special case of classical conditioning of the two-way type (Figure 24). Note the similarity of this model to those proposed by

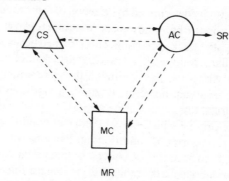

Figure 24. Diagram of instrumental conditioning according to Asratyan: CS, the conditioned stimulus; AC, the alimentary or feeding centre, with SR the salivary response; MC, the motor centre, with MR the motor response (from Asratyan, 1970).

Wyrwicka and Soltysik (Figure 21). Temporary connections can be formed between the US centres, the feeding or alimentary centre (AC), and the motor centre (MC). Since these connections are bidirectional, when the CS activates the AC, it can also simultaneously activate the MC, producing either a salivary or motor response, or both. Classical conditioning refers specifically to the CS–AC connection, instrumental conditioning to the CS–AC–MC, or to the CS–MC connection. Thus the critical difference between classical and instrumental conditioning is that the former reflects stronger forward, the latter stronger backward connections.

It is obvious from the discussion so far that a weak point in Soviet two-way conditioning theory is its failure to account for the greater strength of backward connections in instrumental than in classical conditioning. "Drainage" explanations seem inadequate, as does Asratyan's neural net theory involving the biological significance of stimuli. The only theorist who has seriously attempted to resolve this issue is Razran in his attempts to build a conceptual bridge between Soviet and Western conditioning theories.

Razran (1971) employs the core concept of "habituability" to account for the difference. The strength of the forward connection is directly related to the habituability of the first stimulus, whether CS or US. An inverse relationship holds for the backward connection. Since, in classical conditioning, ORs to the CS are readily habituated, classical procedures favour formation of forward connections. However, since instrumental responses (escape, those concerned with obtaining food) are biologically highly significant, and thus not readily habituated, instrumental procedures favour the development of backward connections. To this extent, the strength of the bidirectional connections in each case is artefactually determined by selection of response systems occupying different positions on the habituation continuum. However, on this basis, it is difficult to see why the backward connection formed between two USs should be stronger that that developed in a US–CS pairing, since the second stimulus (US) in the first case is clearly less habituable than its counterpart in the second. As in the case of Asratyan, however, Razran's hypotheses have not yet been subjected to empirical test.

As yet, the one-process bidirectional theory of conditioning has had little impact on Western theories of conditioning. Reasons for this are unclear. It may be due in part to incomplete understanding of Pavlovian conditioning theory, or of the great plasticity of the cortex in integrating behaviour. What is clear is that the associationist dogma which has guided Western theory emphatically rejects the notion of backward conditioning as an associative phenomenon. This injunction requires that classical and instrumental conditioning be considered different forms of learning, despite the fact that the traditional dichotomy of classical/instrumental responses being restricted to autonomic/skeletal response systems can no longer be endorsed. There is little evidence that the two forms are governed by different empirical laws. On the other hand, Soviet theorists (and, indeed, Western researchers such as Gormezano and Tait) have failed to demonstrate convincingly that bidirectional conditioning occurs along *all* conditioning paradigms.

An alternative to the bidirectional theory is the two-process theory, which still commands support amongst Western learning theorists. Gray has presented evidence for and against this view in his recent book "Elements of a two-process theory of learning" (1975), to which the reader is referred for a fuller account. We shall briefly summarise his argument, which appears to rest on two simple propositions.

(a) Initially, neutral stimuli may acquire motivational, conditional significance through classical conditioning.

(b) Having acquired such significance, these stimuli may guide instrumental behaviour towards, or away from reinforcement (goals).

These propositions are formally grounded in the old Miller–Mowrer theory of avoidance learning, which proposes that:

1. neutral stimuli acquire secondary aversive properties if they are followed by punishment;

2. animals exposed to such stimuli will attempt to terminate this exposure (instrumental component);

3. such CS termination is the critical reinforcing event — in this case, in active avoidance.

Gray draws support for the two-process theory from a number of sources. The most relevant is that involving Sidman avoidance, where internal stimuli monitoring passage of time — specifically the interval between the last response and onset of punishment — become conditioned warning signals for instrumental avoidance. He cites a considerable amount of supportive evidence, of which perhaps the most illustrative is that reported by Rescorla and Lolordo (1965). These authors employed a technique — one which, incidentally, has been used extensively for assessing tranquilliser effects — in which classically conditioned signals (CS → Pun, CS → Rew), off the baseline, are used to manipulate operant responses, whether avoidance (e.g. the Sidman shuttle-box) or appetitive (e.g. bar-pressing for food/water). They trained dogs in Sidman avoidance, US being shock, then exposed them to classical contingencies, US still being shock. The dogs were then returned to the Sidman shuttle-box, and presented the classical CSs. Rescorla and Lolordo report that CSs which were followed by shock in the classical procedure now provoke increased shuttling rate. On the basis of these results, they conclude that the CS acquires fear significance through classical conditioning, then potentiates the instrumental (avoidance) behaviour. Clearly, two distinct processes are involved.

Gray applies the two-process theory to many areas of learning, such as conflict behaviour, where the animal approaches both reward and punishment. Initially, neutral stimuli can become signals for both impending reward and punishment, thus affecting strength of approach (incentive motivation) and avoidance (fear motivation) respectively.

It is obvious that in the present circumstances we cannot fully argue the merits of one- as against two-process theories. As in so many debates in areas of learning and conditioning, data are often ambiguous, the evidence circumstantial, lines of demarcation unclear. In such instances, judgement rests ultimately on personal preference and conviction. We feel that, on balance, the weight of evidence probably supports one-process theory, different relationships rather than different processes differentiating the two forms of conditioning. However, we agree with Schoenfeld (1971), who has proposed that classical and instrumental responses occurring to a CS should be regarded as a biological whole, although it is obvious that under certain conditions the two may be separated. We can, and perhaps should avoid pitting one- against two-process theory by regarding instrumental conditioning as simply another level of sophistication. From an evolutionary point of view, we might propose a multi-level, vertical organisation, involving increasingly complex and "younger" brain systems, extending upwards from sensitisation, to habituation, to classical, then to instrumental conditioning, finally to imitation learning and the various forms of cognition, "lower" forms overlapping with, entering into and infusing "higher" forms. Limits are presumably imposed by phylogeny and the ontogenetic stage of the organism under study.

## Associative Linking: the Neuroanatomical Locus of the CR

Associative learning occurs when potential connections linking centres representing paired stimuli are transformed into functional connections through increased transmittability of synapses linking the neurons belonging to each of the centres. The necessary condition for associative learning is that S must pay attention to the presented pair of stimuli. The physiological basis of attention is the arousal of the corresponding centre. A CR is thus a special case of associative learning in which activation of the recipient (usually the US) centre, as distinct from the transmitting (CS) centre, is "labelled" by its ability to elicit an observable response, so that when the functional connection between these centres is formed, the stimulus activating the latter elicits the response characteristic of the former.

But how are these functional connections made, what determines the ease with which they occur, and how many identifiable links in the reflex chain are observable? We can identify at least four.

### 1. CS Characteristics

Although the relationship of CS intensity to CR acquisition rate has long been recognised by Western learning theorists, the importance of this variable in conditioning has been minimised. Choice of both CS modality and intensity seems to be dictated largely by methodological convenience.

As noted previously, however, the Teplov-Nebylitsyn typology differentiates the strength-sensitivity property, referring to arousability to any sensory stimulus, such as those normally selected as CSs, from dynamism, which describes reflex sensitivity to reinforcement. This distinction traces to views originally advanced by Sechenov and Ukhtomskii. Pavlov's concept of the nature of conditioning was that excitation initiated by the US in one neural centre attracts the weaker excitation initiated by other stimuli present at the same time, in accordance with Ukhtomskii's principle of the dominant. In this way, a temporary connection is formed. However, while Sechenov considered the association to be between two reflexes, the first an orienting reflex (OR) to the CS, the second the US reflex, each of which could be a source of variance, Pavlov seems to have been unconcerned about the distinctive functional characteristics of CS and US. Thus he attached little significance to individual differences in OR for conditioning. While these might be important as an index of external inhibition, the OR was not systematically studied (only five reports concerning OR were published from his laboratories), nor did it emerge as a critical variable in his typological theorising. Pavlov was much more concerned with what he regarded as important cortical mediational processes — irradiation, concentration, and the like — in conditioning.

Clearly, however, the law of strength describes one aspect of the CS–CR relationship. In acquisition, Kupalov (1969) reports that increased CS intensity resulted in his experimental animals (dogs) now jumping a high barrier, which previously, at lower CS intensities, they had refused. He also records that extinction rate of conditioned motor reflexes may differ according to the intensity of CSs presented in extinction, despite equivalent levels of response consolidation. Similar relationships have been demonstrated for classical CRs in animals (Krasuskii, 1964), and for motor CRs in man (Kas'yanov and Fruktov, 1952).

Recently, typological theorists have suggested that the function of excitation generated to the "adequate" CS is to maintain arousal in the cortical projection area until the cortical representation of the US is stabilised in the secondary and perhaps tertiary projection areas. There is convincing evidence, of course, that limbic centres are more in control of the cortex when the animal has learned, and is merely routinely responding to reward, i.e. there is a shift from ARAS to limbic control. Insofar as initial learning is concerned, however, CS properties have a considerable influence on CR acquisition rate. This is considered to be particularly important when the US is not "biologically significant", as in sensory (EEG or PCR) conditioning, where, according to Nebylitsyn (1972), speed of CR development depends largely on strength-sensitivity in the CS modality — a matter of some concern when we consider personality/conditioning research in the West, since many of the reinforcements offered (e.g. aversive white noise) are, arguably, of this type. Generally speaking, a weak to moderately intense CS encourages more rapid CR development in a "weak" or "arousable" than in a strong system, since in the former it creates a relatively stronger focus of cortical excitation. On the other hand, a very intense CS impedes CR development in the weak system, since it provokes earlier onset of transmarginal inhibition. To this extent, therefore, we can describe a factor of CS responsiveness. CS modality, however, is an important consideration. Apart from the fact that stronger cortical excitation is generated to auditory than to visual CSs, for example, implying that auditory CSs evoke more rapid development of CRs than visual CSs, there is the problem that, within-Ss, nervous system sensitivity is modality-specific, i.e. does not correlate across modalities (Wertheimer, 1955; Nebylitsyn, 1957a,b, 1972; Rozhdestvenskaya et al., 1960).

Given these relationships between CS intensity and modality and CR development, what are the actual processes and mechanisms involved? Pavlov and his co-workers initially referred to irradiation and concentration, which they regarded as extremely important laws of neural action, and which they empirically demonstrated, but there was no attempt to identify underlying cortical processes.

Some modern adherents of this school have suggested possible mechanisms. For example, Wyrwicka (1973), on the basis of Morrell's (1967) demonstration that some cortical neurons respond to more than one kind of stimulation, has suggested that sensory traces of stimuli intermingle to form patterns of associations in polymodal brain structures, the sensory traces of the stronger stimuli dominating the sensory traces of the weaker stimuli in the pattern. Activation of the pattern by either stimulus releases the response typical of the stronger stimulus. This is, in fact, a version of dominance theory, which has been influential in a number of models of conditioning (e.g. Razran, 1957).

These combined sensory traces, associations among the neural representations of stimuli, continue for some time after pairing, retention time depending on number of repetitions, stimulus intensities, and the capacity of the neurons involved. The existence of such patterns has been claimed by John and colleagues (John, Shimokochi and Bartlett 1969; John, 1972), and Asratyan (1967). The former have demonstrated that certain aspects of electrical activity evoked by the CS in large ensembles of neurons in various brain regions may be "independent" of that stimulus. This activity, which they describe as "read-out component", refers to release of a specific memory of a learned association, so that one stimulus of the pair evokes a learned pattern of associations typically evoked by the combined stimuli.

Asratyan's data point to the same general conclusions. Where two stimuli of approximately equal intensity are combined — for example, food and electric shock, passive flexion of the leg and air puff — after a number of pairings, either stimulus of the pair evokes both reactions. For example, shock produces not only lifting of the paw, but also salivation. Where one stimulus of the pair is considerably stronger than the other, however, either stimulus evokes the stronger response. Note also that any stimulus superimposed on a background of reflexive responding may elicit the reflexive, rather than the more adaptive response. A good example is Ukhtomskii's (1927) report that after strong reflex excitation of the swallowing centre, stimulation of the motor cortex projection area of an extremity produces swallowing, not movement.

What are the implications for conditioning? Insofar as classical conditioning is concerned, if food, for example, is a stronger stimulus to a hungry animal than tone or light, when the latter, as CSs, produce salivation, it follows that the CR must be a response to traces of sensory changes produced by food — thus "images" of previous reinforcement — which dominate in the pattern of associations. The CR has moved in time from a post- to pre-reinforcement position, so that something additional is present in the pattern of associations. This is a necessary inference from many observations reported — for example, Pavlov's finding that the viscosity of conditioned reflex saliva reflects the quality of the reinforcement (e.g. bread or meat) on the previous trial, and thus its salivogenic effect. Judging from the fact that CR and UR amplitudes are positively correlated within response systems, an observation originally reported by Pavlov (1955) and subsequently strongly supported (e.g. Spence and Taylor, 1951; Barr and McConaghy, 1971) we might argue that the CR is a "mimicked" UR. It is not, however, an exact copy (Kimble, 1961). The question arises, therefore, of how these sensory traces, or at least some elements of the UR, become represented in the pattern of associations?

Insofar as instrumental conditioning is concerned, the associative pattern reflects exactly the sequence of events — tone, instrumental act, food, for example. The instrumental act, because of its pre-reinforcement origin, is present in the initial pattern of associations. Does this imply that instrumental conditioning does not involve the kind of feedback mechanisms which seem to be required in classical conditioning? We might recall that in the former, when a movement is performed which is followed by cessation of drive (e.g. hunger or fear), the CS centre becomes connected with the kinaesthetic centre programming the instrumental act. In alimentary conditioning, this move-ment, executed in the presence of the hunger CS, is followed by presentation of food, which excites the reinforcement centre. A series of feeding responses is then initiated, the strength of these being determined by factors such as gut distension, blood glucose level, and so on. Feedback from these responses "gates" the hunger centres in the lateral hypothalamus and the ventro-medial hypothalamus. In avoidance conditioning, the instrumental response per-formed in the presence of the fear CS is immediately followed by cessation of this CS, which leads to fear reduction. In both cases, there are obviously feedback loops to the hunger and fear centres indicating cessation of hunger and fear, but there seems no necessity for assuming a mechanism anything like that required for the cortical representation of the US in classical conditioning. Instrumental behaviour always precedes reinforcement, i.e. the release from undesirable sensations, and for this reason, the associative pattern, from the outset, consists of sensory traces of the CS, feedback from the instrumental response, and sensory changes related to withdrawal or avoidance of shock, or ingestion of food, in that sequence. Clearly these traces must be blended or intermingled into an associative patterns, but the polymodal cortical neurons described by Wyrwicka (1973) seem adequate to perform this function. We might ask, however, whether similar structures mediate the cortical representation of the US in classical conditioning.

## 2. Cortical Representation of the US

The ability of higher vertebrates to have mental images was recognised by Sechenov and Pavlov. Sechenov (1878) spoke of sensory images, of concrete object thinking in animals. Pavlov, however, did not think of images as having particular biological significance, and did not study them in detail. Anokhin (1958) was perhaps the first to acknowledge the fundamental controlling action of the psychoneural processes responsible for the production of concrete images. However, to avoid the terminology of image and mental representation, he coined the term "acceptor of effect" to represent the residual complex of afferent traces, remnants of previous reinforcements, which are reproduced in the animal on presentation of the CS.

Anokhin cites a considerable amount of evidence from studies involving cross-anastomosis of nerves which suggest that restoration of disturbed function is dependent largely on return signalisation of the degree of success of the first reflex responses to the central nervous system. Such compensation is shown when the relevant peripheral structures are subjected to de-afferentation, or the appropriate cortical area is extirpated. In this connection, of interest is some recent work (Purves, 1980) indicating the complexity of the relationships between nerves and their target organs. Neurones projecting to muscles will degenerate in the absence of the target organ, since the latter produces nerve growth factor (NGF) preventing degeneration of efferent nerves.

According to Anokhin, return afferentation, which moves in a direction opposite to the original effector excitation, and thus has both a correcting and reinforcing action, is implicit in the concept of reinforcement. It is possible to reinforce only something that is already occurring, the addressee of the reinforcement itself. This is the conditioned excitation in the cortex, i.e. the excitation in the cortical representation of the unconditioned centres. In this way, Anokhin has added a fourth element in the reflexive process — afferentation, central selection, efferentation, and return afferentation. We might note that this concept is implicit in many functional theories of perception, in servomechanism theory and cybernetics.

Pavlov, of course, in his later speculations about localisation of cortical conditioned connections, had postulated cortical representation of URs, specific cortical loci which become excited following stimulation of the appropriate receptors, rather than the coupling of the cortical locus of the CS with the subcortical UR centre. This view was based on empirical findings that the combined CR produced by the simultaneous action of two or more positive CSs in the same modality was less than the sum of CR values from the separate reflexes. This can only be explained, reasoned Pavlov, is we assume that the conditioned connection is between two cortical loci, since cortical cells, by comparison with subcortical cells, have such relatively low working capacities that they are unable to summate volleys of impulses from a number of sources. This would not be the case, he argued, if UR representation were exclusively subcortical. Thus his contention (one which, incidentally, we would hesitate to challenge for other reasons) that the actual conditioned connection is between two cortical points. It is his further inference, that the connection is therefore located entirely within the cortex, i.e., within the limits of its own structures, which is inadmissible.

Modern neurophysiological evidence indicates clearly that even if the psychoneural process of image representation is cortically mediated, this reflects processes occurring at more primitive levels. Miniature representation of the cortex occurs at reticular level, where the initial linking takes place. It is, after all, the fronto-pallido-hippocampal system which selects, compares and integrates sensory information at the stage of afferent synthesis. Consolidation of memory traces, clearly a critical event in associative learning, involves hippocampal structures; such consolidation is accompanied by increased hippocampal RNA synthesis (Shumskaya and Korochkin, 1975). Bilateral hippocampal ablation grossly impedes avoidance learning, particularly under stressful conditions (e.g. Gembaryan et al., 1979). Equally impressive data from other sources point to the same overall conclusion. To unduly emphasise cortical "control" in conditioning, therefore, is unwarranted.

But to return to Anokhin's model. He suggests that, since most behaviour is chained, the correct sequence of links can only be achieved if each link receives, in the form of "reinforcement", the appropriate return afferentation. But what determines the final stage, when further reflexive behaviour is checked? This can only be the stage at which the return afferentation from the periphery matches the stored complex of excitations present before the actual reflex act took shape. Such "sanctioning afferentation" corresponds to the "intention" giving rise to the reflex act itself. Physiologically, this requires some form of afferent control apparatus, determining the extent to which the particular return afferentation reaching the brain centres corresponds to this complex. Anokhin describes this mechanism, which is claimed to be located in the frontal regions of the cortex (Shumilina, 1949), as the "acceptor of effect" (Figure 25). We note, however, that this control apparatus, if shown to exist, can operate only in the case of "complex" conditioning, since many ablation studies report conditioning in the absence of virtually all cortex, let alone the frontal cortex.

As we mentioned previously, the nature of the stored complex of excitation is directly dependent on the nature of the previous reinforcement, judging from a good deal of evidence. The fact that the conditioned effector excitation in response to the CS corresponds to the effector excitation produced by the US (although not exactly) which follows it in time, logically requires some cortical representation of the unconditioned centre. It must be afferent, since the US is afferent. As Laptev (1938) has suggested, it is not a definite cortical locus, but a system of afferent cells integrated into a single, complete unit. On CS

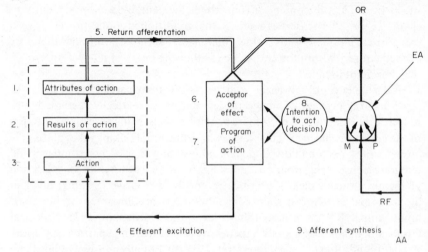

358                                                   THE BIOLOGY OF HUMAN CONDUCT

Figure 25. Anokhin's model describing the behavioural act. The acceptor of effect signals any discrepancy between the outcome (return afferentation) and the goal of the behavioural act. AA is the activating stimulus; RF collaterals to the reticular formation; M is dominant motive, P is memory; EA denotes contextual environmental stimuli, and OR the orienting reaction.

presentation, this group of cells, composed of traces of the UR, becomes excited several seconds before US presentation, producing a CR, which, through return afferentation, is compared with the supplementary complex of afferent excitations deposited by previous experience. Where the stored afferent excitation in the pattern of association which follows the CR is not matched by the UR complex, an OR develops, as, for example, when bread is substituted for meat as reinforcement. In this case, the complex of visual, olfactory and gustatory nerve impulses to the cortex does not match the stored afferent excitation.

Thus Anokhin's "acceptor of effect", or cortical control mechanism, fulfils the function of assessing the results of any reflex act or adaptational effect. It is a psychoneural process of image representation which develops during reinforcement. As Anokhin notes

> being formed under the influence of external events and being a part of each CS, the "acceptor of effect" plays a determining role in adaptive behaviour. On the basis of different impulses affecting sense organs, it determines the degree of precision and adequacy of the resulting act elicited by the original stimulus.

To this extent, it is a physiological analogue of the phenomenological outcome referred to by Thorndike (1935) as "law of effect". We might evaluate this concept in the context of attempts by a number of theorists, previously described, to employ the concept of "effect" to account for classical as well as instrumental conditioning.

What is the neurophysiological mechanism mediating mental images? Beritov (1961) suggests that the neural matrix involved is the complex of short axon stellate cells located in the third and fourth layers of the primary cortical projection areas. These are integrated into a functional network through a complex loop consisting of association neurons and internuncials, lying mainly in the association areas between the projection areas, and in the secondary cortical receptive areas — for example, in areas 18 and 19 for vision. However, while images of the environment are formed on the first trial, being simply connections between receptive stellate cells, in development of CRs images formed in the stellate cells receiving the CS are linked with the large pyramidal effector cells over a number of trials. When the CS image is produced in the secondary receptive areas of the cortex following activation of the short axon stellate cells in the primary receptive area, the conditioned excitation irradiates and excites the cortical representation of the unconditioned centre, the complex of afferent traces (tactile, gustatory, olfactory) which then excites the effector organ — muscle or gland. Note that the cortical representation of the unconditioned centre is excited twice — first by the CS, then by the US.

It could be that the cortical representation of the unconditioned centre — the stored images or traces of the UR — is an additional source of variance in conditioning. While it may be that responsivity in these centres directly reflects responsivity in the subcortical centres mediating reinforcement, under the influence of appropriate drive, there may be differences characterising the cortical cells themselves (strength, for example).

Are there other factors affecting responsivity in these cortical centres mediating the CS and US? At least one additional possibility has been suggested by Asratyan and his colleagues, who have reported data on "switching" or schaltung, a phenomenon observed and studied much earlier by Sechenov and by Magnus (1924), and, more recently, by Konorski and Miller (1936), Vatsuro (1949), Struchkov (1976), for example. Switching refers to the fact that context can serve as a distinct CS, that the context and the designated CS are both components of the stimulus configuration. This proposition has recently attracted a good deal of attention in American conditioning theory (e.g. Rescorla and Wagner, 1972; Estes, 1973).

Asratyan's data, first obtained in 1936, demonstrate that a single indifferent CS can acquire two different signal meanings at the same time — alimentary and defensive, positive and negative, short delay and long delay — by differentially reinforcing the CS (in different rooms, at different times of day, by different experimenters), using in one instance food reinforcement, in the other shock, immediate reinforcement in one situation, delayed reinforcement in the other, and so on. The conditions under which the CS shifts its cue value are denoted switchover factors.

Data reported by Shitov and Lakovleva (1937) are typical. In the morning, metronome beats of 128 per minute were paired, as CS, with food reinforcement; in the afternoon, with the same dogs, in the same room, the same CS was paired with electric shock to the paw. Similar types of discrimination were also developed to the same CS in different rooms, as was development of the same CR to two different CSs, in different rooms, and at different times of day. The fact that these discriminations can be learned and differentially extinguished suggests that excitation and inhibition are not located in the CS focus (contrary to the views of Pavlov, Babkin (1904) and Zeleni (1906), that the CS focus is the site of conditioned inhibition), since in different rooms, and at different times, the same CS evokes different CRs. Nor can these be located in the US focus, since different CSs can evoke the same CRs in different rooms, at different times, to different experimenters, although note the views of Perelzweig (1907) and Anokhin (1932) that the US is the site of conditioned inhibition. Asratyan suggests that the switchover factors (rooms, time of day, experimenters) direct the phasic CRs, and might themselves be regarded as tonic CSs, creating a reflex background on which phasic conditioned reflex activity is superimposed.

The implication of these findings, viz., that a single CS can fully retain the old, as well as the new, cue value, by contrast with the more usual case in which a new cue value displaces the older salience, is that the same locus in the cortex, i.e. the point to which the CS is addressed, is the site of at least two temporary connections at the same time. We should distinguish this type of behaviour — the switchover from one CR pathway to another CR pathway — from that in which excitation is switched from the UCR to the CR pathway. The latter is the basis on which any CR is formed, since conditioning is fundamentally a process in which excitation elicited by a neutral stimulus is switched from its "natural" or unconditional, to a new, conditional pathway. Such switchover activity is obviously an expression of the "leading function" of the highest part of the nervous system (Pavlov, 1951-2). In the former case, some form of differential inhibition, a special blockade of a temporary connection, clearly cannot occur at the cortical site of either CS or US, and thus must be localised somewhere in the structures of the temporary connection itself.

In this connection, of interest are data reported by Daurova (cited by Asratyan, 1962, p. 182) concerning transmarginal inhibition. An alimentary CR was developed to a tone frequency of 1100 cps and 45 dB in one situation, and an avoidance CR to the same stimulus in another situation. Both experiments were conducted on the same day and in no particular order. When both CSs were increased in intensity to 105–115 dB, however, the CS failed to evoke an alimentary CR, but did elicit the avoidance behaviour. Thus the CS was transmarginal for one response, while retaining its positive value for the other. Asratyan suggests, on this basis, that transmarginal inhibition is not localised in the CS focus, as Pavlov maintained, but in subsequent components of the conditioned reflex arc. Exactly where, however, is problematical.[1]

The question arises, of course, of whether social conditioning, conditioning outside artificial laboratory situations, always, or usually, involves contextual variables of the sort referred to in the switching experiments. We would suggest that this is the case, and are reminded of Helson's (1959) emphasis on the importance of such variables in human psychophysical and perceptual responding, and his attempts to apply adaptation level principles — admittedly with little success — in the field of social perception.

There is little doubt that physiological adaptation or tonic conditioned reflex effects are clearly demonstrated in animal behaviour. There are many instances reported in the Soviet literature. A simple example reported by Khachaturian (cf. Asratyan, 1958) will suffice. He reports a study in which reflex salivation to 10 grams food mixture was measured in dogs on two occasions separated by a one week interval. During this period, the dogs were fed on 50 grams identical mixture. Salivation to the 10 grams portion on the second occasion was significantly greater, although gradually reverting to base rate during the seven day trial.

Finally, a brief comment on the finding that the CR is usually not exactly the same as the UR, seldom an exact copy. This might be expected, for a number of reasons. Firstly, although the efferent limbs of CR and UR might be identical, initial pathways involved in their evocation are not. Secondly, the animal is usually not oblivious to the different contexts in which CS and US occur. While a CS acquires aversive properties through association with electric shock, for example, it also signals the imminence of shock. The US does not. Thus, motor response to CS is different from that to US. To the former, the animal may freeze, brace itself against the impending shock, to the latter, there may be increased motor activity. Finally, as we have previously mentioned (Chapter 3) higher nervous functioning in man may be governed by laws different from those applying to lower forms. Additional information may be introduced at higher levels, mediating selections of a CR which is not the same as the UR. The thrust of Vygotsky's theory of signification relates to man's active construction

---

[1]It is difficult to appreciate the logic of this argument. From present knowledge, and assuming that the CS focus is cortical, there is no reason why one CS focus cannot be shut down (transmarginal inhibition) while avoidance behaviour continues. A loud noise is unpleasant irrespective of its particular sensory qualities (such as frequency) which would require cortical processing. In any event, subcortical areas can effectively 'sense' intensity and crude parameters of signals.

of reality, involving the connection of artificially created signs and the fabrication of sign structures to advance personal goals and objectives.


### 3. Unconditional, i.e. US and UR Mechanisms

#### (a) Concepts of arousal

Arousal is usually considered to be uni-polar, and reward-punishment a bi-polar dimension. Often the two are placed orthogonally to provide a definition of any stimulus in two-dimensional space. The arousal axis is shown as arousal potential, that is, the amount of arousal produced by a stimulus, while the $S_{r+}$ or the $S_{r-}$ of the stimulus is the direction in which, and the extent to which, it modifies behaviour in an instrumental situation. Considerable evidence, however, has called into question both the concept of a single arousal dimension, and the assumption that all behaviour modifications of the type described are mediated by one form of reward or punishment system. Specific examples are, for the former, paradoxical sleep, and, for the latter, Gray's claim of equivalence of omission of reward and punishment, and equivalence of omission of punishment and reward.

Most arousal theories attach considerable importance to the role of the ascending reticular activating system (ARAS), the loosely organised region of nerve fibres and nuclei situated along the centre of the brain stem, which, from electrical stimulation and lesion studies, has been shown to control the degree of arousal of the cortex. All levels of the ARAS receive inputs branching off from the main sensory tracts. As a result, sensory stimulation is conveyed upwards to the cortex by this route, as well as directly to the projection areas. In essence, the theory states that the afferent collaterals convey sensory stimulation to the ARAS, which in turn stimulates and arouses the cortex, which can then process more efficiently the sensory information carried by the direct sensory route. If the ARAS of a drowsy animal is electrically stimulated, it becomes alert, the critical observation being that stimulation in other areas, for example, the cortex, does not necessarily produce this effect. By using a combination of stimulation and lesion techniques, we can show that it is stimulation of the ARAS, and not direct stimulation of the cortex via sensory pathways, which is the critical stimulus for arousal. If the ARAS is destroyed, sensory stimulation produces only transient arousal in the animal, the EEG quickly reverting to a somnolent state.

More careful experiments, however, seem to demonstrate that the posterior hypothalamus is more important in behavioural arousal, and the reticular formation in EEG arousal. Lesions in the posterior hypothalamus result in somnolent behaviour, even when stimulation of the ARAS produces EEG desynchronisation. On the other hand, it has been shown that cats with lesions carefully placed in the ARAS can orient towards moving objects. Sectioning the brainstem at the midpontine level produces fast cortical EEG and permanent wakefulness.

In this connection, we should mention the locus coeruleus, Raphé nucleus, and "large cell bodies" which exercise important control over "arousal" and sleep/wake cycles. These are active neural mechanisms which can isolate the cortex by shutting down sensory input and motor output, while still allowing the cortex to function at high levels of activity, as, for example, in dreaming (Hobson and McCarley, 1977).

## (b) Functional relationships between arousal sub-systems

Usually arousal is measured by a number of behavioural indices — CNS (EEG, for example), motor (increased body movements), sensory (lowered thresholds) and autonomic (GSR, heart rate changes, etc.). These roughly quantitative measures were, in the past, assumed to be correlated, since they were thought to be peripheral indices of a central arousal state. A good deal of more recent evidence, however, suggests that this is not the case. Indices tend not to correlate, within-S, this lack of concomitance being formally incorporated in the principle of individual relative response specificity (Lacey and Lacey, 1958b) which we have already referred to in Chapter 2 when reviewing evidence of individual differences in responsivity in different effector systems as one source of variation in nervous system activity over different brain systems. Very briefly, this states that subjects exhibit idiosyncratically specific patterns of autonomic reactivity under stress — some individuals respond maximally in the cardiac system, others in the vasomotor system, others again in the somatic system — such activation hierarchies being reliable upon immediate re-test and across different stressor episodes. Clearly this principle applies also to conditioned response phenomena, probably assuming greatest significance when aversive stimuli, generating pain and fear, are employed as reinforcement; the case for appetitive reinforcement is much less clearcut.

Increasingly in the literature, however, there has been, paradoxically, some suggestion of lawfulness in the very dissociations described by the IRS principle. For example, dissociation between indices seems to be consistently more pronounced at extreme ends of arousal dimensions. During paradoxical sleep and extreme fear, although the animal, behaviourally, appears to be under-aroused, the EEG indicates a high level of alertness. In view of this qualification, many theorists, when referring to arousal, have limited their observations to the middle portion of the dimension, where such dissociations are less extreme, and, in any event, are much less likely to occur.

Again, there have been indications that certain arousal sub-systems at times appear to be almost functionally autonomous, having different growth and maintenance characteristics from those expressed in other (parallel) systems. One of the earliest indications of this was Gantt's observations (Robinson and Gantt, 1947; Gantt, 1976) that while sometimes the salivary, cardiac, respiratory and motor components of OR vary systematically in a co-ordinated, integrated manner, on other occasions certain components predominate, and appear to operate almost independently. This lack of balance or harmony Gantt termed schizokinesis.

Gantt reported that the cardiac system appears to be the most reactive response system. This is clearly demonstrated in salivary CR extinction, where he has noted that while the secretory and motor components of the CR drop out fairly readily, the cardiac CRs persist, and may even increase in strength. Note a similar observation by Gray (1971a); in active avoidance, he reports that shuttle-box behaviour can be extinguished, while the autonomic components of response to the PUN–CS persist. Gantt comments that the animal continues to "remember" with its heart, i.e. emotionally, but not with its movements. Thus it continues to be steered by past emotional memories, preparing it for action no longer required. Other internal events, such as endocrine secretions, which are not followed by the activity necessary to consume such substances, also occur. Spontaneous development of responses of this sort — which often assume neurotic proportions — several years after the removal of the traumatising situation, Gantt (1953) refers to as autokinesis. His term proflex describes the more general process by which the CR is continually being modified, independently of the external environment, probably by interactions among the traces of foci of former conditioned excitations and inhibitions (Gantt, 1976) (cf. also Eysenck's notion of "incubation", p. 458).

Gantt's concept to some extent preempted Lacey's (1956, 1967) view suggesting electro-cortical, somatic and autonomic arousal systems which are not entirely synergistic, and, indeed, may even be semi-independent, and some inferences derivable from the recent multi-process theory of Davidson and Schwartz (1976), which, although concerned primarily with the psychobiology of relaxation, has some obvious implications for arousal theory.

Although relaxation has been extensively employed in psychotherapy, following the pioneer work of Jacobson (1929) and Schultz (1932), as evidenced, for example, in techniques such as systematic desensitisation, where muscular relaxation is thought to antagonise anxiety responses (Wolpe, 1958) and in autogenic training (Luthe, 1963), few investigators have attempted to examine components of relaxation, or to define the concept.

Generally speaking, however, following the lead of Jacobson (1929), who distinguished somatic (respiration, heart rate, etc.) from cognitive effects, many authors differentiate mental/emotional and muscular relaxation (e.g. Rachman, 1968a), although none has systematically looked at the implications of such differences. Davidson and Schwartz (1976) have added a third component, attentional style, referring to openness and awareness of ongoing events, which interacts with somatic and cognitive components. These authors also differentiate left and right hemisphere cognitive and somatic anxiety, particularly the former. They maintain that when S is subjected to unwanted verbal cognitions, he is manifesting left hemisphere mediated cognitive anxiety, and when suffering from visuo-spatial fantasies (e.g. falling into a cave, with accompanying visual and kinaesthetic imagery), anxiety is mediated primarily by the right hemisphere.

There is a good deal of anecdotal and empirical evidence suggesting that, at times, the somatic and cognitive arousal systems are in direct opposition (Eysenck, 1961). A person may be somatically relaxed and physically tired, but cannot fall asleep because his "mind is racing". There may be no "anxiety", as such, expressed, possibly annoyance at not being able to sleep. Alternatively, subjects sometimes complain of bodily tension and autonomic stress without accompanying cognitive symptoms. Often beginning meditators report somatic aches and pains and diffuse muscle tension, despite being "cognitively calm" (Goleman, 1971). To the extent that these forms of anxiety or arousal can vary independently, we can refer to different arousal systems. We might comment also that in this event different relaxation techniques would presumably be effective only in particular circumstances — for example, thought stopping in the case of cognitive but not somatic anxiety, muscular relaxation in the case of somatic but not cognitive anxiety.

Can we advance this argument further to suggest that different arousal systems of the type described may form an integrated, functional whole, in which activity in one system may monitor activity in another? If so, to what purpose?

There is, in fact, a good deal of evidence, drawn from a variety of sources, to suggest a functional relationship of this sort between amount of proprioceptive feedback from the skeletal musculature and the viscera —i.e. from the somatic system — level of emotional arousal, and recall of thematic material.

A widely held psychoanalytic view is that the true aim of repression is to suppress the development of affect (Freud, 1951a,b), and that this demands a constant energy expenditure, which is reflected in chronic muscle tension (Plutchik, 1954). Braatöy (1947, 1952) concluded that habitual postural muscle tension helps neurotics maintain composure by "imprisoning...anxiety", and suggests that if this posture becomes rigid, the anxiety-eliciting stimuli become more suppressed, "forgotten" or unrecognisable. In similar vein, Shatan (1961, 1963) conceived of postural muscles as "hiding places" for repressed memories and emotions, a view subscribed to by Solley and Murphy (1960), who argue that perceptual traces can develop as CSs for strong autonomic feedback following a painful incident, and that "the painful memories are 'locked' in a state of unawareness by the incessant feedback from the tightened muscles" (p. 244). Murphy and Spohn (1968) have expanded this concept by suggesting that defensive muscle tension not only protects a person from his memories, but also from the "reality" impinging on his exteroceptors.

> our bodily tension system... (leads to) a sort of massive elevation of thresholds and rejection of information. There may be such a thing as a generalised gating out, the proprioceptive system acting as a gater. We tighten the body; we drum the fingers; tap with the feet; gasp, over-breathe, and constantly invent new devices for introducing internal "noise" by which to deafen us to unpleasant messages; we chomp and make busy counterstimulation which will have a distraction value (p. 63).

In addition to general defensive systems of this sort, which may be located in the deep back muscles (Braatöy, 1952) or in the thoracic and abdominal muscles (Reich, 1942; Perls, Hefferline and Goodman, 1951; Christiansen, 1966) there have also been suggestions of more specific systems, as, for example, in the case of arm paralysis, which, according to Braatöy (1952), is often associated with repressed feelings of hostility, and serves the function of blocking aggressive impulses and actions.

Firenczi (1930), Reich (1949) and Sullivan (1945) have proposed an obvious corollary to this view. They suggest that the abandonment of rigid postures and tensions may be accompanied by strong emotional discharge or catharsis;

> when stubborn, deeprooted tensions are abandoned ... there is often a dramatic outburst of emotion. The immediate sensation may be an unpleasant, formless anxiety akin to the "uncanny emotion" described by Sullivan as undifferentiated, all-encompassing, poorly distinguished and extremely disquieting (Shatan, 1963, p. 22).

This claim is supported by observational data reporting emotional disturbance, and, in some cases, release of anamnestic material by both normal Ss and psychiatric patients when approaching a relaxed state (e.g. Jacobson, 1938; Wolpe, 1958; Lazarus, 1965a,b; Geer and Katkin, 1966). Reich (1942) states that the relaxation of muscle rigidity liberates affective energy and restores to memory the infantile situation in which the repression occurred. Braatöy (1954) reports that he could precipitate feelings of intense unrest in patients with hysterical paralysis of the arm by simply withdrawing the arm gently from its fixed postition, and that when the patient returned the arm to the original position, the unrest was repressed. Shatan (1963) also observed that when stubborn deep-rooted muscle tensions are abandoned, there are often dramatic outbursts of emotion.

There is some supporting experimental evidence, although there are difficulties of interpretation. Grinker and Spiegel (1945) report that following pentothal relaxation of war neurosis patients, a violent outburst or abreaction sometimes occurs which yields "repressed" thematic material. A similar effect has been reported by Braatöy (1952) describing the results of pentothal relaxation of a female patient with writer's cramp. These two studies are of particular interest, since it could be argued that drug manipulation is the only acceptable methodology for demonstrating disinhibition effects of this type.

Non-drug studies point to the same general conclusion. Davis and Malmo (1961) noted with a female hysteric that during some therapy hours in which she appeared calm and relaxed, EMG recordings were higher than in other sessions in which she was hostile and weeping. Hefferline (1958) reports that when muscle tensions or blocks are removed in normal Ss, there is often spontaneous recall of typical situations, possibly dating back to childhood, when S learned to be tense in this particular manner.

In addition, there are indications that the content of the released imagery is related to the locus of the muscle tension. Braatöy (1952) observed that release of chronic forearm tension, which was a conversion symptom in some of his patients, at times was paralleled by feelings of aggression towards a parental figure. Shagass and Malmo (1954) report an increase in tension in the thigh muscles of an hysteric patient when sexual problems were raised in interview, and an increase in arm tension when feelings of hostility were discussed. Malmo, Shagass and Davis (1950a) report that headache-prone patients showed a rise in forehead EMG recordings whenever traumatic material was uncovered.

Of somewhat broader implication is the study by Barrell and Price (1977), who systematically assigned differential EMG and autonomic defence reactions to questionnaire-derived individual differences in their postulated "confronter-avoider" dimension. Confronters show high levels of EMG activity in conflict situations, avoiders high levels of autonomic activity.

In apparent contradiction to the clinical observations and evidence cited above, there are some indications that muscle relaxation inhibits emotional expression. In systematic desensitisation, for example, muscle relaxation is invoked to inhibit the anxiety elicited by phobic stimuli (Wolpe, 1958, 1961a,b; Rachman, 1967). Jacobson (1938) argues strongly that deep muscle relaxation usually prevents imagery and affect (although, as Braatöy (1954) comments, some of Jacobson's subjects did show emotional disturbance when attempting to relax, but these were excluded from the sample). A similar rationale underlies the use of anxiolytic drugs. A good deal of Western medical evidence attests that drug action breaks the somato-psychic cycle of anxiety–peripheral effects–-more anxiety–more peripheral effects. Such peripheral effects can be autonomic as well as somatic. For example, drugs such as $\beta$-adrenoreceptor blockers (e.g. propranolol), which suppress peripheral symptoms of anxiety in the autonomic system (e.g. tachycardia), also have anxiolytic properties.

It may be, of course, that the abreactions reported by Grinker and Spiegel (1945) and Braatöy (1952) did in fact lead to anxiety reduction, but there is no information specifically on this point in their reports. There is also the question of dosage level, always a critical variable in drug studies. We are reminded of recent suggestions that "inadequate" doses of minor tranquillisers may disinhibit suppressed aggressive impulses, leading, for example, to increased probability of "baby-battering" by anxious, hostile mothers.

Again, it is possible that this conflict of evidence is more apparent than real. Both hyper- and hypotonicity of the skeletal musculature alike may inhibit emotional expression. Certainly there is evidence that both states result in reduced availability of relevant imagery in recall (e.g. Courts, 1942). Moderate levels of tensional input facilitate recall, while little or extreme tension decrements recall, generating the well-known inverted U function. Other factors, however, may also be involved. Mangan, Murphy and Farmer (1980) report that even moderate levels of input, when associated with threat signalled by verbal stimuli, result in reduced recall of semantically related words in a serial recall task.

It could be that the peripheral feedback/anxiety relationship depends to some extent on subject type, and, to this extent, is an expression of individual response specificity. We have previously referred to individual differences in stress reactions. The core concept seems to be "protective boundary", which has appeared under many guises in the literature. It underlies Jung's (1944) mandala formulation. It distinguishes Reich's (1949) armoured S, Kempe's (1956) muscle-tension type, Fisher and Cleveland's (1958) high barrier S, Barrell and Price's (1977) confronter. These have in common that they respond to stress with increased muscle tension. They seem calm and able to deny emotion. The emotionally sensitive S, on the other hand, responds autonomically, showing relatively little increase in muscle tension. To the extent that such a typology has any validity, we might expect the different types to show different effects from relaxation of the peripheral musculature. This point has been well demonstrated by Farmer and Wright (1971), who report that high barrier snake-phobic patients respond to muscle relaxation, and low barrier patients to directed muscular activity, using Lazarus's (1965b) technique, in anxiety inhibition.

There have been a number of suggestions about possible neurophysiological mechanisms involved, the most explicit being that of Gellhorn (1964). In stressing both the somatic and autonomic correlates of arousal, he cites extensive evidence to support his contention that amount and pattern of proprioceptive discharge on the hypothalamus from the musculature per unit time is related to emotional arousal. He claims as supporting evidence the findings of Pasquarelli and Bull (1951), who report that certain postures, presumably determining amount and specificity of proprioceptive discharge, are necessary for the simulation of certain emotions under hypnosis. Note also the lesion studies suggesting that the hypothalamus plays an important role in behavioural arousal. These observations suggest that a certain level and locus of proprioceptive feedback (taking into account the constraints imposed by the IRS principle) is a necessary condition for the occurrence of emotional states, and that when these conditions are not met, emotional arousal is inhibited. Such a relationship was first suggested by Sechenov (1863), and is implicit in the visceral-muscular theory of emotion of James and Lange. Gellhorn (1964) has also postulated a relationship between amount of proprioceptive input and recall of material, in that the facilitative action of hypothalamic-cortical discharge extends to the association areas as well as to the sensory projection areas and the motor cortex. He cites evidence that memory processes are facilitated in moderate but not in extreme emotional states (McGinnies, 1949; Miller, 1950; Rapaport, 1942).

Obviously, many of the relationships suggested are hypothetical, and carefully controlled studies are necessary before more definite conclusions can be drawn. However, at this stage it seems reasonable to postulate a relationship between muscle tonicity and cortical activity, via the hypothalamic-cortical connections, such that cortical activity triggers off muscle responses, which feed back proprioceptive impulses through the extra-reticular system, which, in turn alter overall cortical arousal. If the feedback is moderate, the cortex is aroused, but if too intense, it may produce cortical inhibition in the same way that sensory overload is thought to induce transmarginal inhibition. If so, maintained hypertonicity could permit some control over emotional expression, and presumably the associated imagery.

This general proposition is not at variance with the recently developed hypotheses that the defence reflex, which has both heart rate and muscle tension components, involves in part the raising of sensory thresholds (the perceptual defence effect) and the inhibition of specific cortical activity producing distortion or rejection of the exteroceptive stimulus (Graham and Clifton, 1966; Lacey, 1967; Oken, 1967). Significant neurophysiological events would include: (a) increased muscle tension, which increases cardiac output (Konradi, 1953; Rushmer, 1962); and (b) increased heart rate and blood pressure which lead, via the carotid sinus and aortic baroreceptors, to inhibition of cortical activity (Bonvallet and Block, 1961), and to reduction of sensory intake (Lacey, 1959).

*(c) Reward and punishment systems*

Despite recent controversy, a good deal of evidence from self-stimulation and lesion studies points to a high degree of specificity in response to particular USs within the primary reward (hypothalamus, median forebrain bundle and reticular formation) and aversion (medial hypothalamic fibres to the brain tegmentum) systems. Data from a number of conditioning studies are in general agreement. With the exception of the Barr and McConaghy (1972) study, most reports disclose little, if any, intra-S correlations between UR amplitudes elicited by different rewards and punishments (e.g. Korotkin, 1930; Ivanov-Smolenskii, 1935b; Krasnogorskii, 1935; Anokhin, 1961; Lovibond, 1964), and there would be substantial agreement with Ivanov-Smolenskii's (1935b) observation that

> alongside the general, synthetic type of nervous activity, we may speak of a partial or component type, and in this way describe some separate functions — for example, alimentary, defensive, sexual or orienting-investigatory — in terms of its relatively greater or lesser readiness to acquire new conditioned connections (cited by Teplov, 1956, p. 123 of Gray's (1964b) translation).

Note, however, Ivanov-Smolenskii's reference to a "general, synthetic type". In similar vein, a number of theorists have suggested more general systems mediating reward and punishment.

Gray (1969, 1971a) is perhaps the most explicit. He distinguishes between reactivity to the unconditioned rewards and punishments themselves, where he considers that there are likely to be considerable intra-S differences in the URs elicited by different categories of reward and punishment, and reactivity to stimuli previously paired as classically conditioned CSs with unconditional rewards and punishments. In the latter case, he has suggested two major dimensions of individual differences: (a) a system mediating instrumental behaviour motivated by positive incentive, irrespective of the precise nature of the reward which is contingent on the instrumental response; and (b) a system mediating inhibition of ongoing instrumental behaviour, which is activated by warning of impending punishment, again irrespective of the precise nature of the threatened punishment.

According to theory, "reward mechanisms for approach behaviour", located in the septal area, the median forebrain bundle and the lateral hypothalamus, are activated both by signals of reward and relieving non-punishment, while "punishment mechanisms for passive avoidance", located in the medial forebrain cortex, medial septal nuclei and the hippocampus, are activated by signals of punishment and frustrative non-reward. Omission of punishment ("relief") is detected by a comparator feeding into the reward system, and frustrative non-reward by another comparator feeding into the punishment system.

There are a number of suggestions in the literature of reciprocal inhibitory links between reward and punishment areas (e.g. Anokhin, 1961; Lovibond, 1964; Gray, 1969, 1971a; Berlyne, 1971b). This is a well established finding from lesion studies and studies reporting the effects of simultaneous stimulation of both areas: for example, forebrain (reward) units have been shown to decrease in activity roughly in parallel with increase in inhibition exerted by the punishment system, and to return to normal rates of firing when activity in the punishment area reduces. We should, however, mention a dissenting report from Mikhailova, Pimenova and Simonov (1972) who recorded decreased, rather than increased activity (measured by bar-pressing rate and EEG activity) in reward centres (median forebrain bundle) immediately following cessation of intracranial stimulation, which implies that omission of punishment does not give rise to positive emotion. The authors argue, therefore, that avoidance conditioning through activation of reward centres is unlikely. They also suggest that the positive and negative emotional systems are functionally autonomous.

Lovibond (1964), in advancing the notion of reciprocal inhibitory links between centres mediating different types of reinforcement, suggests that this may account for the lack of correlation between appetitive (sexual) and aversive (shock) CR acquisition rates, arguing that in situations where the criterion CR is an appetitive one, Ss highly arousable in defensive centres may form CRs slowly and with difficulty if the situational stimuli are intense enough to elicit defensive reflexes.

The precise mechanisms involved, however, are unclear. Gray (1969, 1971a) has suggested a symmetrical process, the dominance of reward or punishment depending on which occurs first in time, a possibility which is also suggested by Asratyan's switching experiments (cf. pp. 359–60).

Berlyne (1971b), in his arousal model, has suggested a different mechanism to account for the mutual inhibitory effects of reward and punishment. This is based on the proposition that small increases in arousal, and reduction in arousal from "unpleasant" levels (relief) are rewarding, and that large increases in arousal are unpleasant, and thus punishing. Berlyne distinguishes relief, which is mediated by the secondary reward system, from pleasure, which is mediated by the primary reward system. As the secondary reward system, which is located at the top of the brain stem and the limbic system (the lower parts of the cerebrum) increases in activity, either through omission or termination of punishment, or by reduction in aversive level of arousal, it inhibits the tegmental aversion system, which, in turn, disinhibits the primary reward system, and is thus equivalent to reward.

Berlyne therefore distinguishes relief from pleasure, the latter being the feeling caused by direct stimulation of the primary reward system, the former being the feeling caused by activation of the secondary reward system, which, through inhibition of the punishment system, activates or releases the primary reward system. There is some supporting evidence in that stimulation of the secondary reward areas alleviates the effect of conditioned fear responses on behaviour, and inhibits the tendency to bar-press to switch off stimulation of the tegmental aversion system. Berlyne's model, however, does not possess the inbuilt symmetry of Gray's model, since there is no secondary punishment system postulated to mediate frustrative non-reward.

In this event, might we expect to find that omission of reward has more long-lasting effects than omission of punishment, i.e. to be more akin to direct punishment than omission of punishment is akin to reward? There is little evidence on this point, except perhaps from vicious circle behaviour (VCB). VCB, as described by Mowrer, is a variant of active avoidance, and occurs when the avoidance response is punished. In active avoidance, typically the animal is placed in a shuttle box, a warning tone is presented, and a few seconds later the grid is electrified. To avoid shock, the animal must run, or jump into a safe compartment. This avoidance response is highly resistant to extinction, since the animal effectively reinforces itself every time it makes the avoidance response, even though the shock now never occurs. Reinforcement, according to the classic view, is reduction of fear classically conditioned to the CS.

Gray, however, suggests that the reinforcement resides in the comparison of the expected no-shock in the safe compartment with the registered lack of shock when the animal acutally arrives there. The appropriate comparator system then signals to the reward system. The reinforcement prevents the animal from delaying its avoidance response and testing whether the shock still follows the warning tone.

In VCB, the animal either jumps into brief shock, or has to traverse shock to reach the safe compartment. A question, therefore, is whether the response is appetitive, i.e. jumping to the PUN–CS, or escape/flight from the PUN–CS. Paradoxically, this procedure has been shown to increase the intensity of the active avoidance response, the reason being, according to Gray, that the original training effectively suppresses passive avoidance responses to warning signals, and substitutes some form of approach behaviour. This is supported by the observation that animals which lurch forward in response to shock to the hindpaws show the paradoxical VCB behaviour, yet animals which lurch backwards from shock to the forepaws show more normal inhibition of the punishment response. Thus compatibility of response to punishment with the nature of the approach response is critical – so long as the response is compatible with approach behaviour VCB will be observed, while if it is more compatible with passive avoidance, then the whole mechanism of comparator reinforcement breaks down, and the animal goes into extinction. In VCB, since the punishment is always followed by eventual termination, this will produce reinforcement, just as in the case of ordinary active avoidance, although more so. Old safety signals become even more powerfully reinforcing than previously, despite the fact that they are now associated with punishment.

How does this relate to the question of omission of punishment *vis-à-vis* omission of reward? The VCB situation is balancing one against the other — the animal first experiences omission of reward (when it is shocked), then omission of punishment. Since VCB does not extinguish, it could be claimed that omission of punishment is more critical reinforcement than omission of reward, which, would, incidentally, weigh against Berlyne's model. However, the critical control, in which the sequences are reversed, is not possible, since shock is always eventually terminated.

### (d) Relationships between arousal and reward and punishment systems

One of the oldest postulated relationships is expressed as the Wundt curve (Figure 26). Here the arousal produced by a stimulus, measured by psychophysiological correlates such as GSR, heart rate and so on, plotted against the operation of reward and punishment systems, generates a "hedonic value" continuum. Small increases in arousal have positive reward values, and large increases negative reward, i.e. punishment values. Evidence has been

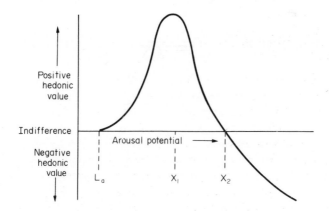

Figure 26. The Wundt curve (adapted from Wundt, 1874; and Berlyne, 1960, 1967).

adduced to show that humans rate small values of salt and sour taste ranges, tone intensities, heat and cold, as rewarding, large values as unpleasant. Similar effects have been shown by rats in their approach to small increases of salt and sour tastes, and avoidance of large increases.

On the basis of these data, McClelland *et al.* (1953) have produced a similar type of curve (Figure 27).

"Discrepancy from adaptation level" (AL), the stimulus level S has adapted to, or is experiencing, denotes the surprise of novelty value of the stimulus. We can view the "butterfly" curve as support for the Wundt curve, in that "discrepancy from AL" should be proportional to arousal potential. Since the curve is symmetrical, it can be reflected to give the Wundt curve.

On this evidence, we might suggest that small increases in arousal correlate with activation of the reward systems, and that the relationship reverses at higher levels, providing that the base line — the adaptive level — is placed in the low to middle intensity range. This is suggested by the fact that small increase in arousal has a parallel in drive induction — a small amount of food makes a hungry animal hungrier, judging from frequency of responses to obtain food in an instrumental situation such as bar-pressing. Since drive reduction is generally regarded as important primary motivation, and since drive level clearly correlates with arousal level, we might also expect reduction of arousal from a high level to be rewarding.

Berlyne postulates that the secondary reward system is activated when arousal reduces from an uncomfortable level, and that the primary reward system is activated when arousal increases by a small amount. Since he locates the secondary reward system in the limbic system, it is of interest to note that electrical stimulation in this region activates the parasympathetic system,

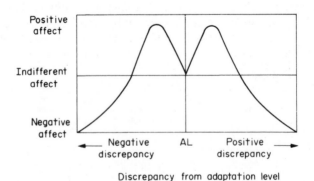

Figure 27. The butterfly curve figuring in the theory of McClelland *et al.* (1953) (from Haber, 1958).

producing de-arousal. In some patients, such treatment can make intractable pain bearable, and temporarily relieve depression.

A problem in considering the relationship between arousal and reward-punishment systems is that the systems governing both seem to be located in the same brain regions — the lower parts — so that both systems receive input from stimuli more or less simultaneously. Gray, in his flow models for avoidance behaviour, explicitly shows the reward-punishment systems activating the arousal systems. However, we have some evidence for the reverse — reduction in high levels of arousal tends to be rewarding. That being said, it is possible that a third factor acts on both systems — for example, blood glucose in hunger mechanisms activating both reward-punishment and arousal systems.

Can reward-punishment and arousal systems be manipulated independently? Some relevant data are available from Schachter's (1971) well-known experiments, in which he demonstrated that the subjective experience of adrenaline injections (adrenaline having a fairly specific action on brain stem arousal systems) is dependent on the social situation — a warm, empathic experimenter elicits feelings of pleasantness and euphoria, while an aggressive interviewer elicits aggressive, hostile reactions. Both types of reaction are exacerbated by adrenaline, compared with placebo controls. Somewhat similar results have been reported by Bem (1972), using amphetamines. However, although overt behaviour, as assessed by observers, was similar to that expressed by Schachter's subjects, this was not particularly congruent with subjects' introspections about their feelings. From these data, we might deduce that, while high levels of arousal intensify emotions thought to be mediated by reward-punishment systems, there are no directional effects inherent in just high level of arousal. This, of course, contradicts the previous findings of directional effects of changes in arousal — positive for small increases and negative for large. It would be of interest, in pursuing this question further, to observe the dose-related interactions between stimulants such as adrenaline, and the directional effects of different social contexts. At present, however, it is impossible to establish whether it is alteration in arousal levels which is monitored by reward-punishment systems, or whether the interaction is opposite, or simply more complex.

## 4. Cognitive Mediational Variables

Interest in this area has focused on three questions:

(a) whether knowledge ("awareness") of the CS–US contingency, i.e. relational learning, is a necessary condition for autonomic conditioning;

(b) whether, and under what conditions, "cognitive" control of involuntary responding is possible;

(c) the role of imagery.


## (a) Awareness of CS–US contingency

Some general aspects of this question have been covered in a number of reviews (cf. Creelman, 1966; Ross, 1971), and in a recent symposium on classical conditioning and the cognitive processes (*Psychophysiology*, Vol. 10, No. 1, 1973). The reader is referred to these sources for more detailed examination of particular issues. At this point, a brief summary of the main conclusions will suffice.

Despite some reservations, there is a consensus that the role of awareness in relational learning depends on the conditioning paradigm employed and on the response mode selected. In single cue eyelid conditioning, for example, where the CS is supraliminal and short-trace, the intact, motivated animal will condition without awareness, i.e. without having to focus attention on what leads to what. Irradiation and concentration of excitation may be sufficient conditions for cortical connecting. The length of the CS–US interval, of course, is critical. In eyelid conditioning, for example, the interval is short, less than 1 second, while for GSR conditioning there appears to be little contingency analysis over CS–US intervals ranging from 0.75 to 6 seconds.

Where the CS is long-trace, however, the situation is different. The animal has to analyse the stimulus situation to establish what the signal is, has to develop some concept to the delay period involved, and must then withhold the CR until the appropriate time through an active inhibitory process. Where the delay period is lengthy (say, 2–3 minutes), and the interval is filled, sophisticated stimulus analysis and efficient strategies of attentional deployment may be required.

Of course, this is not true in all cases. Take, for example, food aversions, where CS–US intervals can be of the order of hours. The critical factor here is the innate "hard-wired" constraints on learning. Much behaviour is pre-programmed by evolution, so that if we set up an experiment in very artificial surroundings it is often easy to ignore what actually happens in the real world. In this connection, we might mention the criticisms of Skinner's experiments, based on high-speed films of pigeon pecking, which showed that the operant could, in fact, be either a swallow (water reward) or a bite (food pellet reward).

There are, of course, different levels of stimulus analysis, and thus different degrees of awareness. Even where S appears unable to estimate the CS–US interval, often a process which appears analogous to temporal conditioning appears, yielding a progressive increase in the latency of the preparatory autonomic activity preceding the US. In some instances, a variety of response-produced cues evoked by the CS may become effectively conditioned although the relationship of these cues to the US cannot be verbalised by S. A somewhat similar situation can occur in the case of compound CSs, where S may be unable to verbalise the relationship of certain CS elements to the US, although these may determine some aspects of his behaviour. Over and above these considerations, we are reminded that phasic CR activity is often "unconsciously" steered by contextual stimuli which provide a tonic CR background on which phasic CR activity is superimposed.

The empirical data reported strongly support Razran's earlier (1955) conceptualisation of the role of cognitive processes in classical conditioning. He differentiated two radically different levels of learning, relational learning and "true conditioning". The first refers to S's awareness of the relatedness amongst different elements of the conditioning paradigm, for example, CR and UR, CS and CR, CR and US. In autonomic conditioning studies, relational learning involving the CS–US relationship is of principal interest. "True conditioning" is simply a consequence of the automatic strengthening effects of repetitive stimulus pairings, and no awareness of the CS–US relationship is necessary. The intellectually competent human operates more at the level of relational learning than of true conditioning, since this occurs more quickly and more strongly, resembling discrete one-trial insight learning.

Insofar as discrimination learning is concerned, since S must be able to discriminate CS+ from CS– in order to respond positively to the former, and inhibit response to the latter, which implies a recognition, as distinct from a detection process, this type of learning is uniquely susceptible to cognitive determination. Inability to discriminate cues can lead to severe behavioural disruption, at times to experimental neurosis. As in the case of single-cue conditioning, however, on occasions S may not be able to verbalise or accurately describe the relationships involved. Baer and Fuhrer (1973), for example, report that differential electrodermal conditioning can still be obtained when S is distracted from recognition of the CS–US contingency by embedding the CS in a probability learning task. Similar results have been reported where ambiguous or complex verbal discriminanda, or a masking technique during the CS–US interval have been employed. On the other hand, verbalisers condition better than non-verbalisers.

In evaluating such results one question at issue is precisely what we mean by awareness. Most theorists accept some concept of graded awareness, which traces historically from Descartes, and finds its modern expression in psychoanalytic and directive state perception theories. Depending on S's arousal state, his defensive posture, and the signal to noise ratio, stimuli which are cortically registered are "recognised" on the basis of feedback from relevant response systems. A good example is the subliminal conditioning data reported by Gershuni *et al* (1948). After S had developed a stable GSR to shock, auditory CS presentation of intensity 8–12 dB below auditory threshold evoked a cortical response, but not GSR, which could only be elicited when CS amplitude was increased to 3–6 dB below threshold. Presumably, in the absence of feedback (the OR), S remains unaware of stimulation, although with CSs of 8–12 dB below threshold, differential responding and extinction can be obtained. Clearly there is a feedback continuum on which different responses can be located. Ss are not normally aware of evoked potentials, for example, but they are cognisant of gross responses such as increased heart rate, changes in skin resistance, which alter homeostatic state. In the middle range, awareness fluctuates, and it may be that cortical connections can be activated without recognition of the eliciting stimulus. In this connection, we might refer to the Hefferline and Perera (1963) report that S imagined (reported) a non-existent (omitted) auditory signal, which had previously been associated with a below-awareness involuntary response (thumb twitch), whenever the latter subsequently occurred.

We should also note, of course, the "purpose" of the recognition process. In the subception experiments reported in the fifties, for example, S appears to be alert to signals in order to defend against impending punishment, and is thus prepared to act on partial cues which normally would be inadequate to elicit a veridical response.

In assessing the significance of knowledge of CS–US contingencies in conditioning, a number of technical and methodological problems arise. What kind of "awareness" are we referring to? To S's awareness of what is being done to him, awareness arising out of what he had been instructed to do, awareness of what he did, awareness of what he is doing? What about awareness *vis-à-vis* expectancy? There can be expectancy about the likelihood, as well as time of occurrence of stimuli. It may be that many of the post-experimental questionnaires used in conditioning studies do not provide a satisfactory definition of awareness. S defined as unaware on one questionnaire might be classed as aware on another. The fact that S cannot report awareness post-experimentally does not necessarily imply that he is unaware of contingencies during conditioning, in the sense of attending to them. Trial-by-trial assessments have been attempted, but intervention of this sort may grossly influence the dependent variables. Attempted control over contingency learning by the use of masking and such tasks introduces serious problems of control and interpretaion.

Another problem which should be noted is that of response specificity. Since correlation between response measures across physiological systems is low, it is perhaps not surprising that CRs in different response modes correlate poorly. It may be that when S emits an autonomic response which has multiple reference — in broad terms, in the electro-cortical, autonomic and somatic arousal systems — some elements in the CR complex may be subject to cognitive mediation, others not. We might also ask whether cognitive mediation applies equally or at all to retention (extinction) as well as to acquisition (conditioning), and whether such effects are restricted to short-term as distinct from long-term "memory processes". These questions have not yet been subjected to systematic enquiry.

Concerning operant conditioning, the problem is somewhat less critical, since reinforcement always follows the instrumental act, and is contingent on it, i.e. the instrumental act is pre-reinforcement in origin, so that the sequence of CS, instrumental act, reinforcement is implicit in the pattern of associations which we describe as instrumental learning. There is general agreement that "knowledge" that the instrumental act has been completed is necessary for operant conditioning to occur. Precisely what "knowledge" means, however, is the subject of continuing debate. Certain theorists persist in the earlier view that operant conditioning involves only voluntary responses, about which the responding S might be expected to have some modicum of awareness. On the other hand, Konorskii (1973), for example, notes that "knowledge" of the instrumental act is not necessary for instrumental learning, simply coincidence between drive states and the appropriate kinaesthetic units located in the basal ganglia or the cortical-kinaesthetic fields.

In normal circumstances, however, it seems reasonable to suggest that feedback "instructs" the animal that the behavioural consequences of the movement are likely to occur. The animal "knows" that he has jumped, or pressed the bar, and thus anticipates release from fear or the imminence of appetitive stimuli. With human Ss, we would expect such "knowledge" and anticipation to be capable of verbal description.

*(b) Voluntary, i.e. cognitive, control of involuntary responses*

There is a good deal of anecdotal material reported concerning control of this sort, although in some cases doubt has been expressed about authenticity. Tuke (1884) reports many such cases, involving, for example, voluntary control of pupillary contraction and dilation. Wenger, Bagchi and Anand (1961) record voluntary arrest of heart rate in an Indian yogi. McClure (1959) reports progressive slowing of pulse, without recourse to breath-holding or the Valsalva Manoeuvre, until almost complete cessation of heart action occurred, followed by a feeling of impending loss of consciousness. Lindsley and Sassonman (1938) report voluntary reflex pilo-erection, and Wenger and Bagchi (1961) voluntary sudomotor control. In some cases the response appears to be elicited by "visualisation" of appropriate stimulus conditions — high temperature in the case of sudomotor activity, for example.

There are at least three sources of experimental evidence pointing to the same general conclusion, that under well specified conditions, and possibly after a long period of training, some Ss can exercise a considerable degree of control over responses normally considered involuntary.

1. The first of these concerns well-authenticated laboratory demonstrations of voluntary control using classical conditioning procedures, and, in some cases, the added dimension of control via substitution of verbal for the sensory CSs which have been classically conditioned to the autonomic responses.

Bair (1901) reported voluntary control over ear movements by pairing voluntary clenching of the jaw with involuntary movements of the ear produced by electrical stimulation of the retrahens muscle, until jaw clenching alone was sufficient to elicit ear movements. Using similar procedures, Shagass (1942) developed voluntary control of the occipital alpha rhythm in human Ss. Hudgins (1933) reported control of pupillary constriction and dilation by verbal command, a finding which has been replicated by Kotliarevsky (1935) with children. While there have been some failures of replication, a number of authors (Jasper and Shagass, 1941; Menzies, 1937) have reported data suggesting that autonomic responses can be conditioned to S's own verbal stimuli.

Similar studies have been reported in the Soviet literature (cf. Bykov, 1954). Ayrapetyants (1956) for example, demonstrated that elicitation or inhibition of the "urge to urinate" could be brought under the control of external CSs through past contiguous association between bladder pressure and the CSs. Linetskii (1961) reports increased rate of urine secretion in human Ss by simply suggesting to them, under hypnosis, that they were drinking water. Platonov (1959), in summarising a good deal of data concerning word as a conditional stimulus, states that under certain conditions verbal stimuli evoke a series of simple and complex physiological reactions, including water and carbohydrate metabolism, hunger and satiety, gastro-intestinal secretions, thermoregulatory and vasomotor activity, for example.

Overall, a good deal of evidence attests that once an externally produced CS can elicit a conditioned autonomic response in a human S, that S can evoke the CR by simply naming, verbally or sub-vocally, or imagining the CS. These studies have been reviewed in a previous section. Worth mentioning also is data on conditioning of opiates, in both animal and man. Self-suggestion, using a placebo, has been shown to have substantial effects.

2. The second line of argument suggests that voluntary control can be developed through the use of operant procedures. This statement is still anathema to many learning theorists, who pursue the original Mowrer (1938)

and Skinner (1938) line that autonomic responses or autonomically mediated behaviour can be modified only by classical, not by instrumental methods. There would still be some agreement with Skinner's comment, "We may reinforce a man with food whenever he 'turns red', but we cannot in this way condition him to blush" (p. 114).

Over the last two decades, however, a good deal of data have been reported to support the proposition that all types of response, whether mediated by the ANS or by the cerebrospinal system, can be modified by both techniques. Operant conditioning of spontaneous GSR has been reported (Kimmel, 1963; 1967; Greene, 1966; May and Johnstone, 1969; *inter alia*), of galvanic skin potential (e.g. Shapiro and Crider, 1967; Shnidman, 1969), and cardiac rate (e.g. Shearn, 1962; Engel and Chism, 1967b; Brener, Kleinman and Gosling, 1969). Although there has been some unevenness in results, and the large variety of methodologies employed in the reported studies make comparisons difficult, the bulk of evidence points to the conclusion that autonomic responses of this sort can be operantly conditioned.

The counter-argument, however, survives. Katkin and Murray (1968), for example, suggest an alternative somatic-mediation explanation of the effects reported, particularly in the case of heart rate, a much favoured response mode, arguing from the well-established proposition that cardiac rate and somatic events are interrelated, particularly in humans and dogs (Obrist, 1968); Ss simply learn to tense or relax their muscles in the experimental situation, thus influencing heart rate. This possibility, however, is contra-indicated in the series of studies reported by Miller and associates, using animals curarised to prevent use of muscular exertion or relaxation to influence the operant. Describing studies in which curarised rats were rewarded with electrical stimulation of the brain (ESB) for relatively fast or slow heart rate, Trowhill (1967) reports "curarised rats rewarded for fast HR showed a reliable increase in rate, while rats rewarded for slow ones showed a reliable decrease". Miller and Di Cara (1967), using a shaping procedure for reinforcement, were able to produce changes of 25% in both slow and fast HR reward groups. Miller and Banuazizi (1968) report that HR and intestinal activity can be conditioned independently, and Di Cara and Miller (1968a) that HR changes in rats can be operantly conditioned, not only using ESB as reinforcement, but also escape from, or avoidance of, shock.

A range of ANS mediated and other normally involuntary responses other than HR have been voluntarily conditioned in rats — blood pressure changes (Di Cara and Miller, 1968b), EEG alpha rhythm amplitude (Kamiya, 1968), intestinal relaxation and contraction (Miller and Banuazizi, 1968), salivation rate (Delse and Feather, 1968; Miller and Carmona, 1967), skin potential responses (Shapiro and Crider, 1966, 1967; Shapiro, Crider and Tursky, 1964), urine formation (Miller and Di Cara, 1968), peripheral vasomotor responses (Di Cara and Miller, 1968c); Kimmel and Kimmel, 1967). The curarised animal studies of Miller and associates (cf. Miller, 1969) are regarded by many as being "as close as possible to a truly definitive series of experiments establishing the phenomenon of instrumental conditioning of autonomically mediated responses" (Katkin and Murray, 1968, p. 65). We would also include in any category of definitive studies the experiment by Wyler (1977) reporting that monkeys can be operantly trained to bidirectionally control the firing rates of normal and epileptic neurones which constitute the epileptic focus.

3. A third method employed to develop "control" over involuntary responses employs continuous and contiguous visual or auditory representation (feedback) of the physiological response system of interest. Thus S, throughout the course of the behavioural sequence, has continuous information about the outcome of his strategies, rather than the limited information provided by a signal indicating that a criterion response has occurred.

From a considerable number of relevant studies reported in the literature, only a few will be noted by way of illustration. Lisina (1958, English translation 1965) for example, subjected her Ss to prolonged, painful electric shock, which produced a non-habituating vasoconstriction, with the occasional appearance of a "hunting reaction", or vasodilation. Shock termination was contingent on the emergence of this reaction. Despite a large number of reinforcements, no change was reported in Ss' records. When Ss were permitted to observe the externalised visual feedback of their vascular reactions, and noted that the pointer movement representing vasodilation was followed by shock termination, however, relatively few reinforcements were required to effect operant vasodilation to shock. Ss were not informed of the connection between the movements of the pointer and the vasomotor changes, and remained unaware that they could voluntarily control the meter needle, and thereby their vasomotor responses. As Gray (1966) comments, the important element is sufficiency of sensory feedback, rather than understanding, by S, of what he is doing, "Subjects reported that they could control the pointer as they liked, although they still did not know how they were doing it" (p. 30). As we noted in discussing the concept of awareness, however, inability to verbalise contingencies does not necessarily imply complete lack of awareness of the contingencies operating.

A number of studies along similar lines have followed this seminal work. Hnatiow and Lang (1965) and Lang, Sronfe and Hastings (1967) used visual displays in reducing heart rate variability, although there have been some dissenting reports (Shearn, 1962; Bower, 1964; Donelson, 1966). Similar effects using other response modes have been demonstrated. Delse and Feather

(1968) report that three out of every ten Ss were able to control salivary rate, providing they could "hear" themselves salivate by the sounding of a tone for every drop of saliva. Kamiya and associates report similar control of high and low amplitude alpha rhythm using auditory feedback (Kamiya, 1968; Nowlis and Kamiya, 1970) — although note the criticism by Plotkin (1976), which Kamiya (1976) has failed to answer, that the effect reported is largely artefactual. Stern and Kaplan (1967) report GSR control through visual feedback, and Stern and Lewis (1968) GSP control employing similar techniques. McPherson (1967) reports voluntary inhibition of all involuntary movement associated with Huntington's chorea, through use of EMG feedback.

The great specificity of control possible when continuous, contiguous feedback of involuntary responses is available is aptly demonstrated in studies reported by Basmajian and colleagues (Basmajian, 1963; Basmajian, Baeza and Fabingar, 1965; Basmajian and Samard, 1967; Scully and Basmajian, 1969), and by a number of other researchers (e.g. Ashworth, Grimsby and Kogleburg, 1967; Harrison and Mortenson, 1963; Kondo, Canter and Beam, 1977) concerning the activity of individual motor neurons or units.

In summarising the overall results of their research programme, Scully and Basmajian (1969) note

> More than 80% of normal people can be trained to isolate the activity of individual motor units within approximately 15 to 30 minutes ... With additional training they can maintain motor units in regular isolated activity, manipulate the frequency of motor unit discharges at will, and even produce specific rhythms of single motor unit activity (p 65).

From their report, voluntary control of specific motor units apparently can be retained by some Ss even after withdrawal of the visual or auditory feedback. However, despite considerable introspection, these Ss could not explain their success, other than to comment that they "thought about the motor unit as they had seen and heard it previously" (p 83).

A recurring theme in many of these studies is that artifical feedback can develop as a CS for the response represented by that feedback. The power of such CSs is indicated in a number of "sham" feedback studies, for example, that reported by Ayrapetyants, Lobanova and Cherkasova (1952). Three volunteer patients with urinary bladder fistulas had their bladders repeatedly distended and relaxed through calibrated inflows of air or liquid solutions, and observed the accompanying bladder compression readings transmitted by means of inserted rubber balloons on a manometer. Subsequently, the experimenter detached the manometer without S's knowledge, and manipulated the dial readings himself. In the three cases, sham high dial readings could produce an urge to urinate, and an associated GSR, although the actual bladder pressure was low, while low dial readings when the actual bladder pressure was high inhibited the urge to urinate. Double the normal amount of internal compression was required before the urge to urinate was elicited. In a later study, Ayrapetyants (1956) demonstrated that a verbal description by E of the sham meter position was sufficient of itself to produce almost the same degree of inhibition or facilitation of the urgency response as S actually seeing the dial readings.

A number of other relevant studies have been reported. Jones (1956) for example, sham conditioned a patient with a history of frequency of micturation — urgency being associated with abnormally low bladder pressures and volumes — to install an appropriate urgency response to bladder pressures and volumes.

Further evidence of the power of externalised feedback as a CS for the processes it represents can also be adduced from the Hefferline and Perera (1963) study. When S occasionally emitted an invisibly small thumb twitch, he received a tone as a signal to press a key. After several conditioning sessions, the tone was progressively diminished to zero. Nevertheless, S continued to press the button whenever he emitted a thumb twitch, and reported that he still heard the tone (p. 834). This suggests that a sensation of the externalised feedback can be elicited under certain conditions by the below-awareness interoceptive feedback of the response previously represented by the externalised feedback. In other words, when externalised feedback is synchronous with involuntary activity, the feedback or imagery not only develops as a CS for the involuntary activity, but the activity itself also develops as a CS for the perception of the feedback previously associated with this activity.

### (c) The role of imagery

In the behaviourist zeitgeist of the 1930s and 1940s, little interest was evinced in imagery, particularly in "sensitive" areas such as conditioning and learning. Nevertheless, instances of changes in autonomic functioning through S "imagining" situations were recorded in the literature (Darrow, 1929a, b; Jacobson, 1932; Rowland, 1936; Shaw, 1938; Menzies, 1941; Arnold, 1946). In the fifties and sixties new developments in areas of biofeedback and self control focused attention on imagery variables; in the past decade, interest has accelerated, and studies have been reported which bear directly on critical aspects of the problem.

Soviet interest has been confined largely, although not exclusively, to the role of imagery in conditioning, to two aspects in particular — image as a psychoneural process mediating classical sensory conditioning, and image as a second signal CS, a "self-regulated internal feedback loop" (Schwartz *et al.* 1976). Platonov's (1959) comment is representative: "Abstraction from reality characteristic of the second signal system is achieved because the image of objects and ideas replaces their concrete effect on the organism". The fact that word can substitute for any sensory stimulus, and thus act as surrogate CS, eliciting the full CR, is recognised as having both therapeutic and theoretical significance. Implications for cognitive control of autonomic processes, however, have been ignored, although some of the Soviet studies, such as those of Lisina and Ayrapetyants, have provided the stimulus for Western research in this area.

Data from both sources point to a number of conclusions. The first concerns single cue (particularly long-trace) conditioning, a question which we have already discussed. To recapitulate briefly, here the "image" of the CS, i.e. the persisting traces of the exteroceptive stimulus, maintains excitation in the cortical projection area until the cortical representation of the US is stabilised. The latter, according to Anokhin (1958), consists of memories, "images" of previous reinforcements, and it is these two "images" which are cortically connected in the process of conditioning. In this sense, the conditioned response is image-driven, and speed of CR development depends, to some extent, on the intensity or vividness of such imagery, which, in turn, partly reflects reactivity in the cortical (and possibly subcortical) structures mediating these effects. In instrumental conditioning, it is equally obvious that feedback (imagery) of the instrumental act is a necessary link in the development of the associative chain.

Concerning cognitive control of involuntary responses, the role of imagery is more complex, and of more critical importance. In this connection, we should distinguish those instances in which feedback develops as a CS for the response represented by that feedback, an issue which is not germane to the present discussion, from those in which feedback is either withdrawn, following which the response can still be voluntarily elicited, or is not used at all. In the first case, it is the CS which is imaged. Examples are the Basmajian studies, studies in which S reports that he is "thinking about the CS" (e.g. Razran, 1935). In the second case, it is the US which is imaged. An example is the Wenger and Bagchi account of S who could sweat voluntarily by imaging a high temperature.

It might be argued that the second case is the "true" instance of cognitive control. In both cases, particularly the latter, we are concerned primarily with the questions of whether images (verbal and non-verbal) can substitute for actual stimuli, and elicit the appropriate autonomic responses, and secondly, whether response amplitude varies as a function of the intensity of imagery, as applies in the case of the actual sensory stimuli (law of strength).

Sechenov (1863) originally argued the case that "from the standpoint of processes, there is not the slightest difference between an actual impression and its signals, and the memory of that impression". In addition to the earlier data cited above, some recent evidence is supportive. Imaged stimuli have similar physiological effects to real stimuli, whether the latter are threatening scenes Van Egeren, Heather and Hein, 1971), stressful versus neutral words (May and Johnstone, 1973), or relate to the differentiation of fear and anger (Weertz and Roberts, 1976). Imagining a fearful stimulus increases both respiratory rate (Rimm and Botrell, 1969) and heart rate (Lang, Melamed and Hart, 1970), in proportion to the vividness of the imagery.

Recent work on control of the salivary response, which has been generally ignored in favour of other autonomic responses such as blood pressure, GSR — which is surprising in view of the historical importance of salivation as an autonomic index in Pavlov's studies — is of particular interest. As in the case of imagery generally, diametrically opposed views have been expressed on the extent to which psychic stimuli such as thoughts of food, anxiety thoughts, can modify salivation. Some researchers (Pavlov, 1904, 1955; Razran, 1934; Monnier, 1968; Lachman, 1973; White, 1978) have expressed strong agreement, others equally strong dissent (Lashley, 1916; Katz, Sutherland and Brown, 1967; Delse and Feather, 1968; Dawes, 1974; Shannon, 1974), the latter supporting Katz *et al's* (1967) view that "the salivary reflex is not subject to acts of will".

White, in a series of studies (1975, 1977a,b, 1978) has reported and reviewed a good deal of data which clarify a number of the contentious issues. He reports that the three cognitive stimuli normally used to produce salivary changes — thoughts of food, anxiety thoughts, non-specific suggestions — are equally effective; that there are large individual differences in the ability to exercise such control; that Ss who believe in their ability to control autonomic responses are able to increase, but not decrease salivation at will, in line with previous findings reported by Engel (1972) and Roberts *et al.* (1975); that sex differences are unimportant; that personally significant imagery (rated preferences for foods) is an important variable in salivary control.

Insofar as the relationship between response amplitude and vividness of imagery is concerned, the data are less equivocal. Arnold (1946) noted that the more vivid the imaginative process, the more pronounced the overt movements. Vividness of imagery has been shown to relate positively to increases in heart rate and decreases in skin resistance (Rowland, 1936); responses to phobic stimuli and accompanying autonomic changes appear to be proportional to the vividness of the image on S's phobic hierarchy (Marks *et al.*, 1971); Rimm and Botrell (1969) report increases in respiratory rates, and Lang, Melamed and Hart (1970) increases in heart rate when imagining a fearful scene, in proportion to the vividness of the image. Schwartz (1973) reports anecdotal material, Gottschalk (1970) and Luria (1968) single case studies, and Schwartz *et al.* (1976) clinical data reporting close relationships between affective images and physiological changes. Hayashi (1971) has reported proportionality between intensity of second signal stimuli and salivation. Finally, Drummond, White and Ashton (1978) report that imagery vividness relates to habituation rate — the more vivid the imagery, the slower the habituation to fear-provoking stimuli. Since large amplitude responses habituate more slowly (Thompson and Spencer, 1966), this finding supports the general proposition that the more vivid the image, the greater the response amplitude.

Large inter-S differences in imagery vividness have been reported (Bates and Adams, 1968; Holland and Matthews, 1970; Drummond, White and Ashton, 1978). Since the imaged stimulus obeys the law of strength, we would expect imagery vividness to be a source of variance in conditioning. There is some evidence to support this (Yaremko, Glanville and Leckhart, 1972; Yaremko and Werner, 1974; Mangan, 1974; Yaremko and Butler, 1975; Mangan, 1978a).

A methodological problem in this area is lack of an appropriate metric. The most commonly used measure is Sheehan's (1967) version of Betts' Questionnaire upon Mental Imagery (1909), which yields visual, auditory, tactile, kinaesthetic, proprioceptive, gustatory and olfactory subjective scales of vividness of imagery. McLemore (1972) has researched the construct validities of the imagery questionnaires, and reports that they are only minimally affected by response styles of acquiescence or social desirability. Imaginal vividness appears to be a unitary attribute across sense modalities (McLemore, 1972; Richardson, 1969).

However, this finding, both intuitively, and from the author's experience with the scale, seems questionable. From post-experimental enquiry, it appears that S often visualises the scene or event (e.g. auditory, kinaesthetic) which he is required to image. For example, where Ss are asked to image the hiss of steam, they often report visualising a kettle, or a train, and presumably base their ratings on this "compound" imagery. Thus ratings could be contaminated by the "setting" visual image, and unless instructions are specifically aimed at controlling this variable, spurious results can be expected. In an unpublished study, the author obtained ratings from two samples of Ss under two sets of instructions; Ss administered QMI in the usual way showed high inter-rating correlations; Ss imaging under instructions to inhibit the visual image, however, showed low intercorrelations between the various imagery modes. On common-sense grounds, this seems entirely reasonable. Since the image stimulus obeys the law of strength, we might expect imagery to be modality-specific, since there is clear evidence that strength-sensitivity does not correlate across modalities.

To briefly summarise the research reviewed. Imagery appears to be an important mediational variable in conditioning, particularly single cue, long-trace conditioning. Verbal and non-verbal images can effectively substitute for CS or US. Image obeys the law of strength, so that amplitude of responses produced by imagery reflects the vividness and relevance of such imagery. There are large individual differences in vividness of imagery. Some Ss seem able to "control" their autonomic responding via imagery, possibly after a good deal of training in appropriate cognitive strategies. This is suggested as the likely explanation of the success some Ss have shown in recent studies of autonomic control (Stephens, Harris and Brady, 1972; Blizard, Cowings and Miller, 1975). We should note, however, the possibility of an interaction between imagery vividness and drive strength, in that a less vivid image should be adequate to evoke a full CR in a hungry animal, but not in a sated animal.

Image, however, may be more than stimulus, as Razran's (1949b) data suggest. When S images a concrete stimulus, such as food, then to the extent that he employs verbal or subvocal cues in retrieval, the activation of non-verbal associates could render the imaged US functionally more intense than the real US. Of possible relevance here is the finding that imagery vividness has been shown to facilitate paired associate learning (Paivio, 1969; Paivio and Yuille, 1969) and that concrete stimuli are more easily connected in paired associate learning than abstract words (Paivio, 1969), possibly because these evoke more, and more intense associations.

More definite conclusions in this area await more sophisticated and definitive experiments.

### Summary

Although at this point it is difficult to derive an entirely satisfactory model of conditioning, it is at least possible to identify a number of sources of individual differences in conditioning, from which we can derive weighted prediction formulae. Some of these sources of variance can be dimensionalised using conventional techniques; in other cases, the metric is not yet available, so that we cannot locate Ss at appropriate points along a continuum.

To start with the "unknowns". Probably the most critical is our lack of knowledge about the underlying associative processes by which elements in the reflexive chain are connected, primarily irradiation and concentration of excitation. In the case of classical conditioning, there is the further problem that, arguably, we need to assume some degree of cortical representation of the US. Thus, cortical coupling, to an extent, is between two "images", one sensory (CS), the other memoric (US/UR), the latter moving from a post- to a pre-reinforcement position during the course of conditioning. In operant conditioning, on the other hand, the pattern of associations reflects the sequence of events as they actually occur. The extent to which these different associative patterns introduce variance into conditioning is problematical.

Insofar as reinforcement mechanisms are concerned, despite the elegance of the reward-punishment models described, we should be wary of too oversimplified an account. In the first place, while there is good evidence for inhibition of the reward by the punishment system, inhibition of the punishment by the reward system has been less well demonstrated. On somewhat more general lines, the fact that shock, for example, with other stimuli normally considered aversive, can become a signal for reward, for which the animal will work, or salivate, indicates that "punishment" can be "rewarding". Reward and punishment, therefore, should not be construed in absolute terms. In this connection, we might particularly note data reported by Asratyan (1958) concerning bidirectional conditioned reflexes. He reports that when a motor defence reflex to "adequate" shock is paired with an alimentary reflex to food, shock can elicit salivation, and vice versa, depending on the sequence of events. More than this; shock can elicit (almost) simultaneous salivation and leg withdrawal, suggesting that reward and punishment centres, or rather their cortical representations, can be activated in parallel (Figure 28). In line with the conditioned reflex model, presumably when shock elicits salivation, food is a stronger stimulus than shock, and when food elicits leg withdrawl, shock is a stronger stimulus than food. But what is the explanation when one stimulus elicits both reactions?

From a purely structural point of view, although there are highly localised centres mediating different classes of incentive, in general, where we find

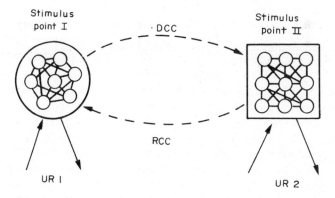

Figure 28. Scheme of the conditioned reflex with bidirectional connection. DCC, direct conditioned connection; RCC, reverse conditioned connection; UR 1, unconditioned reflex No. 1; UR 2, unconditioned reflex No. 2 (from Asratyan, 1958).

punishment areas in the brain, we usually find reward centres in close proximity. For example, the forebrain, one of the "reward mechanisms for approach behaviour" in Gray's system, has punishment centres leading from the limbic system and the thalamus. The thalamus itself contains both reward and punishment centres. If we assume that the cortical US/UR representations topographically reflect the organisation of subcortical structures, as most theorists generally agree, then conditioned connections between reward and punishment centres are entirely possible within the simple conditioned reflex model, being simply connections between closely adjacent cortical loci.

Insofar as the balancing of reward and omission of punishment, and of punishment and omission of reward is concerned, while from the instrumental behavioural point of view we can present some evidence suggesting that these are equivalent, nevertheless at this stage it seems somewhat premature to equate relief with pleasure, and frustration with punishment, as a general behavioural analogue.

As to the "knowns". Obviously we can allocate a major portion of conditioning variance to:

(a) reactivity in the modality of the CS, the importance of this variable varying inversely with the biological significance of the US;

(b) reactivity in the subcortical centres mediating the US, which may determine the responsivity of the cortical representation of the US;

(c) reactivity in the efferent system;

(d) cognitive mediational variables.

The final category is of particular importance in human conditioning. In the past interest in this area has been expressed in a rather obsessive and misplaced concern about the importance of knowledge of CS–US contingencies in relational learning. Clearly it is important, and the arguments can now be relegated to the domain of semantic obscurantism.

Some recent interest has centred on the problem of "cognitive" control over involuntary processes. This appears possible, either through substitution of a verbal for a classically conditioned sensory CS, or, more importantly, through imagery. Depending on imagery vividness, and possibly on S's drive state, considerable control can be exercised over a range of autonomic functioning by S simply imaging a US. Such control appears to be subject to training, a finding which has considerable behavioural and therapeutic significance.

An important secondary gain may be that we are finally being persuaded that human conditioning cannot be encompassed by the relatively simple laws enunciated by Pavlov and Hull. It is considerably more complex than we have chosen to believe, and it is becoming increasingly apparent that antecedent (i.e. "setting") and intervening cognitive variables can profoundly affect the course and outcome of conditioning.

CHAPTER 11

# Socialisation: the Search for "Conscience"

*The fundamental problem of social psychology is the moralisation of the individual into the society into which he is born as an amoral and egoistic infant. There are successive stages, each of which must be traversed by every individual before he can attain the next higher: (1) the stage in which the operation of the instinctive impulses is modified by the influence of reward and punishments; (2) the stage in which conduct is controlled in the main by anticipation of social praise and blame; (3) the highest stage in which conduct is regulated by an ideal that enables a man to act in the way that seems to him right, regardless of the praise or blame of his immediate social environment.*
W. McDougall (1908)

> *I bid you, mock not Eros,*
> *he knows not doubt or shame,*
> *And, unaware of proverbs,*
> *the burn child craves the flame.*

Christopher Morley

## Introduction

IN A very broad sense, socialisation refers to the process whereby individuals are taught to function effectively in society, and is thus concerned with the characteristics they acquire, and the psychological mechanisms through which this is achieved. The aim of socialisation is the substitution of internal control for external sanctions — a shared instead of an egocentric world view — by the internalisation of attitudes and values. Through the process of cognitive representation, future consequences may be transformed into current events which are functionally similar to actual outcomes in their capacity to influence actions.

Such internalised attitudes and values describe "conscience" — the cognitive and affective processes which constitute an internalised moral governor over an individual's conduct (Aronfreed, 1969). It is cognitive in that it implies awareness of the origins and nature of rules of conduct, the ability to evaluate one's own actions and intentions, and to behave in an appropriate manner in the absence of external reinforcement, affective in that social-moral judgement is constrained by feelings of fear (anxiety), obligation, remorse and guilt. Aronfreed suggests that the term should be used only to refer to conduct where substantial changes in motivational state become attached to actions or their cognitive representations. Thus it should be restricted to conduct involving aggressive and sexual behaviour, honesty, truthfulness, aspects of authority, for example.

A critical question is precisely how these changes in motivational state become attached to actions, and a good deal of controversy has centred round this issue. As a consequence, there are many formal theories about socialisation, each containing some truth, and each attracting some empirical support. This applies particularly to the plethora of interactional models, ranging from the crude early social learning model of Bandura and Walters (1963) to the more elegant model of social behaviourism described by Staats (1975, 1980). No one theory, by itself, however, is sufficiently robust to accommodate all the observed phenomena concerning the acquisition of social rules. Nevertheless, from the 1930s and 1940s, when the term socialisation, in its modern sense, first appeared in the sociological-psychological literature — although earlier theorists such as Durkheim and Freud had been actively concerned with problems of socialisation — we can identify two dominant alignments, each of which is very broadly represented in modern approaches to social learning.

The first, the biological/behavioural, regards socialisation as almost synonymous with "education", both terms referring to the active intervention of social agents in the life of the individual to advance culturally approved social goals and roles. Society is thus the active agent, the individual the more-or-less passive recipient. We should note, however, as Danziger (1976) comments, that while education is concerned more with the value of goals, socialisation in this sense is concerned more with their effectiveness, a shift in emphasis which recapitulates the general change from social philosophy to positivistic social science. This view is represented in the culture-personality school of Kardiner, Mead and Gorer, which owes a good deal both to psychoanalytic theory and to the Marxist theory of society, and in "social engineering" theories which employ the language of conditioning to describe techniques of social control.

The second emphasis, which might be denoted social psychological/trans-actional, presupposes the active participation of the child in the ongoing process of social action, a process involving three elements — the person, the environment, and the person/situation interaction — all of these being critical for the understanding of socialisation and the social learning process. The "activity" theory of Vygotsky and modern Soviet developmental theorists such as Leont'ev and Davydov, and the interactional psychology and social behaviourism theories of Endler and Magnusson and Staats, which we have previously described, are the most influential representatives of this approach.

## Social Learning as a Reciprocal Process

In this chapter, we shall attempt to review theory and research reflecting these two broad approaches to social learning. To a degree, of course, this distinction is arbitrary and artificial. There is considerable overlap between the views expressed, the difference being largely one of emphasis. Biological theories of socialisation, such as that described by Eysenck, for example, do, in fact, increasingly emphasise the environment/person interaction term (e.g. Eysenck and Eysenck, 1980). Interactional theories do increasingly pay at least lip service to the importance of biological causal agents (e.g. Staats, 1980). This rapproachement has been encouraged by the impressive evidence reported in the conditioning and developmental literature over the past two decades emphasising that a good deal of learning, particularly social learning, is a reciprocal, transactional process initiated almost from the moment of birth.

We noted in a previous section the somewhat surprising extent to which neonates, from the first day of life, are capable of stimulus analysis and discrimination reversal of a relatively high order (Siqueland and Lipsitt, 1966). They condition readily in both classical and operant modes (e.g. Siqueland and Lipsitt, 1966; Papousek, 1967a,b, 1969). It has been claimed that humans learn better in infancy than at any other period in later life (Lipsitt, 1969). Early learning opportunities clearly affect later learning, learning ability appearing to decline if not exercised. A prime example is the development of sensori-motor skills, where integration of behaviour units into smooth sequences requires a well-ordered programme of operant learning. Of particular interest is Papousek's (1967a) report of large and consistent individual differences in conditioning rates in 3–6-month-old infants, and his observation that these differences are attributable to innately determined differences in higher nervous activity.

From day one, therefore, infants respond in sophisticated ways to environmental contingencies. More than this. They show clear motivation not only to establish "what leads to what" in the environment (Papousek, 1969; Bower, 1974), showing effort and well-developed skill in discovering simple rules, but also in using this knowledge to attain certain goals rapidly and directly. Parents become aware of this early in the child's life. How tyrannical infants can become when they establish that a cry attracts attention, that a smile captures interest! A S Schaffer (1977) observes, such learning is transactional in that at all stages of growth we can detect constant and progressive modifications of behaviour, both parent and child operating within a system of mutuality, whereby the behaviour of one produces effects on the other, which, in turn, modify the behaviour of the first. We have thus a complex network of interacting influences. Individuals play an active role in altering their environment, exercising some control over parents as well as being influenced by them.

In this connection, an important "enabling" mechanism may be the dependency or anaclitic bond with the nurturing adult which is claimed to emerge at around 5–7 months of age. The classic analytic view is that this orginates in the satisfaction of oral needs. Bowlby, on the other hand, takes a more ethological stance in suggesting that the bond is determined by a number of innate, instinctual, response systems (crying, smiling, clinging, following), which are activated by environmental stimuli, and terminated by an object or a person, the actual experience of terminating creating the affectional bond. There may be considerable debate about the origin of this bond. However, there is no doubt about its important role in early learning. A child reared under normal conditions reacts to physical separation from his parents with distress. Psychological separation, i.e. threat of denial of dependency needs, is equally distressing, its reinforcement value depending on the strength of the affectional bond. Anxiety as a consequence of physical or psychological separation is the unavoidable risk in the love relationship with the caring person.

It would be a mistake to suggest, however, that all early learning has this primary, 'transactional' quality. There is an important dimension of infant learning (sometimes referred to as curiosity, exploratory drive), learning which is reinforced by nothing more than the actual seeking and discovery of a solution, learning which reflects the child's active striving towards contact with the external world, one of the basic psychological drives mentioned earlier. Man is not a passive system, attempting to maintain homeostasis with minimal energy output. A decisive role is played by the emerging, creative power of the individual — a view which has been emphasised by European and Soviet psychologists (e.g. Vygotsky, 1972) — by the conscious self-monitoring of performance (Harrè and Secord, 1976). Thus, within the limits of individual differences, the normal child is spontaneously active, his responses being selective, acquisitive, adaptive. Such activity promotes an appropriate level of stimulation through which the child can adjust his behaviour by comparing expected with real stimulation. Inability to detect lawfulness, to create a model, is thought initially to result in increased level of activity, subsequently to decreased level, finally to apathy (Schaffer, 1965; Papousek, 1969). These observations support Pribram's (1967) model postulating two different types of mechanism involved in internal control of emotion — those promoting increased processing of information in an effort to reduce uncertainty, and those limiting information input (and presumably decreasing uncertainty) by a return to the previous level of integration. In this sense, opportunity to explore, and to learn, modulates the infant's emotional life, and exercises a profound influence on the course of socialisation learning. Clearly, the nurturing adult is importantly concerned in creating the conditions necessary for such learning to occur, but her involvement is secondary, not primarily "transactional" in the sense in which we have previously used the term in referring to acquisition of rules of conduct.

Thus, when a child approaches the period of primary socialisation, i.e. that point in time when behaviour is formally shaped through conditioning and observational learning, he carries within himself an already extensive experiential history — experience of active searching or hypothesis testing to develop "models of the environment", and thus effective "coping strategies" (Bruner, 1959), which modulates his level of spontaneous activity and emotional stability — and an established bond with the caring adult.

## A. Biological/Behavioural Theories of Socialisation

### 1. General models of "conditionability"

A number of theorists have postulated general factors of "conditionability" to account for acquisition of socially appropriate behaviour, and for the suppression of socially undesirable or egotistical behaviour. This implies some consistency in rate of acquisition and extinction of conditional responses between learning situations and across response systems. Differential conditioning during socialisation is claimed to account for the consistent behavioural differences in social-moral behaviour which are the basis of personality structure in adults. On the other hand, an assumption implicit in most conditioning models is that appetitive and aversive acquisition and extinction involve different processes, judging from evidence of large intra-S differences in unconditional responses to different appetitive and aversive reinforcements, and from data suggesting that subcortical structures mediating reward and punishment are mutually inhibitory, and that classical and instrumental conditioning are different forms of learning. From this point of view, there are no grounds for anticipating factors of "conditionability".

BASIC MODELS

The theoretical biases of Eysenck and Spence, the most influential theorists in the field of conditioning and personality in recent years, reflect the influence of two great principles of behaviour modification, the Pavlovian notion of contiguity or association, and the Thorndikian principle of hedonism (law of effect). These differences account in part for certain contradictions in the experimental results reported, and for some apparent logical inconsistencies in the development of their postulates and models.

Eysenck's general theory (Eysenck, 1957) concerning the aetiology of personality types is expressed in a series of postulates, of which two are of central importance:

1. the postulate of individual differences states that human beings differ with respect to the speed with which excitation and inhibition are generated, the strength of such excitation and inhibition, and the speed with which inhibition is dissipated;

2. the typological postulate asserts that individuals in whom excitatory potentials are generated weakly and slowly, and in whom reactive inhibition is generated quickly and strongly, and dissipates quickly, are predisposed to develop extraverted patterns of behaviour, and that individuals in whom excitatory potentials are generated quickly and strongly, and in whom reactive inhibition is generated slowly and weakly, and dissipates slowly, are predisposed to develop introverted patterns of behaviour.

The conditioning postulate, which is the cornerstone of Eysenck's behaviour theory, reflects a strong Pavlovian emphasis. It is, in fact, derived from early Pavlovian typology. In line with Pavlov's identification of hysteria with predominance of inhibition (Pavlov, 1927, p. 397), and with Jung's (1924) assumption that hysteria is the neurosis of the extravert, Eysenck proposed that the extravert is the unbalanced inhibitory type,[1] and the introvert the unbalanced excitatory type. Since balance according to excitation was originally assumed by Pavlov to underlie speed of formation of positive and inhibitory CRs, Eysenck hypothesised that introverts will condition quickly and extinguish slowly, and that extraverts will condition slowly and extinguish rapidly. Differential excitatory and inhibitory growth gradients in the two groups, therefore, were assumed to account for differential CR acquisition and extinction rates. In Pavlovian theory, each reinforced trial increases conductivity in the CS–US links in the CNS, so that growth in the acquisition curve reflects growth of excitatory potential in the synapses of the CNS, or in whatever cortical area provides the physiological or neurological locus of the CR. Simililarly, extinction is a function of internal inhibition, in that unreinforced CSs evoke inhibition, or decreased conductivity in the relevant synapses. Thus genetically based differences in the balance of cortical excitation and inhibition shape socialisation learning, via conditioning, to produce the typical extraverted and introverted behaviour patterns.

While this early version of Eysenck's theory appears, at first sight, to be plausible enough, a number of theoretical difficulties, three in particular, were ignored.

(a) Although Pavlov, in his 1932 paper (1941, pp. 102–16) identified hysteria

---

[1]The inhibitory type was subsequently (post-1930) excluded from the Pavlovian typology, presumably because of lack of evidence of a clear type.

with predominance of inhibition, he also noted that some "inhibitory" dogs continued to behave in an adaptive manner, despite frequent collisions between excitatory and inhibitory processes. Presumably these were the strong, but balanced or equilibrated types, and it is difficult to see how these can be accommodated within the Eysenckian typology.

In the early statement of his postulates (1955), Eysenck referred only to reactive inhibition. In the later version, however, (Eysenck, 1957), he referred to excitatory and inhibitory potential, describing excitation and inhibition as if they occupied a single bipolar dimension, so that his two types are superficially similar to Pavlovian unbalanced types. From his subsequent discussions, however, it is obvious that he equates excitatory potential with $_sH_r$, and inhibitory potential with $I_r$, constructs which, in Hullian theory, are independent, so that logically it is possible for an individual to generate both potentials equally strongly. Nevertheless, until 1966, which marks a turning point in his typological theorising, Eysenck continued to emphasise the inhibitory aspect of his postulates, probably because the strongest evidence for differences between Es and Is involved speed of development of reactive inhibition in satiation and reminiscence experiments. In 1965, for example, he suggested that the experimental parameters likely to produce correlations between E and eyeblink conditioning rates are those productive of inhibition — partial reinforcement, and discrimination learning as opposed to single stimulus conditioning. Superior conditioning of Is is thus due to the stronger cortical inhibition in Es depressing conditioning and facilitating extinction, rather than to the greater cortical excitation of Is facilitating acquisition "providing that the optimum degree of excitation has not been reached. As this provision is unlikely to be fulfilled in normal rested subjects, more stress has been laid on the inhibitory postulate" (Eysenck, 1965, p. 258).

(b) Perhaps more importantly, as Nebylitsyn (1966a) points out, Pavlov, in a 1935 paper (1955, pp. 490–1) suggests that hysteria is a product of weakness in the artistic type, and dysthymia a product of weakness in the thinking type. In this event, it is pertinent to ask how the same typological weakness can underlie differences in CR development and extinction between hysterics and dysthymics. Nebylitsyn (1966a) suggests that where better conditioning is reported from dysthymics (and presumably introverts), as, for example, in Halberstam's (1961) study, this may be because verbal ("second-signal") CSs were employed, since dysthymics are "thinkers", "second-signalling" types. In this connection we might note Myasishchev's (1959) report that dysthymics show more expressive GSRs to stimulation in the second signal system, while hysterics respond maximally to first signal, i.e. sensory stimuli.

(c) Eysenck has never seriously considered his second major personality dimension, N, or neuroticism, in relation to personality/conditioning theory.

Although he has consistently maintained that neuroticism, which is orthogonal with extraversion, reflects differences along a dimension of autonomic activation mediated subcortically by the limbic system, in his personality theory Eysenck has continued to emphasise E–I differences, formally anchored in the excitation/inhibition balance hypothesis, as the basis for differential conditioning rates, and to ignore N differences, or to link them to balance through the inferred relationship of neuroticism to introversion. It may be, however, that N, interactively with E, plays a more critical role in conditioning.

Spence (1964), on the other hand, has attached greater significance to drive variables. Since he considered drive to be a function of both relevant need, and the total aggregate strength of existing irrelevant needs, he claimed that level of internal anxiety, or "emotionality", as measured by Taylor's Manifest Anxiety Scale (MAS), for example, should predict aversive conditioning rates. Simply stated, in Hullian terms, increased D multiples with existing $_sH_r$ to produce greater $_sE_r$.

EMPIRICAL STUDIES

(a) Classical conditioning

Extensive testing of these propositions has produced conflicting results. On the one hand, the Maudsley group has reported statistically significant, though small differences (accounting for about 8–10% of the reliable variance) favouring introverts in acquisition of eyeblink and GSR[2] (to shock US) CRs (Eysenck, 1965). On the other hand, evidence of approximately equal weight from Spence's Iowa group has supported a relationship between MAS scores, assumed to measure internal anxiety or proneness to defensive arousal, and thus orthogonal to extraversion[3] and acquisition of aversive CRs (Spence, 1964), particularly under conditions likely to increase S's apprehension (Ominsky and Kimble, 1966). Again, some studies have reported superior conditioning from both introverts and neurotics (e.g. Piers and Kirchner, 1969), and from neurotic introverts, compared with neurotic extraverts and both stable groups (e.g. Mogel, 1969). Finally, a few studies have reported no differences between personality groups (e.g. Morgenson and Martin, 1969).

In attempting to account for these discrepancies, Eysenck has contended that emotionality, or "acute" anxiety, does not contribute to total effective drive strength in classical aversive conditioning (although it may do so in instrumental learning) except when S is under threat or stress, in which case

---

[2]Results from the GSR studies may be suspect. The methodologies employed suggest that responses are probably conditioned orienting responses, a special class of CR which does not obey general laws pertaining to 'true' CR acquisition.

[3]Note, however, Eysenck's claim that MAS reflects both E and N, and, as such, cannot be regarded as orthogonal with E.

emotionality becomes a source of relevant drive. This claim has some independent support (Beam, 1955; Sweetbaum, 1963; results of some of the Iowa studies (cf. Spence, 1964); Kimble, 1961; Ominsky and Kimble, 1966). Thus he discounts the apparent contradiction between the Maudsley and Iowa findings. He suggests that high-N and high-E Ss are innately predisposed to react differently to different classes of stimuli — high-N Ss to emotion-provoking stimuli with innervation of their sympathetic nervous systems, and high-E Ss to inhibition-producing stimuli with cortical inhibition (Eysenck, 1965). Under stressful conditions, therefore, which applied in many of the Iowa studies (use of dentist's chair, darkened room, and so on), under pre-examination or pre-operation stress, or ego-threat, MAS or N differences might be expected to predict conditioning rates, while under non-stressful or mildly irritating conditions, which applied in many of the Maudsley studies, excitatory and inhibitory growth potentials are more likely to contribute to CR acquisition and extinction rates.

> While different individuals are hypothesised to have different potentials for reacting to emotion-provoking or inhibition-producing stimuli, these stimuli can only be translated into observable behaviour under specified conditions, that, is under emotion-producing conditions for Spence, and under inhibition-producing conditions for Eysenck (Eysenck, 1965).

Two other possible explanations have been offered. One is Brody's (1972) suggestion that introverts condition poorly in anxiety-producing situations because of excessive operation of transmarginal inhibition, a point which has also been made by White and Mangan (1972), who observed that N as well as E might be correlated with response amplitude when stimulus intensities approach transmarginal levels.

An alternative possibility is that sampling artefact might be involved (Franks, 1964; White et al., 1969). It is possible that the negative correlation typically reported between E and N (around 0.2–0.4) could bias high-N (or MAS) and low-E samples in favour of a disproportionately high number of high-N/low-E Ss. More rapid acquisition of aversive CRs by these Ss could account in part for the discrepancy between the two sets of data. This hypothesis, however, has never been adequately tested. In any event, we are faced with the problem of explaining why the neurotic introvert should show faster conditioning than other groups.

Insofar as appetitive conditioning is concerned, most of the reported studies have employed one of two types of reinforcement — salivary or sexual.

Only a few salivary conditioning experiments have been reported. Bindra, Paterson and Strzlecki (1955) report no differences between high and low MAS Ss, and Morrish (1974) no difference between high and low N and high and low E subjects in salivary conditioning. The Morrish results are surprising, in view of the clearly established greater unconditional salivation of Is to gustatory stimuli such as lemon juice.

A more encouraging outcome has been reported where sexual USs have been employed. We might predict better conditioning from stable extraverts, in view of the evidence that Es show more rapid growth, higher levels, and greater frequency of sexual excitation (Eysenck, 1971a,b, 1976), and that high N Ss appear to be "susceptible to fear and anxiety to a degree which makes them less likely to indulge in sexual behaviour, to worry about sex, to be disgusted by sex, and to have fewer contacts with sexual partners" (Eysenck, 1971b, p. 594). Questionnaire and interview data from a number of sources — from British (Eysenck, 1976; Mangan, 1978b) and young German and American undergraduate samples (Giese and Schmidt, 1968; Zuckerman *et al.*, 1972) — offer similar descriptions.

Laboratory conditioning of sexual arousal, however, has produced conflicting results. Lovibond (1964), Mangan (1974) and Morrish (1974), the first two studies employing slides of nude females as US with male Ss, the latter a movie portraying erotic scenes, failed to report significant correlations between E-I and speed of CR acquisition. However, Mangan (1978a) and Paisey and Mangan (in press) report that extraversion and stability (low N) add to the prediction of CR acquisition in classical (sexual) GSR conditioning, and Kantorowitz (1978) reports correlations of 0.88 between E and tumescence conditioning, and –0.76 between E and detumescence conditioning. It is arguable, of course, whether tumescence conditioning — a comparison of pre- and post-treatment tumescence to erotic stimuli, the treatment involving S masturbating during a 2-minute exposure to such stimuli over 8 sessions — is "true" conditioning. The same could be said of detumescence conditioning, which involves comparison of pre- and post-orgasm response to a different erotic slide, not associated with treatment. Nevertheless, the results are highly significant, even allowing for smallness of sample (N = 7).

### (b) Operant conditioning

Few studies have been reported relating personality measures to active avoidance, reinforcement being a painful US such as electric shock. Perhaps the most informative is that of Davidson and Payne (1964), who employed a finger withdrawal response, the US being electric shock, and the CS a tone. GSR was simultaneously conditioned to the tone. The authors report that while there were high correlations between acquisition and extinction scores for each conditioning procedure, there were no significant correlations between the two. This, they conclude, argues against a general factor of conditionability, and suggest that this is possibly due to the fact that one type of conditioning depends on contiguity, the other on drive reduction. They report that none of the conditioning indices correlates with introversion, neuroticism or manifest anxiety, as assessed by various questionnaires, nor with an independent psychiatric rating of anxiety based on interview.

By far the most frequently employed methodology in operant conditioning, however, has been a verbal operant paradigm, usually a Taffel-type task in which S is required to construct sentences from a pool of nouns/pronouns, and verbs, reinforcement being comments such as "good", "not so good", delivered by E.

In this connection we could predict that introverts will condition more readily than extraverts to both types of reinforcement, arguing from the original Eysenckian postulate, a prediction which is also derivable from Nebylitsyn's (1966a) contention that introverts, as "thinking", "second-signalling" types, should be more responsive to verbal than to sensory stimuli. On the other hand, Gray would suggest that extraverts are more responsive to signals of reward, introverts to signals of punishment.

A number of studies, employing a Taffel technique, or a variant of this, have reported significant correlations between introversion and verbal "reward" conditioning (e.g., Halberstam, 1961; Quay and Hunt, 1965; Jarwanda, 1966; Helmat, 1971; Gupta, 1970, 1973, 1976; Gupta and Singh, 1971; Jones, 1973), and verbal "punishment" conditioning (e.g. Gupta, 1976).

On the other hand, Fontinelle (1973) has reported that Is condition better than Es under a punishment regime, and Es better than Is under reward conditioning, a result also reported by Seunath (1975) who employed a pursuit rotor learning task with 14–15-year-old Ss. Sadler (1970), Sadler and Mifford (1971) and Otis and Martin (1968) report that stable introverts and neurotic extraverts condition more readily under reward conditions, although, according to Sadler (1970), different searching patterns appear to be mainly responsible for learning differences between groups. Nagpal and Gupta (1979) report that anxious extraverts condition better under reward conditions, and anxious introverts better when punishment is employed.

Overall, the weight of evidence from the verbal conditioning studies confirms Eysenck's original hypothesis — introverts condition more quickly than extraverts, irrespective of reinforcement type — although there is some support for Gray's view that Es are more conditionable under reward conditions. Some failures of prediction (e.g. Miller and Minten, 1972), however, have been recorded.

#### (c) Later versions of Eysenck's theory

In Eysenck's most recent statements about conditioning and personality, there has been a marked change in emphasis. While he referred to both excitatory and inhibitory potentials in his early theorising, until 1966 Eysenck continued to emphasise the inhibitory aspect of his conditioning postulate. In his 1966 and 1972 statements, however, while it is apparent that he still retains two of his inhibition-producing conditions — partial reinforcement and discrimination learning — he now attaches considerably more weight to the excitatory elements in acquisition, especially weak CS and US, and short CS–US intervals.

This re-assessment was based on his own observation of a close relationship between reticular arousal thresholds and introversion which is reflected in the lower thresholds of arousability expressed by introverts in a number of modalities (cf. Eysenck, 1967), and on Gray's (1964a) suggestion that different arousal levels in the reticular formation could account for most of the experimentally determined differences between weak and strong nervous systems.

From this point of view, certain conditions should favour introverts, others extraverts, in CR acquisition. Confirmatory data are reported by Eysenck and Levy (1972). Weak US, short CS–US intervals, and partial reinforcement, in that order, favour Is in acquisition. A combination of the three conditions produces the impressive separation between groups shown in Figures 29, 30 and 31.

The identification of nervous system strength-sensitivity, or "arousability", with extraversion, however, raises a number of problems. Arguing from the original Pavlovian typology, where it was assumed that excitatorily strong Ss develop CRs more rapidly, extraverted (i.e. strong) Ss should condition more readily than introverted (i.e. weak) Ss. Clearly, this is not Eysenck's expectation. If, on the other hand, we adopt the revised Teplov–Nebylitsyn typology, other difficulties arise. According to this view, the sensitive system is characterised not only by a high level of arousability, but also by a low working capacity. Strength-sensitivity is assumed to be a continuous dimension, the distance between the upper and lower thresholds being constant for all reacting systems. Thus, the introverted system, in addition to having lower thresholds of arousability, should also exhaust more rapidly when subjected to ultra-strong stimuli, or to repeated applications of moderately strong stimuli.

But precisely what do we mean by arousability? Arousability in the afferent systems, in the subcortical structures mediating reinforcement, or both? Nebylitsyn (1966a) distinguishes arousability to CS from arousability to US, each of these defining an independent nervous system property.

There is evidence that introverts are more sensitive in a number of afferent systems, show greater unconditional salivation to lemon juice, and greater decrement to swallowed lemon juice, the latter being taken as a measure of transmarginal inhibition. These findings fit the general pattern of introverts being more arousable in both cortical and in subcortical centres than extraverts.

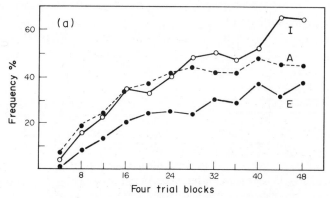

(a) Rate of eyelid conditioning for introverts, ambiverts and extraverts under weak UCS
conditions.

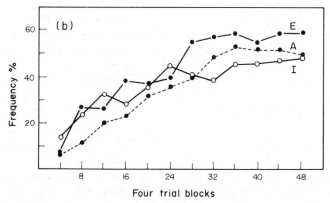

(b) Rate of eyelid conditioning for extraverts, ambiverts and introverts under strong UCS
conditions.
Figure 29 (from Eysenck & Levy, 1972).

On the other hand, there are clear indications that extraverts are more
arousable in the tactual system (Mangan, 1974), that they show stronger sexual
arousal (UR amplitude to erotic stimuli), and that at the strong end of *certain*
stimulus intensity continua the behaviour of Es is more characteristic of the
weak than the strong system, in that they generate transmarginal and reactive
inhibition more readily than Is (White *et al.,* 1969; Mangan and Farmer, 1967;
Zhorov and Yermolayeva-Tomina, 1972).

In counter-argument, it could be claimed that Nebylitsyn's theorem may still
hold — i.e. that the distance between the upper and lower thresholds of response
is the same for all reacting systems — if we measure "distance" as multiples of
jnd. Within Nebylitsyn's model, it is still possible for Is to have both lower

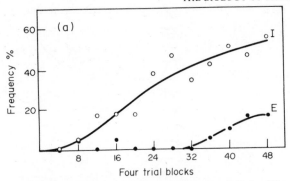

(a) Rate of eyelid conditioning for introverts and extraverts under conditions of partial
reinforcement, weak UCS, and short CS–UCS interval.

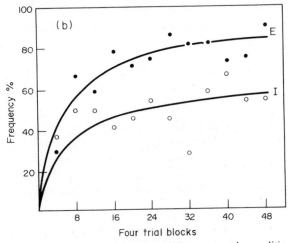

(b) Rate of eyelid conditioning for extraverts and introverts under conditions of 100%
reinforcement, strong UCS, and long CS–UCS interval.
Figure 30 (from Eysenck & Levy, 1972).

absolute thresholds and higher thresholds of transmarginal inhibition, if they
have larger jnds throughout the range of stimulus intensities. From limited
evidence, however, this does not appear to be the case (Farley and Gundrum,
1972).

The problem becomes somewhat more intractable in view of the suggested
relationship between strength-sensitivity and manifest anxiety or neuroticism,
which is orthogonal with extraversion. Lynn (1966) suggests that strength of the
nervous system corresponds to anxiety, Ss with weak nervous systems being
anxious, though he acknowledges that there is little evidence of relationships
between anxiety and the various threshold measures devised by Teplov and his

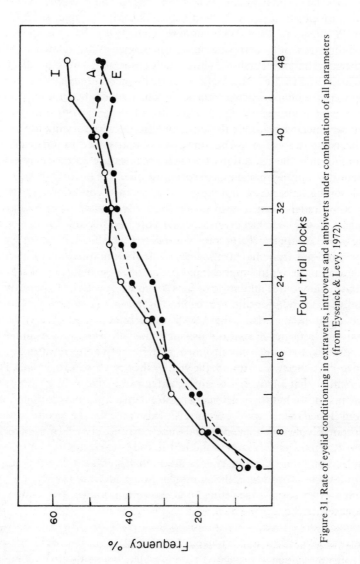

Figure 31. Rate of eyelid conditioning in extraverts, introverts and ambiverts under combination of all parameters (from Eysenck & Levy, 1972).

colleagues. Gray (1965) has proposed that neuroticism may be related to nervous system strength via an underlying component of arousal, a suggestion similar to one originally made by Eysenck (1947). There is some recent support for this proposition (Knowles and Krasner, 1965; Claridge, 1967; Ginsberg, 1969; White et al., 1969; White and Mangan, 1972). There is, of course, the possibility that both extraversion and neuroticism are related to strength-sensitivity, the extraversion factor being associated with specific analyser sensitivity, and the neuroticism factor with the generalised sensitising influence of the mesencephalic reticular arousal system, so that N becomes critical only at transmarginal intensities, i.e. at stimulus intensities strong enough to elicit defensive reflexes, or where the situational stimuli are very intense.

The most serious problem, however, is that posed by Gray (1969). He maintains that the conditions Eysenck specifies are so restrictive that it is difficult to concede that the over-socialisation of the introvert is mediated by conditioning, since we cannot suppose that parental conditioning practices are any more under- than over-arousing (but note the comment by Paisey and Mangan, p. 462). He has proposed, therefore, a different explanation for the better conditioning performance of introverts which is critical for Eysenck's theory. Judging from the extraverting effects of sodium amytal, which, through its action on the septo-hippocampal structures — structures which appear to mediate behavioural inhibition — acts to reduce sensitivity to punishment, he hypothesises a relationship between introversion and activity in the negative feedback loop comprising the ARAS, the orbital-frontal cortex, the medial septal area and the hippocampus, such that introversion is a dimension of susceptibility to signals of punishment and frustrative non-reward. The greater the degree of this susceptibility, the greater the degree of introversion. Thus it is not so much that introverts condition better, rather that they are more prone to punishment, so that when defensive reinforcement is employed, defensive CRs are developed more rapidly, Gray (1970) also postulates a second, orthogonal factor, involving sensitivity to signals of reward and relieving non-punishment. These two axes are oblique to the EPI E and N axes; neurotic introverts are therefore more prone to aversive conditioning, stable extraverts to appetitive conditioning. However, although Nicholson and Gray (1972) and Mangan (1978b) offer some supporting data, these hypotheses have not yet been adequately tested.

### (d) Some recent, more broadly based studies

From the evidence presented to this point, involving, for the most part, simple correlational studies relating extraversion scores to CR acquisition rates, we would be hard pressed to infer a general factor of conditionability. And even if we assume such a factor, the relationships reported are too weak, and the experimental conditions too restrictive, to support a general theory relating conditioning to personality. The inferred neurophysiological variables hardly qualify as critical determinants of personality organisation.

This does not mean, however, that we should abandon the concept of conditionability altogether. The research, on the whole, has been relatively unsophisticated, and the hypothesis only indifferently tested. Nevertheless, there are a few recorded studies in which a wide enough spectrum of psychophysiological variables has been sampled to allow conditionability factors, if such exist, to emerge, and these have signalled more general factors cutting across stimulus and response systems.

One example is the Q analysis reported in Chapter 9, which suggested factors of "arousability", involving responsivity to CS and US, and "inhibitibility", which accounted for a good deal of the variance of both CR extinction and mobility of inhibition.

Mangan (1974, 1978a,b) has reported other relevant data. In the first (1974) study, an attempt was made to establish the contribution of a wide range of measures to the variance of appetitive (sexual) GSR conditioning and extinction. The critical variables, in both cases, were the psychophysiological rather than the cognitive mediational or personality variables.

A further study (Mangan, 1978a) disclosed CR acquisition and extinction factors cutting across appetitive and aversive conditioning paradigms. Rotated factor loadings are shown in Table 36. GSR was response in both cases. Both factors were indexed by variables which, on a priori grounds, were thought to be critical. The extinction factor loads the internal inhibition measures (habituation rate of OR), and, negatively, both afferent arousability (initial amplitude of OR), i.e. responsivity in the modality of the CS, and arousability to the US (appetitive and aversive UR amplitudes). Unstable introverts appear to extinguish CRs more rapidly. The acquisition factor shows positive loadings of variables reflecting responsivity to CS (initial amplitude of OR), and of two of the three measures thought to index unconditional responsivity — appetitive UR amplitude, frequency of sexual outlet). Aversive UR amplitude does not load this factor. However, it was anticipated that the critical aversive US variable would be auditory sensitivity, since for sensitive Ss the 106 dB white noise would be more intense, subjectively, and thus more aversive. We might also expect such Ss to acquire appetitive CRs more rapidly, because of their greater reactivity to the auditory (appetitive) CS. Stable extraverts, from this analysis, are more "conditionable".

There is the possibility, of course, that more of the variance of the acquisition and extinction factors is taken up by appetitive than by aversive responding, or vice versa, so that the pattern of loadings may be biased one way or the other, and thus give a false picture of the content of both factors. For this reason, four

TABLE 36. *Rotated factor loadings (values < 0.30 omitted) (from Mangan, 1978a.*
*Reproduced by permission of J. B. Lippincott Co.)*

|  |  | I | II | III | IV |
|---|---|---|---|---|---|
| 1. Extraversion | | .40 | .30 | | |
| 2. Neuroticism | | .55 | .40 | | .48 |
| 3. Appetitive acquisition | | | .73 | | |
| 4. Appetitive UR amplitude | | .41 | .46 | | |
| 5. Frequency sexual outlet | | | .85 | | |
| 6. Appetitive extinction | | .83 | | | .32 |
| 7. Aversive acquisition | | | .60 | | |
| 8. Aversive UR amplitude | | .39 | | .49 | .46 |
| 9. Aversive extinction | | .55 | .42 | | |
| 10. Tactual ⎫ | | | .31 | | .48 |
| 11. Auditory ⎬ Sensitivity | | .42 | .66 | | |
| 12. Visual ⎭ | | .40 | | .58 | |
| 13. Tactual ⎫ | | .32 | | .74 | |
| 14. Auditory ⎬ Imagery | | | | .82 | |
| 15. Visual ⎭ | | | | .70 | |
| 16. Tactual ⎫ | | .69 | | | |
| 17. Auditory ⎬ Habituation rate | | .44 | | | .34 |
| 18. Visual ⎭ | | .59 | | | |
| 19. Tactual ⎫ | | .32 | .75 | | |
| 20. Auditory ⎬ Initial amplitude | | .30 | .50 | .35 | |
| 21. Visual ⎭ | | .64 | .37 | .30 | .30 |
| 22. SAE Decline | | | | | .91 |
| 23. SAE Recovery | | .55 | | | .34 |

multiple regression analyses were performed, using the 19 psychophysiological and personality variables as predictors, and appetitive and aversive CR acquisition and extinction rates as dependent variables. Results are shown in Table 37. The F statistic in each case shows that the regression is significant.

There are three interesting features of these analyses which were not disclosed in the Principal Components analysis. The first involves the predictive weights and pattern of loadings of the extraversion dimension. E adds to the prediction of both appetitive acquisition and aversive extinction, and I to aversive acquisition and appetitive extinction, an outcome which is deducible from Gray's theory. If structures mediating punishment also mediate frustrative non-reward, and those mediating reward also mediate omission of punishment, we might anticipate patterns of loadings similar to those shown in the present analysis, factors which trangress specific responsivities to particular types of reward and punishment.

Secondly, the fact that tactual and auditory imagery predict appetitive acquisition, and visual imagery aversive acquisition, indicates that imagery in the CS modality is an important mediational variable. We might also argue that tactual imagery, in the appetitive case, is a US-related cognitive mediational

TABLE 37. Step-wise regressions of nineteen psychophysiological, cognitive and personality variables onto the four dependent variables (from Mangan, 1978a. Reproduced by permission of J. B. Lippincott Co.)

(a) Dependent variable — Appetitive acquisition

| Variable | R | R²% change | Simple r | b |
|---|---|---|---|---|
| Freq. sex. out. | .60 | 36 | .60 | 0.102 |
| Vis. init. amp. | .68 | 10 | .51 | 0.687 |
| Aud. sensit. | .72 | 6 | .37 | -0.239 |
| Tact. imagery | .78 | 8 | .40 | 0.808 |
| Aud. imagery | .84 | 11 | -.14 | 0.654 |
| N | .87 | 5 | -.16 | 1.121 |
| Tact. init. ampl. | .89 | 3 | .43 | 1.296 |
| Aud. hab. rate | .92 | 6 | -.26 | 0.739 |
| E | .95 | 5 | .05 | -0.492 |
| Tact. hab. rate | .98 | 5 | -.15 | -0.288 |
| (Constant) | | | | -21.022 |

(b) Dependent variable — Aversive acquisition

| Variable | R | R²% change | Simple r | b |
|---|---|---|---|---|
| Vis. hab. rate | .45 | 21 | -.45 | -0.570 |
| Aud. sensit. | .70 | 29 | .45 | 0.802 |
| Visual imagery | .77 | 10 | .28 | 0.443 |
| E | .85 | 9 | -.04 | -0.491 |
| SAE recovery | .90 | 13 | -.42 | -0.475 |
| Aud. init. amp. | .95 | 9 | .24 | -0.359 |
| (Constant) | | | | 7.330 |

(c) Dependent variable — Appetitive extinction

| Variable | R | R²% change | Simple r | b |
|---|---|---|---|---|
| SAE recovery | .61 | 38 | .61 | 0.217 |
| Aud. hab. rate | .78 | 22 | .56 | 0.216 |
| Tact. hab. rate | .84 | 11 | .56 | 0.206 |
| Freq. sex. outlet | .88 | 6 | .15 | 0.497 |
| Vis. init. ampl. | .91 | 6 | -.55 | -0.408 |
| E | .93 | 5 | -.37 | -0.314 |
| Vis. hab. rate | .95 | 5 | .52 | 0.226 |
| (Constant) | | | | 8.243 |

(d) Dependent variable — Aversive extinction

| Variable | R | R²% change | Simple r | b |
|---|---|---|---|---|
| Aud. sensit. | .47 | 22 | .47 | 0.390 |
| Aud. init. amp. | .56 | 10 | -.17 | -0.281 |
| Aud. hab. rate | .63 | 8 | -.06 | -0.545 |
| Vis. init. amp. | .69 | 7 | -.31 | -0.654 |
| Freq. sex. out. | .74 | 8 | .24 | 0.506 |
| E | .81 | 11 | .13 | -0.282 |
| Aud. imagery | .85 | 6 | -.26 | -0.274 |
| (Constant) | | | | 22.534 |

variable. Although there is some evidence that imagery assists in the process of conditioning, (e.g. Yaremko and Butler, 1975) and in paired associate learning (e.g. Paivio, 1969), and is viewed by most conditioning therapists as a direct potentiator of treatment effects, to the writer's knowledge few studies have been reported in which CS and US modality-specific imagery have been identified as sources of variance in conditioning. Such a finding, of course, is not unexpected, in view of the fairly substantial evidence that introverts experience more vivid mental imagery, and employ such imagery more effectively, in recall, than extraverts (cf. Gralton, Hayes and Richardson, 1979). This could be one of the critical personality-conditioning links, though we have to ask the question of whether this generalises across modalities, or is sensory modality-specific.

Finally, while it is clear that appetitive acquisition is predicted largely by arousability measures, aversive acquistion is predicted about equally by both arousability (auditory sensitivity and visual imagery) and the inverse of inhibition measures (visual habituation rate and SAE recovery). In the aversive list, slow habituation rate is second in order of importance. Thus, weakness of inhibition is as good a predictor of aversive acquisition as strength of excitation. Precisely why this is the case, however, is unclear.

From the analysis, it is tempting to infer general factors of "arousability" and "inhibitibility" across stimulus (CS and US) modalities in both conditioning situations. "Arousability", in the present case, can be operationalised as responsivity to CS and US (initial amplitude to CS, unconditional response to reinforcement), and, from the regression analyses, imagery vividness in the modality of CS and US, which were three of the sources of variance in conditioning identified in previous discussion. There is, of course, the unresolved difficulty of excitation/inhibition balance seemingly determining rate of aversive, but not appetitive acquisition.

In this respect, of interest is a series of studies reported by Paisey and Mangan (in press) comparing acquisition and extinction rates across appetitive and aversive reinforcements, classical and instrumental (in the original Bekhterev sense of instructed motor preconditioning) paradigms, and personality types, the latter being assessed on the basis of a number of personality inventories, including the EPI, Strelau's temperament inventory, and Zuckerman's sensation-seeking scale. In these experiments, differential reactivity to US was partialled out; the authors claim that this more faithfully simulates the level of US stimulation Ss are likely to encounter in everyday life, on the assumption — a basic postulate of the Warsaw school, which we have previously described — that Ss actively seek a level of stimulation consonant with their biologically determined level of reactivity. Thus, while Ss objectively encounter different levels of reward and punishment, subjectively these are equated between-Ss.

The results reported support the following conclusions.

1. Insofar as classical conditioning is concerned, there is a general factor of "conditionability" across appetitive and aversive reinforcement type.

2. Stable extraverts show superior autonomic conditioning, introverts superior motor approach and avoidance learning.

3. Since differential responsivity to US was partialled out, differential conditioning rates are considered to reflect reactivity and activity characteristics (which are negatively correlated) in the afferent/efferent systems involved. Introverts, who are afferently reactive, fail to condition autonomically, but because of their efferent non-active levels, condition well in instructed motor preconditioning. Extraverts, on the other hand, who are afferently non-reactive, condition well autonomically, but condition poorly in instructed motor preconditioning because of their higher levels of efferent activity.

CONDITIONABILITY ACROSS EFFERENT SYSTEMS

One of the few studies in which an attempt has been made to establish conditionability factors across efferent, as distinct from unconditional and conditional afferent, systems is that reported by Barr and McConaghy (1972a), who conditioned penile volume and GSR responses to both aversive (shock) and appetitive (slides of nude females) USs (cf. also the Davidson and Payne (1964) report). They report significant correlations between CR amplitudes in the two conditioning procedures within each response system, data consistent with those reported by Dykman, Mack and Ackerman (1965) from extensive experiments with dogs, employing heart rate, respiratory, blood pressure and motor responses. In agreement with previous findings with both human Ss — by Campbell (1938) employing eyeblink and knee-jerk conditioning, and Bunt and Barendregt (1961) with eyeblink, GSR and alpha desynchronisation responses, for example — and the animal data reported by Dykman, Mack and Ackerman (1965), no significant correlations were reported across response systems. However, when a work ratio measure, rather than raw scores, was employed — this index describing that portion of the total response achieved by the CR at the point of US onset — significant correlations were found across response modalities, in the same and in different conditioning procedures.

Barr and McConaghy's (1972a) claim that they have thus demonstrated factors of conditionability, however, invites much closer examination. The work ratio measure, like any other form of range correction, in effect partials out individual differences in reflex sensitivity to the aversive and sexual USs. Such a procedure certainly corrects for individual response specificity. But at the same time, it eliminates one — if not the major — source of variance in conditioning, since CR and UR amplitudes are highly correlated. It could be argued, of course, that this technique has revealed a common factor running through mediational processes other than those involving responsivity to particular USs — for example, imagery, arousability to CSs, aspects of return afferentiation — which were marked as important sources of variance in conditioning in the previous chapter. We might even suggest that this is in fact, the content of a general factor of excitability, as distinct from conditionability, which, in certain circumstances (where the US is not biologically significant, for example) could strongly influence speed of CR acquisition, and could be related to introversion. Where these conditions are not met, of course, we might expect other relationships to emerge.

A secondary, but important issue for present discussion, is that this technique may obscure relationships between personality dimensions and conditioning rates. If the sexual arousal of Es is more easily conditionable than that of Is because of their greater reflex sensitivity to erotic stimuli, and if the aversive arousal of Is is more readily conditionable than that of Es because of their greater reflex sensitivity to punishment, partialling out individual differences in sexual responsiveness and fearfulness would minimise or completely preclude between-group differences in rates of CR acquisition.

The real problem, of course, is that we lack an appropriate metric by which to make comparisons within and between Ss across response systems, particularly in the case of aversive (stress) conditioning, where the IRS principle seems to operate maximally. In theory, however, there is no reason why individual reactivities in different response systems should not be comparable — for example, cardiac responsivity in the case of subject A, vasomotor responsivity in the case of subject B — providing an appropriate correction term can be devised. Perhaps all that is required is normative data embracing major response systems, on the basis of which S's responsivity can be calculated in units of standard score. Such a procedure would fix the locus of conditionability where it ought to be — in the brain centres — while at the same time preserving idiosyncratic, individual response dispositions (that is, what S experiences phenomenally during the course of conditioning) which, as return afferentiation, probably determines the strength of the cortical representation of the US.

Concerning appetitive conditioning, where it has been suggested that the IRS principle exerts considerably less effect, since particular USs evoke highly specific responses, the problem may be of a different order. Here conditionability implies correlations between primary responses such as penile expansion and parotid secretions. There is no evidence of such relationships. We have noted reservations about the work ratio correction term employed by Barr and McConaghy (1972a). Normative data concerning primary sexual responses are probably unobtainable.

There may be, however, a viable alternative. Even in the most specific appetitive arousal systems, there are clusters of indices which appear to vary concomitantly. For example, in sexual responding, where the primary response is tumescence, a range of secondary responses, such as semi-spastic contractions of facial, abdominal and intercostal muscles, hyperventilation, tachycardia, elevations in systolic and diastolic blood pressure, GSR changes, changes in peripheral blood flow, characterise sexual arousal from initial sexual alertness to the pre-orgasmic plateau of the sexual cycle (Masters and Johnson, 1966). Salivary responding, while not normally as intense as sexual responding, nevertheless has heart rate, blood pressure, GSR characteristics. Even allowing for individual differences in amplitude of primary response, and in patterning of secondary responses, it may be possible to devise composite scores reflecting overall sexual and salivary responsiveness, which would permit between-S comparisons.

Finally, we might again refer briefly to the possibility that broadly based arousal systems, electro-cortical, autonomic and somatic, are related in dynamic, functional systems, activity levels in one system monitoring levels in others. An example cited was high levels of muscle tension "repressing" autonomic arousal and associated memories (Mangan, Murphy and Farmer, 1980). There have been suggestions that dynamic systems of this sort specify personality types, such as those described by Kempe (1956), and, more recently, by Barrell and Price (1977), who refer to a confronter/avoider personality dimension, one type responding to stress in terms of autonomic arousal, the other in terms of somatic arousal.

Clearly, any attempt to establish conditionability factors across response systems must take account of these phenomena.


A GENERAL FACTOR OF "INHIBITIBILITY"

In the study reported by Mangan (1978a) concerning general factors of CR acquisition and extinction, the disclosed content of the extinction factor left a number of important questions unanswered. In addition to the question of excitation/inhibition balance — strength of inhibition and weakness of excitation — determining speed of CR extinction, particularly in the case of aversive extinction, the extinction factor is indexed by a number of inhibitory measures — reactive, internal, transmarginal — which, according to Nebylitsyn (1966a), have little in common.

Historically, this problem has always been a vexing one. Pavlov referred to inhibition as a "curse", and typologists since that time, while describing different forms of inhibition — internal and transmarginal, for example — indexing different nervous system properties, have been uncertain about the content of these forms, and about their interrelationships. Nevertheless, we still find frequent reference, even in the comparative literature, to "inhibitible" types. But what kind of inhibition is referred to? Is there a general, inhibitory factor, as suggested in the analysis described above, of which internal and transmarginal inhibition, for example, are special forms? What is the status of reactive inhibition *vis-a-vis* these other forms?

Pavlov (1932) suggested that transmarginal or protective inhibition, which is assumed to develop when the intensity of stimulation surpasses the working capacity of the cortical cells, is distinct from internal inhibition. Transmarginal inhibition is passive, i.e. unconditioned, so that it is maximally effective on first presentation of the eliciting stimulus, while internal inhibition is active, i.e. conditioned inhibition, developing incrementally over trials, as in CR extinction. However, this distinction seems questionable, since Pavlov recognised an incremental form of transmarginal inhibition involving repeated stimulation of moderate load, as in extinction with reinforcement, a classic measure of excitatory strength, and thus of transmarginal inhibition. As Teplov (1937) notes, however, there is no evidence that the ultra-strong and incremental forms of transmarginal inhibition involve the same neural substrate.

It is possible, of course, that all forms of inhibition have a protective function. This has been suggested by a number of Soviet theorists, who note, for example, that following injections of toxins, drug-induced sleep can abolish certain pathological disorders. They also point to the reported efficacy of sleep therapy in the treatment of traumatic brain injury and shock. Judging from these data, and making the (questionable) assumption that sleep is a form of internal inhibition, it is claimed that the protective role need not differentiate transmarginal from other forms of inhibition.

Nebylitsyn (1966a), on the other hand, maintains that internal inhibition, transmarginal inhibition and inhibitory strength index orthogonal nervous system properties — dynamism of inhibition, excitatory strength and inhibitory strength — and cites evidence suggesting that internal and transmarginal inhibition are independent processes. However, there is little evidence one way or the other concerning inhibitory strength, a nervous system property which has been little investigated. Pavlov mentioned prolongation of differentiation (to the point of disinhibition) as a measure of absolute inhibitory strength, and this was the method employed in determining the inhibitory type, which Eysenck originally equated with extraversion. Subsequent evidence suggests that multiple repetition (Fedorov, 1961a) and increase in the physical intensity (Guseva, 1959, 1961; Zeval'd, 1964) of the differential stimulus produces much the same effect.

Since the Eysenckian typology rests on the proposition that the E is the inhibitory type, inhibition referring here to reactive inhibition, a fatigue measure derived, for instance, from frequency of involuntary rest pauses in tapping tasks, the obvious question arises of the extent to which the processes underlying reactive inhibition also underlie the inhibitory measures used as typological indices.

Eysenck (1967) suggests that reactive inhibition is equivalent in all essential respects to internal inhibition; Nebylitsyn (1966a), however, dismisses any suggestion of similarity. Gray (1967) notes that there are some similarities between reactive and transmarginal inhibition, which seems reasonable if he is referring to the repeated measures, i.e. incremental, form of transmarginal inhibition. If reactive inhibition is akin to fatigue, it might be equated with transmarginal inhibition in the motor system, a property which Mateyev (1961) has identified through factor analysis of ergographic strength measures. However, according to Rozhdestvenskaya et al. (1960), ergographic strength measures load a factor independent of a strength factor indexed by visual and auditory tests.

This problem might be resolved if relevant neurophysiological evidence about underlying processes were available. Again, however, critical data are lacking, although a number of hypotheses have been advanced. For example, postulated transmarginal and inhibitory strength mechanisms include a number inferable from ionic and denaturation theories of excitation, and from Wedenskii's theory of parabiosis. At this point in time, however, there are no grounds for favouring one interpretation over any other. And while the inhibitory effects of brain extracts such as GABA or Florey's Factor I are indisputable, there is no unequivocal evidence of active inhibitory agents at the synaptic junctions similar but opposite in function to known active excitatory agents. Insofar as internal or extinctive inhibition is concerned, suggestions about possible mechanisms range from simple one-stage "fatigue" models, essentially more sophisticated versions of Pavlov's original model, to more robust two-stage models, involving, for example, inhibition, by diencephalic mechanisms, of the neural circuits responsible for beta activity (Roitbak, 1956, 1958a). As in the previous cases, however, there is little precise information about inhibitory blocking agents and/or mechanisms at reticular level.

An obvious recourse is to empirical test. The only relevant study, however, is that reported by Mangan (1978b), who identified five inhibitory factors from a battery of eleven measures of reactive, internal, and transmarginal inhibition, and inhibitory strength. The factor structure is shown in Table 38. The factors, which were identified in terms of their inferred content — internal (factor I), transmarginal (III) and aversive and appetitive inhibitory strength (II and IV) — show considerable overlap. For example, the inhibitory strength measures, which were derived using a battering technique — i.e. presentation of the CS+,

TABLE 38. *Varimax rotated loadings (values <.30 omitted)*
*(from Mangan, 1978b)*

| Variable | | Assumed factor content | Factor | | | | |
|---|---|---|---|---|---|---|---|
| | | | I | II | III | IV | V |
| 1. EPI E | | E | .32 | | | .60 | .65 |
| 2. EPI N | | N | | | .73 | | .39 |
| 3. SAE decl. | | Reactive inhib. | .89 | | | | |
| 4. SAE recov. | | Reactive inhib. | .75 | | .42 | | |
| 5. Aud. | } OR habit | Int. inhib. | | .85 | | | |
| 6. Vis. | | Int. inhib. | | | .65 | | .37 |
| 7. Tact. | | Int. inhib. | | | .35 | .62 | |
| 8. App. | } CR Extinc. | Int. inhib. | .62 | .37 | .47 | .36 | |
| 9. Aver. | | Int. inhib. | .30 | .34 | | .42 | .48 |
| 10. App. | } Spon. rec. | Inhib. strength | | | | .82 | |
| 11. Aver. | | Inhib. strength | | .84 | | | |
| 12. A-I durat. | | | | | | | .92 |
| 13. A-I slope | | Trans. inhib. | .33 | | .70 | | |

following extinction of CR, with decreasing ITIs, until CR recovery — load factors on which internal inhibition in tactual and auditory modalities are strongly represented. Despite this, rather surprisingly, there is no general inhibitory factor. The explanation may lie in the strong modality effect which is evident from the factor structure. Neglecting the personality variables, the measures defining factors II, III and IV are auditory (variables 5 and 11), visual (6 and 13), and tactual (7 and 10). The fact that different inhibitory measures show higher correlations within than across afferent systems may be a demonstration of the "partialness" of nervous system properties which Nebylitsyn (1966a) refers to in the case of excitatory processes, and which is suggested in the Rozhdestvenskaya *et al.* (1961) study.

This "partialness" of inhibitory nervous system properties may be relevant to the question of the neurophysiological locus of CR extinction. If this is localised in the cortical focus of the CS, as a number of theorists have suggested, and if inhibition is modality specific, it is hardly likely that a general CR inhibition factor would emerge across different conditioning situations in which different CSs are employed, as in the present case. We might even predict a similar type of factor structure to that reported. On the other hand, we might recall Daurova's switching data (cf. p. 360), demonstrating that an intense auditory CS (105–115 dB), can be transmarginal for one response (alimentary CR in one room), while retaining its positive signal value for another (avoidance response in another room), which suggests that transmarginal inhibition is localised not in the CS focus, but in subsequent elements of the conditined reflex.

It is possible, of course, that the explanation may lie in the different strengths of the cortical representations of the alimentary and fear US. Dominance theory would suggest that the 105–110 dB CS is sufficiently intense to "rob" the weaker unconditional representation of the alimentary UR, although not the biologically more significant fear response, which (presumably) has stronger limbic system involvement. It may also be that irradiation of inhibition from the CS focus is the critical factor, inhibition encompassing the weaker US focus at an earlier stage. This perhaps explains why response amplitude continues to diminish, rather than the response remaining asymptotic or disappearing altogether, when stimulus intensity is increased beyond TTI. The stronger the stimulus (CS) intensity, the greater the irradiation, involving more and more cell aggregates, so that the response decrements over trials.

The pattern of loadings for E and N in this analysis is of interest. Introversion loads factor IV, suggesting strong inhibition in the tactual system, and stable extraversion factor V, indexed by after-image duration, which is now regarded as an index of lability. Neuroticism has a high loading on factor III, suggesting fast development of inhibition in the visual system. The latter results are replications of previous finding (White and Mangan, 1972; White et al., 1969).

SUMMARY

From the data reviewed in this section, there is increasing support for general factors of classical, and, to a lesser extent, operant "conditionability" which cut across reinforcement type, and show clear, replicable relationships with Eysenck's E and N dimensions. There are, of course, persisting problems, one being the question of individual response specificity, another the implications of the Paisey and Mangan findings that activity and reactivity levels in efferent systems predispose extraverts to condition well autonomically, and introverts to show superior motor approach and avoidance learning. Whether or not we can posulate a general factor of inhibitibility is another matter. Be that as it may, while the stability of these broad "conditionability" factors is less than optimal, and while the percent variance accounted for by personality dimensions is relatively moderate, nonetheless the acquisition data, overall, are promising, and inspire some confidence that appropriate experiments in more realistic behavioural settings may eventually reveal stronger and more stable factors.

## 2. Avoidance conditioning models of socialisation

In search of the biological bases of personality, a number of theorists have adopted a more limited perspective, pointing to the obvious similarity between passive avoidance conditioning and suppression of socially undesirable behaviour as a basis for a theoretical model (the Mowrer–Eysenck conditioning theory of conscience) which attempts to explain one of the important mechanisms of social learning, and the origins of individual differences in the effectiveness of such learning.

According to Mowrer (1960a), avoidance behaviour is mediated through conditioned anxiety responses previously established via the temporal association of punishment with the forbidden behaviour, when the misdemeanour is immediately followed by a slap, withdrawal of love, or some other punishment, administered within the time interval known to produce Pavlovian conditioning (Eysenck, 1965). Socially conforming or moral behaviour reduces the fear/anxiety, although post-transgressional fear, or guilt, cannot be reduced in this way, and persists. Self-criticism, self-abasement and confession might be regarded as strategies for relieving guilt, expressions of the need for punishment postulated in psychoanalytic theory.

Failure to inhibit prescribed behaviour is due to resistance to conditioning, or, more specifically, to inability to develop anticipatory responses (Eysenck, 1960). Thus the unsocialised individual is one who has failed to introject social norms through some defect in the structures mediating avoidance conditioning. As a consequence, he lacks an adequate repertoire of conditioned avoidance responses, collectively the "conscience", which the normal child acquires through the use, by parents, of fear-arousing punishments. Right actions are praised, wrong actions punished, the process being facilitated by the constant labelling practised by parents, teachers and other socialising agents, which help the child to generalise CS–US connections (Eysenck, 1977). This biologically based continuum of responsiveness to conditioning ("conditionability") is anchored at one end to the descriptive dimension psychopathy, and, at the other, to dysthymia, the former representing the extreme of unresponsiveness, the latter the extreme of responsiveness. Amongst normal samples, "conditionability" is reflected in degree of extraversion-introversion, or, more precisely, by characteristic levels of cortical arousal, of which introversion and extraversion are the outward and visible signs.

There are a number of difficulties with this theoretical model. The first concerns the concept of conditionability, which we have discussed at some length in a previous section. We concluded that the hypothesis has not yet been adequately tested — the critical experiments have yet to be done. It was also suggested that there might be a family of variables, rather than a single unitary variable of conditionability, the significance of elements in the conditionability equation varying with particular conditioning paradigms. At this stage, it seems premature to discount the possibility of a conditionability factor. On the other hand, it would be equally unwise to ground a theory on what is in effect an untested hypothesis.

A more critical problem may be that Eysenck's model makes no distinction between aversive and appetitive conditioning, particularly in view of the claim that data from a large number of experiments (cf. review in Hare and Schalling, 1978) indicate that the learning deficits of the psychopath, regarded as the least socialised individual, refer only to learning to avoid signals of impending punishment, specifically social disapproval, while responding as well as normals to material rewards and punishments, and to social rewards, the limiting function in all cases being awareness of CS–US contingencies. Again, it may be, as Gul'dan and Ivannikov (1974) suggest, that psychopaths fail to generalise their learning, thus being unable to usefully employ the results of their experience. We might also refer to evidence that psychopaths do not appear to develop anticipatory SC responses when they observe an aversive stimulus ostensibly delivered to another S (Sutker, 1970; Hare and Graigen, 1974; House and Milligan, 1973; Aniskiewicz, 1973) which is consistent with the observation that psychopaths show little concern for others. Psychopaths thus seem to be unresponsive to anticipated noxious stimuli, whether experienced directly or vicariously.

Might it not be the case, however, that unsocialised individuals show a deficit not in overall conditioning, but in passive avoidance conditioning — learning what not to do, learning to refrain from categories of behaviour which are strongly disapproved of in our society — which a number of authors (e.g. Aronfeed and Reber, 1965) regard as the primary mechanism of socialisation learning?

Until recently, this possibility has not been seriously entertained, probably because learning theorists, from the time of Hull, have addressed their best efforts to subsuming all types of learning under the two broad categories of classical/instrumental, operant/respondent learning. It is only in the last 15 years or so that passive avoidance has been regarded as a distinct type of learning. McCleary (1966) first reported that active and passive avoidance are mediated by different physiological systems, judging from evidence that some hippocampal lesions produce deficits in shock avoidance learning, and that septal lesions grossly interfere with passive avoidance learning, while facilitating active avoidance. The possibility that "aversive inhibitory conditioning" may be evolutionarily and functionally prior to both classical and instrumental conditioning, as Razran (1971) suggests, offers further indirect support for this proposition.

Gray (1975) has been most explicit on this point. We have discussed his views previously. Suffice it to say that Gray has demonstrated that in rats passive avoidance is mediated by a complex of neurocortical systems different from those which mediate classical conditioning, instrumental learning, active avoidance, escape learning. Sodium amylobarbitone selectively and grossly affects passive avoidance behaviour, while leaving other forms relatively unimpaired. According to Gray, conditioned frustrative non-reward is mediated by similar physiological systems to passive avoidance, systems different from those involved in learning under conditions of reward and positive reinforcement, primary punishment and primary non-reward.

Comparatively few studies have been reported directly investigating aspects of social learning in children through avoidance conditioning. The so-called "resistance to temptation" studies are a notable exception. Generally speaking, we are thrown back on data from laboratory studies of conditioning with animals, which raise the awkward question of the generalisability of such findings to human behaviour, and on data from adult clinical groups (variously described as antisocial, asocial, psychopathic) whose avoidance learning deficits are assumed to underlie lack of social-moral development. However, whether such studies provide analogues for social learning in normal infants, i.e. whether we can deduce something of the history and typical features of social-moral conduct in individual Ss and/or groups of Ss from these data is a debatable point.


I) PSYCHOPATHIC/SOCIOPATHIC DEVIANCE

It has been argued that the psychopath represents the unique case of failure of socialisation learning. He is the individual who has failed to introject the norms of conventional social-moral behaviour. As such, it has been claimed that he offers a singular opportunity for testing the personality through conditioning hypothesis.

Primary, or "true" psychopathy — or sociopathy, the terms being interchangeable — is differentiated from secondary, neurotic, dyssocial psychopathy, the former describing a person who is amoral and impulsive, who lacks the restraining influence of guilt and anxiety, and is thus irresponsible and unreliable, displaying poor judgment, superficial affect, impaired "conscience", and inability to profit from experience, the latter describing individuals whose antisocial behaviour is a consequence of unresolved neurotic conflicts and processes. Since he is incapable of inhibiting socially unacceptable, i.e. rule-breaking, behaviour, the psychopath, particularly the primary psychopath, is unable to acquire the rules of the social group in which he lives.

Despite some consensus about the symptomatology of psychopathic deviance, however, there are different points of view about underlying dynamics. What evidence is there that psychopaths are incapable of learning, generally, of learning to avoid, more specifically still, of passive avoidance learning? If so, why? Or are psychopaths unresponsive to, or do they choose to ignore, certain response-reinforcement contingencies? Again, if so, why?

There are essentially two lines of argument.

### (a) Biological deficit

The general thesis is that psychopaths do not learn to avoid noxious stimuli because cues associated with punishment fail to elicit anticipatory fear and anxiety (Lykken, 1957; Hare 1965; Schalling and Levander, 1967; Fenz, Young and Fenz, 1974; Bourdouxhe, 1975). The most widely accepted explanation is Eysenck's (1957, 1961) proposal that this is due to the psychopath's high level of extraversion and neuroticism, existing antisocial tendencies (lack of learned social control) being multiplied by N to produce psychopathic behaviour. Eysenck and Eysenck (1976), more recently, have extended and clarified this view. They now postulate that within the three-dimensional space created by their main personality dimensions (P, E and N), they can construct a set of concentric ellipsoids, whose two focal points lie high on the P dimension and on the E+ N+ quadrant. All persons located within this set of ellipsoids can be designated psychopaths, with those Ss who are located closer to the first focal point (P) being primary psychopaths, those located closer to the second point (E +N+) being described as secondary psychopaths. The latter group is characterised by strong neurotic disturbance. Presumably lack of social-moral control due to poor conditioning applies only to the latter group. We must look elsewhere for the etiology of asocial behaviour in primary psychopaths.

A more specific hypothesis is that deficits in passive avoidance learning provide an explanatory framework for the reported behavioural deficits of clinically diagnosed psychopaths (e.g. Trasler, 1978). Such individuals seem to have difficulty in making use of certain response-produced signals of impending punishment, although they perform just as well as normals in learning situations which are controlled by primary and secondary rewards, or following the onset of an aversive stimulus. The application of pleasant or unpleasant stimuli apparently has similar effects on psychopaths and normals. For example, these groups differ little in cardiac reactivity to simple stimuli such as tones and electric shock (Hare, 1978), in vasomotor response to 80 dB tones and electric shock (Hare, 1968), to slides of nude females (Hare and Quinn, 1971), to injections of saline and adrenaline (Hare, 1972). The psychopath simply fails to respond to signals of impending punishment, i.e. to conditioned aversive stimuli, while showing no such insensitivity to conditioned appetitive stimuli.

*Supportive evidence*

A good deal of data have been reported comparing the conditioning performance of psychopaths with normals, employing both material and social rewards and punishments. The former has usually involved cigarettes or candy as reward, withdrawal of these, or electric shock, as punishment, the latter verbal comments such as "good", "not so good".

A finding of particular interest is that some learning deficits of psychopathic Ss seem to be response-specific. For example, while psychopaths do not appear to show much electrodermal activity in anticipation of a stressor, there is good evidence that they are as proficient as normals in acquisition of anticipatory heart rate and digital vasomotor responses (Hare and Quinn, 1971). Thus, while psychopaths might be poor electrodermal conditioners, they would have to be regarded, on this evidence, as good cardiovascular conditioners. It has even been suggested (Hare and Graigen, 1974) that psychopaths show greater rather than smaller anticipatory heart rate responses, prior to shock, than normals, which has been claimed to reflect the operation of a mechanism for coping with an impending stressor.

Kadlub (1956) reports no differences between psychopathic and normal criminals where reinforcement is verbal or material (cigarettes) reward. Blaylock (1960) reports that psychopathic prisoners, normal prisoners and hospitalised normals all show significant learning under both reward and punishment conditions. On the other hand, Johns and Quay (1962), employing the same technique, report significant improvement on a learning task by neurotic, but not psychopathic Ss, a finding replicated by Quay and Hunt (1965).

A number of explanations have been advanced to explain these contradictory findings. The first is the question of who actually offers the reinforcement. In this connection the findings of Bryan and Kapche (1967) are of interest. They report no differences between psychopaths and normals when verbal reinforcement is presented by acceptable ex-convicts, rather than by graduate student Es. Along similar lines, Bernard and Eisenmann (1967) suggest that the superior conditioning of female psychopaths, compared with normals, to both social approval and monetary reinforcement, may be due to the fact the Es were male, taking into account the impoverished sexual environment from which the sample was drawn. Stewart and Renick (1970) come to the same conclusion when testing male and female psychopaths, using male and female agents. Psychopathic Ss conditioned when reinforced by E of the opposite sex, but not by a same-sexed E. For normal Ss, on the other hand, verbally mediated social approval was reinforcing, irrespective of the sex of E. It appears, therefore, that sex, status and probably many other characteristics of experimenter determine the extent to which psychopaths "comply" with experimental demands.

A second factor is awareness of the response-reinforcement contingency. The importance of this variable with normal Ss has been clearly demonstrated for both classical electrodermal conditioning (e.g. Dawson and Furedy, 1976) and for verbal conditioning (Spielberger, 1962, 1965; Spielberger and De Nike, 1966). If psychopaths are less attentive to reinforcment contingencies, this could explain some of the inconsistencies in the reported findings. Relevant data, however, are not encouraging. Acord (1967) reports no differences between psychopaths and non-psychopaths in the verbalisation of correct contingencies, nor in the amount of learning in a Taffel-type task. Doctor and Craine (1971) report that primary psychopaths condition more readily than secondary, neurotic psychopaths, and that improvement in performance is strongly related to S's awareness of the contingencies involved.

A further consideration is that in most studies one or other psychopathic groups — seldom both — has been compared with normals, and one type of reward and/or punishment employed as reinforcement. An obvious question is the extent to which "awareness" and conditioning correlate across different reinforcement modes within and between groups.

Only one study has been reported (Kling, 1972), in which both social and material reward and punishment have been employed in a verbal conditioning study (Taffel-type sentence construction task) with primary and secondary psychopaths. The social rewards and punishments were E saying "good", "not so good", and the material rewards and punishments tokens exchangeable for cigarettes and candy, and loss of tokens from a fixed number given to S at the commencement of training. Data from this experiment are shown in Table 39 and Figure 32. The data have some interesting features. Firstly, there are no differences in the effects of material and social reinforcement on the verbal conditioning performance of aware psychopaths. Secondly, it is obvious that

TABLE 39. *The number of aware and unaware primary and secondary psychopaths in the verbal and material reward and punishment conditions (from Kling, 1972. Reproduced by permission of John Wiley)*

| | Primary psychopaths | | Secondary psychopaths | |
|---|---|---|---|---|
| | aware | unaware | aware | unaware |
| Verbal reward | 4 | 3 | 5 | 2 |
| Verbal punishment[a] | 0 | 6 | 4 | 3 |
| Material reward | 4 | 3 | 6 | 1 |
| Material punishment | 5 | 2 | 6 | 1 |
| Totals | 13 | 14 | 21 | 7 |

[a] One subject failed to meet the established criterion for awareness applied by the judges. However, a note made by E during the experimental session indicated that this subject had a correlated hypothesis that was sufficient for him to avoid punishment, and he was therefore eliminated from the study.

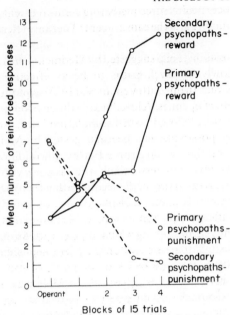

Figure 32. Mean number of reinforced responses for aware primary and secondary psychopaths under reward and punishment (from Kling, 1972. Reproduced by permission of John Wiley.)

psychopaths are more sensitive to tangible (material) than to verbal reinforcement (75% compared with 48%). However, under material reward and punishment conditions, a significantly greater proportion of secondary than of primary psychopaths are aware of the correct contingency. There appears to be little difference between groups insofar as social reward is concerned. In the case of social punishment, however, while more than half the secondary psychopaths were aware of the response-reinforcement contingency, none of the primary psychopaths evinced awareness. From these data, it seems that primary psychopaths are oblivious to, or choose to ignore, social disapproval, which contrasts with their (relatively) greater awareness of, and reactivity to, social rewards, and to material rewards and punishments.

*Mechanisms*

However, even if, for the sake of argument, we accept that physical, symbolic and other cues fail to generate in psychopaths sufficient anticipatory fear for the instigation and reinforcement of avoidance behaviour, particularly when the aversive event is temporally remote (Hare, 1965), is it necessary to infer some defect in the subcortical centres mediating reinforcement, such as the septo-hippocampal structures, as the causal agent? There are alternative "biological" explanations.

There is the possibility, one suggested by Mednick (1975), that fear responses dissipate too slowly in psychopaths to be an effective reinforcement for avoidance behaviour. In line with Venables's (1975) hypothesis, suggesting that recovery rates reflect openness/closedness to the environment, it might be that psychopaths are more "closed" when stimulation is intense or startling.

An interesting possibility has been suggested by Maltzman (1979). He employs his general theory concerning Pavlovian conditioning — that it is a complex process involving essentially the discovery of which signal is significant, a process occurring in the second rather than the first signal system, and thus being primarily a left hemisphere function in dextrals — to identify etiologically significant factors in sociopathy. He notes that the sociopath is as capable as normal Ss in describing what happens in the experiment, such verbal awareness suggesting that the sociopath's left hemisphere is functioning normally. The fact that sociopaths differ from control Ss in differential responsivity, however, suggests, according to Maltzman, that either the left hemisphere is excessively dominant, i.e. Ss display extreme hemispheric asymmetry, that there is a lack of integration or transfer of information between the two hemispheres, or that there is a deficit in the right hemisphere, which involves the first signal system, the perceptual response to environmental change. As yet, however, there is little empirical support for these speculations.

Again it could be argued that the so-called aversive stimulus, in fact, may not be aversive enough. If psychopaths show chronically low levels of arousal, as seem probable — cf. Hare's (1978) analysis of 8 experiments, suggesting that psychopathic prisoners have lower tonic SCs than other inmates ($X^2 = 32.5, df = 60, p < 0.005$) — and are less responsive to stress, as indicated by lower noradrenaline secretions (Bourdouxhe, 1975; Lidberg et al., 1978), they should be less reactive to intense or aversive stimuli than normals. Note also the prospective study by Loeb and Mednick (1976) who report that the 7 Ss from their sample of 104 adolescents who 10 years later had engaged in some form of antisocial delinquent behaviour showed smaller conditioned SC responses, and were less responsive to the US, than were control Ss. A similar explanation has been offered to account for differences between primary and secondary psychopaths. Spielberger, Kling and O'Hagan (1978) suggest that primary psychopaths are lower in trait anxiety, and are less responsive to stress than secondary psychopaths and normals. There is some support for this contention. Primary psychopaths appear to express lower A-state (Hare, 1968; Lykken, 1957; Schachter and Lutane, 1964; Schalling and Levander, 1967; Schalling,

1970, *inter alia*), and lower A-state levels (Lykken, 1957; Schmauk, 1970; Doctor and Craine, 1971) than various comparison groups.

It could be that psychopaths, if chronically under-aroused, show strong stimulation-seeking tendencies, in an attempt to maintain optimal arousal levels. Evidence on this point is generally supportive. Zuckerman (1975) reports data showing, overall, higher levels of questionnaire-measured sensation-seeking from a number of delinquent samples. Eysenck and Eysenck (1976) report significantly elevated P scores in Ss engaged in risky or dangerous occupations, as well as in criminal and drug abuser samples. Earlier data report stronger sensation-seeking tendencies in extraverts, compared with introverts. Extraverts are also subject to more rapid habituation. These biologically based tendencies, in combination, could impel high E and/or high P Ss to actively search for stimulation possessing exciting or arousing qualities, and to display levels of "impulsivity" which cannot be constrained by normal socialisation processes.

The question of impulse control raises a number of problems. As we mentioned in our previous discussion of Eysenck's P dimension, poor impulse control can reflect either excessively strong levels of drive or motivation, or chronically weak inhibition of normal levels of motivation and drive. Thus psychophysiological profiles of Ss exhibiting similar lack of impulse control can be quite different. Again, there has been little attempt in the literature to differentiate control of motor impulses, as opposed to intellectual and emotional behaviours, although Gawecka and Posnaniak (1979) have reported large individual differences among imprisoned psychopaths in need for different types of stimulation — motor, imaginal, sensory — partly as a function of age and experience. It may be that different forms of stimulation-seeking differentiate psychopathic subgroups — poor control over motor impulses, leading to aggressive or assaultive behaviours towards persons and property, characterising imprisoned psychopaths, other varieties of impaired impulse control describing non-criminal psychopaths and other learning disabled individuals. Arguably, psychopaths are no more nor less an homogeneous population than any other. Since they do appear to be characterised by abnormal avoidance learning, however, it seems important to establish to what extent the different psychophysiological deficits we have mentioned contribute to the etiology of the observed behavioural deficit.

### (b) "Functional" explanations

A number of authors have attempted more "dynamic" or functional explanations of the apparent lack of responsivity of psychopaths to signals of punishment. Lykken (1968) and Hare and Graigen (1974), for example, have argued along lines similar to the "attentional deficit" approach to schizo-phrenia, itself a variant of the perceptual defence hypothesis. This proposes that psychopaths may be unusually proficient at "negative preception", which decribes the extent to which a warning signal permits adaptive "tuning out" or attentuation of an expected noxious stimulus (Lykken, McIndoe and Tellegen, 1972). On this basis, it has been argued that there should be greater differences between responses of psychopaths and normals to unsignalled, compared with signalled, shock. However, while there has been some support for the proposition (Blankstein, 1969; Hare, 1972; Mathis, 1970), there have also been failures of prediction (Hare, 1968; 1978; Hinton and O'Neil, 1976).

Even if we do assume some such mechanism, we still have to establish why it operates only in some situations, not in others, only to certain types of reinforcement, on certain occasions, under certain conditions. Schmauk (1970), for example, reports that institutionalised psychopaths do not learn to avoid shocks, do not give anticipatory SC responses, are "unaware" of the contingencies involved. However, when loss of money rather then shock is employed as reinforcement, these Ss do learn to avoid, do give anticipatory SC responses, they are aware of the contingencies involved. In this instance, we would have to argue that psychopaths can learn to avoid one type of aversive US, but are insufficiently aroused/motivated to avoid others. In the Kling (1972) study, awareness of response-reinforcement contingencies appears to be the critical variable, lack of awareness being most prominent when social disapproval is the reinforcement. The obvious question arises of whether S is incapable of, or simply chooses not to attend to certain contingencies. Is he a poor conditioner, or simply not motivated to establish what is going on in particular experiments? If not, why not? We are reminded of the Syndulko et al. (1975) finding that even when their psychopathic Ss were 'aware' of the CS-US contingency, they still failed to give the appropriate SC response.

It has been claimed that psychopaths do not learn as well as others because they are unresponsive to social reinforcement (Cleckley, 1964; Eysenck, 1964; Hare, 1970). In line with this view, Cleckley (1964) has suggested that psychopaths fail to respond with appropriate affect to emotive verbal stimuli— while he is cognisant of the denotative meaning of emotional words, he is incapable of experiencing their emotional or motivational significance. Cleckley (1964) describes this condition as "semantic dementia". Schafer (1948) and Simon, Holzberg and Unger (1951), in similar vein, have observed that while psychopaths are aware of social values, these appear to have no motivational significance.

Again, however, this observation sheds little light on underlying dynamics, although a deficit or insensitivity of this sort is hardly likely to directly involve structures mediating reinforcement. Perhaps it has to do with impaired transfer of effect from first to second signal stimuli. With normal Ss, a direct, one-to-one relationship can be assumed, as we have already described.

On the other hand, a more plausible explanation is that psychopathic Ss are aware of the emotional significance of certain social stimuli, but choose to ignore this. We can only guess at the underlying motivation. It may be a consequence of inconsistent, unpredictable punishment regimes imposed in childhood. If the child cannot match the severity of offence to the nature and severity of punishment, this could produce a "conditioned indifference". If one cannot work out why, one causes to bother. Such confusion, or course, may be compounded by a conflicted relationship between parent and child. Thus, potentially significant CSs, and conditioning contexts, become "de-affected", "irrelevant". A possible consequence is committment to a simple hedonistic principle, and, at the same time, the development and deployment of a set of largely verbal operants — "asocial skills" (pathological lying, for example) — which in some instances prove effective in warding off immediate threats of punishment.

*Social Skills Training*

If this is the case, we might expect Social Skills Training (SST) to have some therapeutic value with psychopathic Ss. SST, which is a therapeutic package aimed at teaching social and interpersonal skills, was originally developed by Wolpe (1958) and subsequently expanded by Argyle (1969), who suggested that socially skilled behaviour can be analysed into component parts and trained as any motor skill.

An increasing literature reports that SST, and its variants such as Personal Effectiveness Training (Liberman *et al.*, 1975), Structured Learning Therapy (Goldstein, 1973), for example, are effective in improving interaction skills (basic conversational skills, heterosexual interactions, interview skills) with a range of client populations — anxious students (Curren, 1975), unassertive college students (McFall and Twentyman, 1973), socially inadequate psychiatric inpatients (Edelstein and Eisler, 1976; Bellack, Hursen and Turner, 1976) — less so with psychiatric outpatients (Argyle, Trower and Bryant, 1974; Marzillier, Lambert and Kellet, 1976).

In the present context, of more immediate interest are those SST studies which have been concerned with certain types of offenders, such as arsonists (Rice and Chaplin, 1979) and male adolecent delinquents (e.g. Spence and Marzillier, 1979). The theoretical background for these studies is a behavioural deficiency model of offending (e.g. Braukman *et al.*, 1975; Goldstein *et al.*, 1978), which proposes that delinquent behaviour is a reflection of inadequate opportunity to observe, display and receive reinforcement for socially appropriate behaviour. However, while some studies (e.g. Spence and

Marzillier, 1979) have reported some limited success, the hypothesis must be regarded as not proven. Clearly, it would be of interest to establish the extent to which a social skills deficit theory of deviance applies in the case of clinically diagnosed psychopaths, the assumption being that if such deviance is attributable to learning rather than skills deficit, SST will be wholly or differentially ineffective.

## SUMMARY

From the published research concerning psychopathic deviance, the overall picture is confusing. Clinically diagnosed psychopaths exhibit personality and psychophysiological characteristics, on the basis of which we might predict, *ex hypothesi,* poor "conditionability", and, as a consequence, inadequate social learning, particularly that involving passive avoidance. The "residual" behaviour is impulsive and egotistical; in the case of the secondary psychopath, this is claimed to be exaggerated by high N, drive which multiplies existing (antisocial) response tendencies. Notwithstanding the elegance and attractiveness of this theory, however, there is some evidence that psychopaths are neither more nor less conditionable than normals to social rewards, and to material rewards and punishments. They appear to be unresponsive, in the main, to social disapproval. The reasons for this apparent inability, or unwillingness to respond to social punishment, with the consequent poor introjection of social norms, however, are uncertain.

In this event, data from psychopathic samples do not allow a critical test of the socialisation learning through conditioning hypothesis. The fact that inappropriate parental practices may lead to socially inappropriate learning in certain instances does not invalidate the hypothesis that, under normal circumstances, such learning is mediated by conditioning, which may be monitored by biologically fixed levels of cortical arousal. With normal samples, the reported data support the proposition that introverts condition more readily to social reward and punishment than extraverts.

## 2) "RESISTANCE TO TEMPTATION" STUDIES

We noted previously the dearth of studies directly investigating social learning in young children through avoidance conditioning. The reasons for this are obvious enough. However, there are some data bearing on the extent to which behavioural inhibition in children is subject to the same parameters of avoidance conditioning as those demonstrated in animal laboratories, and on the extent to which the conditioning parameters involved are modified by the child's capacity to structure, to communicate, to utilise cognitive representations of behaviour sequences, and their outcomes.

Relevant studies are subsumed under the rubric "resistance to temptation". An illustrative account is that reported by Parke and Walters (1967), who required children to make a choice between an attractive and a less attractive toy, discouraging choice of the attractive alternative with an unpleasant auditory stimulus. When E left the room, resistance to temptation was greater in children exposed to loud presentation of the auditory stimulus, compared with those exposed to the milder noise. This finding was replicated by Parke (1969) and Cheyne and Walters (1969). When this simple paradigm is employed, it seems that children behave rather much like experimental animals. The same applies to timing of punishment effects, i.e. when in the action sequence the stimulus is applied. Earlier punishment produces greater resistance to temptation than delay of punishment (Aronfreed and Reber, 1965; Cheyne and Walters, 1969; Parke and Walters, 1967; Walters, Parke and Cane, 1965).

However, when the problem confronting the child is more difficult, for example, when he has to infer principles or rules from his experience of punishment, and apply these in the temptation condition, the effect of severe punishment is no longer to increase the efficacy of training, but to disrupt it (Aronfreed and Leff, 1963). While resistance to temptation in simple situations is positively related to intensity of punishment, in complex situations moderately intense punishments are more effective than severe ones. Timing of punishment effects also disappear in complex situations (Cheyne and Walters, 1969; Parke, 1969; Walters and Andres, 1967). There is apparently an interaction between severity and timing of punishment, in that with mild aversive stimuli the point in the behaviour sequence at which punishment is applied markedly affects resistance to temptation, while severe punishment is effective irrespective of when it occurs in the sequence (Parke, 1969).

However, while certain parameters operate in a similar fashion in both animal and human avoidance learning, there are additional variables of importance in human learning, particularly the capacity to organise experience into structure and rules, recognition of the relevance of external discriminative stimuli and of response-correlated stimuli such as motives and intentions, and the ability to make use of cues and structures furnished through verbal instructions from adults. In the course of development, behaviour which was once public, i.e. governed by external contingencies, becomes represented by an internal cognitive model or set of monitors (Piaget, 1951; Vygotsky, 1972), which carry the motivational and informational functions of many of the externally structured determinants of the child's early experience.

In this transition, direct training through verbal instructions is a powerful addendum to simple conditioning procedures. There is considerable evidence, for example, of the importance of verbal instructions in establishing and maintaining response inhibition. It is clear that provision of a rationale allows the child to attenuate the CS–US interval beyond the temporal limits appropriate for animals (Parke, 1969, 1972). Parke and Murray (1971) have shown that explaining carefully to the child what he is doing wrong is more effective in inducing response inhibition than the application of punishment without explanation, although a combination of the two is best. It is also apparent that the older child makes verbal criticisms of his own behaviour, usually when no one else is present, and in this way gains more control over deviant impulses (Aronfreed, 1964). Presumably verbal self-criticism replaces injunctions and instructions normally provided by other individuals significant to the child, and possibly marks an important stage in the development of internalisation.

Another factor which may be of importance in the development of forms of self-control such as resistance to temptation, one which has been emphasised by social learning theorists, is the role of a pro-social model. In laboratory demonstrations, typically children are instructed not to deviate, and are then exposed to a model who either conforms or fails to comply with the same prohibition. The reported data, however, are inconsistent. Usually models which fail to comply are highly effective — children who observe the model deviate, themselves deviate more than children who have simply been instructed not to deviate (e.g. Grusec et al., 1978). Models conforming to the prohibition, however, are sometime effective (Grusec et al., 1980), sometimes totally ineffective (Stein, 1966; Wolf, 1973), sometimes minimally effective (Rosenkoetten, 1973) or effective only insofar as certain dependent measures are concerned (e.g. Ross, 1971). It may be, as Dinestbier et al. (1975) suggest, that models are more capable of undermining the child's past socialisation in impulse control than of furthering the development of future impulse control. Another point of interest is underlined in a recent study of deviant boys (Perry, Bussey and Perry, 1975) reporting that models who conformed, i.e. resisted temptation, were effective in promoting resistance to temptation. Ss were drawn from a low socio-economic class, and the authors conjecture that resistant models attract more attention from these boys, who are less accustomed to conformity to prohibitions, than from middle-class Ss who have been employed in other studies. Thus, it is the salience of the model's behaviour which is the critical factor.

SUMMARY

Avoidance learning theories undoubtedly throw some light on certain aspects of human social learning. In relatively simple behavioural situations, parameters of animal avoidance learning apply equally to humans. In more complex situations, however, cognitive models, derived from direct verbal training (as well as by other means, described in the next section) modify the simple transformations mediated by conditioning, and to some extent replace behaviour at the level of covert representation. New principles add to, and subtract from, the behavioural norms initially laid down by conditioning.

Insofar as psychopathic deviance is concerned, it may be that impaired passive avoidance learning, indicating some defect in septo-hippocampal functioning, accounts in part for the inability to inhibit egotistical impulses, particularly aggressive and sexual drives. There are, however, viable alternative explanations. We might also note that the discontinuities with normal behaviour shown by psychopaths are not as marked as we would like to believe. Most normal individuals, given appropriate circumstances, viz., the absence of surveillance, of cues which usually threaten punishment, are capable of psychopathic-like behaviour. Rules are seldom completely internalised. Cognitive representations are seldom functionally autonomous.

In any event, young humans are not shaped entirely by passive avoidance conditioning. This is only one aspect, albeit an important one, of behavioural shaping, in the widest sense. Social learning involves what to do, as well as what not to do, learning how to obtain reward as well as how to avoid punishment. It would be difficult to imagine a social learning process in which unwanted responses are repressed through direct application of punishment, while approved responses are established through the tedious and inefficient process of trial and error. High anxiety levels and stereotypy would be inevitable consequences. Most early learning involves a balanced, usually tandem, presentation of both reward and punishment.

### B. Social Learning Theories of Socialisation

We have been describing one channel of socialisation which produces and maintains the child's internalised control over his social behaviour — classical conditioning of emotional responses, and behavioural shaping through aversive and positive outcomes which are contingent on the child's overt acts. The second channel is observational learning, a form of learning which does not require either the constraints normally imposed in classical conditioning, or outcomes of the child's emitted behaviour. What we are concerned with here is the formation of internal monitors, syntheses of the effective and cognitive input from the social environment, which are stored in cognitive models, higher forms of transformations and generalisations of the simple stimulus response connections laid down by conditioning.

### i) Forms of observations learning

It is beyond the scope of this essay to attempt a review of the voluminous literature on observational learning. This has been widely discussed elsewhere, and the reader is referred to original sources (e.g. Goslin, 1969). Only the salient facts concerning imitation of social models, role-taking and identification, and the behavioural effects of observing the consequences of the behaviour of others (vicarious reinforcement) will be briefly noted here.

The study of imitation learning has a long history. The earlier instinct theory has been replaced in recent years by various learning theory interpretations. Allport (1924), Piaget (1951) and Mowrer (1960b) have emphasised the importance of associative and classical conditioning mechanisms, Miller and Dollard (1941) and Skinner (1953) the role of instrumental mechanisms. For imitative learning, the contiguity of sensory events is a critical condition (Bandura, 1969), and for imitative behaviour, the nature of the reinforcement.

A considerable amount of experimental work with animals, children and adults, particularly by Bandura and his group, has shown that the observed behaviour of a model may provoke more or less similar behaviour in the observing subject. The extent and nature of the learning appear to be dependent on features of the model and on the traits and experiences of the observer, particularly vis-à-vis the model. Behaviour, standards and values can all be substantially influenced by imitation. The role of vicarious reinforcement, i.e. the observed reward and punishment for the model behaviour, is particularly important. Bandura (1965a), for example, reports that if a child watches another child transgressing without being punished, the likelihood of the watcher himself breaking the rule is increased. On the other hand, children who observe transgressions of others being punished are less likely to transgress themselves (Walters, Leat and Mezei, 1963; Walters and Parke, 1964). This also seems to be the case when the model's punishment is self-administered (Bandura and Kupers, 1964; Bandura and Whalen, 1965). Some data record striking similarities between observed and performed aggression, which have been taken as evidence that imitation of a model's expressive mode of aggression has acquired some intrinsic functional value for the child (Bandura, 1965a; Bandura, Ross and Ross, 1961, 1963a; Bandura and Walters, 1963; Hicks, 1965). Bandura's (1965a) study is particularly instructive. Under frustrating conditions — they were denied opportunity to continue playing with attractive toys — nursery school children, when compared with a control group, took over many of the aggressive actions of an adult model, punching and pummelling a doll which the adult had previously been observed to mistreat.

It is difficult to interpret such data in terms of operant conditioning, unless we assume the existence of previously learned generalised imitative responses. Here no primary reinforcement is involved, so that the child's imitative aggression must be attributed to some hypothetical past event which did involve external control of responses by means of differential reinforcement.

Such an interpretation, however, would exclude the possibility that novel responses can be learned through the child's observation of the model, which clearly occurred.

A much more plausible explanation involves the mediating function of symbols. Where children imitate novel responses of a model, they are usually able to describe them verbally, which implies that images and symbolic representations of the model's behaviour persist after cessation of the responses they represent. A number of studies provide substantiating data. For example, Bandura, Ross and Ross (1963a) report that a group of children who were asked to verbalise the actions of a model exhibited greater observational learning than other groups who were simply observing or engaging in interfering symbolic exercises. The fact that these latter showed decremented learning underlines the important mediating role of symbolic processes in observational learning.

Through observation, therefore, it appears that a child can acquire a cognitive structure in which certain acts are viewed as appropriate or inappropriate, as leading to reinforcement or to punishment. The fact that observed contingencies, and the actions of others can be pressed into service for different motives suggests that learning through observation is cognitively mediated. Findings, generally, are consistent with the tenets of cognitive (S–S) learning.

There are of course, different views about the precise role of imitation in the development of cognitive structures. Piaget (1951), following a line originally suggested by Baldwin (1906), describes imitation as an active, natural tendency critical for the infant's social and cognitive development, a view which contrasts with the less dynamic role assigned to imitation by other cognitive theorists. While it is true that in a sense all cognition is a copy of the environment, for Piaget cognitive representation implies a distinctive, volitional act, since all images and representations are forms of actions, not simply passive redintegrations of sense impressions.

Most social learning theorists agree that the limitations on imitative behaviour are largely cognitive. Behavioural shaping through imitation and role-taking, and the resulting generalised and autonomous enactment of the absent model's behaviour, presuppose what Aronfreed (1969) terms a "cognitive template", and Bandura (1969) an "image" guiding imitation. Something like this is clearly involved in much infant imitation, such as that involved in language learning. The fact that cognitively higher animals, such as primates, display generalised imitative behaviour and learning (Warden and Jackson, 1935), while this is difficult to teach to most lower animals such as rats (Solomon and Coles, 1954), even by instrumental learning procedures, is another indication of the cognitive underpinnings of imitative behaviour.

However, while there is general recognition of a cognitive skill component in imitative acquisition, most theorists fail to emphasise the importance of stages of imitation, i.e. the fact that radical restructuring of the imitative act normally parallels changes in the child's cognitive structures. Piaget (1951) is one of the few to point to different stages of imitation developing concurrently with different stages of intelligence, from the pseudo-imitative stage at intelligence stage 1, through imitation of new models, of unfamiliar models, to the final stage of freed imitation at intelligence stage 6 (after 18 months), involving imitation of a new action when the model is no longer present.

A related development of some consequence is the maturational growth of moral values and of socially conforming behaviour, which has been emphasised by Piaget (and, following him, Kohlberg, 1969), and a number of psychoanalytic writers. This growth is also linked with, and is dependent on, intellectual development. In the first "heteronomous" stage (up to 8 years), punishment is regarded as the inevitable consequence of infraction of rules externally imposed by authority. The intention or motives of the offender are irrelevant. This stage gradually gives way to the stage of autonomy, where justification for rules is sought in the mutual advantage for members of the group. Punishment is now viewed as a means of restitution. The child tends to judge individual cases on their merits. Importantly, it is probably only at this stage, following the growth of autonomy, that moral rules can become internalised.

Few social learning theorists would question the central role of the child's imitative or role-taking tendencies in the formation of social knowledge. But what distinctions, if any, should we draw between imitation and identification? Freud (1938) maintained that moral "internalisation" results from a process of parental identification, the motivated transfer of norms into the structure of the self system in the years 4–8. Psychoanalytic theories of identification maintain a clear distinction between identification, as a process of structural change in the personality, and ordinary imitation, a distinction which, generally speaking, has been faithfully observed in the literature. It is customary to differentiate the two in terms of a number of criteria, primarily that in identification, modelling is generalised and trans-situational, is persistent, occurs in the absence of the model, is intrinsically motivated, irreversible and non-extinguishable, even when it is not reinforced, or when it is punished, and persists in the absence of reinforcement to which it is instrumental.

Many developmental theorists, however, regard one as shading into the other. Piaget's final stage, for example, refers to imitation in the absence of the model. Aronfreed's (1969) concept of template, and Bandura's (1969) notion of image guiding behaviour have overtones of identification as well as imitation. Thus, developmentally, increasingly more general, evaluative cognitive structures emerge. A critical element is probably anticipation of later positive or aversive outcomes, which, in turn, may be based on cognitive representations of how people have reacted to the child's behaviour in the past. It has been suggested that such structures have some affinity with Rotter's (1966) concept of internal/external locus of control. The value of social reward and punishment is not entirely a function of the concrete stimulus properties of the external outcome of an act, since these may be mediated in part by the cognitive processes which they engage. Reward and punishment may serve as cues which elicit an individual's evaluation of the consequences of his actions for others, or to evoke other cognitive dimensions of value which will control subsequent behaviour.

Clearly mechanisms of this sort are necessary to account for the fact that there are many everyday situations in which the individual is "motivated" to behave illegally or "asocially" — the external contingencies are favourable, in that the outcome is rewarding, there is little, if any, chance of being detected — yet he desists. It is clearly not the case that response inhibition is mediated by memory of previous punishment, since in certain cases the actual behaviour has never previously occurred. Generalised behavioural inhibition is undoubtedly established through punishment of childish misdemeanours, the process of generalisation being enhanced by verbal explanations provided by the parents. In this event, we would expect the most effective internal control to be exercised over behaviour which is within the repertoire of the young child — for example, aggressive behaviour, lying, cruelty, sexual displays — and least effective over those behaviours which are not — for example, drunkenness, tax evasion. Generally speaking, this proves to be the case.

Insofar as the more "positive" social attributes are concerned, generalised behavioural induction seems to follow the same route. Through a variety of experiences, the child develops and incorporates such broad concepts as altruism into his self-concept. From the literature, it is clear that modelling affects the amount, the duration, the direction and the generalisability of altruistic or prosocial behaviour (Rushton, 1976). The effect of primary reinforcement, however, is less clear. Some studies report that positive reinforcement increases (Gelfand et al., 1975; Rushton and Teachman, 1978), and negative reinforcement decreases (Rushton and Teachman, 1978), children's generosity. According to Rushton and Teachman (1978), however, the effect does not generalise across situations, nor are there studies reporting that generosity is maintained when the reinforcement and the reinforcing agent are withdrawn, a necessary condition before we can make inferences about internalisation, before we can refer to a "trait" or disposition of altruism.

It may be that causal attribution is a critical factor. Ross (1976) suggests that reinforcement contingencies will have a different effect, depending on the attributions provided. The reported data, however, are equivocal. While

Rushton and Teachman (1978) report that in their positive reinforcement condition three different attributions, provided for their sample of 8–11 year old boys for their model-induced altruism, failed to have a differential effect, Grusec *et al.* (1978) report that, in a similar situation, a self-oriented attribution was more effective than an externally oriented attribution. Neither had any effect on two influence procedures involving direct instruction.

Over and above these considerations, we should also note the importance of second-order cognitive structures, such as a general respect for rules, which most parents attempt to impart from an early age. Whether or not such rules carry moral conviction is probably irrelevant. Children obey because of a general belief that it is wrong to contravene any rule. In Piaget's terminology, such individuals have not progressed beyond the heteronomous stage of moral development.

With the development of language and greater physical mobility, potential for learning is considerably enhanced, particularly since these are paralleled by increased development of inhibitory control. The child increasingly behaves in a more or less free operant situation, seeking greater authority over the environment to satisfy increasingly energetic demands. Language permits the discovery of norms without the sometimes painful experience of reinforcement, and increasing cognitive capacity confers an awareness of the likely consequences of certain actions, such foreknowledge implying recall of differentiated elements of prior experience. As development proceeds, the child thus acquires an extensive repertoire of cognitive connections which enables him to exercise choice, to provide flexible linking behaviour between a wealth of stimulus configurations he habitually encounters, and their possible affective consequences. Such operant control is, of course, more characteristic of later development.

## ii) The role of nurturance in observational learning

There has been considerable debate in the literature on the question of the extent to which the child's early experience of affection and nurturance influences the affective salience of his social models, and thus his tendency to reproduce model attributes in his own behaviour.

Data are highly contradictory. Some studies report that children are more inclined to reproduce the actions of a nurturant than of a non-nurturant model (Bandura and Huston, 1961; Bandura, Ross and Ross, 1963b; Mussen and Parker, 1965; Mischel and Grusec, 1966), others not (Aronfreed, 1964; Rosenhahn and White, 1967; Stein and Wright, 1964). Others again claim that levels of internalisation are not consistently related to the care or treatment of the young infant, or to pacing processes such as weaning and toilet training (e.g. Allinsmith, 1960; Sears *et al.,* 1965; Whiting and Child, 1953).

On the other hand, a number of writers have maintained that children acquire very generalised dispositions to internalise control over their social conduct, and that variations in parental nurturance is a critical variable in this process (Ausubel, 1963). Here there is the implicit assumption of an identification process similar to that postulated by Freud (1933). Motivation to reproduce the properties of the "love-object" is a major source of the child's identification with his parents. Note, however, that Freud emphasised the punitive and threatening aspects of the parent's behaviour as the most significant source of the child's conscience. In learning theory terms, we would say that many stimulus attributes of the mother (or father) may acquire positive affective value for the child, because of their associations with the experience of approval, affection and care. Thus the child is motivated to reproduce many of the attributes of his nurturant models.

Despite this conflict of evidence, however, there is a modest consensus on a number of points. It is generally conceded, for example, that the learning processes which underlie internalisation are dependent on a certain minimum of nurturance (warmth, affection). It also seems likely that a critical variable may be sensitivity to continuity or change in levels of nurturance, rather than sheer amount of nurturance. Finally, it is clear that extreme parental rejection and punitiveness impede internalisation (Bandura and Walters, 1959; Bronfendenner, 1961; Sears, Maccoby and Lewin, 1957). Children who have experienced low levels of nurturance show poor control over aggressive behaviour, poor sense of responsibility in achievement tasks, indifferent reactions to their own transgressions. Similar data have been reported from institutionalised and concentration camp samples (Freud and Dann, 1951; Goldfarb, 1945a,b). There have also been indications, from cross-cultural studies, that severe early socialisation is associated with incidence of theft and absence of self-blame for illness (Bacon, Child and Barry, 1963; Whiting and Child, 1953).

This is a possible explanation for the conflicting views noted above. Some authors, on the basis of the reported relationship between poor nurturance and inadequate internalisation, have (incorrectly) inferred a positive relationship between a high level of nurturance and effective internalisation. There is no evidence, however, that such is the case. A more reasonable inference is that a certain minimum attachment to the nurturing figure — a threshold of parental nurturance — is a necessary condition for effective internalisation of the child's control over his conduct. Beyond this, there are no grounds for regarding internalisation as a generalised, continuous function of parental nurturance. The fact that there seems to be no direct proportionality between warmth of the model and tendency to imitate has led some theorists (e.g. Danziger, 1976) to suggest an inverted U relationship, with both highly nurturant and highly depriving adults being essentially failures as models.

However, is this nurturance relationship, whatever its true nature, more relevant to reward than to punishment, or vice versa? The limited data available from child-rearing studies are not explicit on this point, although there are indications that this depends, to some extent, on the actual behaviour involved. For example, reward in general seems to be positively correlated with internalisation of achievement motivation (McClelland, 1955), but not of honesty or responsibility (Sears, Rau and Alpert, 1965). This is perhaps a delay of reinforcement effect. More importantly, internalisation of valued social behaviours, such as sharing and honesty, which normally require sustained external support before they come under the control of the child's internal monitors, seem to require a greater degree of nurturance and social attachment from the socialising agents.

Insofar as avoidance learning is concerned, it is possible that level of nurturance could establish the context which determines the salience and the perceived magnitude of punishment, by contrast. A high level of nurturance in the model, for example, could enhance the effectiveness of withdrawal of affection as a component of punishment, thus intensifying the anxiety which motivates imitative and identification behaviour.

Tangential to the question of nurturance is that of the salience of the discipline agent. It is fair to say that socialisation techniques which minimise the salience of such agents have been favoured by those concerned with parental child-rearing (e.g. Aronfreed, 1961; Hoffman, 1970). The assumption is that children who behave in a particular way through fear of punishment are less likely to adopt that behaviour as their own than will children who are less conscious of external pressure. Thus procedures such as reasoning or modelling — any technique which minimises the perception of external pressure — should produce greater internalisation of parental standards than physical punishment or withdrawal of material rewards and privileges.

This general proposition is subsumed under attribution theory, which we have referred to in discussing the growth of altruism, and which claims to provide a mechanism to account for problems of internalisation. This approach has become increasingly attractive to theorists concerned with the development of moral behaviour. Dinestbier et al. (1975) have suggested that although the negative emotional states associated with punishment persist over the individual's lifespan, causal attributions about these states can change. It is these attributions which determine subsequent behaviour. Thus if children attribute anxiety, after transgressing, to fear of being discovered, and punished, they are less likely to suppress deviant behaviour when there is little chance of detection than if anxiety is attributed to violation of personal standards of behaviour (Walters and Grusec, 1977). Any technique which minimises perception of external pressure and coercion is more likely to lead to adoption of a given moral standard. It follows that any means of producing conformity which does not lend itself to externally directed attribution should promote internalisation. However, while there is some support for this hypothesis (Grusec, Saas-Kortsaak and Simutis, 1978) internalisation obviously involves other factors, and a multiple causation explanation is indicated.

In view of the equivocal role of nurturance in modelling, what then is the source of power in the model worth imitating? A number of possibilities have been suggested. For example, Whiting (1960) proposes a status envy theory, essentially a reinterpretation of Freud's oedipal theory. According to this view, the child models himself on that person whose status allows him to consume rewards of which the child feels deprived. Evidence suggests, however, that the child imitates the supplier of rewards, rather than the competitor (Bandura, Ross and Ross, 1963b). In general, crude social power models are implausible, if only because awareness of power presupposes a fairly high level of cognitive development. Imitation, however, is a primitive tendency displayed by infants of less than 12 months of age (Piaget, 1951).

An interesting view is proposed by Danziger (1976), who makes the distinction between personal and positional models, the former being imitated because of personal attributes, the latter because of attributes pertaining to his social position as defined by sex, age and occupation. Importantly, the two kinds of modelling are governed by different conditions. Familiarity may be crucial for personal models; the model's power to threaten may instate him as a personal model, but may have little relevance to positional modelling. What is critical for positional modelling is the model's perceived status in the social system of which he and the child are members. This, in turn, presupposes a certain level of cognitive development. For example, preferential imitation of models of the same sex — the boy's imitation of the aggressiveness of the male model, for example — requires categorisation of himself as belonging to a fixed-gender class, which is possible only at a certain level of cognitive development.

According to Danziger (1976), we should distinguish between the two kinds of power and the two kinds of modelling. Personal modelling is not a prerequisite for positional modelling. There is no evidence, for example, that it is necessary for a boy to identify with a particular example of masculinity before he can adopt a masculine role, or that the adoption of an appropriate sex role depends on a special relationship with a particular parental figure. This being said, however, there are clearly certain conditions common to both forms of modelling, but these are not the primary, initiating factors.

*iii) Internalisation/externalisation balance*

Cognitive representations carry intrinsically reinforcing consequences. But how effective is this control? How free is the socialised individual from the need for external reinforcement, which seems to be required to sustain learned behaviour in animals?

Clearly, there are individual differences in the stability of internalised structures, but over and above this, it appears that many forms of conduct need to have their value continually reinstated by external social reinforcements, which, at times, are not easily observable. Often a young child will effectively suppress an act which has been previously punished, in the absence of surveillance, yet will show no evidence of restraint when the environmental cues are slightly altered. In this case, the environmental cues have probably assumed secondary reinforcing properties, acting as signals of primary aversive stimuli, signals which activate the behavioural inhibition system. To the extent that such signals are functionally autonomous, any alteration in the stimulus configuration might be expected to disinhibit the repressed behaviour.

Such an explanation, however, is far from satisfactory, although it is difficult to imagine what other factors might be relevant. Obviously it has little to do with "awareness". Many authors have noted the discrepancy between conduct and conscience, that is, between the verbal expression of evaluative standards and behaviour in the real social context. There have been numerous reports, dating from Hartshorne and May's (1928) studies, suggesting strongly that the child's verbalised knowledge of social standards in certain situations does not predict his resistance to the opportunity to cheat when he is ostensibly not under surveillance. Children in Western society show, developmentally, an increasingly internalised orientation of conscience, reflected in ability to verbalise contingencies, to evaluate determinants and consequences of conduct (Boehm, 1962; Kohlberg, 1963; Lerner, 1937; Piaget, 1948). However, there is no evidence of corresponding age related increments in the effectiveness with which children control their own behaviour in resistance to temptation situations (e.g. Hartshorne and May, 1928; Sears, Rau and Alpert, 1965). On the other hand, we should recall Kohlberg's (1963, 1969) report of an inverse relationship between degree of internalised orientation of the child's moral decisions in hypothetical conflict situations, and cheating. We might also note the possibility that some of the inconsistencies in the reported data could be due in part to complex motivational links between values and behaviour, which are activated in highly subtle and different ways by the cognitive and affective impact of specific social stimulus situations.

The question of whether extrinsic cues in some form or other are always necessary for behavioural control is a contentious issue. From the animal studies, this in unequivocally the case. With human Ss, however, the picture is much less clear. Data from observational studies indicate that some apparently well-socialised individuals are capable of asocial behaviour to a sometimes extraordinary degree when the normal situational cues are absent or altered (when they are members of invading armies, inmates of concentration camps, for example). Milgram's (1974) experiments vividly demonstrate how easily we are able to deny personal responsibility for our own actions, and how skillfully we are able to rationalise. Ordinary individuals often conceal their true motives; there is normally some discrepancy between conduct and conscience. This, after all, is the rationale of Eysenck's lie scale. A high lie score, reflecting S's unwillingness to admit that he would commit minor transgressions when threat of discovery (and thus punishment) is absent, invalidates the questionnaire.

*iv) The relationship of personality variables to observational learning*

In view of the growing consensus that social learning, like the learning of motor habits, can be mediated by conditioning, the question arises of the relationship of personality variables to vicarious conditioning.

Despite the importance of this issue, very little relevant data are available. To the writer's knowledge, only one study, that of Hinton (1971), has been reported in the literature. He compared the conditioning performance of three groups of Ss, one group being conditioned using a classical paradigm, CS being a tone of 1000 Hz, the US an electric shock, the second group observing a confederate being conditioned in this way, while the third group observed, from videotape, S simulating conditioning of this sort. While groups 1 and 3 conditioned and extinguished normally, there was no relationship between speed of CR acquisition and either E or N. Obviously this is an area on which a great deal more research needs to be done.

The same comment applies in the case of cognitive structures (mainly verbal) which are assumed to possess intrinsically reinforcing properties. As far as we can establish, there is no evidence concerning the relationship of characteristics of these internal monitors to personality variables. We could argue, in line with the Soviet model of verbal conditioning, that, since word substitutes for the sensory CS, and reproduces its aversive or rewarding consequences (we might even agree with Razran that word is more than the sensory CS it connotes), parameters of internalised control over behaviour, and their relationships to personality dimensions, ought to parallel those known to apply in the case of direct avoidance and reward learning. This assumption, however, awaits empirical verification.

It is unfortunate that the dynamics of verbal avoidance learning, in particular, have not been carefully and comprehensively examined in the developmental or conditioning literature. In our culture, where learning is mediated as much by punishment as by reward, normal children quickly acquire a repertoire of verbal strategies or operants to avoid threat of punishment and to obtain reward. We assume that they are usually aware of response-reinforcement contingencies. But what do we mean by "awareness"? It has two distinct elements — recognition that a certain verbalisation removes threat, and understanding of why the threat is pending. Where recognition without understanding occurs, verbal learning may become entirely "instrumental" or utilitarian, as has been suggested in the case of psychopaths, or, in the less extreme case, we may observe the emergence of a disposition, which can assume psychopathological proportions, to constantly emit such operants at the merest suggestion of threat — the profoundly apologetic personality, self-effacing, anxious.

This leads on to our final comment. A real problem in this research area is that clear distinctions between types of learning, which can be simply enough demonstrated in the laboratory, particularly with non-human Ss, are difficult to maintain in social contexts at different developmental levels. Most behavioural situations are highly complex, combining, for example, aspects of active and passive avoidance and reward learning, into highly sophisticated sequences. Even the simplest behavioural unit may contain a wealth of psychological content. This can be replicated, to some extent, in certain more "realistic" laboratory demonstrations, such as in the Taffel-type situation, where paradigms are combined in almost random fashion, depending on S's initial responses. However, undoubtedly most social learning contexts contain additional elements. Consider the example of a child attempting to obtain a sweet without asking. Mother says "no, that's naughty", the child desists (passive avoidance). The child is then told to say "please", and the reward is forthcoming (active avoidance, reward learning). However, usually the child initially expects the verbal operant always to produce reward, and it is only after further experience that he establishes that "please" is an enabling, rather than absolute, operant. Something more than intermittent reinforcement is obviously involved. The child has to analyse the contextual stimulus configuration to establish under what conditions the verbal stimulus is likely to produce reward. The development of congitive strategies of this type is an important facet of social learning.

## Summary

There is no doubt that human social-moral conduct is mediated by cognitive structures, internal monitors which carry some of the motivational content of the externally structured determinants of the child's early experience. Precise mechanisms are uncertain. From a conditioning point of view, it has been argued that parental injunctions, during the course of development, acquire the structural and functional characteristics of CSs. Such CSs have two functions — to identify discriminative stimuli which label permissible and forbidden actions, and to act as secondary aversive stimuli which attach feelings of anxiety, guilt and shame to the undesired behaviour. Injunctions are not themselves primary aversive stimuli, eliciting active responses of defence or flight, but signals of such stimuli, resulting in the stopping or withholding of behaviour. According to Gray (1975), this is an effect similar to that evoked by the CS signalling the non-appearance of an expected reward (Rew–CS), i.e. behavioural inhibition mediated by the septo-hippocampal system.

Cognitive/social learning theorists, however, argue that internalisation is primarily mediated by processes of imitation and identification, which generate a behavioural template, and by vicarious as well as differential reinforcement, which shapes the learning. All these processes play an extremely important role in social learning. Whether or not the average human ever completely internalises social rules, however, is problematical. It seems likely that external contingencies, at least in mild form, perhaps on an intermittent basis, are necessary for consistent control over social-moral behaviour.

## Conclusions

From the research reviewed in this chapter, the following conclusions seem justified.

Insofar as 'conditionability' is concerned:

1. From a number of early studies, involving, for the most part, simple comparisons of Ss drawn from dimensional extremes of E and N in rates of classical CR acquisition, there is a consistent finding that introverts condition more readily than extraverts to aversive USs, particularly under conditions of threat. The between-group differences, however, are relatively small, and it is arguable whether these data, of themselves, provide a solid enough evidential base for Eysenck's conditioning postulate. In any event, where studies have employed a sensory conditioning paradigm, an empirical dictum would insist that we interpret the better conditioning of introverts as due to their greater visual or auditory sensitivity, or lower pain thresholds, rather than to their greater "conditionability", in its widest sense.

2. Gray's hypothesis that introverts are more susceptible to signals of punishment and frustrative non-reward, and extraverts to signals of reward and omission of punishment has only limited support, although the hypothesis has not been adequately tested. There are certainly indications that Is are more reactive to threats of shock, and to corneal air-puffs, and Es more responsive to erotic stimuli, but whether these findings can be generalised to all aversive and

appetitive contexts is another matter. Further, we might argue, on purely intuitive grounds, that while in humans relief might be rewarding, and disappointment unpleasant, the former seems qualitatively different from reward, the latter qualitatively different from punishment. Even if all movements along a postulated hedonic continuum — away from unpleasantness (omission of punishment) or towards satisfaction (reward) — are mediated by common mechanisms, as Gray suggests, this does not necessarily mean that these are experienced, psychologically, as identical events.

3. N is thought to act as a multiplier, potentiating the response S is predisposed to make on the basis of the trait-determinant of extraversion. Since N reflects sensitivity to defensive arousal, individual differences along this dimension have greatest effect when conditions are threatening.

4. From a number of recent studies, there is growing evidence of more general factors cutting across CS, US and UR modalities, factors which are independent of individual reactivities to particular classes of reinforcement. This is clearly implied in the Paisey and Mangan (in press) study, where there is also the suggestion that "reactivity" in afferent and efferent structures relates both to speed of development of autonomic and motor CRs, respectively, and to extraversion-introversion. With some reservations, we might argue for a factor of "excitability", a process factor which involves speed of irradiation and concentration, vividness of imagery, aspects of return afferentation — the latter two variables being critical in stabilising the cortical representation of the US — for example, in addition to a factor of basic "reactivity" in the responding tissues. Depending on the conditioning paradigm employed, individual reactivities to particular classes of reinforcement may be superimposed on this basic predisposition.

This leads to the suggestion, more an addendum, that the structure of psychophysiological parameters of conditioning may parallel that postulated in the case of intellectual abilities and personality dimensions — general factors of excitability and inhibitibility, which enter into all conditioning performance, (equivalent to "$g$", and to superordinate personality factors such as E and N) group factors involving, for example, sensitivity to certain classes of reinforcement (equivalent to ability factors, V, N, K, etc., and to "source" traits) and specific factors unique to particular conditioning paradigms. The relationships of E and N to such hierarchically structured factors will obviously be quite complex.

Insofar as "social" learning is concerned:

5. The suppression of socially undesirable behaviour is thought to be mediated by avoidance conditioning, specifically passive avoidance learning. However, socialisation involves learning what to do, i.e. reward learning, as well as what not to do.

In this respect, we are reminded of the relevance of Cattell's observation that one of the important source traits feeding into second-order extraversion is affectothymia, Guilford's factor of "agreeableness", which derives from a history of successful striving. Discriminating schedules of reward and punishment, encouraging in the child the growth of competence, i.e., the realistic perception of what is possible, consistent with available resources and skills, is a necessary condition for the development of an optimistic, resilient personality. This is probably the developmental experience differentiating the child motivated to succeed from the child motivated to avoid failure, a distinction which may have important implications for personality development.

6. Verbal operant conditioning is obviously a powerful technique in socialisation learning. From the verbal operant conditioning studies with adults, an impressive body of evidence attests that introverts condition more readily to social approval, i.e., reward, than extraverts. These data, however, offer only partial support for the conditionability hypothesis. Too few studies have reported the effects of social disapproval, i.e., punishment, which, in our society, is probably the more frequently used behaviour modifier.

7. Generally speaking, the role of N in social learning has been ignored, a surprising omission in view of the fact that emotionality is acknowledged as a source of drive in instrumental learning. While there is some uncertainty about the precise role of nurturance in acquisition of social-moral habits, there is no doubt that it is a component of "psychological" discipline, which involves primarily threat of withdrawal of love and support. Anxiety, as a result of psychological separation, is the inevitable risk in the relationship with the caring person. Given a minimal threshold of nurturance, normally the child introjects the values and standards of the caretaker, as revealed in reward and punishment contingencies. Eventually the behaviour becomes self-reinforcing. The child "feels good" when behaving appropriately (super-ego development), and self-esteem is enhanced. What makes approval more or less rewarding, and disapproval more or less punishing, lies, to some extent, in the nature of the dependency relationship.

8. In human social learning, cognitive representation of rules of social-moral conduct, guided by processes of imitation, identification and vicarious reinforcement, carry reinforcing consequences. The behaviour of the socialised adult is monitored by cues which have secondary reinforcing properties, the capacity to evoke anxiety when the individual is tempted to behave illegally or asocially. Whether or not these internal monitors, many of which are internalised parental injunctions, ever fully achieve functional autonomy, or whether there is a continuing need for primary reinforcement is a matter of debate. As yet, no data are available relating characteristics of cognitive evaluative structures to personality variables such as E and N.

# CHAPTER 12

# Summary and Conclusions: Some Final Observations

*Give me the luxuries, I can dispense with the necessities.*
Oscar Wilde

ONE OF the purposes of the present volume is to draw parallels between Eastern and Western approaches to personality/temperament. So far, however, all we have managed is a number of analogies based on typological characteristics of groups of Ss differentiated on personality dimensions such as extraversion and neuroticism. At times comparisons have been crude, the findings contradictory, the implications unclear. At this stage in the narrative, therefore, it seems timely to address ourselves to wider issues and to broader perspectives. In preliminary, however, we need a summary statement, a brief review and appreciation of both theories.

Pavlov, in developing his theory of nervism, ascribed behavioural differences in dogs to characteristics of nervous system functioning. However, he showed little interest in human typology, although in his writings he frequently referred to higher-order abstraction, to thinking, to the second signal system, which he claimed to be subject to the same laws governing first signal functioning, and was much concerned, particularly towards the end of his life, with the relationship of typology to psychopathology.

It was Krasnogorskii and Ivanov-Smolenskii who initially advanced human typological theorising, the former identifying four types (mobile, slow, excitable, inhibited) based on cortical-subcortical relationships according to mobility and balance, the latter developing a methodology (the verbal-motor method) for examining typological characteristics in children. In more recent times, a number of research groups, notably those at Moscow, Perm and Warsaw, headed by Teplov and Nebylitsyn, Merlin and Strelau, respectively, have considerably improved methodology and proposed new theoretical formulations. There is now some consensus about appropriate methodology, and agreement that ten orthogonal properties and five secondary, balance properties give a complete account of temperament, of the genotype.

There are, however, a number of flaws in this simple model.

(a) The importance of emotional reactivity has been underplayed or completely ignored, although Soviet theorists have constantly emphasised this aspect of temperament. For example, Rubenstein, one of the most authoritative writers on personality and temperament, as far back as 1946 described the dynamic aspects of personality as sensitivity and impulsiveness, two basic features of temperament. Other theorists (e.g. Levitov, 1952), in similar vein, have construed personality in terms of emotional excitability, specifically the speed of arousal, duration and intensity of emotions, and the speed of mental processes associated with such excitability.

Curiously enough, in this respect, we can draw an interesting comparison with Western personality typologies. For example, in Eysenck's earlier theory, while differences along the extraversion dimension were formally anchored in the excitation/inhibition balance hypothesis, N, or emotionality, was ignored, or linked to balance through the relationship between anxiety and introversion.

To some extent, this omission has been remedied in the later typological models of Nebylitsyn and Strelau. Nebylitsyn contended that the partial nature of nervous system properties, which he had always regarded as a critical problem for typological theory, is due to the specificity of the nervous structures located in the primary, secondary and tertiary zones of the sensory projection areas sited in the retrocentral cortex. On the other hand, more general nervous system properties which affect overall behaviour — more particularly emotional responsivity — and thus constitute the physiological basis of temperament, are located in the anterocentral (frontal) cortex, i.e. in the structurally and functionally more highly developed areas of the brain, which are intimately related to subcortical structures such as the reticular formation, the thalamus, the hypothalamus.

To a degree, Strelau's design is a logical development of Nebylitsyn's model. His two temperament dimensions, reactivity and activity, which, in combination, describe energy level, refer to sensory and emotional reactivity (which, in the case of sensory stimuli, is modality-specific), and to the vigour of goal-directed activity, which involves augmenting or reducing stimulation to attain an optimal level of activation.

(b) Teplov and Nebylitsyn originally defined dynamism as speed of development of conditioned responses. This being the case, we would have to assume that other nervous system properties play a relatively minor role in conditioning. Clearly this is not the case. From Nebylitsyn's later writings, it is obvious that dynamism, in fact, refers to reactivity in the subcortical centres mediating reinforcement. Arguably, this property could also reflect characteristics of the structures mediating cortical representation of the US. Dynamism is only one of the factors, albeit an important one, determining conditioning rate, the significance of each property depending in large measure on the conditioning paradigm employed.

(c) Commonsense, and some data, suggest a degree of dependency between nervous system properties, although an illusion of orthogonality can be created in artificial laboratory conditions. It is obvious that mobility involves both strength of excitation and of inhibition, that dynamism of inhibition has a mobility component. While the exact relationship of mobility and lability has yet to be revealed, they are clearly related. It is possible that second- or third-order factors, such as, for example, Strelau's reactivity and activity dimensions, might be identifiable, suggesting a hierarchical structure of nervous system properties.

A schematic representation of Eastern European typology, in so far as excitation is concerned, is attempted in Table 40. No such schematisation is possible for inhibitory properties, since too little is known about their content.

Clearly, this approach is deductive. The "Pavlovian" strategy aims to identify and describe characteristics of nervous system functioning, and then to relate individual variations in these characteristics to individual differences in behaviour. The critical assumption, therefore, is that CNS events are causal factors producing observable and predictable variations in behaviour. The other side of the coin is the inductive approach adopted by many Western personality theorists; a broad spectrum of behaviour is assessed by questionnaire, and then, through techniques such as factor analysis, major factors are derived, summary descriptions of the common variance distributed through a wide range of items. Nothing is implied about the biological bases of such traits. This requires, additionally, the use of deductive procedures to identify the underlying neurophysiological content of these inductively derived personality dimensions.

This is what Eysenck has attempted to do in outlining his biological theory of personality. From our present vantage point, we can perhaps evaluate his theory — admittedly somewhat superficially — by using two criteria — the similarity between the neurophysiological processes and mechanisms thought to underlie his personality dimensions and the Pavlovian properties as described by Nebylitsyn, and the strength and reliability of the relationships reported between these dimensions and properties.

Insofar as the first criterion is concerned, the available evidence points to some striking agreements. The physicochemical basis of excitatory strength, according to Nebylitsyn, could involve any one of a number of aspects of nerve cell functioning — availability of "messengers", calcium fluxes, for example. Dynamism of excitation reflects reactivity in the RF structures mediating reinforcement. The structure mediating OR habituation, i.e. dynamism of inhibition, is the hippocampus. Mobility seems to be related to level of ACH,

TABLE 40. *The structure of temperament dimensions, incorporating the Nebylitsyn and Strelau revisions of the original Pavlovian typology.*

| Higher order dimensions | Reactivity | | Activity | Temporal characteristics of response | | |
|---|---|---|---|---|---|---|
| | — Sensory | — Emotional — | Energy Level | | | |
| Mediating structures, processes | Fronto-reticular system (RF, frontal cortex, sensory projection areas, cellular processes) | Fronto-limbic system (limbic structures, frontal cortex, esp. mediobasal and orbital structures) | Motor cortex, efferent structures | ACH availability | Structures determining duration of refractory phase | Unknown |
| Nervous system properties | Strength — Primary Secondary / Secondary | Dynamism — Secondary / Primary | | Mobility | Lability | Irradiation and concentration |
| Behavioural correlates | Working capacity, resistance to fatigue and stress | Cortical representation of CS and US (images), aspects of return and sanctioning afferentation / Emotionality; reactivity to US | Responsivity levels in effector systems | Ease in altering signal values of stimuli | Information processing characteristics | Induction effects |
| Integrative mechanisms | — Sensory arousal modulation | Emotional arousal modulation | Motor arousal modulation | Flexibility | Memory | Discrimination |

Ease and speed of adaptation

while lability reflects the action of mechanisms and processes determining duration of the absolute refractory phase. Nebylitsyn's major temperament dimensions, activity and emotionality, are thought to reflect characteristics of the fronto-reticular system (frontal cortex, sensory projection areas and so on) and of the fronto-limbic system (limbic structures, mediobasal/orbital structures of the frontal cortex).

Mechanisms suggested for extraversion are those involved in sensory discrimination and in modulating reticular arousal, and those determining functional characteristics of the septo-hippocampal structures. Neuroticism relates to characteristics of the visceral brain, which includes the hippocampus, septum, amygdala, cingulum and hypothalamus. Activity in certain parts of this system, specifically the septo-hippocampal loop and septo-orbital frontal cortex, underlies E and N differences (Gray, 1971a). Septal stimulation produces behavioural arrest and sleep (Guyton, 1976), as does stimulation of the intra-laminar nuclei of the thalamus. This loop is also linked to extinction of ORs and to signals of non-reward (Vinogradova, 1975).

It has been suggested that level of psychoticism, P, Eysenck's third major personality dimension, is determined by level of sex hormones such as testosterone (leading to high P), and oestrogen (leading to lower P).

Judging from the best information available about mediating structures and processes, therefore, there seem to be good grounds for identifying extraversion and neuroticism with strength and dynamism, and, to a lesser extent, lability of nervous processes. In addition, there is considerable support for this from a number of psychometric and psychophysiological studies.

Extraverts are strong in an excitatory sense, introverts weak, when afferent sensitivity, i.e. sensory threshold, is the measure. Introverts also appear to have lower thresholds of transmarginal inhibition than extraverts, which is in agreement with Nebylitsyn's finding of a high, positive, correlation between upper and lower thresholds of response. Note the paradox, however, that in the RT mode, introverts appear to be stronger, not weaker than extraverts, although plausible reasons for this have been suggested. Extraverts accumulate reactive inhibition more readily than introverts, i.e. are more dynamic in an inhibitory sense, and introverts are claimed to be more dynamic in an excitatory sense (speed of CR formation). Extraverts demonstrate higher mobility of inhibition, and lower lability. There is little evidence one way or the other of any relationship between introversion-extraversion and inhibitory strength. At second-order level, Strelau's factor of reactivity has both emotional sensitivity (impulsivity) and sensory reactivity (broadly based extraversion) components.

There have also been a few reports in the literature relating nervous system properties to individual differences not normally included under the rubric "personality". For example, divergent thinking, in the Guilford sense, relates

452 THE BIOLOGY OF HUMAN CONDUCT

to mobility of inhibition. Lability differences appear to predict efficiency in recall and in information processing, as does excitatory strength. There is no doubt that the general stimulus-intensity-control mechanism which is assumed to underlie Petrie's augmenting/reducing dimension, Freud's "stimulus barrier", for example, is highly similar, perhaps identical, with nervous system strength, although only one direct test of this assumption has been reported (Sales and Throop, 1972). Clearly, findings of this sort open up new and highly promising lines of enquiry.

What of the relationship of introversion to speed of CR acquisition, which is the cornerstone of Eysenck's behaviour theory? There is some evidence that neurotic introverts develop classical CRs more readily when the US is aversive, and the situation threatening, and that stable extraverts are more "conditionable" to appetitive USs. Whether this can be extrapolated to all conditioning situations, however, is a moot point, although, in this connection, we should note recent evidence of relatively broad factors cutting across CS and particularly US modalities, on which E and N, in certain combinations, seem to load. Does this mean that we can equate certain E/N combinations with balance or equilibrium in dynamism, which seems to be implied by Gray? Clearly, there is some substance to this claim, but evidence to hand presents a rather confusing picture, and it seems wiser, for the moment, to suspend judgment.

Insofar as social learning is concerned, there is conflicting evidence about the relationship between E and N and passive avoidance learning, which is claimed to be the main route for socialisation learning. On the other hand, in verbal operant conditioning, Is condition better than Es to social reward. The effects of social punishment, however, are much less clear cut.

## In Prospect

What do we see in prospect for psychophysiology, in particular, for differential psychophysiology? In both areas, there has been disappointingly little progress during the past decade. The reasons for this are obscure, although Ax, when relinquishing editorship of *Psychophysiology* in 1974, made some interesting observations on this point.

He suggests two possible reasons. Firstly, he underlines the lack of recognition by psychophysiologists that the psyche and the soma are two relatively distinct systems, whose interactions are symbolic rather than causal. In the psychosomatic interaction, the physiology changes with experience, such changes complicating and attenuating the interaction to a considerable degree. A similar observation has been made by Strelau (1975a). Biofeedback phenomena, and the Schaltung and cognitive effects mentioned previously, are good cases in point.

Secondly, Ax refers to attempts by psychophysiologists to generate nomothetic laws of behaviour. However, when we combine a unique physiology with a unique experience, we have "uniqueness squared", which makes it highly improbable that we will ever uncover laws which will predict human behaviour. The alternative is to study the individual in detail from birth, and content ourselves with understanding, explaining and predicting his unique behaviour. Only in this way will we be able to account for a substantial portion of the variance of human behaviour. Ax comments:

> I suppose that a science of the individual would lead eventually to each individual becoming the subject of his own psychology, and the major goal of life to achieve maximum understanding of himself, and perfection of his behaviour.

We would decline to adopt such a pessimistic view, suggesting rather (as Ax also agrees) that the nomothetic and idiographic approaches are not incompatible, being natural aspects of science which must be pursued in logical order, and as appropriate for the systems involved, taking into account available methodologies and experimental techniques. Unfortunately, however, this is not the view taken by the principals involved. Soviet differential psychophysiology, to this point, has been almost entirely idiographic, although there are recent signs of a broader, more nomothetic attitude. On the other hand, in the West any idiographic approach to individual differences is treated with considerable reserve, if not open hostility, and it has proved difficult to find appropriate publication outlets for research of this type.

These considerations being noted, where do we go from here? In the following pages, we shall suggest a number of research directions which we think promising. Our selection is idiosyncratic, reflecting our own particular biases and preferences, and is therefore probably not representative, only one sample from a spate of possibilities.

At the simplest, empirical level, we need to know considerably more about properties or processes such as irradiation and concentration, and lability, for example. It is important to map the boundaries of these properties. Equally important is the question of orthogonality, and the identification of higher-order factors. Even in the case of well-researched areas, such as, for example, the characteristics of the orienting response, we need to know a good deal more about the relationships, within-S, between habituation rate, spontaneous fluctuation rate, over-extinction, rise time, recovery function, for example. Too few idiographic studies of this sort have been attempted.

In this respect, we might comment that far too much of the published research at this level can be classed as "busy work" — unsystematic, uncoordinated, without direction or adequate theoretical support. While, at a certain stage of theoretical development, this is perhaps understandable, it is unfortunate that our research ethos still exonerates Thurber's exhortation, "Don't get it right, just get it written".

At a more advanced level, a number of fairly obvious problems suggest themselves. We shall briefly mention a few of these. For example, if we assume semi-independent electro-cortical, autonomic and somatic arousal systems, which, at times, are not synergistic, are nervous system properties differently represented in these systems, as they appear to be in the classic afferent systems? If so, what are the implications? Could this be the explanation of the positive correlation between extraversion and strength when the latter is measured by sensory threshold, and of the negative correlation found between these variables when strength is measured by the RT method?

Again, it would be of considerable interest to investigate Pavlov's claim that the second signal system obeys the same laws which govern first signal responding. Although we know a good deal about semantic generalisation and transfer, and have noted the assertion that at times word is more than the sensory stimulus it designates in its capacity to elicit conditioned responses, what are the semantic correlates, if any, of sensory strength or dynamism? What is, in fact, the role of affect and imagery in learning and conditioning, and to what extent are typological characteristics relevant at this level of functioning?

On a somewhat different tack, what is the relationship of nervous system properties to work styles and attitudes? A good deal of research along these lines has been reported in the Soviet and Eastern European literature, mainly by psychologists at the Urals centre in Perm headed by Merlin (1964, 1967, 1971; 1973a) and by Strelau's Warsaw group.

Perhaps the best documented finding is that nervous system strength shows a significant relationship with stress tolerance, weak nervous systems being less resistant, whether stress is induced by technical breakdowns at different stages in the production cycle, by classroom evaluation of students, by sensory overload, or simply by physical exercise. Merlin's conclusions are in general agreement with the findings of Kevecki's Kiev group, that dogs with strong and equilibrated nervous systems tolerate stress more readily than either weak or strong but unequilibrated nervous systems. Strelau's group reports that highly reactive (i.e. weak) individuals are more easily affected by disorganisation, and that under prolonged stress such Ss develop more, and more severe, functional disorders, which in some cases lead to structural changes, than low reactive individuals.

Merlin has reported that while typological differences, under normal conditions, have little effect on productivity, they do effect work styles, and, as such, are important factors in work scheduling. In this respect, strength and mobility appear to be the important elements. Bagmetov has reported that certain aspects of mental work, particularly warm-up dynamics, fatigue, and changes in work style under emotional tension, are monitored by nervous system strength.

Strelau has also reported a number of studies examining the role of temperament in everyday activity. He makes a distinction between principal and auxiliary actions, the former aimed at achieving a certain goal, the latter creating the most appropriate conditions under which this can occur. S's reactivity level determines the ratio of principal to auxiliary actions. Low reactive individuals show an equilibrium, or a predominance of principal actions, high reactive individuals a predominance of auxiliary over principal actions. The reason for this, according to Strelau, is that auxiliary actions, by facilitating or streamlining principal actions, enable S to avoid tensions. The highly reactive S, who is particularly susceptible to stress, avoids tensions through appropriate auxiliary actions, and can thus act as smoothly and as efficiently as the low reactive S. This strategy applies both in industrial and scholastic contexts. Over and above this, of course, reactivity levels determine to some extent choice of occupation and working conditions. High reactive individuals choose less demanding work and less stressful situations than low reactive persons, who typically opt for stimulating tasks and work contexts of a similar nature.

Strelau does not describe in detail what he means by principal and auxiliary actions. We suspect that he is referring to physical and psychological preparation (auxiliary actions) for the proposed activity (principal action), for example, a teacher preparing a lesson, a workman assembling his tools and "setting up" the job. Presumably the high reactive person, whom we might describe as high on A-state, or emotional lability, in this way forestalls subsequent, possible stressful, emergencies.

Insofar as the relationship of nervous system characteristics to learning is concerned, a number of interesting findings have been reported from East European laboratories. Strelau (personal communication), for example, reports that in rote learning situations, the strong S typically works for long periods, followed by relatively long rest periods, the weak S in short, sharp bursts, interspersed with frequent, short, rest periods. Other things being equal, strong Ss favour a massed practice strategy, weak Ss distributed practice. This, at least superficially, conflicts with the well-established finding that introverted (weak) Ss show later rather than earlier onset of inhibition in such tasks. It is possible, however, that here we are confounding fatigue with monotony. These have opposite relationships with strength-sensitivity (cf. p. 216).

In a somewhat different context, Merlin's group has reported that mobile children (mobility being determined by laboratory test) are more sociable and active in the group, and seem to acquire social skills more readily than inert children, who tend to be sluggish and inactive. The Kiev Institute has also reported relationships between mobility and speed of learning, and we are reminded of the findings, reported earlier, of the relationship of lability and strength to memory functioning and information processing. There is no suggestion, of course, of any relationship between nervous system properties and intellectual endowment, such as mathematical or musical ability. Nervous system constitution provides necessary, but not sufficient, conditions for the development of particular attributes. Thus, high dynamism of excitation, in Nebylitsyn's original sense, is no guarantee of a highly developed capacity for learning. It simply provides appropriate conditions under which learning can flourish.

A rather similar interpretation has been given to the operation of so called "work-attitude" factors in Western personality theory. Factors such as persistance, Webb's $w$ factor, tempo and so on, which are thought to be temperamentally based, similarly provide conditions under which ability factors operate. Is what we call persistence equivalent, in essential respects, to nervous system strength? Can a weak nervous system be persistent?

Another area of interest which recently has commanded attention is the relationship of typology to psychopathology. This was one of Pavlov's later interests, although some of his observations about experimental neurosis and hysteria date from an earlier period.

We have mentioned the reported relationship between stress tolerance and nervous system strength. Further data from the Kiev Institute suggest that dogs with weak or strong but unequilibrated nervous systems are more susceptible to disease, their pathologies are more severe, and therapy is less effective. Strelau's group reports that highly reactive (weak) types, under stress, show more frequent and severe functional disorders. Pervomajski's Ukrainian group has reported relationships between typological factors, particularly strength, and manic-depressive psychosis, epilepsy, neurasthenia, psychasthenia, hysteria and infectious psychosis, which is an extension and continuation of earlier interest in the relationship of typological characteristics to schizophrenia.

Pavlov originally suggested that the weak nervous system, being prone to strong inhibitory reactions, and thus displaying a lower threshold of transmarginal inhibition, was susceptible to schizophrenic-type disorders. Inhibition irradiates, and, at pathological levels, results in the type of effect recorded by Kupalov (1961) in dogs. Kupalov, using a delay paradigm, reported that weak dogs showed initially reduced magnitude of salivary CR, followed, in sequence, by inhibition of CR to the CS, of UR to the US, finally by inhibition of motor movements. Irradiation is considered to be a cortical phenomenon, since delayed reflexes cannot be developed in decorticate animals.

Recently, in the Western literature, there has been the suggestion of two functionally related arousal systems, one governing tonic, the second phasic arousal, a view, which, incidentally, is implicit in Strelau's typological model. This concept, derived initially from two factor theories of arousal control suggested by Lynn (1963), Claridge (1967) and Epstein (Epstein and Coleman, 1970) has been employed to account for the markedly different symptoms — hypo- or hyper-reactivity in autonomic functioning — shown by different groups of schizophrenic patients. Epstein has suggested that the critical defect in schizophrenia is inadequate modulation, by the inhibitory system, of excitation — in effect, lack of an adequate dampening mechanism, this leading to extreme under- or over-responsivity to stimulation.

Although there have been no suggestions that these models are congruent, at first glance this seems plausible, since some of the similarities are striking, and since some of the principals in this area of research, such as Venables and Tizard, have employed the Pavlovian concept of transmarginal inhibition to account for differences in responsivity between schizophrenic groups (Venables and Tizard, 1956, 1958). One schizophrenic "type", the retarded (Claridge, 1967) or non-responder (Gruzelier and Venables, 1974, 1975a,b), could be weak Pavlovian types, under certain conditions developing pathological irradiation of inhibition, thus presenting the picture of a listless, withdrawn, emotionally flat individual. The case for the active, respondent schizophrenic, who shows weak cortical inhibition, and high tonic arousal, is less clear.

On the other hand, while these analogies might be attractive, arguing from the original Pavlovian typology is probably counterproductuve. Irradiation and concentration are now regarded as properties orthogonal to strength, and a good deal more critical research is required before schizophrenic symptomatology can be explained in terms of pathological irradiation of excitation or inhibition.

At a more empirical level, a number of observations by Western theorists concerning the psychophysiology of psychopathology are of interest. As yet, however, there is little evidence of any idiographic approach to these problems, although, in principle, there is no reason why this should not prove fruitful. We can cite at least three examples from the recent literature.

The work of Mednick and Venables on the recovery limb of the OR is a good case in point. They suggest that speed of arousal dissipation, which is reflected in recovery times, predicts psychopathic and schizophrenic deviance, slow recovery times characterising the former, fast recovery times the latter. The underlying theory, which has been described elsewhere, need not concern us here. We need simply to note the practical importance of identification of marker variables of this sort, if indeed, findings are adequately replicated. We would like to enquire, of course, whether, within this general framework, individual differences play a significant role.

The second example has a more general application. Gantt, one of Pavlov's pupils, has, over a period of 40 years, developed concepts of schizokinesis, autokinesis and proflex. These have been discussed elsewhere. Proflex is of particular sigificance. The observation that an aversive CS, over time, may develop increasing capacity to elicit a progressively larger CR, specifically cardiac, has obvious implications for a theory of neurosis.

Along rather similar lines, we might note Eysenck's recent (1979) proposal of a concept of "incubation" which arises from his interpretation of Napalkov's experiment. Napalkov reported that whereas the UR to a single pistol shot was a rise in blood pressure of 50 millimetres, subsequent presentation of the CS, without reinforcement, for 100 trials, produced a CR of a 250 millimetres increase in blood pressure, five times the amplitude of the original UR. Eysenck argues that with repeated CS presentations, the affective component of the CR can act as an effective US, thus incrementing CR strength. In extending his interpretation to the etiology of neurosis, Eysenck suggests that the critical variable is the interaction term between CR amplitude and non-reinforced CS exposure duration. If the US, and hence the CR, is very strong, moderate exposure durations of a non-reinforced CS will result in "incubation" rather than extinction, leading ultimately to "neurotic" CRs. This he terms Pavlovian Type B conditioning.

In Eysenck's view the aim of successful therapy is to maintain the patient below the critical point of the curve relating CR strength to duration of non-reinforced CS exposure, beyond which the CR actually increases in strength. Thus, while lengthy "flooding" by the CS is effective in extinguishing the CR, brief flooding augments it (Figures 33, 34). Sustained flooding by the US also appears to have a similar, but perhaps more extensive, effect, as evidenced in the Leningrad flood incident, recorded by Pavlov, an effect similar to that shown in implosion therapy.

At least superficially, there is some parallel between Gantt's proflex and Eysenck's incubation. It may be that the animals described by Gantt, although experiencing only one CS–US pairing, "incubate" the CR in the intervening period by generating images of the CS. "Remembering the trauma" strengthens the CS–US connection by means of the mechanism described by Eysenck. This, of course, raises the question of whether the amount of CR incubation is trials-or time-dependent, or both. It may be, in addition, that there are large individual differences in the speed and amplitude of incubation and proflex, which, in turn, may be related to typological characteristics. Be that as it may,

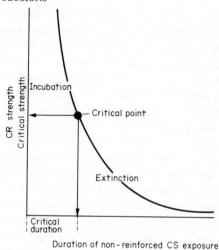

Figure 33. Critical point on the curve relating CR strength to duration of non-reinforced CS exposure demarcating CR incubation or extinction (from Eysenck, 1979).

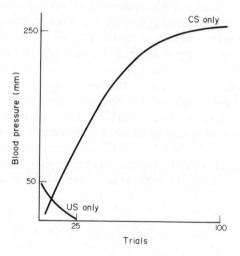

Figure 34. Changes in UR and CR amplitudes over trials in dogs subjected to one CS–US pairing (from Eysenck, 1979).

the parallels between these processes and the development of neurosis, especially phobias, in humans, appear striking.

Finally, might we refer again to a problem of consuming interest to many Western personality theorists, the relationship of conditioning to personality.

While today, few would agree with Sechenov's (1863) bold assertion that: "All acts of conscious and unconscious life are reflexive in origin", thought being "the first two-thirds of the psychic reflex" and emotion "a reflex with an intensified ending", nonetheless a good deal of that social learning which demarcates personality "types" is effected through conditioning. Empirical support for this proposition, however, is weak, although it is fair to comment that the hypothesis has not yet been adequately tested. Nor will it be until we can devise a sophisticated enough model of conditioning to account for all the complexities of human social learning, a model which incorporates, for example, processes such as sanctioning afferentation, the broad steering or tonic reflexes referred to by Asratyan, the complex psyche/soma interactions implied in "cognitive control" of autonomic responses.

The reason why we choose to ignore the vastly increased potential conferred by greater encephalisation in humans, potential which makes conditioning, from the earliest age, a complex and subtle adaptive process, is puzzling. Perhaps it is simply a legacy of behaviourism. But it is surely a truism that man not only observes his own behaviour, both as actor and as audience, as Hobhouse averred, but that the evolutionarily most recent cortical structures endow him with the capacity to explicate such observations and subject them to empirical test. Thus man's unique position in the natural order, an apophthegm recorded in literary as well as scientific lore. Pascal noted the point well: "L'homme n'est qu'un roseau le plus faible de la nature; mais c'est un roseau pensant."

Early in ontogeny, symbolic reactions begin to dominate primary perceptions, and symboling without perceiving tends to become the norm as maturation proceeds. As Razran (1971) aptly comments, "Time-bound biography rather than space-bound contemporaneity is the domicile of man's mind" (p. 184).

Cultural history, of course, also plays its part, a point made many years ago by Sechenov.

> Man juxtaposes not only his experiences of childhood, adolecence, and old age, not only what he saw, say, in America, and here, in Moscow, but also the life of today with that of antiquity ... he becomes a part, so to speak, of the life of the universe without leaving the narrow limits of his terrestrial existence (Sechenov, 1892, p. 201).

The benefits conferred by higher-order symboling and thinking are obvious enough. They range from the capacity to evoke marked behaviour changes through symbolic self-instructions, to acceleration of formal learning through symbolic instructions (the "conditional dominant" of Merlin) without the need for paired conditioning. Perhaps most importantly, it implies increased capacity for planning, that uniquely human discriminant function, which, involving as it does control over the order in which a sequence of operations is to be performed, permits anticipated consequences to qualify and correct antecedents.

At first glance, this seems to conflict with the classical mind-as-reflex Soviet model, as expressed, for example, by Pavlov:

> Vital phenomena that are termed psychic are distinguishable from pure physiological phenomena only in degree of complexity. Whether we call these phenomena psychical or complex-nervous is of little importance, as long as it is realised and recognised that the naturalist approaches them and studies them only objectively, leaving aside the question of essence" (Pavlov, 1903, p. 121).

However, it is clear that while Pavlov strongly rejected "subjective" interpretation of data, this was more a methodological imperative. There are frequent references, in his writings, to the importance of thinking, higher-order symboling. In this regard, we should note that Anokhin's recent description of return and sanctioning afferentation is a formalisation of a theme which has reverberated in Soviet reflexology and psychology for more than a century. Both Sechenov and Pavlov emphasised the importance of kinaesthesis, proprioception, feedback, and this has continued to be emphasised in Soviet psychology generally. Rubinsteyn's assertion is typical: "Psyche is both a conditioned and a conditioning event" (1959, p. 19). Anokhin's affirmation that afferent synthesis is a most crucial aspect of brain activity is essentially a restatement of Pavlov's view that the afferent apparatus is the "creative" link in the reflexive chain.

The quale of conditioning, therefore, is a complex interaction between genetic dispositions, a range of environmental events, and the unfolding power of the individual to think, to symbol, to anticipate and predict possible consequences. The simple models which continue to direct personality/conditioning research — models which imply that the immature nervous system is a tabula rasa, on which environment writes large — have long outlived their usefulness. Until we shake ourselves free from the intellectual serfdom of "the" conditioned reflex, and escape from the often impoverished reality of the intervening variable, we have no reason to expect much more than demonstrations of what are fairly modest relationships — with a few notable exceptions — between personaldity variables, typological indices and conditioning performance. While it may be true, as Nebylitsyn (1972) contends, that typological variables have considerable predictive power when the organism is stressed, and regresses to a more primitive (UR) level of functioning, this has little relevance to the dynamics of normal personality development, which involves the introjection of social norms, the learning of socially appropriate behaviour. To achieve a fuller understanding of this process, we need a new theoretical orientation, a new methodology — a model similar to that constructed, for example, by Piaget and modern Soviet developmentalists, which emphasises observation, over time, of those child/environment interactions which eventually produce the relatively stable transactions we denote personality "traits".

As a case in point, consider the implications of the Vygotsky/Leont'ev/ Strelau reactivity-activity model of temperament for personality-conditioning research. Using this model, Paisey and Mangan (in press) claim that individual differences in reactivity/activity levels in the afferent/efferent systems, rather than differential sensitivity to reinforcement type, account for the personality-conditioning links reported. Extraverts, because of their low reactivity, stimulation-seek by developing more powerful classical CRs, while introverts, because of their low activity levels, develop more expressive motor CRs, all Ss being exposed to USs of equivalent subjective intensities in both conditioning situations.

It could be argued, of course, that this condition is not likely to be encountered in real-life contexts, since environmental contingencies reflect a more-or-less random pattern of reinforcement intensities. Activity theory, however, suggests something quite different. Individuals, increasingly as development proceeds, create their own environments — adaptation is active rather than passive, signification rather than signalisation characterising distinctively human forms of learning and conditioning. A critical feature of this process is the child's vigorous striving to match reward and punishment to idiosyncratic reactivity/activity requirements. In reward learning, the individual actively seeks that level and quality of stimulation which harmonises with his biologically fixed, optimal "hedonic" level. Insofar as punishment is concerned, while undoubtedly differences in reactivity level may amplify or dampen the impact of aversive stimulation, it is nonetheless true that people (parents and teachers) as the major dispensers of punishment in socialisation learning, usually make some attempt to equate level of punishment with its perceived effects on the child, thus unwittingly modifying punishment with the reactivity of the transgressor. The critical observation, therefore, is not so much that different personality groups show differential susceptibility to reinforcement type, in that given arbitrarily fixed (by E) levels of reward and punishment, these groups show poorer or better conditioning. This may be true. But more importantly, each is responsive to that reinforcement level which is appropriate to his individual needs, and each seeks to avoid inappropriate levels of stimulation. We may have to look elsewhere for the "causes" of personality differences.

But to do this, we need new concepts, a new vision. Perhaps we should start by retracing our steps, and looking again at the classical/operant distinction.

Classical and instrumental learning — in Bekhterev's original sense of motor avoidance — refer to passive adaptation, to signalisation, to the consequences of largely unavoidable early experience. This, admittedly, is the bedrock of socialisation. Later reality testing — activity or signification, whatever we choose to call it — presupposes voluntary action leading to operant learning and rule building on the basis of available feedback.

This is nothing particularly original in this. But in our research on the role of conditioning in personality formation, we seem to forget that the conditions we impose in our laboratory experiments determine to a considerable extent the kind of effects we are likely to obtain. Restraining dogs in harnesses, running rats in straight alleys, limit response possibilities. If we restrain the animal and study only his autonomic responses, or allow him to shuttle and study only his jumping, that is our emphasis, not his. The total physiological response profile, however, undoubtedly reflects coping behaviour in a much more general sense. The fact that we restrict our observations to one type of learning context, and to one type of behaviour does not mean that other responses are not present, either overtly (but unmeasured) or in latent form (inhibited motor responses, imagery).

When we look at such response profiles under "real life" conditions, classical/operant distinctions are much harder to justify. For example, consider Kupalov's (1969) experiment describing the development of classically conditioned place reflexes (reflex-chained approach learning) in dogs in an unrestricted environment. We are struck by the similarity of this procedure to the shaping of a discriminated operant. "Real" learning is clearly a complex web of associative linking, and we need to understand both the associative processes involved, and the ways in which these interweave, overlap and combine. This suggests that we should eschew deterministic models of learning in relation to personality development, and turn our attention to the ways in which the child constructs his own reality. What determines his "coping" strategies, i.e. the extent to which he is able to exercise effective control over environmental contingencies? To what extent are these determined by the assimilated structures laid down earlier in ontogeny? What is the nature of the active, integrating principle — the will, the ego?

Vygotsky, nearly 50 years ago, made a similar and equally apt comment about the future of developmental psychology.

"In the person of its best representatives, child psychology has come to the conclusion that the descriptions of man's inner life, as a whole, belong to the poet's or historian's art. This is in effect a declaration of bankruptcy, a reflection of the shaky underpinnings of child psychology, a confession of the impossibility, in principle, of studying the personality within the methodological framework which set the stage for the development of child psychology in the first place. Only a resolute break with the methodological constraints of traditional child psychology can bring us to the study of that higher mental synthesis which has been correctly described as the personality of the child". (L. S. Vygotsky, 1960).

We agree. Only when we incorporate new concepts into personality theory, and new perspectives into personality research can we aspire to a greater understanding of personality dynamics, and thus to the contribution of individual psychophysiological differences to behavioural variance. Only then will we begin to appreciate the complexities of the relationship between the neural and the psychic.

# References

ACKER, L. E. and EDWARDS, A. E. (1964) Transfer of vasoconstriction over a bipolar meaning dimension, *J. Exp. Psychol.* **67,** 1–6.

ACORD, L. D. (1967) Psychopathy and conditioning. Unpublished doctoral dissertation, Case Western Reserve University.

ADAMOVICH-GERASIMOV, V. A. (1959) The limits of trace conditioning in dogs with different types of higher nervous activity. Proceedings of Conference dedicated to the Fortieth Anniversary of the Russian Revolution, Minsk.

ADAMS, J. A. (1961) Human tracking behaviour, *Psychol. Bull.* **58,** 55–79.

ADCOCK, C. J. (1976) *Psychology and theory,* Wellington: Victoria University Press.

ADCOCK, N. V. and ADCOCK, C. J. (1977) The validity of the 16 PF personality structure: a large New Zealand sample item analysis, *J. Behav. Sci.* **2,** 227–37.

ADCOCK, N. V., ADCOCK, C. J. and WALKEY, F. H. (1974) Basic dimensions of personality, *Int. Rev. Appl. Psychol.* **23,** 131–7.

ADER, R. and CONKLIN, P. M. (1963) Handling of pregnant rats: effects of emotionality on their offspring, *Science, N. Y.* **142,** 411–12.

ADRIAN, E. and MATTHEWS, B. M. (1934) The interpretation of potential waves in the cortex. *J. Physiol., Lond.* **81,** 440.

AINSWORTH, M. D. (1962) The effects of maternal deprivation: a review of findings and controversy in the context of research strategy, in, *Deprivation of maternal care,* pp. 197–1159 Geneva: WHO.

AKHIMOVA, M. N. (1971) Individual characteristics of attention and basic properties of the nervous system. Unpublished Dissertation, Kuibyshev.

ALDRICH, C. A., SUNG, C. and KNOP, C. (1945) The crying of newly born babies, *J. Pediat.* **27,** 89–96.

ALEKSANDROVA, N. I. and KLYAGIN, V. S. (1978) Title not given, in, B. M. Teplov (Ed.), *Typological Features of High Nervous Activity in Man,* Vol. 5, p. 103 Moscow: Prosveschchenie. Cited by Gorbunov, Sirotskii and Maravenko (1978).

ALEKSEEVA, M. S. (1953) Determination of types of nervous system in dogs on the basis of different unconditioned reinforcement — alimentary and acid-defence. *Tr. Inst. Fiziol. im. I. P. Pavlova,* **2.**

ALEKSEEVA M. S., ELKIN, V. I. and FEDOROV, V. K. (1964) A comparison of nervous system mobility between rats of the Wistar Strain and rats selectively bred for auditory sensitivity, *Zh. Vyssh. Nerv. Deyat. im. I. P. Pavlova,* **14,** 1.

ALEKSEYENKO, N. YU and BLINKOV, S. M. (1955) Conditioned reactions to tactile stimuli in unilateral injury of the parietal lobe, *Trans. Inst. Vyssh. Nerv. Deyat. im. I. P. Pavlova Ser. Fiziol.* **1,** 235–46.

ALKER, H. A. (1972) Is personality situationally specific or intrapsychically consistent? *J. Personality,* **46,** 1–16.

ALLEN, C. K., HILL, F. A. and WICKENS, D. B. (1963) The orienting reflex as a function of the inter-stimulus interval of compound stimuli. *J. Exp. Psychol.* **83,** 247–54.

465

ALLINSMITH, B. B. (1960) Directness with which anger is expressed, in, D. R. Miller and
  G. E. Swanson (Eds.), *Inner conflict and defence*, pp. 315–36, New York: Holt, Rinehart &
  Winston.
ALLPORT, F. H. (1924) *Social Psychology*, Cambridge, Mass.: Riverside Press.
ALLPORT, G. W. (1955) *Becoming: basic considerations for a psychology of personality*, New
  Haven, Conn.: Yale University Press.
ALLPORT, G. W. (1961) *Pattern and growth in personality*, New York: Holt, Rinehart and Winston.
ALLSOPP, J. E. and EYSENCK, H. J. (1974) Personality as a determinant of paired-associates
  learning, *Percept. Mot. Skills*, **39**, 315–24.
AMINOV, N. A. (1974) Functional states during monotonous work and the balance of the basic
  nervous processes, *Vop. Psikhol.* **2**, 77–83.
ANISKIEWICZ, A. (1973) Autonomic components of vicarious conditioning and psychopathy.
  Doctoral dissertation, Perdue Univ. Ann Arbor, Mich.: Univ. Microfilms No. 73–28, 040.
ANOKHIN, P. K. (1932) Title not given. *Nizhegorodskii Med. Zh.* **7–8.**
ANOKHIN, P. K. (1949) The reflex and the functional system as factors in physiological integration,
  *Fiziol. Zh. SSSR*, **35,** 5.
ANOKHIN, P. K. (1958) *Electroencephalographic analysis of conditioned reflex activity.*
  Moscow: Izd. Medgiz.
ANOKHIN, P. K. (1961) New conceptions of the physiological architecture of the conditioned
  reflex, in, L. F. Delafresnaye (Ed.), *Brain mechanisms and learning*, pp. 188–224, Springfield,
  Ill.: Charles C. Thomas.
ANOKHIN, P. K. (1966) Special features of the afferent apparatus of the conditioned reflex and
  their importance to psychology, in, A. N. Leont'ev, A. R. Luria and A. A. Smirnov (Eds.),
  *Psychological research in the USSR*, Vol. 1, pp. 67–98, Moscow: Prosveshcheniye.
ANOKHIN, P. K. (1969) Cybernetics and the integrative activity of the brain, in, M. Cole and
  I. Maltzman (Eds.), *A handbook of contemporary Soviet psychology*, New York: Basic Books.
ANTONOVA, G. P. (1967) Concerning the after-effect of the basic nervous processes in children,
  in, *New research in pedagogical sciences*, Vol. IX, Moscow: Prosveshcheniye.
ANTONOVA, G. P. (1968) Concerning the age changes in some features of the nervous processes in
  schoolchildren, Proceedings of the Third All-Union Congress of the Society of Psychologists
  of the USSR, Vol. 1, Moscow.
APPELBAUM, J., SILVA, E, E., FRICK, D. and SEGUNDO, J. P. (1960) Specificity and biasing of
  arousal rection habituation. *Electroenceph. Clin. Neurophysiol,* **12,** 829–40.
ARCHER, J. (1973) Tests for emotionality in rats and mice: a review, *Anim. Behav.* **21,** 205–35.
ARGYLE, M. (1964) Introjection: a form of social learning, *Br. J. Psychol.* **55,** 391–402.
ARGYLE, M. (1969) *Social Interaction,* London: Methuen.
ARGYLE, M., TROWER, P. and BRYANT, B. (1974) Explorations in the treatment of personality
  disorders and neuroses by social skills training, *Br. J. Med. Psychol.* **47,** 63.
ARGYLE, M., GRAHAM, J. A., CAMPBELL, A. and WHITE, P. (1979) The rules of different situations,
  *N. Z. Psychol.* **8,** 13–25.
ARKANGELSKII, V. M. (1924) The relative strengths of different kinds of internal inhibition,
  *Tr. Fiziol. Labor. im. I. P. Pavlova,* **1,** 1.
ARMSTRONG, H. E. (1964) The relationship between a dimension of body-image and two measures
  of conditioning. Doctoral dissertation, Syracuse University. Ann Arbor, Michigan: University
  Microfilms, No. 64–8845. *Diss. Abst.* **25,** 2, 1315.
ARNOLD, M. (1946) On the mechanism of suggestion and hypnosis, *J. Abnorm. Psychol.*
  **41,** 107–28.
ARONFREED, J. (1961) The nature, variety, and social patterning of moral responses to
  transgression, *J. Abnorm. Soc. Psychol.* **63,** 223–41.
ARONFREED, J. (1964) The origin of self-criticism, *Psychol. Rev.* **71,** 193–218.
ARONFREED, J. (1968) *Conduct and conscience: the socialization of internalized control over
  behaviour,* New York: Academic Press.
ARONFREED, J. (1969) The concept of internalization, in, D. A. Goslin (Ed.), *Handbook of
  socialization theory and research,* Chicago: Rand McNally.

ARONFREED, J. and LEFF, R. (1963) The effects of intensity of punishment and complexity of discrimination upon the learning of internalized suppression. Unpublished Manuscript, University of Pennsylvania.

ARONFREED, J. and REBER, A. (1965) Internalized behavioral suppression and the timing of social punishment, *J. Personality Soc. Psychol.* **1**, 3–16.

ARTEM'EF, V. V. and BEZLADNOVA, N. I. (1952) Electrical reaction of the auditory area of the cortex of the cerebral hemispheres during formation of a conditioned defensive reflex, *Tr. Fiziol. Labor. im. I. P. Pavlova*, **1**, 228–36.

ASHWORTH, B., GRIMSBY, L. and KOGLEBURG, E. (1967) Comparison of voluntary and reflex activation of motor units, *J. Neurosurg. Psychiat.* **30**, 91–8.

ASRATYAN, E. A. (1937) The cerebral cortex and plasticity of the nervous system, *Usp. Sovrem. Biol.* **4**, 3.

ASRATYAN, E. A. (1958) New data on switching in conditioned reflex activity, *Zh. Vyssh. Nerv. Deyat. im. I. P. Pavlova*, **8**, 3, 305.

ASRATYAN, E. A. (1962) O meste obrazovaniya i funktsional' nyth osnovakh uslovn oy syvogi. *Zh. Vyssh. Nerv. Deyat. im. I. P. Pavlova*, **12**, 3.

ASRATYAN, E. A. (1967) Some peculiarities of formation, functioning and inhibition of conditioned reflexes with two-way connections. *Prog. Brain Res.* **22**, 8–20.

ASRATYAN, E. A. (1970) *Ocherki po fiziologii uslovnych refleksov*, Moscow: Nauka.

ASRATYAN, E. A. (1972) Genesis and localisation of conditioned inhibition, in, R. A. Boakes and M. S. Halliday (Eds.), *Inhibition and learning*. London: Academic Press.

ASRATYAN, E. A. (1981) The two-way connection as a basic principle of neurophysiology, *Pavlov. J. Biol. Sci.* **16**, 1, 1–7.

ATKINSON, R. L. and ROBINSON, N. M. (1961) Paired-associate learning by schizophrenic and normal subjects under conditions of personal and impersonal reward and punishment, *J. Abnorm. Soc. Psychol.* **62**, 322–6.

AUSUBEL, D. P. (1963) The influence of experience on the development of intelligence. Paper read at a Conference on Productive Thinking in Education, sponsored by NEA Project on the Academically Talented Student, Washington, D.C.: Mimeographed.

AVAKYAN, R. V. (1961) The measurement of differential threshold intensities by means of conditioned eyeblink reflexes and verbal report, *Zh. Vyssh. Nerv. Deyat. im. I. P. Pavlov*, **11**, 5.

AX, A. F. (1953) The physiological differentation between fear and anger in humans, *Psychosom. Med.* **15**, 433–42.

AX, A. F. (1974) Editorial, *Psychophysiol.* **11**, 613–14.

AX, A. F. and BAMFORD, J. L. (1970) The GSR recovery limb in chronic schizophrenics, *Psychophysiol.* **7**, 145–7.

AYRAPETYANTS E. SH. (1956) Materials on the physiology of the internal analyser in man, *Tr. Fiziol. Labor. im. I. P. Pavlova*, **5**, 396–406.

AYRAPETYANTS, E. SH., LOBANOVA, L. V. and CHERKASOVA, L. S. (1952) Materials on the physiology of the internal analyser in man, *Tr. Fiziol. Labor. im. I. P. Pavlova*, **1**, 3–20.

AZRIN, N. H., HUTCHINSON, R. R. and HAKE, D. F. (1966) Extinction-induced aggression, *J. Exp. Analysis Behav.* **9**, 191–204.

AZRIN, N. H., HUTCHINSON, R. R. and HAKE, D. F. (1967) Attack, avoidance and escape reactions to aversive shock, *J. Exp. Analysis Behav.* **10**, 131–48.

BABIGHIAN, G., MOUSHEGIAN, G. and RUPERT, A. L. (1975) Central auditory fatigue, *Audiology*, **14**, 72–83.

BABKIN, B. P. (1904) Systematic study of complex-nervous (psychic) phenomena in dogs. Thesis, St. Petersburg: Military Medical Academy.

BABKIN, B. P. (1910) The characteristics of the auditory analyser in dogs, *Tr. Obshchestva Russkikh Vrachey v St. Peterburge*, **77**, 197–232.

BACON, M. K., CHILD, I. L. and BARRY, H. (1963) III. A cross-cultural study of some correlates of crime, *J. Abnorm. Soc. Psychol.* **66**, 291–300.

BADIA, P. and DEFRAN, R. H. (1970) Orienting responses and GSR conditioning: a dilemma. *Psychol. Rev.* **77**, 171–81.

BAER, P. E. and FUHRER, M. J. (1970) Cognitive processes in the differential trace conditioning of electrodermal and vasomotor acitivity, *J. Exp. Psychol.* **84**, 176–8.

BAER, P. E. and FUHRER, M. J. (1973) Unexpected effects of masking: differential EDR conditioning without relational learning, *Psychophysiol.* **10**, 1, 95–9.

BAGSHAW, M. H. and KIMBLE, D. P. (1972) Bimodal EDR orienting response characteristics in limbic lesioned monkeys: correlates with schizophrenic patients. Paper presented to meeting of the Society for Psychophysiological Research, Boston, Mass.

BAGSHAW, M. H., KIMBLE, D. P. and PRIBRAM, K. H. (1965) The GSR of monkeys during orienting and habituation and after ablation of the amygdala, hippocampus and infrotemporal cortex, *Neuropsychologia,* **3**, 111–19.

BAIR, J. (1901) Development of voluntary control, *Psychol. Rev.* **8**, 474–510.

BAKAND, P. (1959) Extraversion/introversion and improvement in an auditory vigilance task, *Br. J. Psychol.* **50**, 325–32.

BALDWIN, J. M. (1906) *Mental developments in the child and the race: methods and processes,* New York: Macmillan.

BALINT, M. (1948) Individual differences of behaviour in early infancy and an objective method for recording them, *J. Genet. Psychol.* **73**, 57–79.

BALL, T. S., BARBER, J. and KOHLER, H. (1975) Galvanic-skin response orienting response as a measure of tactile discrimination in retarded children, *Am. J. Ment. Defic.* **79**, 559–64.

BANDURA, A. (1965a) Influence of model's reinforcement contingencies on the acquisition of imitative responses, *J. Personality Soc. Psychol.* **1**, 589–95.

BANDURA, A. (1965b) Vicarious processes: a case of no-trial learning, in, L. Berkowitz (Ed.), *Advances in experimental social psychology,* Vol. 2, New York: Academic Press.

BANDURA, A. (1969) Social-learning theory of identification processes, in, D. A. Goslin (Ed.) *Handbook of socialization theory and research,* Chicago: Rand McNally.

BANDURA, A. (1978). The self system in reciprocal determinism, *Am. Pschol.* **33**, 344–58.

BANDURA, A. and HUSTON, A. C. (1961) Identification as a process of incidental learning, *J. Abnorm. Soc. Pschol.* **63**, 311–18.

BANDURA, A. and KUPERS, C. J. (1964) Transmission of patterns of self-reinforcement through modelling, *J. Abnorm. Soc. Psychol.* **69**, 1–9.

BANDURA, A. and WALTERS, R. H. (1959) *Adolescent aggression,* New York: Ronald.

BANDURA, A. and WALTERS, R. (1963) *Social learning and personality,* New York: Holt, Rinehart and Winston.

BANDURA, A. and WHALEN, C. K. (1966) The influence of antecedent reinforcement and divergent modelling cues on patterns of self reward, *J. Personality Soc. Psychol.* **3**, 373–82.

BANDURA, A., ROSS, D. and ROSS, S. A. (1961) Transmission of aggression through imitation of aggressive models, *J. Abnorm. Soc. Psychol.* **63**, 575–82.

BANDURA, A., ROSS, D. and ROSS, S. A. (1963a) Imitation of film mediated aggressive models, *J. Abnorm. Soc. Psychol.* **66**, 3–11.

BANDURA, A., ROSS, D. and ROSS, S. A. (1963b) A comparative test of the status envy, social power and secondary reinforcement theories of identification learning, *J. Abnorm. Soc. Psychol.* **67**, 527–34.

BANDURA, A., ROSS, D. and ROSS, S. A. (1963c) Vicarious reinforcement and imitative learning, *J. Abnorm. Soc. Psychol.* **67**, 601–7.

BARCAL, R., SIMON, J. and SOVA, J. (1969) Blood pressure in twins, *Lancet,* **I**, 1321.

BARKHUDARYAN, S. S. (1956) Characteristics of dogs with intermediate types of nervous system, *Tr. Inst. Fiziol. im. I. P. Pavlova.* **5**.

BARKHUDARYAN, S. S. (1964) On the mechanisms of origination and localization of different forms of conditioned inhibition, in, E. A. Asratyan and V. N. Andreyeva (Eds.) 10th Conference of the I. P. Pavlov All-Union Physiological Society, Yerevan Vol. 2, Topics of Scientific Papers, No. 1, 131–2. Moscow-Leningrad: Izd. Nauka. English translation (1965), Foreign Technology Division, Air-Force Systems Command, Wright Patterson Air Force Base, Ohio.

BARNES, G. (1975) Extraversion and pain, *Br. J. Soc. Clin. Psychol,* **14**, 303–8.

BARONENKO, V. A., SKIDANOVA, M. M., ILYINA, T. K. and ARTEMYEVA, G. A. (1979) The influence of mental work on efficiency and reliability of voluntary motor activity, *Zh. Vyssh. Nerv. Deyat, im. I. P. Pavlova*, **29**, 34–41.

BARR, M. L. (1974) *The human nervous system: an anatomical viewpoint*, 2nd ed., New York: Harper.

BARR, R. F. and McCONAGHY, N. (1971) Penile volume responses to appetitive and aversive stimuli in relation to sexual orientation and conditioning performance, *Br. J. Psychiat.* **119**, 377–83.

BARR, R. F. and McCONAGHY, N. (1972a) A general factor of conditionability: a study of galvanic skin responses and penile responses, *Behav. Res. Ther.* **10**, 215–27.

BARR, R. F. and McCONAGHY, N. (1972b) Conditioning in relation to conceptual thinking, *Br. J. Psychiat.* **121**, 299–310.

BARRELL, J. J. and PRICE, D. D. (1977) Two experimental orientations toward a stressful situation and their related somatic and visceral responses, *Psychophysiol.* **14**, 517–21.

BARRY, H. and SYMMES, D. (1963) Reinforcing effects of illumination change in different phases of the rat's diurnal cycle, *J. Comp. Physiol. Psychol.* **56**, 117–19.

BARRY, H., WAGNER, A. R. and MILLER, N. E. (1962) Effects of alochol and amobarbitol on performance inhibited by experimental extinction, *J. Comp. Physiol. Psychol.* **55**, 464–8.

BARRY, R. J. (1975) Low intensity auditory stimulation and the GSR orienting response, *Physiol. Psychol.* **3**, 1, 98–100.

BARRY, R. P. (1976) Failure to find the "local" EEG OR to low-level auditory stimulation, *Physiol. Psychol.* **4**, 170–4.

BARTOL, C. K. and COSTELLO, N. (1976) Extraversion as a funtion of temporal duration of electrical shock: an exploratory study, *Percept. Mot. Skills*, **42**, 3, 1174.

BASMAJIAN, J. V. (1963) Conscious control of single nerve cells, *New Scient.* **20**, 662–4.

BASMAJIAN, J. V. and SAMARD, T. G. (1967) Effects of distracting movements on the control of trained motor units, *Am. J. Phys. Med.* **46**, 1427–40.

BASMAJIAN, J. V., BAEZA, M. and FABINGAR, C. (1965) Conscious control and training of individual spinal motor neurons in normal human subjects, *J. New Drugs*, **5**, 78–85.

BASSIN, F. V. and SERKOVA, M. P. K. (1956) Elektrografii izmeneniy myschechnogo tonusa predshestvuyushchikh proizviol'nomu dvizheniyu pri organicheskikh narusheniyakh motoriki. *Zh. Nevropat. Psikhiat.* **56**, 2.

BATES, J. F. and ADAMS, D. (1968) The influence of mental stress on the flow of saliva in man, *Arch. Oral Biol.* **13**, 593–6.

BAUMEISTER A. A., SPAIN, C. J. and ELLIS, N. R. (1963) A note on alpha-block duration in normals and retardates, *Am. J. Ment. Defic.* **67**, 723–5.

BEACH, F. A. (1965) Problems of classification, description and measurement. Symposium: Evolving methodology in the study of behaviour. Michigan State University. Unpublished.

BEAM, J. C. (1955) Serial learning and conditioning under real-life stress, *J. Abnorm. Soc. Psychol.* **51**, 543–51.

BECKER-CARUS, C. (1971) Relationships between EEG, personality and vigilance, *Electroenceph. Clin. Neurophysiol.* **30**, 519–36.

BECKMAN, F. H. and STEIN, M. I. (1961) A note on the relationship between percent alpha time and efficiency in problem solving, *J. Pscyhol.* **51**, 169–72.

BEKHTEREV, V. M. (1907) *Objektive Psychologie oder Psycho-reflexologie, die Lehre von den Assoziations-reflexen*, Leipzig and Berlin: Teubner, 1913.

BELLACK, A. S., HERSEN, M. and TURNER, S. M. (1976) Generalisation effects of social skills training in chronic schizophrenics: an experimental analysis, *Behav. Res. Ther.* **14**, 391–8.

BELLONI, M. L. (1964) The relationship of the orienting reaction and manifest anxiety to paired associates learning. Unpublished doctoral dissertation, University of California, Los Angeles, 1964. Cited by Maltzman and Raskin (1965).

BELYAEVA, Z. V. (1979) Vegetative-somatic components of motor responses to direct verbal stimuli, *Zh. Vyssh. Nerv. Deyat. im. I. P. Pavlova*, **29**, 42–6.

BELYAEVA-EXEMPLYASKAYA, S. N. (1961) The significance of personal tempo and rhythm in everyday life, *Vop. Psikhol.* **2**.

BEM, D. J. (1972) Self-perception theory, in, L. Berkowitz (Ed.), *Advances in experimental social psychology*, Vol. 6, New York: Academic Press.

BEM, D. J. and FUNDER, D. C. (1978) Predicting more of the people more of the time: assessing the personality of situations, *Psychol. Rev.* **85**, 485–501.

BENDIG, A. W. (1962) Factor analysis of the Guilford-Zimmerman Temperament Survey, *J. Genet. Psychol.* **67**, 21–6.

BENITEZ, L. D., ELDREDGE, D. H. and TEMPLER, J. W. (1972) Sensory threshold shift in the chinchilla: electrophysioloigcal correlates, *J. Acoust. Soc. Am.* **52**, 1115–23.

BERG, W. K. (1970) Heart rate and vasomotor responses as a function of stimulus duration and intensity. Unpublished M.A. thesis, University of Wisconsin.

BERG, W. K. (1974) Cardiac orienting responses of six and sixteen week old infants, *J. Exp. Child Psychol.* **17**, 2, 203–312.

BERGER, L. A. (1964) A comparison of the physiological functioning of normals and psychiatric patients, *Psychol. Rep.* **15**, 183–7.

BERGMAN, D. and ESCALONA, S. K. (1949) Unusual sensitivities in very young children, in, *The PSA Study of the Child*, Vol III/IV, New York: International Universities Press.

BERITOV, I. S. (1924) On the fundamental nervous processes in the cortex of the cerebral hemispheres, *Brain*, **47**, 109–48, 358–76.

BERITOV, I. S. (1928) Charakteristik und gegenseitige Wirkung der Angeborenen. Reflexakte des Verhaltens der Tiere. *1,11 Mitt. J. Exper. Biol. Med., Moscow*, **20**, 106–16, 117–30.

BERITOV, I. S. (1930) Science about behaviour as reflexology. *Usp. Éksp. Biol., Moscow*, **15**, 3.

BERITOV, I. S. (1932) *Individually acquired activity of the central nervous system*, Tbilisi: GIZ.

BERITOV, I. S. (1961) *Neural mechanisms of the behaviour of higher vertebrates*, Moscow: Akad. Nauk SSSR. English translation (1965) by W. T. Liberson, Boston: Little, Brown.

BERKOWITZ, L. (1969) Simple views of aggression: an essay review. *Am. Scient.* **57**, 372–83.

BERKSON, G. (1961) Responsiveness of the mentally deficient, *Am. J. Ment. Defic.* **66**, 277–86.

BERKSON, G., HERMELIN, B. and O'CONNOR, N. (1961) Physiological responses of normals and institutionalised mental defectives to repeated stimuli, *J. Ment. Defic. Res.* **5**, 1, 30–9.

BERLYNE, D. E. (1960) *Conflict, arousal and curiosity*, New York: McGraw-Hill.

BERLYNE, D. E. (1966) Curiosity and exploration, *Science, N. Y.* **153**, 25–33.

BERLYNE, D. E. (1967) Arousal and reinforcement, in, D. Levine (Ed.), *Nebraska Symposium on Motivation*, Lincoln, Neb.: University of Nebrasks Press.

BERLYNE, D. E. (1968) Behaviour Theory as Personality Theory, in, E. F. Borgatta and W. W. Lambert (Eds.), *Handbook of personality theory and research*, Chicago: Rand McNally.

BERLYNE, D. E. (1971a) Affective aspects of aesthetic communication. Paper to Symposium on "Affect and Communication". Erindale College, University of Toronto: Academic Press.

BERLYNE, D. E. (1971b) *Aesthetics and psychobiology*, New York: Appleton-Century-Crofts.

BERLYNE, D. E. and LEWIS, J. L. (1963) Effect of heightened arousal on exploratory behaviour, *Can. J. Psychol.* **17**, 398–411.

BERNARD, J. L. and EISEMANN, R. (1967) Verbal conditioning in sociopaths with social and monetary reinforcement, *J. Personality Soc. Psychol.* **6**, 203–6.

BERNSTEIN, A. S. (1964) The galvanic skin response orienting reflex among chronic schizophrenics, *Psychon. Sci.* **1**, 391–2.

BERNSTEIN, A. S. (1967) The orienting reflex as a research tool in the study of psychotic populations, in, I. Lluttkay-Nedieky, L. Cigarek, V. Zikmund and I. Kellerova (Eds.), *Mechanisms of orienting reaction in man*, Bratislava: Slovak Academy of Sciences.

BERNSTEIN, A. S. (1968) The orienting response and direction of stimulus change. *Psychonom. Sci.* **12**, 127–8.

BERNSTEIN, A. S. (1969) To what does the orienting response respond? *Psychophysiol.* **6**, 338–50.

BERNSTEIN, A. S. (1970) Phasic electrodermal orienting response in chronic schizophrenics: II. Response to auditory signals of varying intensity, *J. Abnorm. Psychol.* **75**, 146–56.

BERNSTEIN, A. S., TAYLOR, K., AUSTEN, B. G., NATHANSON, M. and SCARPELLI, A. (1971)

The orienting response and apparent movement toward or away from the observer, *J. Exp. Psychol.* **87**, 37–45.

BERRY, J. L. and MARTIN, B. (1957) G.S.R. reactivity as a function of anxiety, instructions and sex, *J. Abnorm. Soc. Psychol.* **54**, 9–12.

BERRY, W. and IMUS, H. (1935) Quantitative aspects of flight of colors, *Am. J. Psychol.* **47**, 449–57.

BETTS, G. H. (1909) *The distribution and functions of neural imagery,* New York: Columbia University Teachers' College Contributions to Education Series, No. 26.

BIALOWAS, D. (1976) Submission to group pressure and reactivity as an example of the effects of temperamental traits on social behaviour. Unpublished M.A. Thesis, Warsaw University.

BINDRA, D., PATERSON, A. L. and STRZLECKI, J. (1955) The relation between anxiety and conditioning, *Can. J. Psychol.* **9**, 1–5.

BIRCHALL, P. M. A. and CLARIDGE, G. S. (1979) Augmenting-reducing of the visual-evoked potential as a function of changes in skin conductance level, *Psychophysiol.* **16**, 482–90.

BIRYUKOV, D. A. (1958) The nature of orienting reactions, in, L. G. Voronin, A. N. Leont'iev, A. R. Luria, E. N. Sokolov and O. S. Vinogradova (Eds.) *The orienting reflex and orienting – investigatory activity* pp. 20–5 Moscow: Akad. Pedagog. Nauk RSFSR.

BIRYUKOVA, Z. I. (1961) *An investigation of typological features of higher nervous activity in sportsmen,* Moscow: Izd. Fikzul'tura i Sport.

BITTERMAN, M. E. and HOLTZMAN, W. H. (1952) Conditioning and extinction of the galvanic skin response as a function of anxiety, *J. Abnorm. Soc. Psychol.* **47**, 615–23.

BLAKEMORE, C. and MITCHELL, D. E. (1973) Environmental modification of the visual cortex and the neural basis of learning and memory, *Nature, Lond.* **241**, 467–8.

BLAKESLEE, E. A., MYNON, K., HAMERNIK, R. and HENDERSON, D. (1978) Asymptotic threshold shift in chinchillas exposed to impulse noise, *J. Acoust. Soc. Am.* March, 876–82.

BLANKSTEIN, K. R. (1969) Patterns of autonomic functioning in primary and secondary psychopaths. Unpublished Master's thesis, University of Waterloo.

BLAYLOCK, J. J. (1960) Verbal conditioning performance of psychopaths and non-psychopaths under verbal reward and punishment, *Diss. Abstr.* **21**, 1628.

BLIZARD, D. A., COWINGS, P. and MILLER, N. E. (1975) Visceral responses to opposite types of autogenic-training imagery, *Biol. Psychol.* **3**, 49–55.

BLOCK, J. (1957) A study of affective responsiveness in a lie-detector situation, *J. Abnorm. Soc. Psychol.* **55**, 11–15.

BLOCK, J. (1965) *The Challenge of Response Sets,* New York: Appleton-Century-Crofts.

BLOCK, J. (1967) Monozygotic twin similarities in multiple psychophysiologic parameters and meaures, *Recent Adv. Biol. Psychiat.* **9**, 105–18.

BLOCK, J. (1977) Advancing the psychology of personality: paradigmatic shift or improving the quality of research? in, D. Magnusson and N. S. Endler (Eds.) *Personality at the crossroads: current issues in interactional psychology,* Hillsdale, New Jersey: Erlbaum.

BLOCK, J. and BLOCK, J. (1979) The role of ego-control and ego-resiliency in the organisation of behaviour, in, W. A. Collins (Ed.), *Minnesota Symposium on Child Psychology,* Vol. 13, New York: Laurence Erlbaum.

BLOCK, V. and BONVALLET, M. (1960) Le déclenchement des réponses électrodermales à partir du système réticulaire facilitation. *J. Physiol. Pathol. Gen.* **52**, 25–6.

BLOKH, L. S. (1940) The peculiarities of negative induction connected with age and the cerbral cortex, in, *Sbovmik. Pob. Redaktsili Professora, A. G. Ivanova-Smolenskogo,* (1940) Moscow. Cited by E. I. Boiko, (1957).

BLONSKY, P. P. (1961) *Selected pedagogical works,* Moscow: APN, RSFSR.

BLURTON-JONES, N. G. (Ed.) (1972a) *Ethological studies of child behaviour,* Cambridge: Cambridge University Press.

BLURTON-JONES, N. G. (1972b) Categories of child-child interaction, in, N. G. Blurton-Jones (Ed.) (1972a).

BLURTON-JONES N, G, (1972c) Non-verbal communication in children, in, R. A. Hinde (Ed.), *Non-verbal communication,* Cambridge: Cambridge University Press.

BOBROVA, M. V. (1960) Dependence of magnitude of chronaxie in reflexive responding on typological features in dogs, *Zh. Vyssh. Nerv. Devat. im. I. P. Pavlova*, **10**, 4.

BOEHM, L. (1962) The development of conscience: a comparison of American children of different mental and socioeconomic levels, *Child Dev.* **33**, 575–90.

BOHLIN, G. (1972) Susceptibility to sleep during habituation procedure as related to individual differences, *J. Exp. Res. Person.* **6**, 248–54.

BOHLIN, G. (1976) Delayed habituation of the electrodermal response as a function of increased level of arousal, *Psychophysiol.* **13**, 345–51.

BOIKO, E. I. (Ed.) (1957) *Studies in higher neuro-dynamics as related to problems of psychology*, Moscow: Akad. Pedagog. Nauk RSFSR, Institute Psikhologii. English translation by A. Ferber (1961), Washington: CFSTI, U.S. Department of Commerce, No. TT-60-21168.

BOIKO, E. I. (1961) Reaction time and the physiological law of strength, in, *Common problems of psychology and physiology*, Moscow: Izd. Acad. Pedagog. Nauk RSFSR.

BOIKO, E. I. (1964) *Reaction time in man*, Moscow: Meditsina.

BOKHAROVA S. P. and LAKTIONOV, A. N. (1972) Izuchenie interferentsii v kratkovremennoy pamyah v svyazi s tipologicheskimi osobennostyami nervnoy sistemy, *Vop. Psikhol*, **1**.

BOND, M. R., GLYNN, J. P. and THOMAS, D. G. (1976) The relation between pain and personality in patients needing Pentazosine (Forstral) after surgery, *J. Psychosom. Res.* **20**, 4, 369–81.

BONE, R. N. and EYSENCK, H. J. (1972) Extraversion, field dependance and the Stroop test, *Percept. Mot. Skills*, **72**, 34 (3), 874–84.

BONVALLET, M. and BLOCK, V. (1961) Bulbar control of cortical arousal, *Science, N.Y.* **133**, 1133–4.

BORGE, G. F., BUCHSBAUM, M. and GODWIN, F. (1971) Neurophysiological correlates of affective disorders, *Arch. Gen. Psychiat.* **24**, 501–4.

BORISOVA, M. N. (1959) Determination of discriminative thresholds and elaboration of fine sensory differentiations as a means of studying the concentration of excitation, in, Teplov, B. M. (Ed.), *Typological features on higher nervous activity in man*, Vol. 2, Moscow: Akad. Pedagog. Nauk RSFSR.

BORISOVA, M. N. (1965) Individual differences and typological correlates of simple reactions, in, B. M. Teplov (Ed.), *Typological features of higher nervous activity in man*, Vol. 4, Moscow: Akad. Pedagog, Nauk RSFSR.

BORISOVA, M. N. (1969) Concerning the typological significanced of certain indices of motor reactions, in, V. D. Nebylitsyn (Ed.), *Problems of differential psychophysiology*, Vol. 6, pp. 38–57, Moscow: Prosveshchenique.

BORISOVA, M. N. (1972) Concentration of nervous processes as an individual typological feature of higher nervous acitivty, in, V. D. Nebylitsyn and J. A. Gray (Eds.), *The biological basis of individual behaviour*, pp. 29–40, London: Academic Press.

BORISOVA, M. N., GUREVICH, K. M., YERMOLEYEVA-TOMINA, L. B., KOLODNAYA, A. T., RAVICH-SHCHERBO, I. V. and SCHWARTZ, L. A. (1963) Materials for comparative studies of various indices of the mobility of the nervous system in man, in, B. M. Teplov(Ed.), *Typological features of higher nervous activity in man*, Vol. 3, Moscow: Akad. Pedagog. Nauk RSFSR.

BOUCHARD, T. J. (1972) The 16 PF test, in, O. K. Buros (Ed.), *VIIth mental measurements year book*, pp. 329–32, New Jersey: Gryphon Press.

BOURDOUXHE, S. (1975) Concerning psychopathy, *Feuill. Psychiat. Liège*, **8**, 17–26.

BOWER, A. C. and DAS, J. P. (1972) Acquisition and reversal of orienting response to word signals, *Br. J. Psychol.* **63**, 195–203.

BOWER, S. M. (1964) Self instructed heart rate change: a methodological evaluation, *Diss. Abstr.* **24**, 12, 5559.

BOWER, T. G. R. (1972) Object perception in infants, *Percept.* **1**, 1.

BOWER, T. G. R. (1973) *The development of reaching in infants*, Unpublished monograph.

BOWER, T. G. R. (1974) *Development in infancy*, San Francisco: W. H. Freeman and Co.

BOWER, T. G. R., BROUGHTON, J. M. and MOORE, M. K. (1971) The development of the object concept as manifested by changes in the tracking behaviour of infants betwen 7 and 20 weeks of age, *J. Exp. Child. Psychol.* **11,** 2.

BOWERS, K. S. (1973) Situationism in psychology: an analysis and a critique, *Pschol. Rev.* **80,** 307–36.

BOWLBY, J. (1947) *Forty-four juvenile thieves: their characters and home life,* London: Baillière, Tindall and Cox.

BOWLBY, J. (1951) *Maternal care and mental health,* Geneva: W.H.O.

BOWLBY, J. (1973) *Attachment and loss,* Vol. II: Separation, anxiety and anger, London: Hogarth.

BOZHOVICH, L. I. (1976) The concept of the cultural-historical development of the mind and its prospects, *Vop. Psikhol.* **2,** 29–39.

BRAATÖY, T. (1947) De Nervöse sinn, *Medisinsk psykologi og psykoterapi,* Oslo: Cappelin.

BRAATÖY, T. (1952) Psychology vs. anatomy in the treatment of "arm neurosis" with physiotherapy, *J. Nerv. Ment. Dis.* **115,** 215–45.

BRAATÖY, T. (1954) *Fundamentals of psychoanalytic technique,* New York: Wiley.

BRADLEY, P. B. (1957) The central action of certain drugs in relation to the RF of the brain, in, H. M. Jasper, (Ed.), *Reticular formation of the brain,* pp. 123–49 Boston: Little Brown.

BRAUKMAN, C. J., FIXEN, D. L., PHILLIPS, E. L. and WOLF, M. M. (1975) Behavioural approaches to treatment in the crime and delinquency field, *Criminology,* **13,** 299–331.

BREMER, E. and STOUPEL, N. (1959) De la modification des réponses sensorielles corticales dans l'éveil réticulaire, *Archs. Int. Physiol.* **67,** 240–75.

BRENER, J., KLEINMAN, R. A. and GOSLING, W. H. (1969) The effects of different exposures to augmented sensory feedback on the control of heart rate, *Psychophysiol.* **5,** 510–16.

BRIDGER, W. H. and REISER, M. F. (1959) Psychophysiological studies of the neonate: an approach toward the methodological and theoretical problems involved, *Psychosom. Med.* **21,** 265–76.

BRINDLEY, G. S. (1959) The discrimination of after-images. *J. Physiol., Lond.* **147,** 194–203.

BROADHURST, A. and GLASS, A. (1969) Relationship of personality measures to the alpha rhythm of the electroencephalogram, *Br. J. Psychiat.* **115,** 199–204.

BROADHURST, P. L. (1959) The interaction of task difficulty and motivation: the Yerkes-Dodson Law revived, *Acta Psychol.* **16,** 321–37.

BROADHURST, P. L. (1960) Experiments in psychogenetics, in, H. J. Eysenck (Ed.), *Experiments in personality,* London: Routledge and Kegan Paul.

BROADHURST, P. L. (1969) Psychogenetic selection: a study of the Roman high and low avoidance strains of rats, *Behav. Res. Ther.* **2,** 273–80.

BROADHURST, P. L. (1975) The Maudsley reactive and non-reactive strains of rats: a survey, *Behav. Genet.* **5,** 299–319.

BRODY, N. (1972) *Personality: research and theory,* New York: Academic Press.

BROGDEN, W. J. (1939a) The effect of frequency of reinforcement upon the level of conditioning, *J. Exp. Psychol.* **24,** 419–31.

BROGDEN, W. J. (1939b) Sensory preconditioning. *J. Exp. Psychol.* **25,** 323–32.

BROFENDENNER, U. (1961) Some familial antecedents of responsibility and leadership in adolescents, in, L. Petrullo and B. M. Bass (Eds.) *Leadership and interpersonal behaviour,* pp. 239–72, New York: Holt, Rinehart & Winston.

BRONSTEIN, A. I. (1927) The effect of the inter-stimulus interval on the latency of a motor conditioned reflex in man, *Fiziol. Zh. SSSR,* **10,** 3–4.

BROUGHTON, R. J., POIRET, R. and TASSINARI, C. A. (1965) The electrodermogram (Tarchanoff effect) during sleep, *Electroenceph. Clin. Neurophysiol.* **18,** 69, 1.

BROWN, J. S. (1969) Factors affecting self-punitive locomotor behaviour, in, B. A. Campbell and R. M. Church (Eds.) *Punishment and aversive behaviour,* pp. 467–514, New York: Appleton-Century-Crofts.

BROWN, R. A., FADER, K. and BARBER, T. X. (1973) Responsiveness to pain: stimulus-specificity versus generality, *Psychol. Rec.* **23,** 1–7.

BROWNE, J. A. and HOWARTH, E. A. (1977) A comprehensive factor analysis of personality questionnaire items: a test of twenty putative factor hypotheses, *Multiv. Behav. Res.* **12**, 399–427.
BROWNFIELD, M. K. (1965) Sex and stimulus time differences in after-image durations, *Percept. Mot. Skills,* **21**, 446.
BRUELL, J. M. (1969) Genetics and adaptive significance of emotional defecation in mice, *Ann. N.Y. Acad. Sci.* **157**, 825–30.
BRUNER, J. S. (1959) The cognitive consequences of early sensory deprivation, *Psychosom. Med.* **21**, 89–95.
BRUNER, J. S. (1973) Organisation of early skilled action. *Child Dev.* **44**, 1–11.
BRUNN, K., MARKKANEN, T. and PARTENEN, J. (1967) *Inheritance of Drinking Behaviour, a Study of Adult Twins,* Helsinki: Finnish Foundation for Alcohol Studies.
BRYAN, J. H. and KAPCHE, R. (1967) Psychopathy and verbal conditioning, *J. Abnorm. Psychol.* **72**, 71–3.
BUCHSBAUM, M. (1974) Average evoked response and stimulus intensity in identical and fraternal twins, *Physiol. Psychol.* **2**, 365–70.
BUCHSBAUM, M. (1975) Averaged evoked response augmenting/reducing in schizophrenia and affective disorders, in, D. Freedman (Ed.), *Biology of the major psychoses,* pp. 129–42, New York: Raven Press.
BUCHSBAUM, M. and PFEFFERBAUM, A. (1971) Individual differences in stimulus intensity response, *Psychophysiol.* **8**, 600–11.
BUCHSBAUM, M. and SILVERMAN, J. (1969) Stimulus intensity control and the cortical evoked response, *Psychosom. Med.* **30**, 12–22.
BUCHSBAUM, M. S., DAVIS, G. C. and BUNNEY, W. E. (Jr.) (1977) Naloxone alters pain perception and somatosensory evoked potentials in normal subjects, *Nature, Lond.* **270**, 620–2.
BUCHSBAUM, M., GOODWIN, F., MURPHY, D. and BORGE, G. (1971) AER in affective disorders, *Am. J. Psychiat.* **128**, 19–25.
BÜHLER, K. (1907) Tatsachen und Probleme Zu einer Psychologie der Denkvorgage, I. Über Gedanken, *Arch. ges. Psychol.* **9**, 207–365.
BUNDY, R. S. and FITZGERALD, H. E. (1975) Stimulus specificity of electrodermal recovery time: an examination and reinterpretation of the evidence, *Psychophysiol.* **12**, 1, 406–11.
BUNT, A. VAN DE and BARENDREGT, J. T. (1961) Intercorrelations of three measures of conditioning, in, J. T. Barendregt (Ed.), *Research in psychodiagnostics,* pp. 146–56, The Hague: Mounton.
BURAKOVA, N. S. (1976) Characteristics of conditioning in dogs raised in partial intra-species isolation, *Zh. Vyssh. Nerv. Deyat. im. I. P. Pavlova,* **26**, 1195–9.
BURCH, N. R. and GRIENER, T. H. (1960) A bioelectric scale of human alertness: concurrent recordings of the EEG and GSR, *Psychiat. Res. Rep.* **12**, 183–93.
BURT, C. (1966) The genetic determination of differences in intelligence: a study of monozygotic twins reared together and apart, *Br. J. Psychol.* **57**, 146.
BURT, C. and HOWARD, M. (1956) The multifactorial theory of inheritance and its application to intelligence, *Br. J. Statist. Psychol.* **8**, 3, 95–131.
BUSS, A. H. (1966) *Psychopathology,* New York: Wiley.
BUSS, A. H. (1977) The trait-situation controversy and the concept of interaction. *Person. Soc. Psychol. Bull.* **3**, 196–201.
BUSS, A. H., PLOMIN, R. A. and WILLERMAN, L. (1973) The inheritance of temperaments. *J. Personality,* **41**, 513–24.
BUTTERS, N. and ROSVOLD, H. E. (1968) Effect of caudate and septal nuclei lesions on resistance to extinction and delayed alteration. *J. Comp. Physiol. Psychol.* **65**, 397–403.
BYKOV, K. M. (Ed.) (1952) *Problems of the physiology of interoception,* Moscow: Akad. Nauk SSSR.
BYKOV, K. M. (1953) New data on the physiology and pathology of the cerebral cortex, *Proc. XIX Inter. Cong. Psychol.* Montreal.
BYKOV, K. M. (1954) *The cerebral cortex and the internal organs,* Moscow: Foreign Languages Publishing House. Translated (1959) from 1954 (3rd) edition by R. Hodes and A. Kilbey.

CADORET, R. J. (1963) Relationship between autonomic response patterns and conditioned learning, *Percept. Mot. Skills,* **16,** 67–85.

CADORET, R. J., CUNNINGHAM, L., LOFTUS, R. and EDWARDS, J. (1975) Studies of adoptees from psychiatrically disturbed biologic parents, *J. Pediat.* **87,** 301–6.

CALHOUN, J. B. (1962) A "behavioral sink", in, E. Bliss (Ed.), *Roots of behaviour,* pp. 295–315 New York: Harper.

CALLOWAY, E. (1959) The influence of amobarbital (amylobarbitone) and methamphetamine on the focus of attention, *J. Ment. Sci.* **105,** 382–92.

CALLOWAY, E. (1975) *Brain electrical potentials and individual psychological differences,* New York: Grune & Stratton.

CAMPBELL, A. A. (1938) The inter-relations of two measures of conditioning in man, *J. Exp. Psychol.* **22,** 225–43.

CANNON, W. B. (1963) *Bodily changes in pain, hunger, fear and rage,* New York: Harper & Row (originally published: (1915) Appleton-Century Co.).

CANTER, S. (1973) Some aspects of cognitive function in twins, in, G. Claridge, S. Canter and W. I. Hume (Eds.) (1973).

CAREY, W. B., LIPTON, W. L. and MEYERS, R. A. (1974) Temperament in adopted and foster babies, *Child Welfare* **53,** 352–9.

CARLIER, M. (1979) An attempt to validate Strelau's questionnaire. Paper presented at the International Conference on Temperament, Need for Simulation, and Activity, Warsaw.

CARRIER, N. A., MALPASS, L. F. and ORTON K. D. (1961) *Response of bright, normal and retarded children to learning tasks,* Carbondale: South Illinois University.

CARROLL, D. and POKARA, J. (1976) The effects of threat of shock on SCR habituation to simple auditory stimuli, *Physiol. Psychol.* **4,** 94–8.

CARROLL, D. and SURTEES, P. C. (1976) The electrodermal component of the orienting response in blind and deaf individuals, *Br. J. Psychol.* **67,** 367–75.

CARTER, H. D. (1933) Twin similarities in personality traits, *J. Genet. Psychol.* **43,** 312–21.

CARTER, H. D. (1935) Twin similarities in emotional traits, *Character Person.* **4,** 61–78.

CASEY, J. and MCMANIS, D. I. (1971) Salivary response to lemon juice as a measure of introversion in children, *Percept. Mot. Skills,* **33,** 1059–65.

CASSELL, W. A. and FISHER, S. (1963) Body-image boundaries and histamine flare reaction, *Psychosom. Med.* **25,** 344–50.

CATTELL, R. B. (1947) Confirmation and clarification of primary personality factors, *Psychometrika,* **12.** 197–220.

CATTELL, R. B. (1957) *Personality and motivation: structure and measurement,* Yonkers. N.Y.: World.

CATTELL, R. B. (1960) The multiple abstract variance analysis equations and solutions for nature-nurture research on continuous variables. *Psychol. Rev.* **67,** 353–72.

CATTELL, R. B. (1965) Methodological and conceptual advances in evaluating hereditary and environmental influences and their interaction, in, S. G. Vandenberg (Ed.), *Methods and goals in human behaviour genetics,* New York: Academic Press.

CATTELL, R. B. (1966) The scree test for the number of factors, *Multiv. Behav. Res.* **1,** 245–76.

CATTELL, R. B. and WARBURTON, F. W. (1967) *Objective personality and motivation tests: a theoretical introduction and practical compendium.* Urbana: Univeristy of Illinois Press.

CATTELL, R. B., BLEWETT, D. B. and BELOFF, J. R. (1955) The inheritance of personality: multiple-variance analysis of approximate nature-nurture ratios for primary personality factors in Q-data, *Am. J. Hum. Genet.* **7,** 122–46.

CATTELL, R. B., EBER, H. W. and TATSUOKA, M. M. (1970) *Handbook for the sixteen personality factor questionnaire,* Champaign, Illinois: IPAT.

CAVALLI-SFORZA, L. L. and BODMER, W. F. (1971) *The genetics of human populations,* San Francisco: W. H. Freeman.

CAVANAUGH, D. K. (1958) Improvement in the performance of schizophrenics on concept formation tasks as a function of motivational change, *J. Abnorm. Soc. Psychol.* **57,** 8–12.

CERNACEK, J. and PODIVINSKY, F. (1972) Certain characteristics of the ontogeny of motor dominance in postnatal development, *Bratisl. Lék. Listy,* **58,** 4.

CHAINOVA, A. D. (1971) *Problems of engineering psychology,* Vol. 2, p. 197 Moscow: APN SSSR.

CHANG, H. T. (1959) The evoked potential, in, W. Field, H. W. Magoun, and V. E. Hall (Eds.), *Handbook of physiology. Section 1, Neurophysiology, 1,* Washington D.C.: American Physiological Soceity.

CHEN-JUNG, H. (1973) Effects of stimulus change on orienting reflex, *Bull. Educ. Psychol.* **3,** 15–44.

CHERKES, V. A. (1958) Razdrazhenie khvostatogo yadra i uslovnye dvigatel'nye refleksy. 18-e soveshchenie po problemam vysshey nernoy deyatel'nosti. Leningrad: Tezisy dokladov.

CHESS, S. (1979) The importance of temperament in the handicapped child. Paper given at International Conference on Temperament, Need for Stimulation and Activity, Warsaw.

CHEYNE, J. A. and WALTERS, R. H. (1969) Intensity of punishment, timing of punishment, and cognitive structure as determinants of response inhibition, *J. Exp. Child Psychol.* **7,** 231–49.

CHIRKOVA, T. I. (1967) On the question of methods of studying the traits of children of the weak type of higher nervous activity, *Trans. Gorky. Pedagog. Institute,* **84.**

CHRISTIANSEN, B. (1966) *Studies in respiration and personality, Vol 4:* Suggestions concerning the interpretation of respiratory test scores and an elaboration of problems for further research, Oslo: Institute for Social Research.

CHUDNOVSKY, V. E. (1963) Experimental studies of the properties of type of nervous system of pre-school children, *Vop. Psikhol.* **3.**

CHUDNOVSKY, V. E. (1967) Concerning the specificity of typological features in preschool children, in, B. M. Teplov (Ed.), *Typological features of higher nervous activity in man,* Vol. 5, Moscow: Prosveshcheniye.

CHUPRIKOVA, N. I. (1952) Title and source not given. Cited by E. I. Boiko, Reciprocity of conditioned reflex processes in complex system reactions, in, E. I. Boiko (Ed.) (1957).

CHUPRIKOVA, N. I. (1954) The dynamics of excitation during the combination of visual and motor reactions, Moscow: Akad. Pedagog. Nauk RSFSR, No. 53.

CHUPRIKOVA, N. I. (1955) Irradiation and concentration of excitation in the visual analyser of man, *Zh. Vyssh. Nerv. Deyat. im. I. P. Pavlova,* **5,** 4.

CHUPRIKOVA, N. I. (1967) *Slovo kak faktor upravleniya v vysshey nervnov deyatel'nosti cheloveka,* Moscow: Prosveshcheniye.

CHUPRIKOVA, N. I. (1972) The completion of temporary connections through speech, *Soviet Psychol.* Spring.

CIGÁNEK, L. (1961) The EEG response (evoked potential) to light stimulus in man, *Electroenceph. Clin. Neurophysiol.* **13,** 165–72.

CIGÁNEK, L. (1969) Variability of the human visual evoked potential: normative data, *Electroenceph. Clin. Neurophysiol.* **27,** 35–42.

CLARIDGE, G. S. (1960) The excitation-inhibition balance in neurotics, in, H. J. Eysenck (Ed.), *Experiments in Personality,* Vol. 2, New York: Praeger.

CLARIDGE, G. S. (1961) Arousal and inhibition as determinants of the performance of neurotics, *Br. J. Psychol.* **52,** 53–63.

CLARIDGE, G. S. (1967) *Personality and Arousal,* Oxford: Pergamon Press.

CLARIDGE, G. S. (1972) The schizophrenics as nervous types, *Br. J. Psychiat.* **121,** 1.

CLARIDGE, G. S. (1973) A nervous typological analysis of personality variation in normal twins, in, G. S. Claridge, S. Canter and S. I. Hume (Eds.), *Personality differences and biological variations: a study of twins,* Oxford: Pergamon Press.

CLARIDGE, G. S. and CHAPPA, H. J. (1973) Psychoticism: a study of biological basis in normal subjects, *Br. J. Soc. Clin. Psychol.* **12,** 175.

CLARIDGE, G. and MANGAN, G. L. (forthcoming) Genetics of human nervous system functioning, in, S. Haber (Ed.), *Handbook of behaviour genetics,* New York: Lawrence Erlbaum.

CLARIDGE, G. S., CANTER, S. and HUME, S. I. (Eds.) (1973) *Personality differences and biological variations: a study of twins,* Oxford: Pergamon Press.

CLARK, J. W. and BINDRA, D. (1954) Individual differences in pain thresholds, *Can. J. Psychol.* **10,** 69–76.

CLARK, W. C., BROWN, J. C. and RUTSCHMAAN, J. (1967) Flicker sensitivity and response bias in psychiatric patients and normal subjects. *J. Abnorm. Psychol.* **72**, 35–42.

CLARKE, A. M. and CLARKE, A. D. B. (1976) *Early experience: myth and evidence,* London: Open Books.

CLAUSEN, J. and KARRER, R. (1968) Orienting response-frequency of occurrence and relationships to other autonomic variables, *Am. J. Ment. Defic.* **73**, 455–64.

CLECKLEY, G. (1964) *The mask of sanity: an attempt to clarify some issues about the so-called psychopathic personality,* 4th ed., St. Louis, Mo.: C. V. Mosby.

CLEVELAND, S. E., REITMAN, E. E. and BREWER, E. J. (Jr.) (1965) Psychological factors in juvenile rheumatoid arthritis, *Arthritis Rheum.* **8**, 1152–8.

COHEN, D. J., DIBBLE, E. and GRAWE, J. M. (1977 Father's and Mother's perceptions of children's personality, *Archs. Gen. Psychiat.* **34**, 4, 480–7.

COHEN, D. J. and SILVERMAN, A. J. (1959) Psychophysiolgical investigation of vascular response variability, *J. Psychosom. Res.* **3**,, 185–210.

COHEN, S. I., SILVERMAN, A. J. and SCHMAVONIAN, B. M. (1959) Psychophysiological mechanisms of stress tolerance. *Semi-Annual Report,* Div. Psychophysiol. Res., Dept. Psychiatry, Duke University Medical Centre.

COLES, M. G. H., GALE, A. and KLINE, P. (1971) Personality and habituation of the orienting reaction: tonic and response measures of electrodermal activity, *Psychophysiol.* **8**, 54–63.

COLLMAN, R. D. (1931) The psychogalvanic reactions of exceptional and normal school children, *Teach. Coll. Contrib. Educ.* **469**.

COLLMAN, R. D. (1959) The galvanic skin responses of mentally retarded and other children in England, *Am. J. Def.* **63**, 626–32.

COOMBS, C. H. (1938) Adaptation of the galvanic response to auditory stimuli, *J. Exp. Psychol.* **22**, 244–68.

COOPER, J. R., BLOOM, E. E. and ROTH, R. H. (1978) *The Biochemical Basis of Neuropharmacology,* New York: Oxford University Press.

COOPER, R. M. and ZUBEK, J. P. (1958) Effects of enriched and restricted early environment on the learning ability of bright and dull rats, *Can. J. Psychol.* **12**, 159–64.

CORCORAN, D. J. W. (1964) The relation between introversion and salivation, *Am. J. Psychol.* **77**, 298–300.

CORCORAN, D. J. W. (1965) Personality and the inverted-U relation, *Br. J. Psychol.* **56**, 267–73.

CORMAN, O. D. (1967) Stimulus generalisation of habituation of the galvanic skin response, *J. Exp. Psychol.* **74**, 236–40.

CORSON, S. A. and CORSON, E. (1976) Philosophical and historical roots of Pavlovian psychobiology, in, S. A. Corson (Ed.), *Psychiatry and psychology in the U.S.S.R.* New York: Plenum Press.

COSTELLO, C. G. (1964) Ego-involvement, success and failure: a review of the literature, in, H. J. Eysenck (Ed.), *Experiments in motivation,* Oxford: Pergamon.

COURTER, R. J., WATTENMAKER, R. A. and AX, A. F. (1965) Physiological concomitants of psychological differentiation, *Psychophysiol.* **1**, 282–90.

COURTS, F. A. (1942) Relation between muscular tension and performance, *Psychol. Bull.* **39**, 347–67.

COUSINS, L. R. (1976) Individual differences in the orienting reflex and children's discrimination learning, *Psychophysiol.* **13**, 5, 479–87.

CRAIG, J. V., ORTMAN, L. L. and GUHL, A. M. (1965) Genetic selection for social dominance ability in chickens, *Anim. Behav.* **13**, 114–31.

CREELMAN, M. B. (1966) *The experimental investigation of meaning: a review of the literature,* New York: Springer.

CRIDER, A. and AUGENBAUM, C. R. (1975) Auditory vigilance correlates of electrodermal response habituation speed, *Psychophysiol.* **12**, 36–40.

CRIDER, A. and LUNN, L. L. (1971) Electrodermal lability as a personality dimension, *J. Exp. Res. Person.* **5**, 145–50.

CROOK, M. N. (1937) Intra-family relationship in personality test performance, *Psychol. Rec.* **1**, 479–502.

CURREN, J. P. (1975) An evaluation of a skills training programme and a systematic desensitisation program in reducing dating anxiety, *Behav. Res. Ther.* **13**, 65–8.

DANIEL, R. S. (1967) Alpha and theta EEG in vigilance, *Percept. Mot. Skills,* **25**, 697–703.

DANILOVA, L. K. (1966) Dinamika izmeneniy pervichnykh otvetov na zvukovye razdrazhiteli v protesse vyrabotki uslovnogo oboronitel'nogo refleksa. 21-e soveshchanie po problemam vysshey nervnoy deyatel'nosti Tezisy i referaty dokladov. Moscow — Leningrad: Nauka.

DANILOVA, N. N. (1956) Conference on the electrophysiology of the central nervous system.

DANILOVA, N. N. (1959) The orienting reflex and the reaction of reorganising cerebral bio-currents in response to a rhythmic visual stimulus, in, E. N. Sokolov (Ed.), *The orienting reflex and problems of higher nervous activity,* Moscow: Akad. Pedagog. Nauk RSFSR.

DANZIGER, K. (1976) *Socialization,* Harmondsworth, Penguin Modern Psychology.

DARROW, C. W. (1927) Sensory, secretory and electrical changes in the skin following bodily excitation, *J. Exp. Psychol.* **10**, 197–226.

DARROW, C. W. (1929a) Differences in the physiological reactions to sensory and ideational stimuli, *Psychol. Bull.* **26**, 185–201.

DARROW, C. W. (1929b) Electrical and circulatory responses to brief and ideational stimuli *J. Exp. Psychol.* **12**, 267–300.

DARROW, C. W. (1933) The functional significance of the galvanic skin reflex and perspiration in the backs and palms of the hands, *Psychol. Bull.* **30**, 7–12.

DAS, J. P. and BOWER, A. C. (1971) Orienting responses of mentally retarded and normal subjects toward signals, *Br. J. Psychol.* **62**, 83–96.

DAUROVA, F. K. (1960) Proceedings of the XIX Conference on Problems of Higher Nervous Activity (in Russian).

DAUROVA, F. K. (1962) The localization of transmarginal inhibition in elements of the reflex arc, *Tr. Inst. Vyssh. Nervn. Deyat. im. I. P. Pavlova,* **7**.

DAUROVA, F. K. (1963) Binary conditioned reflex, in, E. Gutmann and P. Hicks (Eds.), *Central and peripheral mechanisms of motor functions,* pp. 161–6. Prague: Vydavaterstvo. Ceskoslovenkey Akademie Vied.

DAVIDENKOV, S. N. (1947) *Evolyutsionno — geneticheskiye problemy v neuropatologii,* Leningrad.

DAVIDSON, P. O. and McDOUGAL, C. E. A. (1969) Personality and pain tolerance measures, *Percept. Mot. Skills,* **28**, 787–90.

DAVIDSON, P. O. and PAYNE, R. W. (1964) Introversion, neuroticism and conditioning, *J. Abnorm. Soc. Psychol.* **68**, 2, 136–43.

DAVIDSON, P. O., PAYNE, R. W. and SLOAN, R. B. (1966) Cortical inhibition, drive level and conditioning, *J. Abnorm. Psychol.* **71**, 310.

DAVIDSON, R. J. and SCHWARTZ, G. E. (1976) Patterns of cerebral lateralization during cardiac biofeedback versus the self-regulation of emotion: sex differences, *Psychophysiol.* **13**, 62–8.

DAVIS, A. D. (1960) Some physiological correlates of Rorschach body image productions, *J. Abnorm. Soc. Psychol.* **60**, 432–6.

DAVIS, F. H. and MALMO, R. B. (1951) Electromyographic recording during interview, *Am. J. Psychiat.* **107**, 908–15.

DAVIS, H. and DAVIS, P. A. (1976) Action potentials of the brain in normal persons and in normal states of cerebral activity, *Arch. Neurol. Psychiat.* **36**, 1214–24.

DAVIS, M. and WAGNER, A. R. (1967) Habituation of startle response under incremental sequence of stimulus intensities, *J. Comp. Physiol. Psychol.* **67**, 486–92.

DAVIS, R. C. (1934) Modification of the galvanic skin reflex by daily repetition of the stimulus, *J. Exp. Psychol.* **17**, 504–35.

DAVIS, R. C. (1957) Continuous recording of arterial pressure: an analysis of the problem, *J. Comp. Physiol. Psychol.* **50**, 524–9.

DAVIS, R. C. and BUCHWALD, A. M. (1957) An exploration of somatic response patterns: stimulus and sex differences, *J. Comp. Physiol. Psychol.* **50**, 44–52.

DAVIS, R. C., BUCHWALD, A. M. and FRANKMAN, R. W. (1955) Autonomic and muscular responses and their relation to simple stimuli, *Psychol. Monogr.* **69**, 20 (whole No. 405).

DAVYDOV, V. V. (1976) Major development in developmental and educational psychology at the present stage of development of education, *Vop. Psikhol.* **4**, 3–15.

DAWES, C. (1974) Rhythms in salivary flow rate and composition, *Int. J. Chronobiol.* **2**, 253–79.

DAWSON, M. and FUREDY, J. (1976) The role of awareness in differential autonomic classical conditioning: the necessary-gate hypothesis, *Psychophysiol.* **13**, 50–3.

DE LANGE, STORM, VAN LEEUWEN, W. and WERRE, J. (1962) Correlations between psychological and electroencephalographic characteristics, in, *Electroencephalographic investigations of higher nervous activity*, Moscow: Izd. Akad. Nauk SSSR.

DE LOACHE, J. S. (1976) Rate of habituation and visual memory in infants, *Child Dev.* **47**, 1, 145–52.

DELSE, F. C. and FEATHER, B. W. (1968) The effect of augmented sensory feedback on the control of salivation, *Psychophysiol.* **5**, 15–21.

DEMBER, W. N. and EARLE, R. M. (1957) Analysis of exploratory manipulatory and curiosity behaviours, *Psychol. Rev.* **64**, 91–6.

DENENBERG, V. H. (1967) Stimulation in infancy, emotional reactivity and exploratory behaviour, in, D. C. Glass (Ed.), *Neurophysiology and emotion*, New York: Rockefeller University Press.

DENENBERG, V. H. and ZARROW, M. X. (1970) Rat Pax, *Psychol. Today*, **3**, 45–7.

DENENBERG, V. H., HUDGINS, G. A. and ZARROW, M. X. (1964) Mice reared with rats: modification of behavior by early experience with another species, *Science N. Y.* **143**, 380–1.

DENENBERG, V. H., PASCHKE, R. E. and ZARROW, M. X. (1968) Killing of mice prevented by early interaction between two species, *Psychonom. Sci.* **11**, 39.

DENENBERG, V. H., ROSENBERG, K. M., PASCHKE, R. E. and ZARROW, M. X. (1969) Mice reared with rat aunts: effects of plasma corticosterone and open field activity, *Nature Lond.* **221**, 73–4.

DEPUE, R. A. (1976) An activity-withdrawal distinction in schizophrenia: behavioral, clinical, brain damage and neurophysiological correlates, *J. Abnorm. Psychol.* **85**, 174–85.

DEPUE, R. A. and FOWLES, D. C. (1973) Electrodermal activity as an index of arousal in schizophrenics, *Psychol. Bull.* **79**, 233–8.

DEPUE, R. A. and FOWLES, D. C. (1976) Electrodermal activity and schizophrenia: the problem of stimulus intensity modulation, *Psychol. Bull.* **83**, 192–3.

DEPUE, R. A., DUBICKI, M. D. and MCCARTHY, T. (1975) Differential recovery of intellectual, associational and psychophysiological functioning in withdrawn and active schizophrenics, *J. Abnorm. Psychol.* **84**, 325–30.

DI CARA, L. V. and MILLER, N. E. (1968a) Changes in heart rate instrumentally learned by curarized rats as avoidance responses, *J. Comp. Physiol. Psychol.* **65**, 8–12.

DI CARA, L. V. and MILLER, N. E. (1968b) Instrumental learning of systolic blood pressure responses by curarized rats: dissociation of cardiac and vascular changes, *Psychosom. Med.* **30**, 489–94.

DI CARA, L. V. and MILLER, N. E. (1968c) Instrumental learning of vasomotor responses by rats: learning to respond differentially in the two ears, *Science*, N.Y. **159**, 1485–6.

DINESTBIER, R. A., HILLMAN, D., LEHNHOLT, J., HILLMAN, J. and VALKENAAR, M. C. (1975) An emotion-attribution approach to moral behaviour: interfacing cognitive and avoidance theories of moral development, *Psychol. Rev.* **82**, 299–315.

DMITRIEV, L. I., BELYAKOVA, L. I., BONDARENKO, T. T. and NIKOLAEV, G. V. (1956) A study of the orienting and defensive reflexes in schizophrenics at different stages in the course of the disease, *Zh. Nevropath. Psikhiat.* **68**, 5, 713–19.

DOCTOR, R. M. and CRAINE, W. H. (1971) Modification of drug language usage of primary and neurotic psychopaths, *J. Abnorm. Psychol.* **77**, 174–80.

DODT, E. (1956) Centrifugal impulses in the rabbit's retina, *J. Neurophysiol.* **19**, 301–7.

DOLLARD, J. and MILLER, N. E. (1950) *Personality and psychotherapy*, New York: McGraw-Hill.

DOLLARD, J., DOOB, L. W., MILLER, N. E., MOWRER, O. H. and SEARS, R. R. (1939) *Frustration and aggression*, New Haven: Yale University Press.

DONELSON, F. E. (1966) Discrimination and control of human heart rate, *Diss. Abstr.* 1967, 4571-B.

DONGIER, M. and BOSTEM, A. (1967) Essais d'application en psychiatrie de la variation contingente negative, *Acta. Neurol. Psychiat. Belg.* **67**, 8, 640–5.

DORMANN, M. F. and HOFFMANN, R. (1973) Short-term habituation of the infant auditory evoked potential, *J. Speech Hear. Res.* **16**, 4, 637–64.

DOSTALEK, C. (1964) *Rucklaufige bedingte Verbindungen in ihrem Zusammenhand mit dem Wesen der hoheren Nervenlatigkeit,* Berlin: VEB Verlag.

DOUGLAS, R. J. (1972) Pavlovian conditioning and the brain, in, R. A. Boakes and M. S. Halliday (Eds.), *Inhibition and learning,* pp. 529–53, New York; Academic Press.

DOUGLAS, R. J. and PRIBRAM, K. M. (1966) Learning and limbic lesions, *Neuropsychologia,* **4**, 197–220.

DOWNIE, W. W., BOYLE, J. A., GREIG, W. R., BUCHANAN, W. W. and ALEPA, F. P. (1969) Relative roles of genetic and environmental factors in control of blood pressure in normotensive subjects, *Br. Heart J.* **31**, 21–5.

DRUMMOND, P., WHITE, K. and ASHTON, R. (1978) Imagery vividness affects habituation rate, *Psychophysiol.* **15**, 3, 193–5.

DUBININ, N. P. (1971a) Philosophical and sociological aspects of human genetics, *Vop. Filos.* **1**.

DUBININ, N. P. (1971b) The population conception and typological thinking in the problem of man, *Vop. Filos,* **10**.

DUBOS, R. (1965) *Man adapting,* New Haven: Yale University Press.

DUFFY, E. (1934) Emotion: an example of the need for reorientation in psychology, *Psychol. Rev.* **41**, 239–43.

DUMENKO, V. N. (1955) Izmeneniya reaktivnosti yader raztich nykh analizatorov pri sochetanii razdrazhiteley, *Tr. Inst. Vyssh. Nerv. Deyat. im. I. P. Pavlova, Ser. Fiziol.* **1**.

DUMENKO, V. N. (1975) Formation of linear relations of potentials in the dog neocortex in a dynamic stereotype, *Zh. Vyssh. Nerv. Deyat. im. I. P. Pavlova,* **25**, 925–33.

DUMONT, S. and DELL, P. (1958) Fécilitations spécifiques et non-spécifiques des réponses visuelles corticales, *J. Physiol. Paris,* **15**, 261–4.

DUNSTONE, J. J., DZENDOLET, G. and HENCKERUTH, O. (1964) Effect of some personality variables on electrical vestibular stimulation, *Percept. Mot. Skills,* **18**, 689–95.

DUSTMAN, R. E. and BECK, E. C. (1965) The visual evoked response in twins, *Electroenceph. Clin. Neurophysiol.* **19**, 570–5.

DWORKIN, R. H. (1978) Genetic influences on cross-situational consistency, in, W. E. Nance (Ed.) *Twin research: psychology and methodology,* pp. 49–56, New York: Alan R. Liss.

DWORKIN, R. H. (1979) Genetic and environmental influences on person-situation interactions, *J. Res. Person.* **13**, 279–93.

DWORKIN, R. H., BURKE, B. W., MAHER, B. A. and GOTTESMAN, I. I. (1976) A longitudinal study of the genetics of personality, *J. Personality Soc. Psycho.* **34**, 510–18.

DWORKIN, R. H., BURKE, B. W., MAHER, B. A. and GOTTESMAN, I. I. (1977) Gentic influences on the organization and development of personality, *Dev. Psychol.* **13**, 164–5.

DYKMAN, R. A. (1965) Towards a theory of classical conditioning: cognitive, emotional and motor components of the conditioned response, in, D. Maher (Ed.), *Experimental approaches to personality,* Vol. 2, pp. 229–317, New York: Academic Press.

DYKMAN, R. A. (1976) Conditioning as sensitisation. *Pavlov. J. Biol. Sc.* **11**, 24–36.

DYKMAN, R. A., MACK, R. L. and ACKERMAN, P. T. (1965) Towards the evaluation of autonomic and motor components of the nonavoidance conditional reflexes in the dog, *Psychophysiol.* **1** 3, 209–30.

DYKMAN, R. A., REESE, W. G., GALBRECHT, L. R. and THOMASSON, P. J. (1959) Psycho-physiological reactions to novel stimuli: measurement, adaptation and relationship of psychological and physiological variables in the normal human, *Ann. N.Y. Acad. Sci.* **79**, 43–107.

DYKMAN, R. A., REECE, W. G., GALBRECHT, C. R., ACKERMAN, P. T. and SUNDERMAN, R. S. (1968) Autonomic responses in psychiatric patients, *Ann. N. Y. Acad. Sci.* **147**, 237–303.

EAVES, L. J. (1973) The structure of genotype and environmental covariation for personality measurements: an analysis of the PEN, *Br. J. Soc. Clin. Psychol.* **12**, 275–82.

EAVES, L. J. and EYSENCK, H. J. (1975) The nature of extraversion: a general analysis, *J. Personality Soc. Psychol.* **32**, 1, 102–12.

EAVES, L. J. and EYSENCK, H. J. (1976) A genetic model for psychoticism, *Behav. Genet.* **6**, 3, 359–62.

EAVES, L. J. and EYSENCK, H. J. (1977) A genotype-environmental model of psychoticism. *Adv. Behavl. Res. Ther.* **1**, 5–26.

EAVES, L. J. and YOUNG, P. A. (1981) Genetical theory and personality differences, in, R. Lynn (Ed.), *Dimensions of personality,* pp. 130–79, Oxford: Pergamon.

EBBINGHAUS, H. (1885) *Untersuchungen zur experimentellen Psychologie.* Leipzig: Duncker A. Humboldt. Translated by H. Ruyer and C. E. Bussenius, New York: Columbian Teacher's College, 1913.

ECCLES, D. (1959) *Physiology of Nerve Cells,* Moscow: Izdatel'stvo Inostrannoi Literatury. English edition, Baltimore, Md.: Johns Hopkins Press.

EDELBERG, R. (1964) Effect of vasoconstriction on galvanic skin response amplitude, *J. Appl. Physiol.* **19**, 427–30.

EDELBERG, R. (1970) The information content of the recovery limb of the electrodermal response, *Psychophysiol.* **6**, 527–39.

EDELBERG, R. (1972a) Electrical activity of the skin: its measurement and uses in psychophysiology, in, N. S. Greenfield and R. A. Sternback (Eds.), *Handbook of psychophysiology,* pp. 367–418 New York: Holt, Reinhart and Winston.

EDELBERG, R. (1972b) Electrodermal recovery rate, goal orientation and aversion. *Psychophysiol.* **9**, 512.

EDELBERG, R. (1973) Mechanisms of electrodermal adaptations for locomotion, manipulation or defense, in, F. Stellar and J. M. Sprague (Eds.), *Progress in physiological psychology,* Vol. 5, pp. 155–210, London: Academic Press.

EDELSTEIN, B. and EISLER, R. (1976) Effects of modeling and modeling with instructions and feedback on the behavioural components of social skills. *Behav. Ther.* **7**, 382–9.

EDWARDS, D. A. (1968) Mice: fighting by neonatally androgenized females, *Science, N. Y.* **161**, 1027–8.

EDWARDS, D. C. (1974) Stimulus intensity and recency contrasts and orienting response strength. *Psychophysiol.* **11**, 543–7.

EDWARDS, D. C. (1975a) Stimulus intensity reduction following habituation, *Psychophysiol.* **12**, 1, 12–14.

EDWARDS, D. C. (1975b) Within mode quality and intensity changes of habituated stimuli, *Biol. Psychol.* **3**, 4, 295–9.

EDWARDS, J. A. and SIDDLE, D. A. (1976) Dishabituation of the electrodermal orienting response following decay of sensitization, *Biol. Psychol.* **4**, 12–28.

EICHENWALD, H. F. and FRY, P. C. (1969) Nutrition and learning, *Science N. Y.* **163**, 644–8.

EINSTEIN, A. (1965) *On differentiation in science,* Moscow, Fiz. i real'nost.

EKEHAMMER, B. (1974) Interactionism in personality, from a historic perspective, *Psychol. Bull.* **81**, 1026–48.

ELIASZ, A. (1973a) Temperament traits and reaction preferences depending on stimulation load, *Pol. Psychol. Bull.* **4**, 103–14.

ELIASZ, A. (1973b) Need for stimulation and need for achievement, *Psychologia Wychowaucza,* **16**, 562–79.

ELIASZ, A. (1974a) *Temperament and personality,* Wroclaw: Ossolineum.

ELIASZ, A. (1974b) The role of temperament traits in the formation of personality trials, in, J. Strelau (Ed.), *The role of temperament traits in action,* pp. 27–43, Wroclaw: Ossolineum.

ELIASZ, A. (1974c) Activity-reactive and operant- and choice of situations differing in stimulation load, in, J. Strelau (Ed.), *The role of temperament traits in action,* pp. 135–41, Wroclaw: Ossolineum.

ELIASZ, A. (1979) Temporal stability of reactivity, *Pol. Psychol. Bull.* **10**, 187–98.

EL'KIN, D. G. (1955) The characteristics of conditioned reflexes to a complex verbal stimulus, *Vop. Psikhol.* **1**, 4, 79–89.

EL'KIN, V. L. and KHORUZHEVA, S. A. (1975) Major properties of nervous processes in twins, *Zh. Vyssh. Nervn. Deyat. im. I. P. Pavlova,* **25,** 1.

EL'KONIN, D. B. (1971) Problems of periods in the mental development of the child, *Vop. Psikhol.* **41.**

ELLIOT, D. N., RIACH, W. and SILBIGER, H. R. (1962) Effects of auditory fatigue upon intensity discrimination, *J. Acoust. Soc. Am.* **34.**

ELLIS, N. R. (1963) The stimulus trace and behavioural inadequacy, in, N. R. Ellis (Ed.) *Handbook of mental deficiency,* pp. 229–325, New York: McGraw-Hill.

ELLIS, N. R. and SLOAN, W. (1958) The relationship between intelligence and skin conductance, *Am. J. Ment. Defic.* **63,** 304–6.

ENDLER, N. S.and MAGNUSSON, D. (1976) Toward an interactional psychology of personality, *Psychol. Bull.* **83,** 956–74.

ENDLER, N. S., MAGNUSSON, D., EKEHAMMAR, B. and OKADA, M. (1976) The multidimensionality of state and trait anxiety, *Scand. J. Psychol.* **17,** 81–96.

ENDLER, N. S., HUNT, J. McV. and ROSENSTEIN, A. J. (1962) An S-R inventory of anxiousness, *Psychol. Monogr.* **76,** 17 (whole No. 536).

ENGEL, B. T. (1972) Operant conditioning of cardiac functioning: a status report, *Psychophysiol.* **9,** 161–77.

ENGEL, B. T. and CHISM, R. A. (1967a) Effect of increases and decreases in breathing rate on heart rate and pulse volume, *Psychophysiol.* **4,** 83–9.

ENGEL, B. T. and CHISM, R. A. (1967b) Operant conditioning of heart rate speeding. *Psychophysiol.* **3,** 418–26.

ENGEL, B. T. and MOOS, R. H. (1967) The generality of specificity, *Archs. Gen. Psychiat.* **16,** 574–81.

ENGELS, F. (1940) *Dialectics of Nature,* New York.

EPSTEIN, S. (1973) Expectancy and magnitude of reaction to a noxious UCS, *Psychophysiol.* **10,** 100–7.

EPSTEIN, S. (1977) Traits are alive and well, in, D. Magnusson and N. S. Endler (Eds.), *Personality at the crossroads: current issues in interactional psychology,* Hillsdale, N.J.: Erlbaum.

EPSTEIN, S. (1979) The stability of behaviour: 1. On predicting most of the people much of the time, *J. Personality Soc. Psychol.* **37,** 7, 1097–26.

EPSTEIN, S. and COLEMAN, M. (1970) Drive theories of schizophrenia, *Psychosom. Med.* **32,** 113–40.

EPSTEIN, S. and FENZ, W. D. (1970) Habituation to a loud sound as a function of manifest anxiety, *J. Abnorm. Psychol.* **75,** 189–4.

ERMEEV, N. S. and FEDOROV, V. K. (1963) O svyazi mezhdu skovost'yu vryabotki i peredelki dvukh usloynykh electrooboronitel'nykh refleksov. *XX soveshchanie po problemam vysshey nervnoy deyatel'nosti.*

ERTL, J. P. (1969) Neural efficiency and human intelligence: final report. US Office of Education Project No. 9–0105.

ERTL, J. P. (1971) Fourier analysis of evoked potentials and human intelligence, *Nature, Lond.* **230,** 525–6.

ERTL, J. P. and SCHAFER, E. W. P. (1967) Cortical activity preceding speech, *Life Sci.* **6,** 473–9.

ESCALONA, S. K. (1968) *The roots of individuality: normal patterns of development in infancy,* London: Tavistock.

ESCALONA, S. K. and HEIDER, G. (1959) *Prediction and outcome: a study of child development,* New York: Basic Books.

ESTES, W. K. (1973) Memory and conditioning, in, F. J. McGuigan and D. B. Lumsden (Eds.), *Contemporary approaches to conditioning and learning,* Washington D.C.: Winston.

EVANS, C. R., LONGDEN, M., NEWMAN, E. A. and PAY, B. E. (1967) Auditory "stabilized images" fragmentation and distortion of words with repeated presentation, *National Physical Laboratory Auto Report,* **30.**

EYSENCK, H. J. (1947) *Dimensions of personality,* London: Routledge & Kegan Paul.

EYSENCK, H. J. (1955) Cortical inhibition, figural after-effect and theory of personality, *J. Abnorm. Soc. Psychol.* **51,** 94–106.

## REFERENCES

EYSENCK, H. J. (1957) *The dynamics of anxiety and hysteria,* London: Routledge & Kegan Paul.

EYSENCK, H. J. (Ed.) (1960) *Experiments in personality,* Vol. 1, Routledge and Kegan Paul.

EYSENCK, H. J. (1961) The effects of psychotherapy, in, H. J. Eysenck (Ed.), *Handbook of abnormal psychology,* New York: Basic Books.

EYSENCK, H. J. (1962) FAE, personality and intersensory comparisons, *Percept. Mot. Skills,* **15,** 2, 405-6.

EYSENCK, H. J. (1964) *Crime and Personality,* London: Routledge and Kegan Paul.

EYSENCK, H. J. (1965) Extraversion and the acquisition of eyeblink and GSR conditioned responses, *Psychol. Bull.* **63,** 258-70.

EYSENCK, H. J. (1966) Conditioning, introversion-extraversion and the strength of the nervous system, in V. D. Nebylitsyn (Ed.) *Symposium 9: Physiological bases of individual psychological differences,* pp. 33-44, Proceedings of the 18th International Congress of Psychology, Moscow.

EYSENCK, H. J. (1967) *The biolgical basis of personality,* Springfield: C. C. Thomas.

EYSENCK, H. J. (1971a) Personality and attitude to sex: a factorial study. *J. Personality,* **21,** 355-76.

EYSENCK, H. J. (1971b) Personality and sexual adjustment, *Br. J. Psychiat.* **118,** 593-608.

EYSENCK, H. J. (1972a) Human typology, higher nervous activity, and factor analysis, in, V. D. Nebylitsyn and J. A. Gray (Eds.), *Biological bases of individual behaviour,* pp. 165-81, London: Academic Press.

EYSENCK, H. J. (1972b) Primaries or second-order factors: a critical consideration of Cattell's 16 PF battery, *Br. J. Soc. Clin. Psychol.* **11,** 265-9.

EYSENCK, H. J. (1976) *Sex and Personality,* London: Open Books.

EYSENCK, H. J. (1977) Psychosis and psychoticism: a reply to Bishop, *J. Abnorm. Psychol.* **86,** 427-30.

EYSENCK, H. J. (1979) Lecture given at the Department of Experimental Psychology, Oxford University.

EYSENCK, H. J. and EYSENCK, S. B. G. (1964) *Manual of the Eysenck personality inventory,* London: University of London Press.

EYSENCK, H. J. and EYSENCK, S. B. G. (1967) On the unitary nature of extraversion, *Acta Psychol.* **26,** 383-90.

EYSENCK, H. J. and EYSENCK, S. B. G. (1969) *Personality structure and measurement,* London: Routledge and Kegan Paul.

EYSENCK, H. J. and EYSENCK, S. B. G. (1975) *Manual of the Eysenck personality questionnaire (junior and adult),* London: Hodder & Stoughton Educational.

EYSENCK, H. J. and EYSENCK, S. B. G. (1976) *Psychoticism as a dimension of personality,* London: Hodder & Stoughton Educational.

EYSENCK, H. J. and EYSENCK, S. B. G. (1977) The place of impulsiveness in a dimensional system of personality description. *Br. J. Soc. Clin. Psychol.* **16,** 57-68.

EYSENCK, H. J. and LEVY, A. (1972) Conditioning, Introversion-Extraversion and the Strength of the Nervous System, in, V. D. Nebylitsyn and J. A. Gray (Eds.), *Biological bases of individual behaviour,* pp. 206-20, London: Academic Press.

EYSENCK, H. J. and PRELL, D. B. (1951) The inheritance of neuroticism: an experimental study, *J. Ment. Sci.* **97,** 441-67.

EYSENCK, M. W. and EYSENCK, H. J. (1980) Mischel and the concept of personality, *Br. J. Psychol.* **71,** 191-204.

EYSENCK, S. B. G. and EYSENCK, H. J. (1963a) On the dual nature of extraversion, *Br. J. Soc. Clin. Psychol.* **2,** 46-55.

EYSENCK, S. B. G. and EYSENCK, H. J. (1963b) Acquiesence response set in personality questionnaires, *Life Sci.* **2,** 144-7.

EYSENCK, S. B. G. and EYSENCK, H. J. (1963c) An experimental investigation of "desirability" response set in a personality questionnaire, *Life Sci.* **2,** 343-55.

EYSENCK, S. B. G. and EYSENCK, H. J. (1963d) The validity of questionnaire and rating assessments of extraversion and neuroticism and their factorial stability, *Br. J. Psychol.* **54,** 51-62.

EYSENCK, S. B. G. and EYSENCK, H. J. (1967a) Physiological reactivity to sensory stimulation as a measure of personality, *Psychol. Rep.* **20**, 45–6.

EYSENCK, S. B. G. and EYSENCK, H. J. (1967b) Salivary response to lemon juice as a measure of introversion, *Percept. Mot. Skills,* **24**, 1047–53.

EYSENCK, S. B. G. and EYSENCK, H. J. (1971a) Crime and personality: item analysis of questionnaire responses, *Br. J. Crim.* **11**, 49–62.

EYSENCK, S. B. J. and EYSENCK, H. J. (1971b) Attitudes to sex, personality and lie scale scores, *Percept. Mot. Skills,* **33**, 216–18.

FARLEY, F. H. and GUNDRUM, R. A. (1972) Arousal, personality and pitch discrimination, *J. Auditory Res.* **12**, 4, 285–90.

FARMER, R. G. and WRIGHT, J. M. C. (1971) Muscular reactivity and systematic desnsitization, *Behav. Ther.* **2**, 1–10.

FEDEROV, V. K. (1951) Study of mobility of nervous processes in mice, *Fiziol. Zh. SSSR,* **37**, 2.

FEDOROV, V. K. (1961) Comparison of results of different studies of basic properties of higher nervous activity in mice, *Zh. Vyssh. Nerv. Deyat. im. I. P. Pavlova,* **11**, 4.

FEDOROV, V. K. (1964) Validity of some indices of mobility of the nervous processes, in, *Methods of study of the typological features of higher nervous activity in animals,* Moscow: Izd. Nauka.

FEDOROV, V. K. (Ed.) (1969) *Behaviour Genetics,* Leningrad: Nauka.

FENCHEL, G. H. (1958) Cognitive rigidity as a behavioural variabie manifested in intellectual and perceptual tasks by an outpatient population. Unpublished doctoral dissertation, New York University. Cited by H. A. Witkin, R. B. Dyk, H. F. Faterson, D. R. Goodenough and S. A. Karp, (1962) 146.

FENTON, G. W. and SCOTTON, L. (1967) Personality and the alpha rhythm, *Br. J. Psychiat.* **113**, 1283–9.

FENZ, W. D., YOUNG, M. J. and FENZ, H. G. (1974) Differences in the modulation of cardiac activity between psychopaths and normal controls, *Psychosom. Med.* **36**, 488–502.

FERRARO, D. P. and YORK, K. M. (1968) Punishment effects in rats selectively bred for emotional elimination, *Psychosom. Sci.* **10**, 177–8.

FESHBACH, S. (1964) The function of aggression and the regulation of aggressive drive, *Psychol. Rev.* **71**, 257–72.

FESTINGER, L. (1957) *A Theory of Cognitive Dissonance,* Evanston, Ill.: Row, Peterson.

FINE, B. J. (1972) Field dependence, introversion and neuroticism: Eysenck and Witkin united, *Psychol. Rep.* **31**, 3, 939–56.

FINE, B. J. and DANFORTH, A. V. (1975) Field dependence, extraversion and perception of the vertical: empirical and theoretical perspectives of the rod and frame test, *Percept. Mot. Skills,* **40**, 3, 683–93.

FIRENCZI, S. (1930) The principle of relaxation and neocartharsis, *Int. J. Psychoanalysis,* **11**, 428–43.

FISCHER, R., GRIFFIN, F. and ROCKEY, M. L. (1966) Gustatory chemoreception in man: multi-disciplinary aspects and perspectives, *Perspect. Biol. Med.* **9**, 549–77.

FISHER, A. E. (1955) The effects of differential early treatment of the social and exploratory behaviour of puppies. Unpublished Ph.D. dissertation, Penn. State University.

FISHER, L. E. and KOTSES, H. (1974) Experimenter and subject sex effects in the skin conductance response, *Psychophysiol.* **11**, 191–6.

FISHER, R. A. (1918) The correlation between relations on the supposition of Mendelian inheritance, *Trans. R. Soc. Edinb.* **52**, 399–433.

FISHER, S. (1963) A further appraisal of the body boundary concept. *J. Consult. Psychol.* **27**, 62–74.

FISHER, S. (1964) Sex differences in body perception, *Psychol. Monogr.* **78**, 14, (Whole No. 591).

FISHER, S. and CLEVELAND, S. E. (1958) *Body image and personality,* Princeton, N.J.: Van Nostrand.

FISKE, D. W. and MADDI, S. R. (1967) A conceptual framework, in, D. W. Fiske and S. R. Maddi (Eds.) *Functions of varied experience,* Homewood: The Dorsey Press.

FLYNN, J. P. (1973) Patterning mechanisms, patterned reflexes, and attack behaviour in cats, *Neb. Symp. Motiv.* **1972**, 125–53.

FONTINELLE, D. (1973) Effects of reward-punishment, introverion-extraversion and neuroticism on verbal conditioning. *Diss. Abstr. Int.* **33**, 12–13, 6076.

FOWLES, D. C. (1974) Mechanisms of electrodermal activity, in, R. F. Thompson and M. M. Patterson (Eds.), *Methods of physiological psychology,* Vol. 1, Part C, New York: Academic Press.

FOWLES, D C., ROBERTS, R. and NAGIE, K. (1977) The influence of introversion-extraversion on the skin conductance response to stress and stimulus intensity, *J. Res. Person.* **11**, 2, 129–46.

FOWLES, D. C., WATT, N. F., MAHER, B. A. and GRIMSPOON, L. (1970) Autonomic arousal in good and poor pre-morbid schizophrenics, *Br. J. Soc. Clin. Psychol.* **9**, 135–47.

FRANKENHAEUSER, A., NORDLEDEN, B., MYRSTEN, A. L. and POST, B. (1971) Psychophysiological reactions to under-stimulation and over-stimulation, *Acta Psychol.* **35**, 4, 298–308.

FRANKS, C. M. (Ed.) (1964) *Conditioning techniques in clinical practice and research,* New York: Springer.

FRANZ, S. I. (1899) Afterimage, *Psychol. Monogr.* **3**, 59.

FREEDMAN, D. G. (1965) An ethological approach to the genetical study of human behaviour, in, S. Vandenberg (Ed.), *Methods and goals in human behaviour genetics,* New York: Academic Press.

FREEDMAN, D. G. and KELLER, B. (1963) Inheritance of behaviour in infants, *Science N. Y.* **140**, 196–8.

FREEMAN, B. L., JOHNSON, J. T. and LONG, C. L. (1972) Semantic generalization of the orienting response, *J. Exp. Res. Person.* **6**, 39–43.

FREEMAN, G. L. and KATZOFF, E. T. (1942) Individual differences in physiological reactions to stimulation and their relation to other measures of emotionality, *J. Exp. Psychol. 33,* 527–37.

FRENCH, J. D. (1957) The reticular formation, in, *The handbook of physiology,* Section 1, Neurophysiology, Vol. II, pp. 1281–1306, Washington, D.C.: Amer. Physiol. Soc.

FRENCH, J. W. (1973) *Toward the establishment of non-cognitive factors through literature search and interpretation,* Princeton, N.J.: Educ. Testing Service.

FREUD, A. and DANN, S. (1951) An experiment in group upbringing, in, *The psychoanalytic study of the child,* Vol. VI, pp. 127–168, New York: International University Press.

FREUD, S. (1933) *New introductory lectures on psychoanalysis,* London: Hogarth.

FREUD, S. (1938) *An outline of psychoanalysis,* London: Hogarth.

FREUD, S. (1951a) The unconscious, in, E. Jones (Ed.) (1952) *Collected papers of Sigmund Freud,* Vol. 4, Papers on metapsychology, Papers on applied psychoanalysis, London: International Psychoanalytic Press.

FREUD, S. (1951b) Repression, in, E. Jones (Ed.) (1952) *Collected papers of Sigmund Freud,* Vol. 4. Papers on metapsychology, Papers on applied psychoanalysis. London: International Psychoanalytic Press.

FRIED, R., FRIEDMAN, M. and WELCH, L. (1967) High and low anxiety and GSR adaptation, *Psychonom. Sci.* **9**, 635–6.

FRIED, R., KORN, S. and WELCH, L. (1966) Effect of change in sequential visual stimuli on GSR adaptation, *J. Exp. Psychol.* **72**, 325–7.

FRIED, R., WELCH, L. and FRIEDMAN, M. (1966) Stimulus novelty and intra-series primacy in GSR adaption, *Percept. Psychophysics,* **1**, 345–6.

FRIED, R., WELCH, L., FRIEDMAN, M. and GLUCK, S. (1967) Is no-stimulus a stimulus? *J. Exp. Psychol.* **73**, 145–6.

FRIEDMAN, S., BRUNO, A. L. and VIETZ, E. P. (1974) New-born habituation to visual stimuli; a sex difference in novelty detection, *J. Exp. Child Psychol.* **18**, 242–51.

FRIES, M. (1954) Some hypotheses on the role of congenital activity type in personality development, *Int. J. Psychoanal.* **35**, 206–7.

FRIES, M. and WOLF, P. (1954) Some hypotheses on the role of congenital activity type in personality development, *Psychoanal. Study, Child.* **8**, 48–64.

FRIGON, JEAN-YVES (1976) Extraversion, neuroticism and strength of the nervous system, *Br. J. Psychol.* **67**, 467–74.

FRITH, C. D. (1967) The interaction of noise and personality with critical flicker fusion performance, *Br. J. Psychol.* **58**, 127–31.

FRITH, M (1973) Habituation during sleep, *Psychophysiol.* **10**, 43–51.

FROMM, E. (1956) Lecture to the American Ortho-psychiatric Association, April 13th (reported in The New York Times).

FUREDY, J. J. (1968) Human orienting reaction as a function of electrodermal versus plethysmographic response modes and single versus alternating stimulus series, *J. Exp. Psychol.* **77**, 70–8.

FUREDY, J. J. (1972) Electrodermal recovery time as a supra-sensitive autonomic index of anticipated intensity of threatened shock, *Psychophysiol.* **9**, 281–2.

FUREDY, J. J. (1974) Experimental assessments of the importance of controlling for contingency factors in human classical differential electrodermal and plethysmographic conditioning, *Psychophysiol.* **11**, 3, 308–15.

FUREDY, J. J. and KLAJNER, F. (1974) On evaluating autonomic and verbal indices of negative preception, *Psychophysiol.* **11**, 2, 121–4.

FURNHAM, A. (1981) Personality and activity preference, *Br. J. Soc. Psychol.* **20**, 57–68.

GALAMBOS, R., SHEATZ, G. and VERNIER, V. G. (1956) Electrophysiological correlates of a conditioned response in cats, *Science, N.Y.* **123**, 376–7.

GALBRECHT, L. R., DYKMAN, R. A., REESE, W. G. and SUZUKI, T. (1965) Intrasession adaptation and intersession extinction of the components of the orienting response, *J. Exp. Psychol.* **70**, 585–97.

GALE, A., COLES, M. and BLAYDON, J. (1969) Extraversion-introversion and the EEG, *Br. J. Psychol.* **60**, 209–23.

GALE, A., COLES, M., KLINE, P. and PENFORD, V. (1971) Extraversion-introversion, neuroticism and the EEG: basal and response measures during habituation of the orienting response, *Br. J. Psychol.* **62**, 4, 533–43.

GANTT, W. H. (1941) Relation between unconditioned and conditioned reflex: inhibition of CR by UR, *Am. J. Physiol.* **133**, 2, 266.

GANTT, W. H. (1942) The origin and development of nervous disturbances experimentally produced. *Am. J. Psychiat.* **98**, 475–81.

GANTT, W. H. (1943) Measures of susceptibility to nervous breakdown, *Am. J. Psychiat.* **99**, 839–49.

GANTT, W. H. (1944) Experimental basis for neurotic behaviour, *Psychosom. Med. Monogr.* **4**, 3–4.

GANTT, W. H. (1953) The physiological basis of psychiatry: the conditional reflex, in, J. Wortis (Ed.), *Basic problems of psychiatry*, pp. 778–98, New York: Grune & Stratton.

GANTT, W. H. (1958) Normal and abnormal adaptations — homeostasis, schizokinesis and autokinesis: diseases of the nervous system. Monograph supplement, **18**, 7.

GANTT, W. H. (1976) Neo-Pavlovianism, in, D. I Mostofsky (Ed.), *Behaviour control and modification of physiological activity*, Englewood Cliffs, N.J.: Prentice-Hall.

GARDNER, E. (1968) *Fundamentals of neurology*, 5th ed., W. B. Saunders.

GARDNER, R. W. (1961) Cognitive controls of attention deployment as determinants of visual illusions, *J. Abnorm. Soc. Psychol.* **62**, 120–7.

GARDNER, R. W. (1964) The development of cognitive structures, in, C. Scheerer (Ed.), *Cognition: therapy, research, promise*, pp. 147–272, Ne York: Harper and Row.

GARDNER, R. W. (1971) Evolution and brain injury: the impact of deprivation on cognitive-affective structures, *Bull. Menninger Clin.* **35**, 113–24.

GARMEZY, N. (1974) Children at risk: the search for the antecedents of schizophrenia, Part 2: Ongoing research programs, issues and intervention, *Schiz. Bull.* **1**, Experimental issue No. 9, 55–125, No. 10, 199–207.

GASTAUT, A. and ROGET, A. (1962) Uchastie osnovnykh funktsional'nykh struktur golovnogo mozya v mekhanizmakh vysshey nervnoy deyatel'nosti, in, *Elektroentsefalograficheskoe issledovanie vysshey nervnoy deyatel'nosti,* Moscow: AN SSSR.

GASTAUT, H. (1957) The brain stem and cerebral electrogenesis in relation to consciousness, in, *Brain mechanisms and consciousness,* pp. 249–83, Springfield, Ill.: Charles C. Thomas.

GASTAUT, H. (1958) Some aspects of the neurophysiological basis of conditioned reflexes and behaviour. In, G. E. Wolstenholme and M. O'Connor (Eds.) *Neurological Basis of Behaviour* (Ciba Foundation Symposium) Boston: Little, Brown.

GASTAUT, H. and BERT, J. (1961) Electroencephalographic detection of sleep induced by repetitive sensory stimulation, in, G. E. W. Wolstenholme and M. O'Connor (Eds.) *The nature of sleep,* pp. 260–71, London: Churchill.

GASTAUT, H., GASTAUT, G., ROGET, A., CORRIOL, J. and NAGUET, R. (1951) Étude électrographie du cycle d'excitabilité cortical, *Electroenceph. Clin. Neurophysiol.* **3,** 401–28.

GATCHEL, R. J. (1975) Effects of inter-stimulus interval length on short- and long-term habituation of autonomic components of the orienting responses, *Physiol. Psychol.* **3,** 2, 133–6.

GATCHEL, R. J. and GASS, F. (1976) Effects of arousal level on short- and long-term habituation of the orienting response, *Physiol. Psychol.* **4,** 66–8.

GATCHEL, R. J. and LANG, P. J. (1974) Effects of inter-stimulus interval length and variability on habituation of autonomic components of the orienting response, *J. Exp. Psychol.* **103,** 802–4.

GAWECKA, H. and POZNANIAK, W. (1979) Reactivity and stimulation-seeking in psychopathic delinquents and neurotic patients, *Pol. Psychol. Bull.* **10,** 175–85.

GAZZANIGA, M. S. (1970) *The Bisected Brain.* New York: Appleton-Century-Crofts.

GEDEVANISHVILI, D. M. (1960) *Voprosy vysshey nervnoi deyatel'nosti uslovnykh* refleksovna, 21 mezhdunarodnom kongresse fiziologicheskikh nauk. Tbilisi: Sabgota Sakartvelo.

GEER, J. H. (1967) Some basic parameters of the orienting response, in, I. Ruttkay-Medecky, L. Ciganek, V. Zikmund and E. Kellerova (Eds.), *Mechanisms of orienting reactions in man,* pp. 237–44, Bratislava: Slovak Academy of Sciences.

GEER, J. H. (1969) Generalisation of inhibition in the orienting response, *Psychophysiol.* **6,** 197–201.

GEER, J. H. and KATKIN, E. S. (1966) Treatment of insomnia using a variant of systematic desensitization, *J. Abnorm. Psychol.* **71,** 161–4.

GELFAND, D. M., HARTMANN, D. P., GROMER, C. C., SMITH, C. L. and PAGE, B. C. (1975) The effects of instructional prompts and praise on children's donation rates, *Child Dev.* **46,** 980–3.

GELLHORN, E. (1964) Motion and emotion: the role of proprioception in the physiology and pathology of the emotions, *Psychol. Rev.* **71,** 457–72.

GEMBARYAN, L. S., HECHT, K., SARAKOSOV, G. T., KOVAL, I. N., KAZARYAN, G. M., GARIBYAN, A. A. and SARKISYAN, J. S. (1979) On the role of the hippocampus in conditioned activity, *Zh. Vyssh. Nerv. Deyat. im. I. P. Pavlova,* **1,** 56–63.

GEON, E. (1961) Expression of individuality in the tempo of human activity, *Vop. Psikhol.* **2.**

GERSHUNI, G. (1958) Regulation of the afferent flow in the auditory system, Gagra Colloquium, Vol. 3, 10th All Union Congress of Physiology, **1,** 149.

GERSHUNI, G. V., KOZHEVNIKOV, V. A., MARUSEVA, A. M. and CHISTOVICH, L. A. (1948) Characteristics of the formation of temporary connections to unaware auditory stimuli in man, *Byull. Eksp. Biol. Med.* **26,** 3, 205–9.

GERSHUNI, G. V., KOZHEVNIKOV, V. A., MARUSEVA, A. M. AVAKYAN, R. V., RADIONOVA, F. A. ALTMAN, J. A. and SOROKO, V. F. (1960) Modifications in electrical responses to the auditory stimulus in different states of higher nervous activity. The Moscow Colloquium on Electroencephalography of Higher Nervous Activity, *Electroenceph. Clin. Neurophysiol. Suppl.* **13,** 115–25.

GIANNITROPANI, D. (1966) Electroencephalographic differences between resting and mental multiplication, *Percept. Mot. Skills,* **22,** 399–405.

GIANNITROPANI, D. (1969) EEG average frequency and intelligence, *Electroenceph. Clin. Neurophysiol.* **27,** 480–6.

GIESE, H.and SCHMIDT, G. (1968) *Studenten Sexualitat,* Hamburg: Rowohlt.

GINSBERG, B.E. (1967) Genetic parameters in behavioural research, in, J. Hirsch (Ed.) *Behaviour-genetic analysis,* New York: McGraw-Hill.

GINSBERG, B. E. (1968) Breeding structure and social behaviour of mammals: a servo-mechanism for the avoidance of panmixia, in D. C. Glass (Ed.), *Genetics,* New York: Rockefellow University Press, 117–28.

GINSBERG, B. E. and ALLEE, W. C. (1942) Some effects of conditioning on social dominance and subordination in inbred strains of mice, *Physiol. Zoöl.* **15,** 485–506.

GINSBERG, N. (1969) Extraversion and adaptation to intermittent light, *Percept. Mot Skills,* **28,** 195–201.

GINSBERG, S. and FUREDY, J. F. (1974) Stimulus repetition, change and assessments of sensitivities of relationships among an electrodermal and two plethysmographic components of the orienting response, *Psychophysiol.* **11,** 1, 35–43.

GLASS, A. and BROADHURST, A. (1966) Relationship being EEG as a measure of cortical activity and personality measures, *Electroenceph. Clin. Neurophysiol.* **21,** 309.

GLUKHOVA, R. I. and VOROBEVA, A. L. (1974) Study of certain psychophysiological parameters of intellectual work capacity in school-age twins, in, *New Studies in Developmental Physiology,* No. 9, Moscow: Izd. Pedagogika.

GOLDFARB, W. (1945a) Effects of psychological deprivation in infancy and subsequent stimulation, *Am. J. Psychiat.* **102,** 18–33.

GOLDFARB, W. (1945b) Psychological privation in infancy and subsequent adjustment, *Am. J. Orthopsytchiat.* **15,** 247–55.

GOLDSTEIN, A. P. (1973) *Structured learning therapy: towards a psychotherapy for the poor,* New York: Academic Press.

GOLDSTEIN, A. P., SHERMAN, H., GERSHAW, N. J., SPRAFKIN, R. P. and GLICK, B. (1978) Training aggressive adolescents in pro-social behaviours, *J. Youth Adol.* **7,** 73–93.

GOLDSTEIN, I. B. (1964) Physiological responses in anxious women patients: a study of autonomic activity and muscle tension, *Archs. Gen. Psychiat.* **10,** 382–8.

GOLDSTEIN, M. J. and ACKER, C. W. (1967) Psychophysiological reactions to films by chronic schizophrenics: Quote II: Individual differences in resting levels in reactivity, *J. Abnorm. Psychol.* **72,** 23–9.

GOLEMAN, D. (1971) Meditation as meta-therapy: hypothesis toward a proposed fifth state of consciousness, *J. Transpersonal. Psychol.* **3,** 1–25.

GOLIKOV, N. V. (1950) *Fiziologicheskaya Labil'nosti i ee izmeneniya pri osnovnykh nervnykh protsessakh.* L.G.U.

GOLUBEVA, E. A. (1964) Reaktsiya perestroyki biotokov mozga i tipologicheskie svoystva nervnoy sistemy, in, *Tipologicheskie osobennosti vysshey nervnoy deyatel'nosti cheloveka,* Vol. 4, Moscow: APN RSFSR.

GOLUBEVA, E. A. (1972a) The driving reaction as a method of study in differential psychophysiology, in, V. D. Nebylitsyn and J. A. Gray (Eds.) *Biological basis of individual behaviour,* London: Academic Press.

GOLUBEVA, E. A. (1972b) Study of the bioelectric correlates of memory in differential psychophysiology, *Vop. Psikhol.* **18,** 1, 25–36.

GOLUBEVA, E. A. (1972c) Driving reaction as a method of study in differential psychophysiology, in, V. D. Nebylitsyn (Ed.), *Problems of differential psychophysiology,* Vol. 7, Moscow: Pedagogika.

GOLUBEVA, E. A. (1973) The study of bioelectric correlates of memory in differential psychology, *Soviet Psychol.***11,** 71–92.

GOLUBEVA, E. A. (1976) Electrophysiological study of the properties of the human nervous system and individual characteristics of human memory. Unpublished doctoral dissertation, Moscow University.

GOLUBEVA, E. A. and GUSEVA, E. P. (1972) Properties of the nervous system as a factor of efficiency in involuntary and voluntary memorization, in, V. D. Nebylitsyn (Ed.), *Problems of differential psychophysiology,* Vol. 7, Moscow: Pedagogika.

GOLUBEVA, E. A. and ROZDESTVENSKAYA, V. I. (1969) Changes in cerebral biocurrents in the course of mental activity and typological differences in lability and dynamic character of the nervous system, in, V. D. Nebylitsyn (Ed.), *Problems in differential psychophysiology,* Vol. 6, Moscow: Prosveshcheniye.

GOLUBEVA, E. A. and ROZHDESTVENSKAYA, V. I. (1969) Change in the bioelectric potentials of the brain in the course of mental activity and typological differences in lability and dynamism of the nervous system, in, V. D. Nebylitsyn (Ed.), *Problems of differential psychophysiology,* Vol. 6, Moscow: Prosveshcheniye.

GOLUBEVA, E. A. and SHVARTS, L. A. (1965) Correlation of the bio-electric potential indices of mobility with the critical flicker frequency and the speed of restoration of visual sensitivity, in, B. M. Teplov (Ed.), *Typological features of higher nervous activity in man,* Vol. 4, Moscow: Prosveshcheniye.

GOLUBEVA, E. A. and TRUBNIKOVA, R. S. (1970) O korrelyatsiyakh produktivnosti pamyati s siloy nervnoy sistemy, *Vop. Psikhol.* 2.

GOLUBEVA, E. A. and VASILENKO, T. K. (1965) Effect of caffeine on the bio-electric potential indices in early stages of psychic fatigue, in, B. M. Teplov (Ed.), *Typological features of higher nervous activity in Man,* Vol 4, Moscow: Prosveshcheniye.

GOLUBEVA, E. A., GUSEVA, E. P. and TRUBNIKOVA, R. S. (1970) Svoystva nervnoy sistemy kak faktor produktivnosti neproizvol'nogo i proizvol'nogo zapominaniya. *Psikhologicheskie mekhanizimy pamyati i ee zakonomernosti v protsesse obucheniya.* Khar'kov.

GOODMAN, L. S. and GILMAN, A. (1971) *The pharmacological basis of therapeutics,* 4th ed., New York: Macmillan.

GOODRICK, C. (1970) Light- and dark.contingent bar-pressing in the rat as a function of age and motivation, *J. Comp. Physiol. Psychol.* 73, 100–4.

GORBUNOV, V. V., SIROTSKII, V. V. and MARAVENKO, N. V. (1978) EEG changes in humans under stress, *Soviet Psychol.* 17, 1.

GORMEZANO, I. and COLEMAN, S. R. (1973) The law of effect and CR contingent modification of the UCS. *Condit. Reflex,* 8, 41–56.

GORMEZANO, I. and TAIT, R. W. (1976) The Pavlovian analysis of instrumental conditioning, *Pavlov. J. Biol. Sc.* 11, 37–55.

GORSUCH, R. L. and CATTELL, R. B. (1967) Second stratum personality factors defined in the questionnaire realm by the 16PF. *Multiv. Behav. Res.* 2, 211–24.

GORYNSKA, E. and STRELAU, J. (1979) Basic traits of the temporal characteristics of behaviour and their measurement by an inventory technique. *Pol. Psychol. Bull.,* 10, 199–207.

GOSLIN, D. A. (1969) *The handbook of socialization theory and research,* Chicago: Rand McNally.

GOTTESMAN, I. I. (1963a) Genetic aspects of intelligent behaviour, in, N. Ellis (Ed.), *Handbook of mental deficiency: psychological theory and research,* New York: McGraw-Hill.

GOTTESMAN, I. I. (1963b) Heritability of personality: a demonstration, *Psychol. Monogr.* 77, 9, 1–21.

GOTTESMAN, I. I. (1965) Personality and natural selection, in, S. G. Vandenberg (Ed.), *Methods and goals in human behaviour genetics,* New York: Academic Press.

GOTTESMAN, I. I. (1966) Genetic variance in adaptive personality traits, *J. Child. Psychol. Psychiat.* 7, 199–208.

GOTTESMAN, I. I. (1967) Biogenetics of race and class, in, M. Deutsch and A. R. Jensen (Eds.), *Race, social class and psychological development,* New York: Holt, Rinehart and Winston.

GOTTESMAN, I. I. (1968) Severity/concordance and diagnostic refinement in the Maudsley-Bethlem schizophrenic twin study, in, D. Rosenthal and S. S. Kety (Eds.), *The transmission of schizophrenia,* pp. 37–48, London: Pergamon Press.

GOTTESMAN, I. I. (1974) Developmental genetics and ontogenetic psychology: overdue detente and propositions from a matchmaker, in, A. D. Pick (Ed.), *Minnesota symposia on child psychology,* Vol. 8, Minneapolis: University of Minnesota Press.

GOTTESMAN, I. I. and SHIELDS, J. (1966a) Contributions of twin studies to perspectives in schizophrenia, in, B. A. Maher (Ed.), *Progress in experimental personality research,* New York: Academic Press.

GOTTESMAN, I. I. and SHIELDS, J. (1966b) Schizophrenia in twins. 16 years' consecutive admissions to a psychiatric clinic, *Br. J. Psychiat.* **112,** 489, 809–18.

GOTTESMAN, I. I. and SHIELDS, J. (1972) *Schizophrenia and genetics,* London: Academic Press.

GOTTESMAN, I. I. and SHIELDS, J. (1973) Genetic theorising and schizophrenia, *Br. J. Psychiat.* **122,** 15–30.

GOTTSCHALK, L. A. (1970) Self-induced visual imagery, affect arousal and autonomic correlates, *Psychosomatics,* **15,** 166–9.

GRAHAM, F. K. (1973) Habituation and dishabituation of responses innervated by the autonomic nervous system, in, H. V. S. Peeke and M. J. Herz (Eds.), *Habituation,* Vol. 1, pp. 163–218, London: Academic Press.

GRAHAM, F. K. and CLIFTON, R. K. (1966) Heart-rate change as a component of the orienting response, *Psychol. Bull* **65,** 305–20.

GRALTON, M. A., HAYES, Y. A. and RICHARDSON, T. E. (1979) Introversion-extraversion and mental imagery, *J. Ment. Imag.* **3,** 1–10.

GRANGER, G. W. (1953) Personality and visual perception: a review, *J. Ment. Sci.* **99,** 8–43.

GRANGER, G. W. (1957) Night vision and psychotic disorders: a review of experimental studies, *J. Ment. Sci.* **103,** 48–79.

GRANGER, G. W. (1960) Abnormalities of sensory perception, in, H. J. Eysenck (Ed.) *Handbook of Abnormal Psychology,* London: Pitman.

GRANGER, G. W. and IKEDA, H. (1968) Drugs and visual perception, in, A. Herxheimer (Ed.), *Drugs and sensory functions,* London: Churchill.

GRANIT, R. (1955) Centrifugal and antichronic effects on ganglion cells of the retina, *J. Neurophysiol.* **18,** 388–411.

GRASTYAN, E. (1959) The hippocampus and higher nervous activity, in, M. A. Brazier (Ed.), *The central nervous system and behaviour,* New York: Josiah Macey Foundation.

GRAY, A. L. (1975) Autonomic correlates of chronic schizophrenia: reaction time, *J. Abnorm. Psychol.* **84,** 189–96.

GRAY, J. A. (1964a) Strength of the nervous system and levels of arousal: a reinterpretation, In: J. A. Gray (Ed.) (1964b) pp. 289–366.

GRAY, J. A. (Ed.) (1964b) Pavlov's typology: recent theoretical and experimental developments from the laboratory of B. M. Teplov, London: Pergamon Press.

GRAY, J. A. (1964c) Stength of the nervous system as a dimension of personality in man, in, J. A. Gray (Ed.), (1964b).

GRAY, J. A. (1965) Stimulus intensity dynamism, *Psychol. Bull.* **63,** 180–96.

GRAY, J. A. (1966) Attention, consciousness and voluntary control of behaviour in Soviet psychology: philosophical roots and research branches: N. O'Connor (Ed.), *Present day Russian psychology,* pp 1–38, Sydney: Pergamon.

GRAY, J. A. (1967) Strength of the nervous system, introversion-extraversion, conditionability and arousal, *Behav. Res. Ther.* **5,** 151–69.

GRAY, J. A. (1968) Strength of the nervous system, introversion-extraversion, conditionability and arousal, *Vop. Psikhol.* **3,** 77–88.

GRAY, J. A. (1969) Sodium amobarbital and effects on frustrative non-reward, *J. Comp. Physiol. Psychol.* **69,** 55–64.

GRAY, J. A. (1970) The psycho-physiological basis of introversion-extraversion, *Behav. Res. Ther.* **8,** 249–66.

GRAY, J. A. (1971a) *The psychology of fear and stress,* London: Weidenfeld and Nicholson.

GRAY, J. A. (1971b) Sex differences in emotional behaviour in mammals, including man: endocrine bases, *Acta Psychol.* **35,** 29–46.

GRAY, J. A. (1975) *Elements of a two-process theory of learning,* London: Academic Press.

GRAY, J. A. and BALL, G. G. (1970) Frequency-specific relation between hippocampal theta rhythm, behaviour and amobarbital action, *Science, N. Y.* **168,** 1246–8.

GREENE, W. A. (1966) Operant conditioning of the GSR using partial reinforcement, *Psychol. Rep.* **19,** 571–8.

GREENGARD, P. (1974) Characterisation of the dopamine receptors in the mammalian caudate nucleus, *J. Psychiat. Res.* **11**, 87.

GRIM, P. F. and WHITE, J. H. (1965) Effects of stimulus change on GSR and reaction time, *J. Exp. Psychol.* **69**, 414–6.

GRINGS, W. W. (1960) Preparatory set variables related to classical conditioning of autonomic responses, *Psychol. Rev.* **67**, 243–52.

GRINGS, W. W. (1969) Compound stimulus transfer in human classical conditioning. Paper read at Conference on Classical Conditioning. McMaster University.

GRINGS, W. W. (1973) Cognitive factors in electrodermal conditioning, *Psychol. Bull.* **79**, 200–10.

GRINGS, W. W. and KIMMEL, H. D. (1959) Compound stimulus transfer for different sense modalities, *Psychol. Rep.* **5**, 253–60.

GRINKER, R. R. and SPIEGEL, J. P. (1945) *Men Under Stress,* Philadelphia: Blakiston.

GROVES, P. M. and THOMPSON, R. F. (1970) Habituation: a dual process theory, *Psychol. Rev.* **77**, 419–50.

GROVES, P. M., LEE, D. and THOMPSON, R. F. (1969) Effects of stimulus frequency and intensity on habituation and sensitisation in the acute spinal cat, *Physiol. Beh.* **4**, 383–88.

GRUSEC, J. E., SAAS-KORTSAAK, P., and SIMUTIS, Z. M. (1978) The role of example and moral exhortation in the training of altruism, *Child. Dev.* **49**, 920–3.

GRUSEC, J. E., KUCZYNSKI, L., RUSHTON, J. P. and SIMUTIS, Z. M. (1978) Modelling, direct instruction and attributions: effects on altruism, *Dev. Psychol.* **14**, 1, 51–7.

GRUSH, J. E., COLES, M. G., FERGUSON, A. Y. and McGEE, J. (1973) Habituation, memory and the evaluative dimension of personality, *J. Res. Person.* **7**, 2, 159.

GRUZELIER, J. H. (1973) Bilateral asymmetry of skin conductance orienting activity and levels in schizophrenics, *Biol. Psychol.* 21–42.

GRUZELIER, J. and HAMMOND, N. V. (1976) Schizophrenia: a dominant hemispheric temporal-limbic disorder? *Res. Comm. Psychol. Psychiat. Behav.* **1**, 33–72.

GRUZELIER, J. H. and VENABLES, P. H. (1972) Skin conductance orienting activity in a heterogeneous sample of schizophrenics, *J. Nerv. Ment. Dis.* **155**, 277–87.

GRUZELIER, J. H. and VENABLES, P. H. (1973) Skin conductance responses to tones with and without attentional significance in schizophrenic and non-schizophrenic patients, *Neuropsychologia,* **11**, 221–30.

GRUZELIER, J. H. and VENABLES, P. H. (1974) Two-flash threshold, sensitivity and beta in normal subjects and schizophrenics, *Q. J. Exp. Psychol.* **26**, 594–604.

GRUZELIER, J. H. and VENABLES, P. H. (1975a) Relations between two-flash discrimination and electrodermal activity re-examined in schizophrenics and normals, *J. Psychiat. Res.* **12**, 73–85.

GRUZELIER, J. H. and VENABLES, P. H. (1975b) Evidence of high and low levels of physiological arousal in schizophrenics, *Psychophysiol.* **12**, 66–73.

GRUZELIER, J. H., LYKKEN, D. T. and VENABLES, P. H. (1972) Schizophrenia and arousal revisited: two-flash thresholds and electrodermal activity in activated and non-activated conditions, *Archs Gen. Psychiat.* **26**, 47, 432.

GRZEGOLOWSKA-KLARKOWSKA, H. (1978) *Effect of reactivity and current state of activation on defense mechanism use,* Cited by J. Strelau (1980).

GUHL, A. M., CRAIG, J. V. and MUELLER, C. D. (1960) Selective breeding for aggressiveness in chickens, *Poult. Sci.* **39**, 970–80.

GUILFORD, J. P. (1975) Factors and factors of personality, *Psychol. Bull.* **82**, 802–14.

GUILFORD, J. P. (1977) Will the real factor of extraversion-introversion please stand up? A reply to Eysenck, *Psychol. Bull.* **84**, 412–16.

GUILFORD, J. P. and MERRIFIELD, P. R. (1960) The structure of intellect model: Its uses and implications: studies of aptitudes of high-level personnel. Report of Psychological Laboratory, No. 24, University of Southern California.

GUILFORD, J. P. and ZIMMERMAN, W. S. (1956) Fourteen dimensions of temperament, *Psychol. Monogr.* **70**, Whole No. 417.

GUL'DAN, V. V. and IVANNIKOV, V. A. (1974) Traits in the formation and use of past experience in psychopathic personalities, *Zh. Nevropat. Psikhiat.* **74**, 1830–6.

GUMP, P. V. (1955) Relation of efficiency of recognition to personality variables. Unpublished doctoral dissertation, University of Colorado. Cited by H. A. Witkin, R. B. Dyk, H. F. Faterson, D. R. Goodenough and S. A. Karp (1962),

GUPTA, B. S. (1970) The effect of extraversion and stimulant and depressant drugs on verbal conditioning, *Acta Psychol.* **34**, 505–10.

GUPTA, B. S. (1973) The effects of stimulant and depressant drugs on verbal conditioning, *Br. J. Psychol.* **64**, 553–7.

GUPTA, B. S. (1976) Extraversion and reinforcement in verbal operant conditioning, *Br. J. Psychol.* **67**, 47–52.

GUPTA, B. S. and NAGPAL, M. (1978) Impulsivity/sociability and reinforcement in verbal operant conditioning, *Br. J. Psychol.* **69**, 203–6.

GUPTA, B. S. and SINGH, S. D. (1971) The effect of extraversion, neuroticism and a depressant drug on verbal conditioning, *Indian J. Exp. Psychol.* **5**. 15–17.

GUREVICH, K. M. (1963) After effect of positive and inhibitory stimuli in the motor reaction, in, B. M. Teplov (Ed.), *Typological features of higher nervous activity in man*, Vol 3, Moscow: Akad. Pedagog. Nauk RSFSR.

GUREVICH, B. and KOLESNIKOV, M. S. (1955) Determination of type of nervous system in animals under freely moving conditions, *J. Physiol.* **41**, 3.

GUSELINIKOV, V. I. and PIVOVAROV, A. S. (1979) Mechanisms of adaptation of electro-excitable membrane of cortical neurone, *Zh. Vyssh. Nerv. Deyat. im. I. P. Pavlova*, **29**, 358–70.

GUSEVA, E. G. (1959) Investigation of the limits of cortical (conditioned) inhibition. *Tr. Inst. Fiziol. im. I. P. Pavlova*, **1**.

GUSEVA, E. G. (1961) Limis of the conditioned inhibition process in dogs with different types of nervous systems, *Zh. Vyssh. Nerv. Deyat. im. I. P. Pavlova*, **11**, 6.

GUSEVA, E. P. (1975) The relationship between voluntary and involuntary retention and certain characteristics of EEG in adolescents and adults, *Vop. Psikhol.* **2**, 128–35.

GUYTON, A. C. (1976) *Organ physiology: structure and function of the nervous system,* London: Saunders.

GYURDZHIAN, A. A. (1954) Izmenenie chuvstvitel'nosti analizatora k razdrazheniyu v rezul'tate prevrashcheniya poslednego v uslovnoveflektornyv signal, *Dokl. Acad. Nauk. SSSR,* **96**, 6, **101**, 6.

GYURDZHIAN, A. A. (1955) Izmenie chuvstvitel'nosti analizatora k razdrashcheniya posledrego v uslovnoreflektornyy signal, *Dok. Akad. Nauk SSSR,* **96**, 6, **101**, 6.

HABER, R. N. (1958) Discrepancy from adaptation level as a source of affect. *J. Exp. Psychol.* **56**, 370–5.

HAGBARTH, K. and KERR, D. (1954) Central influenes on spinal afferent conduction. *J. Neurophysiol.* **17**, 295–307.

HAIDER, M. (1967) Expectancy orienting reactions and the cortical evoked responses, in, I. Luttkay-Nedicky, L. Ciganek, V. Zikmund and T. Kellerova (Eds.), *Mechanisms of orienting reactions in man,* Bratislava: Slovak Academy of Sciences.

HALBERSTAM, J. L. (1961) Some personality correlates of conditioning, generalization and extinction, *Psychosom. Med.* **23**, 67–76.

HALL, C. S. (1934) Emotional behaviour in the rat: 1: Defecation and urination as measures of individual differences in emotionality, *J. Comp. Psychol.* **18**, 385–403.

HALL, C. S. (1941) Temperament: a survey of animal studies, *Psychol. Bull.* **38**, 909–43.

HALL, C. S. (1951) The genetics of behaviour, in, S. S. Stevens (Ed.), *Handbook of experimental psychology,* pp. 304–29, New York: Wiley.

HALL, C. S. and KLEIN, S. J. (1942) Individual differences in aggressiveness in rats, *J. Comp. Psychol.* **33**, 371–83.

HALL, R. J. and WILSONCROFT, W. E. (1964) Prolonged visual afterimages, *Psychosom. Sci.* **1**, 267–8.

HAMMERMAN, A., FOGEL, S, and STEIN, J. A. (1972) The development of "cortical models": differential effects of mode of stimulus presentation, *Int. J. Psychobiol.* **2**, 4, 249–58.

HARDESTY, D. and BEVAN, W. (1965) Response latency as a function of the temporal pattern of stimulation, *Psychol. Rec.* **15**, 385–92.

HARDT, J. V. and KAMIYA, J. (1976) Some comments on Plotkin's self-regulation of electroencephalographic alpha, *J. Exp. Psychol, General*, **105**, 1, 100–8.

HARE, R. D. (1965) Temporal gradient of fear arousal in psychopaths, *J. Abnorm. Psychol.* **70**, 442–5.

HARE, R. D. (1968) Psychopathy, autonomic functioning and the orienting response, *J. Abnorm. Psychol. Monogr. Suppl.* **73**, 1–24.

HARE, R. D. (1970) *Psychopathy: theory and research*, New York: Wiley.

HARE, R. D. (1972) Dissociation of conditioned electrodermal and cardiovascular responses in psychopathy. Paper presented to Society for Psychophysiological Research, Boston, Massachusetts.

HARE, R. D. (1978) Electrodermal and cariovascular correlates of psychopathy, in, R. D. HARE and D. SCHALLING (Eds.) *Psychopathic behaviour: approaches to research.* Chichester, N.Y.: Wiley.

HARE, R. D. and GRAIGEN, D. (1974) Psychopathy and physiological activity in a mixed-motive game situation, *Psychophysiol.* **11**, 197–206.

HARE, R. D. and QUINN, M. (1971) Psychopathy and autonomic conditioning. *J. Abnorm. Psychol.* **77**, 223–39.

HARE, R. D. and SCHALLING, D. (1978) *Psychopathic behavior: approaches to research,* Chichester, N. Y.: Wiley.

HARLOW, H. F. (1958) The nature of love, *Am. Psychol.* **13**, 673–85.

HARLOW, H. F. and HARLOW, M. K. (1962) Social deprivation in monkeys, *Scient. Am.* **207**, 5, 137–46.

HARLOW, H. F. and HARLOW, M. K. (1966) Learning to love, *Am. Scient.* **54**, 244–72.

HARLOW, H. F. and HARLOW, M. K. (1967) The young monkeys, *Psychol. Today*, **1**.

HARRÈ, R. and P. F. SECORD (1972) *The explanation of social behaviour*, Oxford: Basil Blackwell.

HARRIS, J. D. and RAWNSLEY, A. I. (1953) The locus of short duration auditory fatigue or "adaption", *J. Exp. Psychol.* **46**, 457–61.

HARRIS, W. (1960) Stress and perception: the effects of intense noise stimulation and noxious stimulation upon peripheral performance. Ph.D. dissertation, University of Southern California.

HARRISON, V. F. and MORTENSON, O. A. (1963) Identification and voluntary control of single motor unit activity in the tibialis anterior muscle, *Anat. Rec.* **144**, 107–16.

HART, J. D. (1974) Physiological responses of anxious and normal subjects to simple signal and non-signal auditory stimuli, *Psychophysiol.* **11**, 4, 443–51.

HARTMAN, T. F. (1963) Semantic transfer of the differential conditioned eyelid response from words to objects, *J. Exp. Psychol.* **65**, 194–200.

HARTSHORNE, H. and MAY, M. A. (1928) *Studies in the nature of character,* Vol. 1, Studies in deceit, New York: Macmillan.

HARTSBORNE, H. and MAY, M. A. (1929) *Studies in service and self-control,* New York: Macmillan.

HARTSHORNE, H. and SHUTTLEWORTH, F. K. (1930) *Studies in the organization of character,* New York: Macmillan.

HASLAM, D. R. (1967) Individual differences in pain threshold and level of arousal, *Br. J. Psychol.* **58**, 139–42.

HAYASHI, T. (1971) An experimental study of the second-signalling systems of man through printed language, *Condit. Reflex,* **6**, 11–21.

HAYNES, H., WHITE, B. L. and HELD, R. (1963) Visual accommodation in human infants, *Science, N. Y.* **148**, 528–30.

HEBB, D. O. (1949) *The organization of behaviour,* New York: Wiley.

HEBB, D. O. (1955) Drives and the C.N.S. (conceptual nervous system), *Psychol. Rev.* **62**, 243–54.

HEBB, D. O. (1956) The distinction between "classical" and "instrumental". *Can. J. Psychol.* **10,** 165–6.

HECHT, T., HECHT, K., CHOINOWSKI, S. and TREPTOW, K. (1976) Influence of breeding albino rats in groups and isolated on resistance to the effect of an emotional stimulus, *Zh. Vyssh. Nerv. Deyat. im. I. P. Pavlova,* **26,** 1200–7.

HEFFERLINE, R. F. (1958) The role of proprioception in the control of behaviour, *Trans. N. Y. Acad. Sci.* **20,** 739–64.

HEFFERLINE, R. F. and PERERA, T. B. (1963) Proprioceptive discimination of a covert operant without its observation by the subject, *Science, N. Y.* **139,** 355, 834–5.

HELMAT, H. (1971) Extraversion, neuroticism and verbal conditioning of affective self-disclosure, *J. Counselling Psychol.* **18,** 1, 64–9.

HELSON, H. (1959) Adaptation level theory, in, S. Koch (Ed.), *Psychology: a study of a science, Vol. 1, Sensory, perceptual and physiological foundations,* pp. 565–621, New York: McGraw-Hill.

HELSON, H. (1964) Current trends and issues in adaptation-level theory, *Am. Psychol.* **19,** 26–38.

HENDERSON, N. D. (1967) Prior treatment effects on open field behaviour of mice – a genetic analysis, *Anim. Behav.* **15,** 364-76.

HENDRICKSON, E. (1974) Personal communication. Cited by E. Calloway, *Brain electrical potentials and individual psychological differences,* New York and London: Grune & Stratton.

HENINGER, G. R., McDONALD, R. K., GOFF, W. R. and SOLLBERGER, A. (1969) Diurnal variation in the cerebral evoked potential and EEG, *Arch. Neurol.* **21,** 330–7.

HENRY, G. and TEAS, D. (1968) AER and loudness: analysis of response estimates, *J. Speech Hear. Res.* **11,** 334–42.

HERMELIN, B. and O'CONNOR, N. (1968) Measures of the occipital alpha rhythm in normal, subnormal and autistic children, *Br. J. Psychiat.* **114,** 603–10.

HERŃANDEZ-PÉON, R. and SCHERRER, H. (1955) Habituation to acoustic stimulae in the cochlear nucleus, *Proc. Fedn Am. Socs Exp. Biol.* **14,** 132.

HERŃANDEZ-PÉON, R., SCHERRER, H. and JOUVET, M. (1956) Modification of electrical activity in the cochlear nucleus during "attention" in unanaesthetized cats, *Science N. Y.* **133,** 331–2.

HERON, W. T. (1941) The inheritance of brightness and dullness in maze learning ability in the rat. *J. Genet. Psychol.* **59,** 41–9.

HERON, W. T. and SKINNER, B. F. (1940) The rate of extinction in maze-bright and maze-dull rats, *Psychol. Rec.* **4,** 11–18.

HERRINGTON, R. N. and CLARIDGE, G. S. (1965) Sedation threshold and Archimedes' spiral after-effect in early psychosis, *J. Psychiat. Res.* **3,** 159.

HESTON, L. L. (1966) Psychiatric disorders in foster home reared children of schizophrenic mothers, *Br. J. Psychiat.* **112,** 489, 819–25.

HEUBEL, D. H., HENSON, C. O., RUPERT, A. and GALAMBOS, R. (1959) Attention units in the auditory cortex, *Science, N. Y.* **129,** 1279–80.

HICKS, D. J. (1965) Imitation and retention of film-mediated aggressive peer and adult models, *J. Personality Soc. Psychol.* **2,** 97–100.

HIEATT, D. J. and TONG, J. E. (1968) Diferences between normals and schizophrenics on activation-induced change in two-flash fusion thresholds, *Br. J. Psychiat.* **115,** 477–8.

HIGGINS, J. D., TURSKY, B. and SCHWARTZ, G. E. (1971) Shock elicited pain and its reduction by concurrent tactile simulation, *Science, N. Y.* **172,** 866–7.

HILDEBRAND, H. P. (1953) A factorial study of introversion-extraversion by means of objective tests. Ph.D. Thesis, University of London.

HILLYARD, S. A. (1969) Relationships between the contingent negative variation (CNV) and reaction time, *Physiol. Behav.* **4,** 351–7.

HIMMELWEIT, H. (1945) Speed and accuracy of work as related to temperament, *Br. J. Psychol.* **36,** 132–44.

HINTON, D. E. (1971) An investigation of vicarious conditioning, generalization, and extinction, and their relationships to Eysenck's extraversion factor. *Diss. Abstr. Int.* **31**, 11-B, 6936.

HINTON, J. and O'NEIL, M. (1976) Psychophysiological response profiles: an outline of pilot research leading to possible computer predictions of recidivism. Paper presented at NATO Advanced Study Institute on Computer Prediction in Parole, Cambridge.

HIRSH, I. J. and BILGER, R. C. (1955) Auditory-threshold recovery after exposure to pure tones, *J. Acoust. Soc. Am.* **27**, 1186–93.

HIRSCHMAN, R. and BRUMBAUGH-BEUHLER, B. (1975) Electrodermal habituation and subjective response: effects of manifest anxiety and autonomic arousal, *J. Abnorm. Psychol.* **84**, 46–50.

HNATIOW, M. and LANG, P. J. (1965) Learned stabilization of cardiac rate, *Psychopsyiol.* **1**, 330–6.

HOBSON, A. J. and MCCARLEY, R. W. (1977) The brain as a dream state generator: an activation-synthesis hypothesis of the dream process, *Am. J. Psychiat.* **134**, 1335–48.

HOFFMAN, M. L. (1970) Moral development, in, P. H. Mussen (Ed.), *Manual of child psychology*, New York: Wiley.

HOGARTH, R. M. (1974) Monozygotic and dyzygotic twins reared together: sensitivity of heritability estimates, *Brit. J. Math. Stat. Psychol.* **27**, 1, 1–13.

HOLLAND, H. C. (1960) Measures of perceptual functions, in, H. J. Eysenck (Ed.), *Experiments in Personality*, Vol. II. New York: Humanities Press.

HOLLAND, H. C. and GOMEZ, B H. (1963) The effects of stimulant and depressant drugs upon visual figural after-effects, in, H. J. Eysenck (Ed.), *Experiments with drugs*, New York: Pergamon.

HONZIK, M. P. (1964) Personality consistency and change: some comments on papers by Bayley, MacFarlane, Moss, Kagan and Murphy, *Vita Hum.* **7**, 139–42.

HORN, J. M., PLOMIN, R. and ROSENMAN, R. (1976) Heritability of personality traits in adult male twins, *Behav. Genet.* **6**, 17–30.

HORNE, J. A. and OSTBERG, O. (1975) Time of day effects on extraversion and salivation, *Biol. Psychol.* **3**, 4, 301–7.

HOUSE, T. H. and MILLIGAN, W. L. (1973) Heart rate and galvanic skin responses to modelled distress in prison psychopaths, *Newsletter for Research in Mental Health and Behavioural Sciences*, **15**, 36–40.

HOWARD, J. A. (1979) Person-situation interaction models, *Personality Soc. Psychol. Bull.*, **5**, 2, 191–5.

HOWARTH, E. (1972) A factor analysis of selected markers for objective personality factors, *Multiv. Behav. Res.* **7**, 451–76.

HOWARTH, E. (1976) Were Cattell's "personality sphere" factors correctly identified in the first instance? *Br. J. Psychol.* **67**, 213–30.

HOWARTH, E. (1980) Major factors of personality, *J. Psychol.* **104**, 171–83.

HOWARTH, E. and BROWNE, J. A. (1971a) An item factor analysis of the 16PF, Personality: An International Journal, **2**, 117–39.

HOWARTH, E. and BROWNE, J. A. (1971b) Investigation of personality factors in a Canadian context, *Can. J. Behav. Sci.* **3**, 161–73.

HOWE, E. S. (1958) GSR conditioning in anxiety states, normals and chronic functional schizophrenic subjects, *J. Abnorm. Soc. Psychol.* **56**, 183–9.

HOZIMA, N., SUGIMEIRA, N., YAMAGUEHI, K. and HOSAKA, M. (1973) A method of classifying the mentally retarded by use of the skin potential reflex, *Jap. J. Spec. Educ.* **11**, 21–6.

HUDGINS, C. V. (1933) Conditioning and the voluntary control of the pupillary light reflex, *J. Genet. Psychol.* **8**, 3–51.

HUDGINS, G. A., DENENBERG, V. H. and ZARROW, M. X. (1968) Mice reared with rats: effects of preweaning and postweaning social interactions upon adult behaviour, *Behaviour*, **30**, 259–74.

HUME, W. I. (1968) The dimensions of central nervous arousal, *Bull. Br. Psychol. Soc.* **21**, 111.

HUME, W. I. (1973) Physiological measures in twins, in, G. Claridge, S. Canter and W. I. Hume

(Eds.) *Personality differences and biological variations: a study of twins,* pp. 87–114, London: Pergamon.

HUNTER-DUVAN, I. M. and ELLIOT, D. M. (1972) Effects of intense auditory stimulation: hearing losses and inner ear changes in the squirrel monkey, *J. Acoust. Soc. Am.* **52,** 1181–92.

HUTCHINSON, R. R. and RENFREW, J. W. (1966) Stalking attack and eating behaviours elicited from the same sites in the hypothalamus, *J. Comp. Physiol. Psychol.* **61,** 360–7.

INGRAM, E. and FITZGERALD, H. E. (1974) Individual differences in infant orienting and autonomic conditioning, *Dev. Psychobiol.* **71,** 4, 359–67.

INOUYE, E. (1961) Heritability of EEG patterns analysed by frequency analyser. II. Int. Conf. Human. Genetics, Rome.

IPPOLOTOV, F. V. (1966) Interanalyzer differences in the strength of the nervous system in man, *Vop. Psikhol.* No. 2.

IPPOLOTOV, F. V. (1967) Interanalyzer differences in the parameter of sensitivity-strength (excitation) for vision, audition and touch, in, B. M. Teplov (Ed.) *Typological features of higher nervous activity in man,* Vol. 5, Moscow: Prosveshchenie.

IRWIN, D. A., REBERT, C. S., MCADAM, D. W. and KNOTT, J. R. (1966) Slow potential changes (CNV) in the human EEG as a function of motivation variables, *Electroenceph. Clin. Neurophysiol.* **21,** 412–13.

ISON, J. R. and ROSEN, A. J. (1967) The effects of amobarbital sodium on differential instrumental conditioning and subsequent extinction, *Psychopharmacologia,* **10,** 417–25.

IVANOV-SMOLENSKII, A. G. (1932) Passive-defensive reflexes and the strong type of nervous system, *Tr. Fiziol. Labor. im. I. P. Pavlova,* **4,** 1–2.

IVANOV-SMOLENSKII, A. G. (Ed.) (1933) *Experimental studies of higher nervous activity in children,* Moscow: GIZ.

IVANOV-SMOLENSKII, A. G. (1935a) Experimental studies of the interaction of direct and symbolic projections in man's cortex, *Arkh. Biol. Nauk,* **38,** 1, 59–79.

IVANOV-SMOLENSKII, A. G. (1935b) Experimental studies of the child's higher nervous activity. *Fiziol. Zh. SSSR,* **19,** 119–55.

IVANOV-SMOLENSKII, A. G. (1953) On some who have fought for the purity of Pavlovian theory, *Zh. Vyssh. Nervn. Deyat. im. I. P. Pavlova,* **3,** 5.

JACKSON, D. N. (1958) Independence and resistance to perceptual field forces, *J. Abnorm. Soc. Psychol.* **56,** 279–82.

JACKSON, D. N. (1974) Amplitude and habituation of the orienting reflex as a function of stimulus intensity, Psychophysiol. **11,** 647–59.

JACOBSON, E. (1929) *Progressive relaxation,* Chicago: University of Chicago Press.

JACOBSON, E. (1932) Electrophysiology of mental activities, *Am. J. Psychol.* **44,** 677–94.

JAMES, J. P. and HUGHES, G. R. (1969) Generalisation of habituation of the GSR to white noise of varying intensities, *Psychonom. Sci.* **14,** 163–4.

JAMES, J. P., DANIELS, K. R. and HANSON, B. (1974) Over-habituation and spontaneous recovery of of the galvanic skin response, *J. Exp. Psychol.* **102,** 4, 732–4.

JANIS, I. I., MEHL, G. F., HAGAN, J. and HOLT, R. R. (1969) *Personality: dynamics, development and assessment,* New York: Harcourt, Brace & World.

JARWANDA, J. S. (1966) Age, sex, and personality variables in verbal conditioning and its modification by drugs. Unpublished Ph.D. Thesis, Punjab University.

JASPER, H. (1957) The electrical signs of cortical activity, *Psychol. Bull.* **34,** 7.

JASPER, H. and CRUICKSHANK, R. M. (1937) Electroencephalography, II, Visual stimulation and the after image as affecting the occipital alpha rhythm, *J. Genet. Psychol* **17,** 29–48.

JASPER, H. and SHAGASS, C. (1941) Conscious time judgements related to conditioned time intervals and voluntary control of the alpha rhythm, *J. Exp. Psychol.* **28,** 503–8.

JASTRZEBSKA, A., NOWAKOWSKA, J. and STRELAU, J. (1974) Temperament traits, resistance to stress and aetiopathogenesis of ulcers in the digestive tract, in, J. STRELAU (Ed.), *The role of temperament traits in action,* pp. 217–28, Wroclaw: Ossolineum.

JINKS, J. L. and FULKER, D. W. (1970) Comparison of the biometric genetical MAVA and classical approaches to the analysis of human behaviour, *Psychol. Bull.* **73**, 311-49.

JIRSA, R. E. (1974) The prognostic implications of 6 K C/S in audiology, *J. Auditory Res.* **14**, 3, 192-94.

JOHANNSEN, W. J. (1964) Motivation in schizophrenic performance: a review, Psychol. Rep. **15**, 839-70.

JOHN, E. R. (1972) Switchboard vs. statistical theories of learning and memory. *Science, N. Y.* **177**, 850-64.

JOHN, E. R., SHIMOKOCHI, M. and BARTLETT, F. (1969) Neural readout from memory during generalization, *Science, N. Y.* **164**, 1534-6.

JOHNS, J. H. and QUAY, H. C. (1962) The effect of social reward on verbal conditioning in psychopathic and neurotic military offenders, *J. Consult. Psychol.* **26**, 217-20.

JOHNSON, L. C. (1963) Some attributes of spontaneous autonomic activity, *J. Comp. Physiol. Psychol.* **56**, 415-22.

JOHNSON, L. C. and LUBIN, A. (1967) The orienting reflex during waking and sleeping, *Electroenceph. Clin. Neurophysiol.* **22**, 11.

JONES, B. and MISHKIN, M. (1972) Limbic lesions and the problem of stimulus-reinforcement associations, *Exp. Neurol.* **36**, 362-77.

JONES, H. E. (1955) Perceived differences among twins, *Eugen. Q.* **2**, 98-102.

JONES, H. G. (1956) The application of conditioning and learning techniques to the treatment of a psychiatric patient, *J. Abnorm. Soc. Psychol.* **52**, 414-20.

JONES, P. A. (1973) The effect of types of reward on the operant conditioning of extraverts, *Diss. Abstr. Int.* **33**, 12-13, 6080.

JONES, R. (1965) Analysis of variance of the half diallel table, *Heredity, Lond.* **20**, 117-21.

JOSHI, R. T. (1974) Field dependence, anxiety and personality, *Percept. Mot. Skills*, **38**, 3, 1328.

JOST, H. and SONTAG, L. W. (1944) The genetic factor in autonomic nervous system function, *Psychosom. Med.* **6**, 308-10.

JOUVET, M. (1961) Recherches sur les méchanismes neurophysiologiques du sommeil et de l'apprêtrissage négatif, in, *Brain mechanisms and learning*, Springfield.

JOUVET, M. and HERNÁNDEZ-PÉON, R. (1957) Méchanismes neurophysiologiques concernant l'habituation, l'attention et le conditionnement, *Electroenceph. Clin. Neurophysiol.* Suppl. 6.

JUEL-NEILSON, N. and HARVALD, B. (1958) The electroencephalogram in uniovular twins brought up apart, *Acta Genet. Statist. Med.* **8**, 57-64.

JUNG, C. G. (1924) *Psychological types*, London: Routledge & Kegan Paul.

JUNG, C. G. (1944) *Psychology and alchemy*, New York: Pantheon.

JUNG, R. (1961) Neuronal integration in the visual cortex and its significance for visual information, in, W. H. Rosenblith (Ed.), *Sensory communication*, New York: Wiley.

JUS, A. and JUS, C. (1960) Étude de l'extinction part répétition de l'expression EEG du réflexe d'orientation et de l'action du frein externe sur les réactions EEG aux différents stimuli chez l'homme, in, H. H. Jasper and G. D. Smirnov (Eds.), *The Moscow colloquium on electroencephalography of higher nervous activity, Electroenceph. Clin. Neurophysiol.* Suppl. 13.

KADLUB, K. J. (1956) The effeects of two types of reinforcement on the performance of psychopathic and normal criminals, *Diss. Abstr.* **16**, 1946-7.

KAGAN, J. and MOSS, H. A. (1960) The stability of passive and dependent behaviour from childhood through adulthood, *Child. Dev.* **31**, 577-91.

KAGAN, J. and MOSS, H. A. (1962) *Birth to maturity: a study in psychological development*, New York: Wiley.

KALYUTKIN, YU. N., ZYRYANOVA, N. G. and SUKHOBSKAYA, G. S. (1972) Influence of neuro-dynamic factors on individual characteristics of problem solving, in, V. D. Nebylitsyn, and J. A. Gray (Eds.), *Biological bases of individual behaviour*, pp. 334-46, London: Academic Press.

KAMANO, D. K., MARTIN, L. K. and POWELL, B. J. (1966) Avoidance response acquisition and amobarbital dosage levels, *Psychopharmacologia*, **8**, 319–23.

KAMIN, L. J. (1955) Relations between discrimination, apparatus stress and the Taylor scale, *J. Abnorm. Soc. Psychol.* **51**, 595–9.

KAMITAKE, M. (1963) Studies on hereditary versus environmental factors in psychological functions by use of twin method, *Jap. J. Psychol.* **33** 6.

KAMIYA, J. (1968) Conscious control of brain waves, *Psychol. Today,* **1**, 57–60.

KANTOROWITZ, D. A. (1978) Personality and conditioning of tumescence and detumescence. *Behav. Res. Ther.* **16**, 117–23.

KAPUSTNIK, O. P. (1930) The interrelation between direct conditioned stimuli and their verbal symbols, *Tr. Lab. Fiziol. Vyssh. Nervn. Deyat. Reb.*, **2**, (*Psychol. Abstra.* **8**, 152).

KAPUSTNIK, O. P. and FADEEVA, V. K. (1930) Extinction of conditioned reflexes in children 5–12 years of age. *Tr. Lab. Fiziol. Vyssh. Nervyn. Deyat. Reb.* **2**, 19–41.

KARPILOVA, N. L. (1964) On the regulation of the limit of delayed inhibition, in, E. A. Asratyan and V. N. Andreyeva (Eds.), cf. Barkhudaryan (1964), 609–610.

KARSON, S. and O'DELL, J. W. (1974) Is the 16 PF factorially valid? *J. Person. Assess.* **38**, 104–14.

KAS'YANOV, V. M. and FRUKTOV, A. L. (1952) Influence of the strength of a sound stimulus on the speed of motor acts in man, *Fiziol. Zh. SSSR*, **38**, 681–7.

KATKIN, E. S. (1965a) The relationship between manifest anxiety and two indices or autonomic response to stress, *J. Personality Soc. Psychol.* **2**, 324–33.

KATKIN, E. S. (1965b) The relationship between a measure of transitory anxiety and spontaneous autonomic activity. Paper read at the Midwestern Psychological Association Meeting.

KATKIN, E. S. and McCUBBIN, R. J. (1969) Habituation of the orienting response as a function of individual differences in anxiety and autonomic lability, *J. Abnorm. Psychol.* **74**, 54–60.

KATKIN, E. S. and MURRAY, E. N. (1968) Instrumental conditioning of autonomically mediated behaviour: theoretical and methodological issues. *Psychol. Bull.* **70**, 52–68.

KATZ, R. A., SUTHERLAND, R. C. and BROWN, C. C. (1967) Measurement of salivation, in, C. C. Brown (Ed.), *Methods in psychophysiology,* pp. 173–91, Baltimore: Williams & Wilkins Co.

KAUFMAN, H. (1970) *Aggression and altruism,* New York: Holt, Rinehart & Winston.

KAZATKIN, N. I., MIROZYANTS, N. S. and KHOKHITVA, A. P. (1953) Conditioned orienting in infants during the first year of life, *Zh. Vyssh. Nerv. Deyat. im. I. P. Pavlova,* **3**, 192–202.

KEARSLEY, R. B. (1974) The new-born's response to auditory stimulation: a demonstration of orienting and defensive behaviour, *Child Dev.* **44**, 582–91.

KELLER, F. S. and SHOENFIELD, W. N. (1950) *Principles of psychology,* New York: Appleton.

KELLER, M. (1942) Mediated generalisation: generalisation of a conditioned galvanic response established to a pictured object, *Am. J. Psychol.* **56**, 438–48.

KELLY, D., BROWN, C. and SHAFFER, J. (1970) A comparison of physiological and psychological measurements on anxious patients and normal controls, *Psychophysiol.* **6**, 429–41.

KEMPE, J. E. (1956) An experimental investigation of the relationship between certain personality characteristics and physiological responses to stress in a normal population. Unpublished doctoral dissertation, Michigan State University. Cited by I. B. Goldstein (1964) Role of Muscle Tension in Personality Theory, *Psychol. Bull.* **61**, 418–25.

KESLER, P. and WEALE, J. M. (1974) Hippocampal damage and schizophrenia: a critique of Mednick's theory, *J. Abnorm. Psychol.* **83**, 91–6.

KEUSS, P. J. and ORLEBEKE, J. F. (1977) Transmarginal inhibition in a reaction time task as a function of extraversion and neuroticism, *Acta Psychol.* **41**, 2–3, 139.

KHACHATURIAN, M. KH. (Unpublished data, in, E. A. Asratyan (Ed.) (1965) *Compensatory adaptations and reflex activity,* Ch. 4, p. 141, Oxford: Pergamon Press.

KHARCHENKO, P. D. (1960) *Delayed conditioned reflexes,* Kiev.

KHILCHENKO, A. Y. (1958) Method of investigating the mobility of the basic nervous processes in man, *Zh. Vyssh. Nerv. Deyat. im. I. P. Pavlova,* **8**, 6.

KHOZAK, L. E. (1933) Study of the orienting-investigatory food-seeking and passive-defensive conditioned reflexes in school-age children, in, *Experimental investigations of nervous activity in children*, Moscow.

KHRIZMAN, T. P. (1975) Organisation of spatial-temporal relations of the brain electric processes in children's response to verbal commands, *Zh. Vyssh. Nerv. Deyat. im. I. P. Pavlova*, **25**, 690–9.

KIMBLE, D. P. and RAY, R. (1965) Reflex habituation and potentiation in *Rava pipiens. Anim. Behav.* **13**, 550–3.

KIMBLE, G. A. (1961) *Conditioning and learning, 2nd ed.*, New York: Appleton-Century-Crofts.

KIMMEL, H. D. (1963) Mangement of conditioned fear, *Psychol. Rep.* **12**, 313–14.

KIMMEL, H. D. (1967) Instrumental conditioning of autonomically mediated behaviour, *Psychol. Bull.* **67**, 337–45.

KIMMEL, H. D. (1973) Reflex "habituality" as a basis for differentiating between classical and instrumental conditioning, *Condit. Reflex.* **8**, 10–27.

KIMMEL, H. D. (1976) Cherchez la difference! *Pavlov J. Biol. Sc.* **11**, 56–65.

KIMMEL, H. D. and KIMMEL, E. (1965) Sex differences in adaptation of the GSR under repeated applications of a visual stimulus, *J. Exp. Psychol.* **70**, 536–7.

KIMMEL, H. D. and KIMMEL, E. (1967) Inter-effector influences in operant autonomic conditioning, *Psychonom. Sci.* **9**, 191–2.

KIMMEL, H. D. and REYNOLDS, T. W. (1971) On the locus of extinctive inhibition, *Acta. Neurobiol. Exper.* **31**, 227–36.

KIMMEL, H. D. and TERRANT, F. R. (1968) Bias due to individual differences in yoked control designs, *Behav. Res. Meth. Instrumentation*, **1**, 11–14.

KIMMEL, H. D., HILL, F. A. and FOWLER, R. L. (1962) Intersensory generlization in compound classical conditioning, *Psychol. Rep.* **11**, 631–6.

KLIMOV, D. T. (1929) The mechanism of generalisation of conditioned reflexes, *Tr. Fiziol. Lab. im. I. P. Pavlova,* **3**, 2–3.

KLIMOV, Y. A. (1960) Some features of the motorium with respect to typological differences in the mobility of nervous processes, *Vop. Psikhol.* **3**.

KLIMOV, Y. A. (1967) Typological differences in adaptation to extreme conditions of diagnostic experiment, in, *Typological studies in the psychology of personality,* Perm: Transactions of the Perm Pedagogical Institute, 4.

KLING, J. K. (1972) The effects of verbal and material reward and punishment in the verbal conditioning of primary and secondary psychopaths, in R. D. Hare and D. Schalling (Eds.) *Psychopathic behavior: approaches to research,* Chichester, N.Y.: Wiley.

KLONOWICZ, T. (1974a) Effects of reactivity and type of instruction on performance of simple construction tasks, in, J. Strelau (Ed.), *The role of temperamental traits in action,* pp. 143–52, Wroclaw: Ossolineum.

KLONOWICZ, T. (1974b) Reactivity and fitness for the occupation of operator, *Pol. Psychol. Bull.* **5**, 129–36.

KLONOWICZ, T. (1979) Transformation ability, temperament traits and individual experience. *Pol. Psychol. Bull.* **10**, 215–23.

KLONOWICZ, T. and CZYZLOWSKA, M. (1974) Level of reactivity and level of performance: a contribution to the conception of individual style of action. Paper presented at the International Conference on Temperament and Personality, Warsaw.

KLYAGIN, V. S. and KOVALEV, A. N. (1974) Statistical analysis of EEGs and diagnosis of nervous system strength, in, *Diagnostic problems of mental development,* Tallin.

KNOTT, J. (1939) Some effects of "mental set" on the electrophysiological processes of the human cerebral cortex, *J. Exp. Psychol.* **24**, 4.

KNOTT, J. and IRWIN, D. A. (1968) Anxiety, stress and the contingent negative variation (CNV), *Electroenceph. Clin. Neurophysiol.* **24**, 286–7.

KNOWLES, J. B. and KRASNER, L. (1965) Extraversion and duration of the Archimedes spiral after-effect, *Percept. Mot. Skills,* **20**, 997–1000.

KOEPKE, J. E. and PRIBRAM, K. H. (1966) Habituation of GSR as a function of stimulus duration and spontaneous activity, *J. Comp. Physiol. Psychol.* **61**, 442–8.

KOEPKE, J. E. and PRIBRAM, K. H. (1967) Habituation of the vasoconstriction response as a function of stimulus duration and anxiety, *J. Comp. Physiol. Psychol.* **64**, 502–4.

KOFFMAN, G. and PRESSEY, A. W. (1967) Sex differences on a group test of FAE, *Psychonom. Sci.* **8**, 511–12.

KOGAN, A. B. (1960) Structural foundations of the nature of the temporary connections of the conditioned reflex, *Gagrskiye Besedy,* **3**, 191–212.

KOHLBERG, L. (1963) The development of children's orientations toward a moral order, I, Sequence in the development of moral thought, *Vita Hum.* **6**, 11–33.

KOHLBERG, L. (1968) Early education: a cognitive-developmental view, *Child Dev.* **39**, 1013–62.

KOHLBERG, L. (1969) *Stage and sequence: the developmental approach to moralization,* New York: Holt, Rinehart & Winston.

KOHLER, C. (1976) Habituation of the orienting response after medial and lateral septal lesions in the albino rat, *Behav. Biol.* **16**, 1, 63–72.

KOHLER, W., HELD, R. and O'CONNELL, D. N. (1952) An investigation of cortical currents, *Proc. Am. Phil. Soc.* **96**, 290–330.

KOK, E. P. (1975) Similarities and differences in the higher functions of symmetric sections of the right and left cerebral hemispheres, *Fiziologia Cheloveka,* **3**.

KOKORINA, E. P. (1963) Measurement of basic nervous processes in the determination of higher nervous activity using the motor method with food reinforcement, *Zh. Vyssh. Nervn. Deyat. im. I. P. Pavlova,* **8**, 2.

KOKORINA, E. P. (1964) Metodika issledovaniya vysshey nervnoy deyatel'nosti Krupnogo rogatogo skota, in, *Metodika izucheniya tipologicheskikh osobennostey vysshey nervnoy deyatel'nosti u zhivotnyk.* Moscow & Leningrad: Nauka.

KOLAROVA, Z. J. (1968) *Physiology of higher nervous activity in children,* Moscow.

KOLESNIKOV, M. S. (1953) Material on the description of the weak type of nervous system, *Tr. Inst. Fiziol. im. I. P. Pavlova,* **2**.

KOLESNIKOV, M. S. (1953) The development of typological properties of higher nervous activity during ontogenesis. *Tr. Instit. Fiziol. im. I. P. Pavlova.*

KOLESNIKOV, M. S. (1963) *The weak kind of nervous system in animals,* Minsk.

KOLESNIKOV, M. S. and TROSHIKHIN, V. A. (1951) The small standard battery tests for determining type of higher nervous activity in the dog, *Zh. Vyssh. Nervn. Deyat. im. I. P. Pavlova,* **1**, 5.

KOLODNAYA, A. YA. (1957) Izmeneniya elektricheskoy aktivnosti myshts pri vyrabotke dvigatel'nykh differentsirovok u cheloveka, in, *Voprosy izucheniya vysshey neyrodinamiki v svyazi s problemami psikhologii,* Moscow: APN RSFSR.

KOLODNAYA, A. YA. (1963a) Examples of individual differences in the EMGs of man, in, B. M. Teplov (Ed.) *Typological Features of Higher Nervous Activity in Man,* Vol. 3, Moscow: Akad. Pedagog. Nauk RSFSR.

KOLODNAYA, A. YA. (1963b) Features of concentration of nervous processes according to different levels of balance, in, B. M. Teplov (Ed.) *Typological features of higher nervous activity in man,* Vol. 3, Moscow: Akad. Pedagog. Nauk RSFSR.

KOLOMEYTSEVA, I. A. (1979) Dynamics of brain electrical activity during long-term immobilisation, *Zh. Vyssh. Nerv. Deyat. im. I. P. Pavlova,* **29**, 337–44.

KOLOSOVA, T. E. and FORMICHEVA, E. E. (1979) Inter-hemispheric irradiation of excitation depending on individual characteristics of animals, *Zh. Vyssh. Nerv. Deyat. im. I. P. Pavlova,* **29**, 543–7.

KOL'TSOVA, M. M. (1967) *Generalization as a function of the brain,* Leningrad: Nauka.

KOL'TSOVA, M. M. (1972) Physiological role of verbal signals in the development of voluntary movements, *Zh. Vyssh. Nerv. Deyat. im. I. P. Pavlova,* **22**, 1, 10–15.

KOL'TSOVA, M. M. (1973) *Motor activity and the development of cerebral functions in the child,* Moscow.

REFERENCES                                                                    501

KONDO, C. Y., CANTER, A. and BEAM, J. A. (1977) Intersession interval and reductions in frontalis EMG during bio-feedback training, *Psychophysiol.* **14**, 15–17.

KONDRAT'EVA, I. I. (1974) The role of the significance factor in reactions to signals of different intensities, *Vop. Psikhol.* **6**, 107–16.

KONORSKI, J. (1948a) *Conditioned reflexes and neuron organisation,* Cambridge: Cambridge University Press.

KONORSKI, J. (1948b) The problem of internal inhibition, *Tr. Ob. Sessii Posvyash. 10-letiya so Dnya Smerti I. P. Pavlova,* 225–9.

KONORSKI, J. (1967) *Integrative activity of the brain: an interdisciplinary approach,* Chicago: University of Chicago Press.

KONORSKI, J. (1973) On two types of conditional reflexes: general laws of association, *Condit. Reflex,* **8**, 2–9.

KONORSKI, J. and LAWICKA, W. (1959) Physiological mechanism of delayed reactions, *Acta Biol. Exps. Vars.* **19**, 175–96.

KONORSKI, J. and MILLER, S. (1936) Conditioned reflexes of the motor analyzer, *Tr. Fiziol. Lab. I. P. Pavlova,* **6**, 1, 119–288.

KONRADI, G. (1953) Circulatory changes in various states of the body, in, K. Bykov (Ed.), *Textbook of physiology,* pp. 172–9. Moscow: Peace Publishers.

KOPYLOV, A. G. (1956) Evaluation of the functional state of the human brain by the method of electroencephalographic curves of rhythm assimilation, in, *Problems of the theory and practice of electrophysiology of the central nervous system,* Leningrad.

KOPYLOV, A. G. (1957) Method of electroencephalographic curves of rhythm assimilation. *Conference on problems of electrophysiology of the central nervous system,* Leningrad.

KOPYLOV, A. G. (1960) Dynamics of the process of rhythm assimilation as a criterion of the functional properties of the brain. *Transactions of Scientific Conference dedicated to the memory of N. Y. Wedenskii,* Vologda.

KORBATOV, B. M. (1956) Study of the dynamic transmission of a conditioned connection from one cortical signalling system to the other, in, A. G. Ivanov-Smolenskii (Ed.), *Works of the Institute of Higher Nervous Activity: patho-physiological series,* Vol. II, Moscow: Akad. Nauk SSSR.

KORIAT, A., AVERILL, J. R. and MALMSTROM, E. J. (1973) Individual differences in habituations: some methodological and conceptual issues, *J. Res. Person.* **7**, 88–101.

KORNER, A. F. (1964) Some hypotheses regarding the significance of individual differences at birth for later development, *The psychoanalytic study of the child,* XIX, New York: International Universities Press.

KOROTKIN, I. (1930) Comparative description of higher nervous activity in the child with alimentary and defensive reinforcement, in, *Basic mechanisms of conditioned reflex activity in the child,* Moscow.

KOSTOMAROVA, N. M. (1953) Title not given. Cited in E. I. Boiko (Ed.) (1957) *Reciprocity of conditioned reflex processes in complex system reactions.*

KOTLIAREVSKII, L. I. (1933) Orientirovochno-issledovatel'skiye uslovnye refleksy na prostye i sinteticheskiye razdrazhiteli u detei shkol'nogo vozrasta, sb. *"Eksperimental'nye issledovaniya vyssh. nervn. deyat. rebenka".*

KOTLIAREVSKII, L. I. (1935) The formation of pupillary conditioned reflexes and of a differentiation in response to both direct and verbal stimuli, *Arkh. Biol. Nauk,* **39**, 477–89. Cited in W. H. Viogt (1968) Conditioning the human pupillary response, *Percept. Mot. Skills,* **26**, 976–82 (p. 976).

KOTLIAREVSKII, L. I. (1936) Cardio-vascular conditioned reflexes to direct and to verbal stimuli. *Fiziol. Zh. SSSR,* **20**, 228–42.

KOVALEV, A. N., SMIRNOV, L. M. and RABINOVICH, L. A. (1976) The relationship between the internal structure of EEGs and emotionality, *Novye Issled. Psikhol.* **1**.

KOZAK, K. and WESTERMAN, R. (1966) Basic patterns of plastic change in the mammalian nervous system, *Soc. Exp. Biol.* **20**, 509–44.

KOZCIELAK, R. (1979) The role of nervous system traits in inventive creativity, *Pol. Psychol. Bull.* **10,** 225–32.

KOZIELECKI, J. (1968) *Problems in the psychology of thinking,* Warsaw: PWN.

KOZLOVA, L. N., ROGATNYKH, A. A. and SERGEYEVA, L. L. (1979) On the age characteristics of different properties of higher nervous activity type in dogs, *Zh. Vyssh. Nerv. Deyat. im. I. P. Pavlova,* 64–71.

KOZLOWSKI, C. (1977) Demand for stimulation and probability preferences in gambling decisions, *Pol. Psychol. Bull.* **8,** 67–73.

KRASNOGORSKII, N. I. (1935) Physiological activity of the brain in children as a new approach to paediatric problems, in, *Development of studies on the physiological activity of the brain in children,* Moscow.

KRASNOGORSKII, N. I. (1954) *Study of higher nervous activity of man and animals,* Moscow: Medgiz.

KRASUSKII, V. K. (1964) Specification of types of higher nervous activity in dogs using the salivary method, in, *Methods of study of the typological features of higher nervous activity in animals,* Moscow: Izd. Nauka.

KRAUS, O. and KULKA, E. (1958) *Night and smog* (in Czech), Prague: Nasuboysko.

KRECHEVSKY, I. (1933) The hereditary nature of "hypotheses", *J. Comp. Psychol.* **16,** 99–116.

KREPS, YE. M. (1924) An attempt to give an individual description of the experimental animal, *Tr. Fiziol. Labor. im. I. P. Pavlova,* **1,** 1.

KRETSCHMER, E. (1921) *Korperbau und Charakter,* Berlin.

KRUPNOV, A. I. (1971) Dynamic characteristics of active behaviour and their electro-encephalographic correlates. Dissertation, Moscow University.

KRUSHINSKII, L. V. (1949) Inheritance of passive-defensive behaviour (cowardice) as connected with types of nervous system in the dog, *Tr. Inst. Evol. Fiziol. Patol. Vyssh. Nervn. Deyat.* **1.**

KRUSHINSKII, L. V. (1962) *Animal behaviour: its normal and abnormal development,* translated by Basil Haigh, New York: Consultants Bureau.

KRYSHOVA, N. A., BELIAEVA, Z. V., DMITRIEVA, A. F., ZHILINSKAIE, M. A. and PERNOV, L. G. (1962) Investigation of the higher nervous activity and of certain vegetative features in twins, *Soviet Psychol. Psychiat.* **1,** 36–41.

KUO, Z. Y. (1967) *The dynamics of behaviour development,* New York: Random House.

KUPALOV, P. S. (1960) Experimental neuroses, in S. N. Davidenkov (Ed.) *Handbook of neurology,* Vol. 6, Neuroses, epilepsy and narcolepsy, pp. 9–43, Moscow: Medgiz.

KUPALOV, P. S. (1961) Some normal and pathological properties of nervous processes in the brain, in, *Pavlovian conference on higher nervous activity. N. Y. Acad. Sci.* **92,** 1046–53.

KUPALOV, P. S. (1969) The formation of conditioned place reflexes, in, M. Cole and I. Maltzman (Eds.), *A handbook of contemporary Soviet psychology,* pp. 735–62, New York. Basic Books.

LACEY, J. I. (1950) Individual differences in somatic response patterns, *J. Comp. Physiol. Psychol.* **43,** 338–50.

LACEY, J. I. (1956) The evaluation of autonomic responses; towards a general solution, *Ann. N. Y. Acad. Sci.* **67,** 123–64.

LACEY, J. I. (1959) Psychophysiological approaches to the evaluation of psychotherapeutic process and outcome, in, E. A. Rubenstein and M. B. Parlott (Eds.), *Research in psychotherapy,* pp. 160–208, American Psychological Association, Washington, D.C.

LACEY, J. I. (1967) Somatic response patterning and stress: some revisions of activation theory, in, M. H. Appley and R. Trumbull (Eds.), *Psychological stress,* pp. 14–42, New York: Appleton-Century-Crofts.

LACEY, J. I. and LACEY, B. C. (1958a) The relationship of resting autonomic activity to motor impulsivity, *Res. Publ. Ass. Ner. Ment. Dis.* **36,** 144–209.

LACEY, J. I. and LACEY, B. C. (1958b) Verification and extension of the principle of autonomic response-stereotyping, *Am. J. Psychol.* **71,** 50–73.

LACEY, J. I. and LACEY, B. C. (1962) The law of initial values in the longitudinal study of autonomic constitution: reproducibility of autonomic responses and response patterns over a four-year interval, *Ann. N.Y. Acad. Sci.* **98**, 1257–90.

LACEY, J. I. and SMITH, R. L. (1954) Conditioning and generalization of unconscious anxiety, *Science N.Y.* **120**, 1045–52.

LACEY, J. I. and VAN LEHN, R. (1952) Differential emphasis in somatic response to stress, *Psychosom. Med.* **14**, 73–81.

LACEY, J. I., BATEMAN, D. E. and VAN LEHN, R. (1953) Autonomic response specificity: an experimental study, *Psychosom. Med.* **15**, 8–21.

LACHMAN, S. J. (1973) *Psychosomatic disorders: a behavioristic interpretation,* New York: Wiley.

LADER, M. H. (1967) Palmar skin conductance measures in anxiety and phobic states, *J. Psychonom. Res.* **11**, 271–81.

LADER, M. H. and SARTORIOUS, N. (1968) Anxiety in patients with hysterical conversion symptoms, *J. Neurol. Neurosurg. Psychiat.* **31**, 490–5.

LADER, M. H. and WING, L. (1964) Habituation of the psychogalvanic reflex in patients with anxiety states and in normal states, *J. Neurol. Neurosurg. Psychiat.* **27**, 210–18.

LADER, M. H. and WING, L. (1966) *Physiological measures, sedative drugs, and morbid anxiety,* London: Oxford University Press.

LAGERSPITZ, K. (1961) Genetic and social causes of aggressive behaviour in mice, *Scand. J. Psychol.* **2**, 167–73.

LAGERSPITZ, K. and WUORINEN, K. (1965) A cross-fostering experiment with mice selectively bred for aggressiveness and non-aggressiveness, *Inst. Psychol. Univ. Turku.* **17**, 1–6.

LAGERSPITZ, K., TIRRI, R. and LAGERSPITZ, M. J. (1968) Neurochemical and endocrinal studies of mice selectively bred for aggressiveness, *Scand. J. Psychol.* **9**, 157–60.

LAGUTINA, N. I. (1958) The structure of orienting reflexes, in, L. G. Voronin, A. N. Leont'ev, A. R. Luria, E. N. Sokolov and O. S. Vinogradova (Eds.), *The orienting reflex and orienting-investigatory activity,* pp. 80–6, Moscow: Akad. Pedagog. Nauk RSFSR.

LANG, P. J. and BUSS, A. H. (1965) Psychological deficit in schizophrenia, II, Interference and activation, *J. Abnorm. Psychol.* **70**, 77–106.

LANG, P. J., MELAMED, B. G. and HART, J. A. (1970) A physiological analysis of fear modification using an automated desensitization procedure, *J. Abnorm. Psychol.* **76**, 220–34.

LANG, P. J., SRONFE, A. and HASTINGS, J. E. (1967) Effects of feedback and instrumental set on the control of cardiac-rate variability, *J. Exp. Psychol.* **75**, 425–31.

LANGMEIER, J. and MATEJCEK, Z. (1975) *Psychological deprivation in early childhood,* G. L. Mangan (Ed.), Brisbane: University of Queensland Press.

LANSING, R. W., SCHWARTZ, E. and LINDSLEY, D. B. (1958) Reaction time and EEG activation under alerted and non-alerted conditions, *J. Exp. Psychol.* **58**, 1–7.

LAPTEV, I. I. (1938) *Proceedings of the third conference on physiological problems,* **34**, Moscow.

LASHLEY, K. S. (1916) Reflex secretion of the human parotid gland, *J. Exp. Psychol.* **1**, 461–93.

LÁT, J. (1962) Über die Möglichkeit der Beeinflussung der Entwicklung der individuellen psychosomatischen Konstitution, *Biol. Lebensäller Tag,* 222–6.

LATMARIZOVA, A. F. (1947) *Physiological indices of functional mobility.* Leningrad.

LAURENCE, D. R. (1973) *Clinical pharmacology,* Edinburgh: Churchill Livingstone.

LAZARUS, A. A. (1965a) Behaviour therapy, incomplete treatment and symptom substitution, *J. Nerv. Ment. Dis.* **140**, 80–6.

LAZARUS, A. A. (1965b) A preliminary report on the use of directed muscular activity in counter-conditioning, *Behav. Res. Ther.* **2**, 301–3.

LEITENBERG, H., AGRAS, W. S. and BARLOW, D. H. (1969) Contribution of selective positive reinforcement and therapeutic instructions to systematic desensitization therapy, *J. Abnorm. Psychol.* **74**, 113–18.

LEITES, N. S. (1956) The problem of typological differences in the after-effects of excitatory and inhibitory processes, in, B. M. Teplov (Ed.), *Typological features of higher nervous activity in man,* Vol. I, Moscow: Acad. Pedagog. Nauk RSFSR.

# 504 THE BIOLOGY OF HUMAN CONDUCT

LEITES, N. S. (1972) Problems of interrelationship between typological features and age, in, V. D. Nebylitsyn and J. A. Gray (Eds.), *Biological bases of individual behaviour*, London: Academic Press.

LENNENBERG, H. H., REBELSKY, F. and NICHOLS, J. (1965) The vocalisation of infants born to deaf and hearing parents, *Hum. Dev.* **8**, 23–37.

LENNOX, W. G., GIBBS, F. A. and GIBBS, E. L. (1945) The brain wave pattern, an hereditary trait: evidence from 74 "normal" pairs of twins. *J. Hered.* **36**, 233–43.

LEONT'EV, A. N. (1972) *Problems of the development of the mind*, 3rd Ed., Moscow, NGU.

LEONT'EV, A. N. (1975) *Activity, consciousness, personality*, Moscow: Politizdat.

LEONT'EV, A. A. (1977) Some new trends in Soviet psycholinguistics, *Soviet Psychol.* **15**, 2.

LEPIKHOVA, L. A. (1974) Physiological basis of "psychic tempo". *Vop. Psikhol.* **7**.

LERNER, E. (1937) *Constraint areas and the moral judgment of children*, Menasha, Wisc.: George Banta Publ. Co.

LESTER, B. M. (1975) Cardiac habituation of the orienting response to an auditory signal in infants of varying nutritional states, *Dev. Psychol.* **11**, 4, 432–42.

LESTER, D. (1976) The relationship between some dimensions of personality, *Psychology*, **13**, 1, 58–60.

LETTVIN, J. Y., MATURANN, H. R., McCULLOCH, W. S. and PITTS, W. H. (1961) What the frog's eye tells the frog's brain, *Proc. Inst. Radio Engrs.* **47**, 1940–51.

LEVINE, F. M., TURSKY, B. and NICHOLS, D. C. (1966) Tolerance for pain, extraversion and neuroticism: failure to replicate results, *Percept. Mot. Skills*, **23**, 847–50.

LEVINE, J. D., GORDON, N. C. and FIELDS, H. L. (1978) The mechanisms of placebo analgesia, *Lancet*, September 23rd.

LEVINE, S. (1962) Psychophysiological effects of infantile stimulation, in, E. L. Bliss (Ed.), *Roots of behaviour*, New York: Harper.

LEVINE, S. (1968) Influence of infantile stimulation on the response to stress during preweaning development, *Dev. Psychobiol.* **1**, 67–70.

LEVINSON, J. Z. (1968) Flicker fusion phenomena, *Science, N. Y.* **160**, 21–8.

LEVITOV, N. D. (1952) *Voprosy Psikhologii Kharaktera*, 1st ed. (2nd ed., 1956).

LEWIS, E. G., DUSTMAN, R. F. and BECK, E. C. (1972) Evoked response similarity in monozygotic, dizygotic and unrelated individuals: a comparative study, *Electroenceph. Clin. Neurophysiol.* **32**, 309–16.

LEWIS, M. and HORWITZ, M. (1969) The meaning of an orienting response: a study in the hierarchical order of attending. Paper presented at the Meeting of the Society for Research in Child Development, Santa Monica, California.

LEWIS, M., BARTELS, B., FADEL, D. and CAMPBELL, H. (1966) Infant attention: the effect of familiar and novel visual stimuli as a function of age. Paper read at the 32nd Annual Meeting of Eastern Psychological Association, New York.

LIBERMAN, R. P., KING, L. W., DE RISI, W. J. and McCANN, M. (1975) *Personal effectiveness: guiding people to assert themselves and improve their social skills*, Champaign, Ill.; Research Press.

LIDBERG, L., LEVANDER, S. and SCHALLING, D. (1974) Habituation of the digital vasoconstrictive orienting response, *J. Exp. Psychol.* **102**, 4, 700–5.

LIDBERG, L., LEVANDER, S., SCHALLING, D. and LIDBERG, Y. (1978) Urinary catecholamines, stress, and psychopathy: a study of arrested men awaiting trial, *Psychosom. Med.* Report No. 15 from the Laboratory of Clinical Stress Research, Stockholm.

LIDDELL, H. S. (1958) A biological bases for psychopathology, in, P. H. Hoch and J. Zubin (Eds.), *Problems of addiction and habituation*, New York: Grune.

LIGHT, E. F. (1972) A study of the relationship between characteristics of ego boundary and extraversion-introversion, *Diss. Abstr. Int.* **33**, 5-b, 23–6.

LINCOLN, G. A., YOUNGSON, R. W. and SHORT, R. V. (1970) The social and sexual behaviour of the red deer stag, *J. Reprod. Fertil.* Suppl. **11**, 71–103.

LINDSLEY, D. B. (1951) Emotions, in, S. S. Stevens (Ed.), *Handbook of experimental psychology*, New York: Wiley.

LINDSLEY, D. B. (1957) Psychophysiology and motivation, in, M. R. Jones (Ed.), *Nebraska symposium on motivation,* Lincoln: Nebraska University Press.

LINDSLEY, D. B. (1958) The reticular system and perceptual discrimination, in, H. A. Jasper (Ed.), *Reticular formation of the brain,* pp. 513–34, Boston: Little Brown.

LINDSLEY, D. B. (1962) The reticular system and the process of perceptual discrimination, in, *Reticular formation of the brain.* International Symposium. Moscow: Publishers of Medical Literature.

LINDSLEY, D. B. and SASSONMAN, W. H. (1938) Autonomic activity and brain potentials associated with "voluntary" control of the pilomotors (*m.m. arretoresilorum*), *J. Neurophysiol.* **1,** 342–9.

LINDZEY, G., WINSTON, H. and MANOSEVITZ, M. (1961) Social dominance in inbred mouse strains, *Nature, Lond.* **191,** 474–6.

LINETSKII, M. L. (1961) Urine secretion after suggested drinking of water, *Zh. Vyssh. Nerv. Deyat. im. I. P. Pavlova,* **11,** 32–5.

LIPSITT, L. (1969) Learning capacities of the human infant, in, R. J. Robinson (Ed.), *Brain and early behaviour,* London: Academic Press.

LISINA, M. I. (1958) The role of orientation in the transformation of involuntary into voluntary reactions, in, L. G. Voronin, A. N. Leont'ev, A. R. Luria, E. N. Sokolov and O. S. Vinogradova (Eds.), *The orienting reflex and orienting-investigatory activity,* pp. 338–44, Moscow: Akad. Pedagog. Nauk RSFSR. English translation (1965), Baltimore, Awevvian Institute of Biological Science, pp. 450–6.

LIVANOV, M. N. (1962) O zamykanii uslovnykh svyazey (po materialam elektrofiziologicheskikh issledovaniy), in, *Elektroentsefalografichesko issledovanie vysshey nervnoy deyatel'nosti,* Moscow: Medgiz.

LIVANOV, M. N. (1969) The application of electronic-computer techniques to the analysis of bioelectric processes in the brain, in, M. Cole and I. Maltzman (Eds.), *A handbook of contemporary Soviet psychology,* pp. 717–34, New York: Basic Books.

LIVANOV, M. N., GAVRILOVA, N. A. and ASLANOV, A. S. (1966a) Correlations of biopotentials in the frontal regions of the human cortex, in, A. R. Luria and E. D. Khomskaya (Eds.), *Frontal lobes and the regulation of mental processes,* Moscow.

LIVANOV, M. N., GAVRILOVA, N. A. and ASLANOV, A. S. (1966b) On the reflection of some mental state in the spatial distribution of biopotentials in the human cortex. XVIIIth International Psychological Congress. Symposium 6: Electrophysiological correlates of behaviour, Moscow.

LOBB, H., MOFFITT, A. and GAMLIN, P. (1966) Frustration and adaptation in relation to discrimination learning ability of mentally defective children, *Am. J. Ment. Defic.* **71,** 256–65.

LOCKHART, R. A. (1972) Interrelations between response amplitude, latency, rise time, and the Edelberg recovery measure of the galvanic skin response, *Psychophysiol.* **9,** 437–42.

LOEB, J. and MEDNICK, S. A. (1976) A social behaviour and electrodermal response patterns, in, K. O. Christiansen and S. A. Mednick (Eds.), *Crime, society and biology — a new perspective,* New York: Gardner Press.

LOEB, M. and SMITH, R. P. (1967) Relation of induced tinnitus to physical characteristics of the inducing stimuli, *J. Acoust. Soc. Am.* **42,** 2, 493–5.

LOMOV, B. F. (1977) Sixty years of Soviet Psychology, *Studia Psychologica,* **4,** 266–73.

LONDON, I. D. (1954) Research on sensory interaction in the Soviet Union, *Psychol. Bull.* **51,** 531–68.

LOO, R. (1976) Field dependence and the Eysenck personality inventory, *Percept. Mot. Skills,* **43,** 2, 614.

LORENTE DE NO, R. (1943) Cerebral cortex, in, J. B. Fulton (Ed.), *Physiology of the nervous system,* Fairlawn, New York: Oxford University Press.

LORENZ, K. (1966) *On aggression,* New York: Harcourt, Brace.

LOSEN, S. N. (1961) The differential effects of censure on the problem solving behaviour of schizophrenics and normal subjects, *J. Personality,* **29,** 258–72.

LOVCHIKOV, V. A. (1975) Dependence of the magnitude of conditional salivation in dogs on the dose of caffeine, *Zh. Vyssh. Nerv. Deyat. im. I. P. Pavlova,* **25,** 949–52.

LOVELESS, N. E. and SANFORD, J. A. (1974) Slow potential correlates of preparatory set, *Biol. Psychol.* **1,** 303–14.

LOVIBOND, S. H. (1963) Conceptual thinking, personality and conditioning, *Br. J. Soc. Clin. Psychol.* **2,** 100–11.

LOVIBOND, S. H. (1964) Personality and conditioning, in, B. A. Maher (Ed.), *Progress in experimental personality research,* Vol. 1, New York: Academic Press.

LOVIBOND, S. H. (1969) in, G. L. Mangan and L. D. Bainbridge (Eds.), *Behaviour therapy.* Proceedings of a symposium held by the Queensland branch of the Australian Psychological Society, 1967. Brisbane: University of Queensland Press.

LOW, M. D., BORDA, R. P., FROST, J. D. (Jr.) and KELLAWAY, P. (1966) Surface-negative-slow potential shift associated with conditioning in man, *Neurology,* **16,** 771–82.

LUBORSKY, L. (1967) Individual differences in cognitive style as a determinant of vaso-constriction orienting response, in, I. Luttkay-Nedicky, L. Ciganek, V. Zikmund and E. Kellerova (Eds.), *Mechanisms of orienting reaction in man,* Bratislava: Slovak Academy of Sciences.

LUBORSKY, L., BLINDER, B. and SCHIMEK, J. (1965) Looking, recording and GSR as a function of defense, *J. Abnorm. Psychol.* **60,** 270–80.

LÜSCHER, E. and ZWISLOCKI, J. (1949) Adaptation of the ear to sound stimuli, *J. Acoust. Soc. Am.* **21,** 135–9.

LURIA, A. R. (1925) Psychoanalysis as a system of monistic psychology, in, K. P. Kornilov (Ed.), *Psikhologiya i Marksizm,* pp. 47–80, Leningrad: Gosizdat.

LURIA, A. R. (1932) *The nature of human conflicts,* New York: Liveright.

LURIA, A. R. (1959) The directive role of speech in development and dissociation. *Word,* **15,** 2–3.

LURIA, A. R. (1962) *Higher cortical functions in man and their disturbance with local lesions of the brain,* Moscow.

LURIA, A. R. (1963a) *The mentally retarded child,* New York: Macmillan.

LURIA, A. R. (1963b) *The human brain and psychic* (mental) *processes,* Moscow: Akad. Pedagog. Nauk RSFSR.

LURIA, A. R. (1966a) Frontal lobes and regulation of behaviour, in, A. R. Luria and E. O. Khomskaya (Eds.), *Frontal lobes and the regulation of mental processes,* Moscow.

LURIA, A. R. (1966b) *Human brain and psychological processes,* New York: Harper.

LURIA, A. R. (1968) *The mind of a mnemonist,* Translated by L. Solataroff, New York: Basic Books.

LURIA, A. R. (1978a) *The selected writings of A. R. Luria,* Ed. M. Cole, New York: M. E. Sharpe, Inc.

LURIA, A. R. (1978b) *The working brain,* Penguin Press: Allen Lane.

LURIA, A. R. and TSVETHOVA, L. S. (1966) *Neuropsychological analysis of problem solving,* Moscow: Prosveshchenie.

LURIA, A. R. and VINOGRADOVA, O. S. (1959) An objective investigation of the dynamics of semantic systems. *Br. J. Psychol.* **50,** 89–105.

LUTHE, W. (1963) Autogenic training: method, research and application in medicine, *Am. J. Psychother.* **17,** 174–95.

LYAKH, G. S. (1968a) Articulatory and auditory mimicry in the first months of life, *Zh. Vyssh. Nerv. Deyat. im. I. P. Pavlova,* **18,** 831–5.

LYAKH, G. S. (1968b) Characteristics of conditioned connections in mimo-articulatory and auditory components of speech stimuli in the first year of life, *Zh. Vyssh. Nerv. Deyat. im. I. P. Pavlova.* **18,** 1069–71.

LYKKEN, D. T. (1957) A study of anxiety in the sociopathic personality, *J. Abnorm. Soc. Psychol.* **55,** 6–10.

LYKKEN, D. T. (1962) Preception in the rat: autonomic response to shock as a function of length of warning period, *Science, N.Y.* **137,** 665–6.

LYKKEN, D. T. (1968) Neuropsychology and psychophysiology in personality research, in,

E. Borgatta and W. Lambert (Eds.), *Handbook of personality theory and research,* Chicago: Rand McNally.

LYKKEN, D. T. and TELLEGEN, A. (1974) On the validity of the preception hypothesis, *Psychophysiol.* **11**, 2, 125–32.

LYKKEN, D. T., MACINDOE, I. and TELLEGEN, A. (1972) Preception: autonomic response to shock as a function of predictability in time and locus, *Psychophysiol.* **9**, 318–33.

LYKKEN, D. T., TELLEGEN, A. and THORKELSON, K. (1974) Ectentic determination of EEG frequency spectra, *Biol. Psychol.* **14**, 248–59.

LYNN, R. (1963) Russian theory and research on schizophrenia, *Psychol. Bull.* **60**, 486–98.

LYNN, R. (1966) *Attention, arousal and the orientation reaction,* London: Pergamon.

LYNN, R. and EYSENCK, H. J. (1961) Tolerance for pain, extraversion and neuroticism, *Percept. Mot. Skills,* **12**, 161–2.

MCCALL, R. B., HOGARTY, P. S., HAMILTON, J. S. and VINCENT, J. M. (1973) Habituation rate of the infant's response to visual discrepancies, *Child Dev.* **44**, 2, 280–7.

MCCALLUM, W. C. and WALTER, W. G. (1967) La variation contingente négative en psychiatrie. Colloque sur l'étude de la variation contingente négative. Liège.

MCCLEARY, R. A. (1966) Response-modulating functions of the limbic system: initiation and suppression, in, E. Stellar and J. M. Sprague (Eds.), *Progress in physiological psychology,* Vol. 1, pp. 209–72, New York: Academic Press.

MCCLELLAND, D. C. (1955) Some social consequences of achievement motivation, in, M. R. Jones (Ed.), *Nebraska Symposium on motivation,* Vol. III, pp. 41–65, Lincoln, Neb.: University of Nebraska Press.

MCCLELLAND, D. C., ATKINSON, J. W., CLARK, R. A. and LOWELL, E. L. (1953) *The achievement motive,* New York: Appleton-Century-Crofts.

MCCLURE, C. M. (1959) Cardiac arrest through volition, *Calif. Med.* **90**, 440–1.

MCCUBBIN, R. J. and KATKIN, E. S. (1971) Magnitude of the orienting response as a function of extent and quality of stimulus change, *J. Exp. Psychol.* **88**, 182–8.

MCDONALD, D. G., JOHNSON, L. C. and HORD, D. J. (1964) Habituation of the orienting response in alert and drowsy subjects, *Psychophysiol.* **1**, 163–73.

MCDONNELL, G. J. and CARPENTER, J. A. (1959) Anxiety, skin conductance and alcohol: a study of the relation between anxiety and skin conductance and the effect of alcohol on the conductance of subjects in the group, *Q. J. Stud. Alcohol,* **20**, 38–52.

MCDONNELL, G. J. and CARPENTER, J. A. (1960) Manifest anxiety and pre-stimulus conductance levels, *J. Abnorm. Soc. Psychol.* **60**, 437–8.

MCDOUGALL, W. (1908) *An introduction to social psychology,* London: Methuen.

MCDOWELL, H. S. (1937) Frequency of choice of play materials by pre-school children, *Child Dev.* **8**, 305–10.

MCEWAN, P. and ROGER, R. S. (1960) Some individual differences in figural after-effects, *Br. J. Psychol.* **51**, 1–8.

MCFALL, R. M. and TWENTYMAN, C. T. (1973) Four experiments on the relative contributions of rehearsal, modelling and coaching to assertion training, *J. Abnorm. Psychol.* **81**, 199–218.

MACFARLANE, A. (1974) *The psychology of childbirth,* London: Fontana/Open Books.

MCGINNIES, E. (1949) Emotionality and perceptual defence, *Psychol. Rev.* **56**, 244–51.

MCGINNIES, D. (1973) Cardiovascular responses during habituation and mental activity in anxious men and women, *Biol. Psychol.* **1**, 115–23.

MCGRADE, B. J., KESSEN, W. and LATZENDORFF, A. (1965) Activity in the human newborn as related to delivery difficulty, *Child Dev.* **36**, 73–9.

MACIEJCZYK, J. (1974) Reactivity and decision making in a difficult situation in pilots, in, J. Strelau (Ed.), *The role of temperament traits in action,* Wroclaw: Ossolineum.

MACKWORTH, J. F. (1969) *Vigilance and habituation,* Harmonsworth: Penguin Books.

MACKWORTH, J. F. (1970) *Vigilance and attention,* Harmondsworth: Penguin Books.

MACKWORTH, N. H. (1957) Vigilance, *Adv. Sc.* 389–93.

McLean, V., Ohman, A. and Lader, M. (1975) Effects of attention, activation and stimulus regularity on short-term "habituation" of the average evoked response, *Biol. Psychol.* **3**, 57–60.

McLemore, C. L. (1972) Imagery and desensitisation, *Behav. Res. Ther.* **10**, 51–57.

McNemar, Q. (1933) Twin resemblances in motor skills and the effect of practice thereon. *J. Gen. Psychol.* **42**, 70–99.

McPherson, E. L. R. (1967) Control of involuntary movement. *Behav. Res. Ther.* **5**, 143–6.

McReynolds, P. (1960) Anxiety, perception and schizophrenia, in, D. D. Jackson (Ed.), *The aetiology of schizophrenia,* pp. 248–92, New York: Basic Books.

McReynolds, P. and Bryant, J. (1956) Tendency to obtain new percepts as a function of the level of unassimilated percepts, *Percept. Mot. Skills,* **6**, 183–6.

Madlung, K. (1935) Über den Einfluss der typologischen Verauflagung auf die Flimmergrenzen, *Untersuch. Psychol. Phil. Pad.* **10**, 70–8.

Magnus, R. (1924) *Körperstellung,* Berlin.

Magnusson, D. and Endler, N. S. (1977) Interaction psychology: current issues and future prospects, in, D. Magnusson and N. S. Endler (Eds.), *Personality at the crossroads: current issues in interactional psychology,* Hillsdale: W. J. Erlbaum.

Magoun, H. W. (1963) *The waking brain,* 2nd ed., Springfield, Ill.: Thomas.

Maizel, N. I. (1956) A study of typological differences in the balance of the processes of excitation and inhibition by the method of the photo-chemical reflex, in, B. M. Teplov (Ed.), *Typological features of higher nervous activity in man,* Vol. 1, Moscow: Akad. Pedagog. Nauk RSFSR.

Malev, J. S. (1966) Body image, body symptoms and body reactivity in children, *J. Psychosom. Res.* **10**, 281–9.

Malmo, R. B. (1955) Activation: a neurophysiological dimension, *Psychol. Rev.* **66**, 367–86.

Malmo, R. B. and Shagass, C. (1949) Physiological studies of reaction to stress in anxiety states and early schizophrenia, *Psychosom. Med.* **11**, 9–24.

Malmo, R. B., Shagass, C. and Davis, F. M. (1950a) Symptom specificity and bodily reactions during psychiatric interview, *Psychosom. Med.* **12**, 362–76.

Malmo, R. B., Shagass, C. and Davis, F. M. (1950b) Specificity of bodily reactions under stress: a physiological study of somatic symptom mechanisms in psychiatric patients, *Res. Publ. Assoc. Res. Nerv. Ment. Dis.* **29**, 231–61.

Malmo, R. B., Shagass, C., Davis, J., Cleghorn, R., Graham, B. and Goodman, A. (1948) Standardized pain stimulation as controlled stress in physiological studies of psychoneurosis, *Science, N.Y.* **108**, 509–11.

Maltzman, I. (1967) Individual differences in alterations: the orienting reflex, in: R. M. Gagul (Ed.), *Learning and individual differences,* pp. 94–112, Columbus, Ohio: Charles E. Merrill Books Inc.

Maltzman, I. (1968) Theoretical conceptions of semantic conditioning and generalization, in, T. R. Dixon and P. L. Horton (eds.), *Verbal behaviour and general behaviour theory,* pp. 291–339, Englewood Cliffs, N.J.: Prentice-Hall.

Maltzman, I. (1979) Classical conditioning and sociopathy. *Pavlov. J. Biol. Science,* **14**, 2, 133–43.

Maltzman, I. and Langdon, B. (1969) Semantic generalisation of the GSR as a function of semantic distance of the orienting reflex. *J. Exp. Psychol.* **80**, 207–14.

Maltzman, I. and Mandell, M. P. (1968) The orienting reflex as a predictor of learning and performance, *J. Exp. Res. Person.* **3**, 99–106.

Maltzman, I. and Raskin, D. C. (1965) Effects of individual differences in the orienting response on conditioning and complex processes, *J. Exp. Res. Personality,* **1**, 1–16.

Maltzman, I., Smith, M. J., Kantor, W. and Mandell, M. P. (1971) Effects of stress on habituation of the orienting reflex, *J. Exp. Psychol.* **87**, 207–14.

Malyugina, L. L., Mironova, A. I., Fedorov, V. K. and Shabad, L. M. (1963) The significance of typological features of higher nervous activity in the development of malignant tumors, *Zh. Vyssh. Nerv. Deyat. im. I. P. Pavlova,* **8**, 6.

Mandler, G. (1975) *Mind and Evolution,* New York: Wiley.

Mangan, G. L. (1958a) Method-of-approach factors in the testing of middle-aged subjects, *J. Geront.* **13**, 1.

MANGAN, G. L. (1958b) Rigidity factors in the testing of middle-aged subjects, *J. Geront.* **13**, 3.

MANGAN, G. L. (1959) A study of speed, power and related temperament variables. *Brit. J. Educ. Psychol.* **XXIX**, 144–54.

MANGAN, G. L. (1967a) The relation of neo-Pavlovian properties of higher nervous activity and western personality dimensions, II, The relation of mobility to perceptual flexibility, *J. Exp. Res. Person.* **2**, 107–16.

MANGAN, G. L. (1967b) The relation of neo-Pavlovian properties of higher nervous activity and western personality dimensions, III, The relation of transformation mobility to thinking flexibility, *J. Exp. Res. Person.* **2**, 117–23.

MANGAN, G. L. (1967c) The relation of neo-Pavlovian properties of higher nervous activity and western personality dimensions, IV, A factor analytic study of extraversion and flexibility and the sensitivity and mobility of the nervous system, *J. Exp. Res. Person.* **2**, 124–7.

MANGAN, G. L. (1974) Personality and conditioning: some personality, cognitive and psychophysiological parameters of classical appetitive (sexual) GSR conditioning, *Pavlov. J. Biol. Sc.* **9**, 3, 125–35.

MANGAN, G. L. (1978a) Factors of conditionability and their relationship to personality types, *Pavlov J. Biol. Sci.* **13**, 4, 226–35.

MANGAN, G. L. (1978b) Inhibitory ease: a personality type? *Pavlov J. Biol. Sci.* **13**, 3, 177–81.

MANGAN, G. L. (1978c) The relationship of mobility of inhibition to rate of inhibitory growth and measures of flexibility, extraversion and neuroticism. *J. Gen. Psychol.* **99**, 271–9.

MANGAN, G. L. and FARMER, R. (1967) The relation of neo-Pavlovian properties of higher nervous activity and western personality dimensions, I, The relation of nervous strength and sensitivity to extraversion, *J. Exp. Res. Person.* **2**, 101–6.

MANGAN, G. L. and O'GORMAN, J. (1969) The relation of initial amplitude and rate of extinction of orienting response to extraversion and neuroticism, *J. Exp. Res. Person.* **3**.

MANGAN, G. L. and PAISEY, T. (1980) New perspectives in temperament/personality research: the "behavioural" model of the Warsaw group, *Pavlov J. Biol. Sci.* **15**, 4, 159–70.

MANGAN, G. L. and SEELEY, B. (1974) Arousal in chronic and acute schizophrenics. Unpublished paper, obtainable from the author.

MANGAN, G. L., MURPHY, G. and FARMER, R. G. (1980) The role of muscle tension in "repression", *Pavlov J. Biol. Sci.* **15**, 4, 172–6.

MANGAN, G. L., QUARTERMAIN, D. and VAUGHAN, G. (1959) Relationship between Taylor MAS scores and group conformity, *Percept. Mot. Skills.* **9**, 207–9.

MANGAN, G. L., QUARTERMAIN, D. and VAUGHAN, G. (1960) Taylor MAS and group conformity pressure, *J. Abnorm. Soc. Psychol.* **61**, 1, 146–7.

MARBUTOVICH, I. O. and PODKOPAYEV, N. A. (1936) The conditioned reflex as an association, *Tr. Fiziol. Lab. im. I. P. Pavlova,* **6**, 2, 5–25.

MARCHMAN, J. N. (1973) Neuroticism, extraversion and electrodermal orienting response, *Diss. Abstr.* **34**, 4-b, 1776.

MARICQ, H. R. and EDELBERG, R. (1975) Electrodermal recovery rate in a schizophrenic population, *Psychophysiol.* **12**, 630–3.

MARKOVA, A. K. and ABRAMOVA, G. S. (1977) Individual differences and their significance for educational psychology, *Vop. Psikhol.* **2**, 96–104.

MARKS, I., MARSET, P., BOULONGOURIS, J. and HUSON, J. (1971) Physiological accompaniments of neutral and phobic imagery, *Psychol. Med.* **1**, 299–307.

MARTIN, I. (1960) The effects of depressant drugs on palmar skin resistance and adaptation, in, H. J. Eysenck (Ed.), *Experiments in personality,* Vol. 1, pp. 197–220, London: Routledge & Kegan Paul.

MARTIN, I. and RUST, J. (1976) Habituation and structure of the electrodermal system, *Psychophysiol.* **13**, 6, 554–62.

MARTIN, J. E. and INGLIS, J. (1965) Pain tolerance and narcotic addiction. *Br. J. Soc. Clin. Psychol.,* **4**, 224–9.

MARTIN, N. G., EAVES, L. J., KEARSY, M. J. and DAVIES, P. (1978) The power of the classical twin study, *Heredity, Lond.* **40**, 97–116.

MARTON, M. and URBAN, LA. (1966) An electroencephalographic investigation of individual differences in the process of conditioning, in, V. D. Nebylitsyn (organiser), Symposium 9, Physiological bases of individual psychological differences, pp. 106–9, XVIII International Congress of Psychology, Moscow.

MARUSEVA, A. M. and CHRISTOVICH, L. A. (1954) Ob izmenenii deyatel'nosti zvukovogo analizatora cheloveka pod vliyaniem slovesnykh vozdeystviy primenyavshikhsya v eksperimentakh po fiziologii organov chuvstv, *Zh. Vyssh. Nerv. Deyat. im. I. P. Pavlova.* **4,** 4.

MARUSHEVSKY, M. O. (1957) Problems of psychology, *Vop. Psikhol.* **1.**

MARUSHEVSKY, M. O. (1957) On the interaction of the two signal systems in orientation reactions, *Vop. Psikhol.* **3,** 78–87.

MARX, K. (1950) *Das Kapital,* Vol. I, Moscow: Gospolitizdat.

MARZILLIER, J. S., LAMBERT, C. and KELLETT, J. (1976) A controlled evaluation of systematic desensitisation and social skills training for socially inadequate psychiatric patients, *Behav. Res. Ther.* **14,** 225–38.

MASTERS, W. H. and JOHNSON, V. E. (1966) *Human sexual response.* London: Churchill.

MATEYEV, D. (1961) Excitation, inhibition, fatigue and recovery, *Fiziol. Zh. SSSR,* **47,** 1282–9.

MATHENY, A. P. (1975) Twins: concordance for Piagetian-equivalent items derived from the Bayley mental test, *Dev. Psychol.* **11,** 2, 224–7.

MATHENY, A. P. and DOLIN, A. B. (1975) Persons, situations and time: a genetic view of behavioral change in children, *J. Personality Soc. Psychol.* **32,** 6, 1106–10.

MATHENY, A. P., DOLIN, A. B. and WILSON, R. S. (1976) Twins: within pair similarity on Bayley's infant behavior record, *J. Genet. Psychol.* **128,** 2, 263–70.

MATHER, K. (1949) *Biometrical genetics.* London: Methuen.

MATHERS, J. A. L., OSBORNE, R. H. and DEGEORGE, F. V. (1961) Studies of blood pressure, heart rate and the electrocardiogram in adult twins, *Am. Heart J.* **62,** 634–42.

MATHIS, H. (1970) Emotional responsivity in the antisocial personality. Doctoral Dissertation, The George Washington University. Ann Arbor, Mich.: University Microfilms, No. 71-12, 299.

MATTHIES, H. (1980) Pharmacology of learning and memory, *Trends Pharmac. Sciences,* **1,** 12, 333–6.

MATYSIAK, J. (1977) Reactivity in rats measured by reaction time to nearthreshold stimuli and "open-field" behaviour, *Pol. Psychol. Bull.* **8,** 95–8.

MATYSIAK, J. (1978) Effectiveness of avoidance learning in rats differing in reactivity, *Przeglad Psychol.* **21,** 2, 307–13.

MATYSIAK, J. (1979a) Self-exposure to sensory stimuli of different modalities in rats, *Pol. Psychol. Bull.* **10,** 159–65.

MATYSIAK, J. (1979b) Activity motivated by the sensory drive, *Pol. Psychol. Bull.* **10,** 209–14.

MAY, J. R. and JOHNSTONE, H. J. (1969) Positive reinforcement and suppression of spontaneous GSR activity, *J. Exp. Psychol.* **80,** 193–5.

MAY, J. R. and JOHNSTONE, H. J. (1973) Physiological activity to internally elicited arousal and inhibitory thoughts, *J. Abnorm Psychol.* **82,** 239–45.

MAYOROV, F. P. (1938) Inertness of the inhibitory process in a dog of the strong equilibrated type, *Trans. Fiziol. Lab. im. I. P. Pavlova,* **8.**

MAYS, L. E. (1973) Hippocampal unit activity during arousal and orienting, *Diss. Abstr. Int.* **34,** 6-B, 1776–2942.

MECACCI, L. (1979) *Brain and history: the relationship between neurophysiology and psychology in Soviet research,* New York: Brunner/Mazel.

MEDEISOS, E. E. and MCMANIS, D. L. (1974) Assessment of introversion-extraversion in children: brief report, *Percept. Mot. Skills,* **38,** 2, 429–30.

MEDNICK, M. T. (1957) Mediated generalization and the incubation effect as a function of manifest anxiety, *J. Abnorm. Psychol.* **55,** 315–21.

MEDNICK, S. A. (1970) Breakdown in individuals at high-risk for schizophrenia: possible predispositional perinatal factors, *Ment. Hyg., Lond.* **54,** 50–63.

MEDNICK, S. A. (1974) electrodermal recovery and psychopathology, in, S. A. Mednick,

F. Schulsinger, J. Higgins and B. Bell (Eds.), *Genetics, environment and psychopathology,* Amsterdam and Oxford: North-Holland Publishing Co.

MEDNICK, S. A. (1975) Autonomic nervous system recovery and psychopathy, *Scand. J. Behavl. Ther.* **4,** 55–68.

MEDNICK, S. A. (1976) Berkson's fallacy and high risk research. Paper presented to the 2nd Rochester International Conference on Schizophrenia, Rochester, N.Y.

MEDNICK, S. A. and SCHULSINGER, F. (1968) Some pre-morbid characteristics related to breakdown in children with schizophrenic mothers, in, D. Rosenthal and S. S. Kety (Eds.), *The transmission of schizophrenia,* Oxford: Pergamon Press.

MEILI, R. (1957a) *Anfänge der Charakterentwicklung,* Bern and Stuttgart: Verlag Hans Huber.

MEILI, R. (1957b) Angstenstehung bei Kleinkindern. *Schweiz. Z. Psychol.* **14,** 195–212.

MELIKHOVA, E. F. (1964) Correlational analysis of the results of different investigations of strength, balance and mobility of nervous processes, *Zh. Vyssh. Nerv. Deyat. im. I. P. Pavlova,* **14,** 5.

MELNICHUK, P. V. (1958) A study of the electrical activity of the brain by means of rhythmic stimulation in children who have survived a closed injury of the skull. Dissertation, Moscow University.

MELNICK, W. (1976) Human asymptotic threshold shift, in, D. Henderson, R. Mamernik, D. S. Dosanjh and J. Mills (Eds.), *Effects of noise on hearing,* New York: Raven Press.

MELZACK, R. and WALL, P. D. (1965) Pain mechanisms: a new theory, *Science, N.Y.* **150,** 971–9.

MENZIES, R. (1937) Conditioned vasomotor responses in human subjects, *J. Psychol.* **4,** 75–120.

MENZIES, R. (1941) Further studies in conditioned vaso-motor responses in human subjects, *J. Exp. Psychol.* **29,** 457–82.

MERLIN, V. S. (1955) The role of temperament in the assessment of emotional interactions, *Vop. Psikhol.* **6.**

MERLIN, V. S. (1958a) Study of the properties of types of higher nervous activity in man using the GSR method, *Vop. Psikhol.* **5.**

MERLIN, V. S. (1958b) Distinctive features of the orienting and non-orienting conditioned reflex in the expression of the voluntary act, *Izd. Akad. Pedagog. Nauk RSFSR,* **3.**

MERLIN, V. S. (1964) *Outline of a theory of temperament,* Moscow: Prosveshchenie.

MERLIN, V. S. (1967) The relationship between social-typical and individual characteristics of the personality, *Vop. Psikhol.* **4,** 34–43.

MERLIN, V. S. (1971) Roznice typologiczne we ivplywie negatywnej i pozytywnej oceny na podzielnose uwagi, in, J. Strelau (Ed.), *Zagadniema psychologii roznie indywidualnych,* pp. 116–31, Warszawa: PWN.

MERLIN, V. S. (Ed.) (1973a) *Outline of a Theory of Temperament,* Perm: Izd. Permskoye Kniznoye.

MERLIN, V. S. (1973b) Types of functional dependency between temperamental traits and properties of the nervous system, *Vop. Psikhol.* **19,** 6, 39–50.

MERLINO, F. J. (1975) Metatheoretical isolationism reconsidered: its impact for developmental theories, *Hum. Dev.* **18,** 391–5.

MESHCHEVSKII, R. M. (1955) Izmenenie elktricheskoy aktivnosti v korkovom kontse zritel'nogo krolika pri obrazovanii uslovnogo oboronitel'nogo refleksa, *Tr. Inst. Vyssh. Nerv. Deyat. Ser. Fiziol,* **1.**

MESHCHEVSKII, R. M. and SMIRNOV, G. D. (1961) Concerning the origin of the rhythmic reaction of the cerebral cortex to flickering light, *Dokl. Akad. Nauk SSSR,* **139,** 1.

MESHKOVA, T. A. (1974) Study of the genetic basis of various resting EEG parameters in humans by a twin method. Candidate's dissertation, University of Moscow.

MESHKOVA, T. A. and SMIRNOV, L. M. (1978) The genetic basis of individual differences in the human EEG at rest, *Vop. Psikhol.* **5,** 66–75.

MEYER, I. O. (1963) *Osnovnyne svoystva nervnykh protsessov u detey doshkol'nogo vozrasta.* Tbilisi.

MIALL, W. E., HENEAGE, P., KHOSIA, T., LOVELL, H. and MOORE, F. (1967) Factors influencing the degree of resemblance in arterial pressure in close relatives. *Clin. Sci.* **33,** 271–83.

MICCO, D. J. (1973) A further look at the behavioural deficit following injury to the hippocampus, *Diss. Abstr. Int.* **34,** 4-B, 1777.

MICCO, D. J. and SCHWARTZ, M. (1971) Effects of hippocampal lesions upon the development of Pavlovian internal inhibition in rats, *J. Comp. Physiol. Psychol.* **76,** 3, 371–7.

MIKHAILOVA, N. G., PIMENOVA, T. G. and SIMONOV, P. V. (1972) Does the cessation of negative stimulation result in the activation of the positive emotional areas of the brain? *Dokl. Akad. Nauk SSSR,* **204,** 4, 1017–20.

MIKHEYEV, V. F. (1972) The effect of heredity on individual differences in some memory processes, *Vop. Psikhol.* **18,** 4, 61–7.

MIKHEYEV, V. F. (1979) The role of genetic factors in the formation of human trace reactions, *Zh. Vyssh. Deyat. Nerv. im. I. P. Pavlova,* **29,** 510–17.

MILGRAM, S. (1974) *Obedience to authority: an experimental view,* London: Tavistock.

MILLER, A. and MINTEN, F. (1972) Relationships of extraversion and introversion to verbal operant conditioning for aware and unaware subjects, *Psychol. Rep.* **31,** 3, 848–50.

MILLER, J. G. (1950) The experimental study of unconscious processes, in, M. L. Remert (Ed.), *Feelings and emotions,* pp. 261–7, New York: McGraw-Hill.

MILLER, N. E. (1951) Learnable drives and rewards, in, S. S. Stevens (Ed.), *Handbook of experimental psychology,* pp. 435–72, New York: Wiley.

MILLER, N. E. (1959) Liberalisation of basic S-R concepts: extensions to conflict, behaviour, motivation and social learning, in, S. Koch (Ed.), *Psychology: A study of a science,* Vol. II, New York: McGraw-Hill.

MILLER, N. E. (1964) The analysis of motivational effects illustrated by experiments on amylobarbitone, in, H. Steinberg (Ed.), *Animal behaviour and drug action,* pp. 1–18, London: Churchill.

MILLER, N. E. (1969) Learning of visceral and glandular responses, *Science, N.Y.* **163,** 434–45.

MILLER, N. E. (1972) Visceral learning: recent difficulties with curanized rats and significant problems for human research, Symposium, University of North Carolina.

MILLER, N. E. and BANUAZIZI, A. (1968) Instrumental learning by curarized rats of a specific visceral response, intestinal or cardiac, *J. Comp. Physiol. Psychol.* **65,** 1–7.

MILLER, N. E. and CARMONA, A. (1967) Modification of a visceral response, salivation in thirsty dogs, by instrumental training with water reward, *J. Comp. Physiol. Psychol.* **63,** 1–6.

MILLER, N. E. and DI CARA, L. (1967) Instrumental learning of heart-rate changes in curanized rats: shaping and specificity to discriminate stimulus, *J. Comp. Physiol. Psychol.* **63,** 12–19.

MILLER, N. E. and DI CARA, L. V. (1968) Instrumental learning of urine formation by rats: changes in renal blood flow, *Am. J. Physiol.* **215,** 677–83.

MILLER, N. E. and DOLLARD, J. (1941) *Social learning and imitation,* New Haven: Yale University Press.

MILLER, S. and KONORSKI, J. (1928) Sur une forme particulière des réflexes conditionnels, *C. r. Soc. Biol.* **99,** 1115–57.

MILLS, J. A. and TALO, S. A. (1972) Temporary threshold shifts produced by exposure to high frequency noise, *J. Speech Hear. Res.* **15,** 624–31.

MIRDAL, G. M., ROSENTHAL, D., WENDER, P. H. and SCHULSINGER, F. (1977) Perinatal complications in offspring of psychotic parents, *Br. J. Psychiat.* **130,** 495–505.

MISCHEL, W. (1968) *Personality and assessment,* London: Wiley.

MISCHEL, W. (1969) Continuity and change in personality, *Am. Psychol.* **24,** 1012–18.

MISCHEL, W. (1973a) Toward a cognitive social learning reconceptualization of personality, *Psychol. Rev.* **80,** 252–83.

MISCHEL, W. (1973b) On the empirical dilemmas of psychodynamic approaches: Issues and alternatives, *J. Abnorm. Psychol.* **82,** 335–44.

MISCHEL, W. (1977) The interaction of person and situation, in, D. Magnusson and N. S. Endler (Eds.), *Personality at the crossroads: current issues in interactional psychology,* Hillsdale, N.J.: Erlbaum.

MISCHEL, W. (1979) On the interface of cognition and personality: beyond the person-situation debate. *Am. Psychol.* **34,** 745–54.

MISCHEL, W. and GRUSEC, J. (1966) Determinants of the rehearsal and transmission of neutral and aversive behaviours, *J. Personality Soc. Psychol.* **2**, 197–205.

MITTLER, P. (1971) *The study of twins,* London: Penguin.

MOGEL, S. (1969) A comparison of dysthymics in the conditioning and extinction of a finger withdrawal response. Ph.D. Thesis, University of Kentucky.

MOLDOVSKAYA, S. I. (1964) Relationship between mobility of basic nervous processes, working capacity of cortical cells and the speed of re-establishing the signal value of the CS in children. Proceedings of Psychological Conference, Kiev.

MONNIER, M. (1956) *Problems in modern physiology of the nervous and muscular systems,* Tbilisi.

MONNIER, M. (1968) functions of the nervous system, in, M. Monnier (Ed.), *General physiological autonomic functions,* Vol. 1, pp. 385–93, Amsterdam: Elsevier.

MOREAU, T. (1976) Modality differences in the habituation and dishabituation of cardiac responsiveness in the human newborn. *Dev. Psychobiol.* **9**, 109–17.

MORGENSON, D. F. and MARTIN, I. (1968) The orienting response as a predicter of autonomic conditioning, *J. Exp. Res. Person.* **3**, 89–98.

MORGENSON, D. F. and MARTIN, I. (1969) Personality, awareness and autonomic conditioning, *Psychophysiol.* **5**, 5, 536–47.

MORRELL, F. (1967) Electrical signs of sensor coding, in, G. C. Quaston, T. Melnechuk and F. O. Schmitt (Eds.), *The neurosciences: a study program,* New York: Rockefeller University Press.

MORRELL, F. and JASPER, H. (1955) Conditioning of cortical electrical activity in the monkey, *Electroenceph. Clin. Neurophysiol.* **7**, 4.

MORRISH, R. (1974) Appetitive and aversive conditioning and personality. Unpublished doctoral dissertation, University of Queensland.

MORSH, J. E. and ABOTT, H. D. (1945) An investigation of after-images, *J. Comp. Psychol.* **38**, 47–63.

MORTON, N. E. (1975) Analysis of family resemblance and group differences, *Social Biol.* **22**, 111–16.

MORUZZI, G. (1958) Synchronizing influences of the brain stem and the inhibiting mechanisms underlying the production of sleep by sensory stimulation, in, H. H. Jasper and G. D. Smirnov (Eds.), Moscow colloquium on electroencephalography of higher nervous activity, *Electroenceph. Clin. Neurophysiol.* Suppl. 13, 1960, 231–57.

MORUZZI, G. (1960) Synchronising influences of the brainstem and the inhibitory mechanisms underlying the production of sleep by sensory stimulation, in, H. A. Jasper and G. D. Smirnov (Eds.), Moscow Colloquium of Electroencephalography and Clinical Neurophysiology.

MORUZZI, G. and MAGOUN, H. W. (1949) Brain stem reticular formation and activation of the EEG, *Electroenceph. Clin. Neurophysiol.* **1**, 455–73.

MOSGOVOY, V. D. (1973) Study of brain-wave factors and their relationship to intellectual activity. Candidate's Dissertation, University of Moscow.

MOSGOVOY, V. D. (1974) Study of the genetic determinateness of attention parameters, in, *Correlation between the biological and the social in human development,* Symposium proceedings, Vil'nyus, Moscow.

MOSGOVOY, V. D. (1978) Genetic determination of voluntary attention, in, B. M. Lomov and I. V. Ravich-Shcherbo (Eds.), *Problems in the genetics of psychophysiology,* pp. 244–53, Moscow: Inst. Psikhol. Akad. Nauk SSSR: Izd. Nauka.

MOSGOVOY, V. D. (1979) The genetic determination of voluntary attention. *Soviet Psychol.* **17**, 53–67.

MOTOKAWA, K., YAMASHITA, E. and OGAWA, T. (1957) Responses of retinal network to electrical stimulation, *Tohoku J. Exp. Med.* **71**, 41–53.

MOWRER, O. H. (1938) Preparatory set (expectancy) — a determinant in motivation and learning, *Psychol. Rev.* **45**, 62–91.

MOWRER, O. H. (1960a) *Learning theory and behaviour,* New York: Wiley.

MOWRER, O. H. (1960b) *Learning theory and the symbolic processes,* New York: Wiley.

MUNDY-CASTLE, A. C. (1953) An analysis of central responses to photic stimulation in normal adults, *Electroenceph. Clin. Neurophysiol.* **5**, 1.

MUNDY-CASTLE, A. C. (1957) *Conditionnement et réactivité en électroencéphalographie,* Paris: Masson.

MUNDY-CASTLE, A. C. and MCKIEVER, B. L. (1953) The psychophysiological significance of the galvanic skin response, *J. Exp. Psychol.* **46**, 15–24.

MURAWSKI, B. J. (1960) Flicker fusion thresholds in control subjects and identical twins, *J. Appl. Physiol.* **15**, 246–9.

MURPHY, G. and SPOHN, H. E. (1968) *Encounter with reality,* Boston: Houghton Mifflin.

MUSSEN, P. and PARKER, A. L. (1965) Mother nurturance and girl's incidental imitative learning, *J. Personality Soc. Psychol.* **2**, 94–7.

MYASISHCHEV, V. N. (1959) Some problems in observational studies in the neuropsychiatric clinic, in, *Some problems of present-day physiology,* Leningrad: Izd. Medgiz.

NAGPAL, M. and GUPTA, B. S. (1979) Personality reinforcement and verbal operant conditioning, *Br. J. Psychol.* **70,** 471–6.

NARBUTOVICH, I. O. and PODKOPAEV, N. A. (1936) The conditioned reflex as an association, *Tr. Fiziol. Lab. im. I. P. Pavlova.* **6,** 2, 5–25.

NARIKASHVILI, S. P. (1944) The influence of acoustic stimuli on the course of the Purkinje after-image, *Izv. Akad. Nauk SSSR, Ser. Biol.* **3,**, 139–55. Cited by London (1954).

NARIKASHVILI, S. P. (1946) The visual after-image of Purkinje and its modifications under the influence of indirect stimulation. Unpublished dissertation, Pavlov Physiological Institute. Cited by London (1954).

NASONOV, D. N. (1959) *The local reaction of protoplasm and spreading excitation,* Moscow.

NAUTA, W. J. (1964) Some efferent connections of the prefrontal cortex in the monkey, in, J. M. Warren and K. Akert (Eds.), *The frontal granular cortex and behaviour,* New York: McGraw-Hill.

NAUTA, W. J. (1971) The problem of the frontal lobe: a reinterpretation, *J. Psychiat. Res.* **8,** 167–87.

NEBYLITSYN, V. D. (1956) The relationship between sensitivity and strength of the nervous system, in, B. M. Teplov (Ed.), *Typological features of higher nervous activity in man,* Vol. 1, Moscow: Akad. Pedagog. Nauk RSFSR.

NEBYLITSYN, V. D. (1957a) A study of the strength and sensitivity of the nervous system. Candidate's Thesis, University of Moscow.

NEBYLITSYN, V. D. (1957b) Individual differences in strength-sensitivity in the visual and auditory analysers, *Vop. Psikhol.* **4**.

NEBYLITSYN, V. D. (1959) An investigation of the connection between sensitivity and strength of the nervous system, in, B. M. Teplov (Ed.), *Typological properties of higher nervous activity in man,* Vol. 2, pp. 48–82, Moscow: Akad. Pedagog. Nauk RSFSR. English translation by J. A. Gray in J. A. Gray (Ed.) (1964b) pp. 402–5.

NEBYLITSYN, V. D. (1960a) Reaction time and strength of the nervous system: first report, *Izd. Akad. Pedagog. Nauk RSFSR.*

NEBYLITSYN, V. D. (1960b) Reaction time and strength of the nervous system. *Izd. Akad. Pedagog. Nauk RSFSR,* **2,** No. 5.

NEBYLITSYN, V. D. (1960c) The correlation between some indices of electrical excitability of the eye and strength of the nervous system, *Izd. Akad. Pedagog. Nauk RSFSR,* **2.**

NEBYLITSYN, V. D. (1961a) Individual differences in the strength and sensitivity of both visual and auditory analysers, in, N. O'Connor (Ed.), *Recent Soviet psychology,* Oxford: Pergamon.

NEBYLITSYN, V. D. (1961b) Extinction with reinforcement of conditioned EEG as an index of strength of nervous system, *Izd. Akad. Pedagog. Nauk RSFSR,* **3.**

NEBYLITSYN, V. D. (1963a) The structure of the basic properties of the nervous system, *Vop. Psikhol.* **4**.

NEBYLITSYN, V. D. (1963b) An electroencephalographic study of the properties of strength and balance of the nervous processes in man using factor analysis, in, B. M. Teplov (Ed.), *Typological features of higher nervous activity in man,* Vol. 3, Moscow: Akad. Pedagog. Nauk RSFSR.

NEBYLITSYN, V. D. (1964a) The problem of balance of the nervous processes, *Vop. Psikhol.* **6.**

NEBYLITSYN, V. D. (1964b) The photic driving reaction as a function of the intensity of the pulsing light. *Zh. Vyssh. Nerv. Deyat. I. P. Pavlova,* **14,** 4.

NEBYLITSYN, V. D. (1965) Extinction with reinforcement of electro-cortical conditioned reflexes as an index of excitatory strength of the nervous system, in, B. M. Teplov (Ed.) *Typological features of higher nervous activity in man*, Vol. 4, Moscow: Akad. Pedagog. Nauk RSFSR.

NEBYLITSYN, V. D. (1966a) *Fundamental properties of the human nervous system*, Moscow: Proveshcheniye. English Translation, G. L. Mangan (Ed.) (1972) New York: Plenum.

NEBYLITSYN, V. D. (1966b) *Report in the Proceedings of the 18th International Congress of Psychology*, Moscow.

NEBYLITSYN, V. D. (1972) The problem of general and partial properties of the nervous system, in, V. D. Nebylitsyn and J. A. Gray (Eds.), *Biological basis of individual behaviour*, London: Academic Press.

NEBYLITSYN, V. D. (1973) Current problems of differential psychophysiology, *Soviet Psychol.* 11, 47–70.

NEBYLITSYN, V. D., GOLUBEVA, E. A., RAVICH-SHCHERBO, I. V. and YERMOLAEVA-TOMINA, L. B. (1965) A comparative study of short methods of measuring basic properties of the nervous system in man, in, B. M. Teplov (Ed.), *Typological features of higher nervous activity in man*, Vol. 4, Moscow: Akad. Pedagog. Nauk RSFSR.

NEILON, P. (1964) Shirley's babies after fifteen years, in, R. C. Stendler (Ed.), *Readings in child behaviour and development*, 2nd ed, New York: Harcourt Brace & World.

NELSEN, J. M., PELLEY, K. and GOLDSTEIN, L. (1973) Chronic nicotine treatment in rats: EEG amplitude and variability changes occurring within and between structures, *Res. Comm. Chem. Pathol. Pharmacol.* 5, 694–704.

NEUMYVAKA-KAPUSTNIK, D. P. and PLASKIN, A. I. (1964) Functional differences in the spinal cord systems in dogs with different types of nervous system, *Zh. Vyssh. Nerv. Deyat. im. I. P. Pavlova*, 14, 1.

NEVA, E. and HICKS, R. (1970) A new look at an old issue: manifest anxiety scale validity, *J. Consult. Clin. Psychol.* 35, 3, 406–8.

NEWBIGGING, P. L. (1954) The relationship between perspective and embedded figures, *Can. J. Psychol.* 8, 204–8.

NEWMAN, H. H., FREEMAN, F. N. and HOLZINGER, K. (1937) *Twins: a study of heredity and environment*, Chicago: University of Chicago Press.

NICHOLLS, E. G. (1955) The relation between certain personality variables and the figural after-effect. Unpublished doctoral dissertation, University of London. Cited by H. J. Eysenck (1957) p. 158.

NICHOLS, R. C. (1965) The national merit twin study, in, S. G. Vandenberg (Ed.), *Multivariate analysis of twin differences in methods and goals in human behaviour genetics*, New York: Academic Press.

NICHOLS, R. C. (1966) The resemblance of twins in personality and interests, *National Merit Scholarship Corporation Research Reports*, 2, 1–23.

NICHOLS, R. C. and BILBRO, W. C. (1966) The diagnosis of twin zygosity, *Acta Genet. Statist. Med.* 16, 265–75.

NICHOLSON, J. N. and GRAY, J. A. (1972) Peak shift, behavioural contrast and stimulus generalization as related to personality and development in children, *Br. J. Psychol.* 63, 47–63.

NIELSEN, T. C. and PETERSEN, K. E. (1976) Elecrodermal correlates of extraversion, trait anxiety and schizophrenism, *Scand. J. Psychol.* 17, 73–80.

NIES, R. (1964) The orienting reflex as conceptually distinct from drive. Unpublished doctoral dissertation, University of California, Los Angeles. Cited by Maltzman and Raskin (1965).

NIKOLAEV, P. N. (1911) Contribution à l'analyse des réflexes conditionnels complexes, *Arch. Sci. Bio., St. Petersb.* 16, 411–44.

NIKOLAEVA, N. I. (1953) Ob izmenenii vozbudinosti nervnykh struktur golvnogo mozga pri obrazovanii uslovnykh refleksov. Doctoral dissertation, Rostov-na-Donu.

NIKOLAEVA, N. I. (1955) Izmeneniya vozkudimosti raznykh oblastey kory golvonogo mozga pri obrazovanii dvigatel'nykh uslovnykh refleksov, *Fiziol. Zh. SSSR*, 41, 1.

NIKOLAEVA, V. V. (1957) The delayed conditioned reflex and the dynamics of extinction, *Tr. Inst. Fiziol. im. I. P. Pavlova*, 6.

NOBLE, C. E. (1950) Conditioned generalisation of the galvanic skin response to a subvocal stimulus, *J. Exp. Psychol.* **40**, 15–25.

NOIROT, E. (1972) The onset of maternal behaviour in rats, hamsters and mice: a selective review, *Adv. Study Behav.* **4**, 107–46.

NORMAN, W. T. (1969) To see ourselves as others see us: relations among self-perceptions, peer-perceptions and expected peer-perceptions of personality attributes, *Multiv. Behav. Res.* **4**, 417–43.

NOWLIS, D. P. and KAMIYA, J. (1970) The control of electroencephalographic alpha rhythms through auditory feedback and the associated mental activity, *Psychophysiol.* **6**, 476–84.

NUTTIN, J. (1965) *Le structure de la personalité*, Paris: Presses Universitaires de France.

OBRATSOVA, G. A. (1964) *Problems of the ontogeny of higher nervous activity*, Moscow: Nauka.

OBRIST, P. A. (1968) Heart rate and somatic-motor coupling during classical aversive conditioning in humans, *J. Exp. Psychol.* **77**, 180–93.

O'CONNOR, K. and VENABLES, P. H. (1956) A note on the basal level of skin conductance and Binet I.Q., *Br. J. Psychol.* **48**, 148–9.

O'GORMAN, J. G. (1968) Individual differences and the orientation reaction. Paper presented to the 3rd Annual Conference of the Australian Psychological Society, Brisbane.

O'GORMAN, J. G. (1971) Habituation of the orienting reaction as a function of stumulus information, *Psychonom. Sci.* **22**, 331–2.

O'GORMAN, J. G. (1972) Electrodermal lability and recovery of the habituated OR, *Aust. J. Psychol.* **24**, 241–4.

O'GORMAN, J. G. and JAMIESON, R. D. (1975) The incremental stimulus intensity effect and habituation of autonomic responses in man, *Physiol. Psychol.* **3**, 4, 385–9.

O'GORMAN, J. G., MANGAN, G. L. and GOWEN, J. (1970) Selective habituation of the galvanic skin response component of the orientation reaction to an auditory stimulus, *Psychophysiol.* **6**, 716–21.

O'HANLON, J. F. (1965) Adrenalin and noradrenalin: relation to performance in a visual vigilance task, *Science, N.Y.* **150**, 507–9.

O'LEARY, K. S. (1965) Preference for variability of stimuli as a function of experimentally induced anxiety, *Psychol. Rep.* **16**, 1202.

OKEN, D. (1967) The psychophysiology and psychoendocrinology of stress and emotion, in, M. M. Appley and R. Trumbull (Eds.), *Psychological stress*, pp. 43–76, New York: Appleton-Century-Crofts.

OLDS, J. and OLDS, M. (1965) Drives, rewards and the brain. In: F. Barron and W. C. Dement (Eds.) *New directions in Psychology*, Vol. 2, pp. 329–410, New York: Holt, Rinehart & Winston.

OL'SHANNIKOVA, A. E. (1974) The sign of dominant emotions and background EEG parameters in humans by a twin method. Abstract of candidate's dissertation, Moscow University.

OL'SHANNIKOVA, A. E. and ALEKSANDROVA, N. I. (1969) On the reliability of indices of motor reaction, *Problemy Differentsialnoi Psikhofiziologii,* **6**, 252–65.

OLWEUS, D. (1973) *Hackkycklingar och översittare*, Stockholm: Almgvist and Wiksell.

OLWEUS, D. (1974) *Aggression in schools.* Washington: Hemisphere Publishing Corporation.

OLWEUS, D. (1977a) A critical analysis of the "modern" interactionnalist position, in, D. Magnusson and N. S. Endler (Eds.), *Personality at the crossroads: current issues in interactional psychology*, Hillsdale N. J.: Erlbaum.

OLWEUS, D. (1977b) Aggression and peer acceptance in pre-adolescent boys: two short-term longitudinal studies of ratings, *Child Dev.* **48**, 1301–13.

OMINSKY, M. and KIMBLE, G. A. (1966) Anxiety and eyelid conditioning, *J. Exp. Psychol.* **71**, 471–2.

OR, W. C. and STERN, J. A. (1960) The effect of stimulus information on habituation rate. Paper presented at the annual meeting of the Society for Psychophysiological Research, Monte Rey, California.

ORBELI, L. A. (1947) The second-signal system, *Fiziol. Zh. SSSR,* **33**, 675–87.

ORBELI, L. A. (1949) *Problems of higher nervous activity*, Moscow: Akad. Nauk SSSR.

ORBELI, L. A. (1950) The dialectical method in the physiology of the nervous system, *Fiziol. Zh. SSSR*, **36**, 5–18.

ORBELI, L. A. (1958) Basic problems and methods of evolutionary physiology, in, D. A. Biryukov (Ed.), *Evolution of functions of the nervous system*, pp. 7–17 Leningrad: Medgiz.

ORLEBEKE, J. F. (1972) *Arousal, extraversion and strength of the nervous system*, Assen: Van Gorkum.

ORNSTEIN, R. (1972) *The Psychology of Consciousness*, New York: Harcourt Brace Jovanovich Inc.

OSBORNE, R. H., DE GEORGE, F. V. and MATHERS, J. A. L. (1963) The variability of blood pressure: basal and casual measurements in adult twins, *Am. Heart J.* **66**, 176–83.

OSBORNE, R. T. (1970) Heritability estimates for the visual evoked response. *Life Sci.* **9**, 481–90.

OSGOOD, C. E. (1953) *Method and theory in experimental psychology*, New York: Oxford University Press.

OSGOOD, C. E. (1961) Comments on Professor Bousfield's paper, in, C. N. Cofer (Ed.), *Verbal learning and general behaviour theory*, Englewood Cliffs: Prentice-Hall.

OSWALD, I. (1960) Falling asleep open-eyed during intense rhythmic stimulation, *Br. Med. J.* **1**, 1450–5.

OSWALD, I. (1962) *Sleeping and waking: physiology and psychology*, Amsterdam: Elsevier.

OTIS, G. D. and MARTIN, R. B. (1968) Interaction of extraversion and anxiety in an instrumental avoidance task, *J. Exp. Res. Person,* **3**, 57–9.

OTTINGER, D. R. and SIMMONS, J. E. (1964) Behaviour of human neonates and prenatal maternal anxiety, *Psychol. Rep.* **14**, 391–4.

OVERTON, W. F. and REESE, H. W. (1973) Models of development: methodological implications, in, J. R. Nesselroade and H. W. Reese (Eds.), *Life span developmental psychology: methodological issues,* pp. 15–45 New York: Academic Press.

PAISEY, T. J. H. and MANGAN, G. L. (1980) The relationship of extraversion, neuroticism and sensation-seeking to questionnaire-derived measures of nervous system properties, *Pavlov J. Biol. Sci.* **15**, 3, 115–22.

PAISEY, T. J. H. and MANGAN, G. L. (forthcoming) A developmental model of conditioning and personality: activity and reactivity constraints, in, *Contemporary approaches to temperament: an East-West dialogue.* Pergamon.

PAIVIO, A. (1969) Mental imagery in associative learning and memory, *Psychol. Rev.* **76**, 3, 241–63.

PAIVIO, A. and YUILLE, J. C. (1967) Mediation instructions and word attributes in paired-associate learning, *Psychonom. Sci.* **8**, 65–6.

PALEY, I. M. (1968) The multifactor study of certain individual typological features of man and their relation to differences in nervous-system strength, *Probl. obshchei, sotsial'noi i inzhenervnoi psikhol.* **2**, 112–27. Also in *Soviet Psychol.* Winter 1970–1.

PALEY, I. M., ZAGULINA, P. L., IVANOVA, Y. A., LEVEVA, S. N. and LISENKOVA, V. P. (1966) Complex investigation of some individual and typological characteristics in man, in, B. G. Ananev and D. A. Kerimov (Eds.), *Man and society*, Leningrad: Leningrad University Press.

PALLADIN, A. (1906) Formation of laboratory conditioned reflexes to sums of stimuli, *Trans. Obsh. Russ, Vrachey v St. Peterburge,* **73**, 393–401.

PANFEROV, YU. K. (1926) Chained conditioned reflexes in children, in, *Papers, 2nd All-Union Congress of Physiology,* 153–6, Leningrad.

PANTELEYEVA, T. A. (1977) An investigation of the transformation of motor habits as a function of genotype. *Vop. Psikhol.,* No. 4, 106–10.

PANTELEYEVA, T. A. and SHLYAKHTA, N. F. (1978) Genetic components of certain indices of lability of nervous processes, in, B. M. Lomov and I. V. Ravich-Shcherbo (Eds.), *Problems in the genetics of psychophysiology,* pp. 127–36 Moscow: Inst. Psikhol. Akad. Nauk SSSR, Izd. Nauka.

PAPOUSEK, H. (1967a) Conditioning during early postnatal development, in, T. Brackbill and G. G. Thompson (Eds.), *Behaviour in infancy and early childhood,* pp. 259–74, New York: Free.

PAPOUSEK, H. (1967b) Genetics and child development, in, J. N. Spuhler, *Genetic diversity and human development,* pp. 171–86, Chicago: Aldine.

518                                                                THE BIOLOGY OF HUMAN CONDUCT

PAPOUSEK, H. (1969) Development of learning ability in children in the first months of life (in Czech). Dissertation thesis, Charles University, Prague.

PARKE, R. D. (1969) Effectiveness of punishment as an interaction of intensity, timing, agent nurturance and cognitive structuring, *Child Dev.* **40**, 213–36.

PARKE, R. D. (1972) Some effects of punishment on children's behaviour, in, U. Bronfenbrenner (Ed.), *Influences on human development*, Hinsdale, Ill.: Dryden Press.

PARKE, R. D. and MURRAY, S. (1971) Re-instatement: a technique for increasing stability of inhibition in children. Unpublished manuscript, University of Wisconsin. Quoted in R. D. Parke (1972).

PARKE, R. D. and WALTERS, R. H. (1967) Some factors influencing the efficacy of punishment training for inducing response inhibition, *Monographs of the Society for Research in Child Development*, **32** (Whole No. 109).

PARTANEN, J., BRUUN, K. and MARKKANEN, T. (1966) *Inheritance of drinking behaviour: a study on intelligence, personality and use of alcohol of adult twins*, Stockholm: Almquist.

PASQUARELLI, B. and BULL, N. (1951) Experimental investigations of the body-mind continuum in affective states, *J. Nerv. Ment. Dis.* **113**, 512–21.

PATTERSON, T. (1976a) Skin conductance recovery and pupillometrics in chronic schizophrenia, *Psychophysiol. 13*, 189–95.

PATTERSON, T. (1976b) Skin conductance responding/non-responding and pupillometrics in chronic schizophrenia: a confirmation of Gruzelier and Venables, *J. Nerv. Ment. Dis.* **163**, 200–9.

PAVLOV, I. P. (1903) Experimental psychology and psychophysiology of animals, *Izv. Voyenno-Meditsinskoy Akademii*, **7**, 2, 121.

PAVLOV, I. P. (1904) Sur la sécrétion psychique des glands salivaires (phénomènes nerveux complexes dans le travail de glandes salivaires), *Arch. Int. Physiol.* **1**, 119–35.

PAVLOV, I. P. (1915) *Conditions of active and resting states of the cerebral hemispheres. Moscow.*

PAVLOV, I. P. (1924) *Wednesdays, December 5th,* Moscow: Akad. Nauk SSSR.

PAVLOV, I. P. (1927) *Conditioned Reflexes.* Translated and edited by G. V. Anrep (1960, sixth printing). New York: International Publishers.

PAVLOV, I. P. (1927) *Lectures on the work of the large hemispheres of the brain.* Moscow-Leningrad: GIZ.

PAVLOV, I. P. (1928) *Lectures on the conditioned reflex.* Translated and edited by W. H. Gantt. New York: Liveright Publishing Corp.

PAVLOV, I. P. (1932) The reply of a physiologist to psychologists, *Psychol. Rev.* **39**, 91–127.

PAVLOV, I. P. (1933) Essai d'une interprétation physiologique de l'hystérie, *Encéphale*, **28**, 288–95.

PAVLOV, I. P. (1935) Wednesdays, Jan. 23, in, *Selected works*, (1955) Moscow: Foreign Languages Publishing House.

PAVLOV, I. P. (1941) *Conditioned reflexes and psychiatry,* Edited by W. H. Gantt, New York: International Publishers.

PAVLOV, I. P. (1949) *Wednesdays,* Vols I-III, Moscow-Leningrad: Geva Screnus.

PAVLOV, I. P. (1951–2) *Complete Works,* Vol. 3, Books. 2, Moscow: Akad. Nauk SSSR.

PAVLOV, I. P. (1955) *Selected Works.* Translated by S. Belsky, Moscow: Foreign Languages Publishing House.

PAWLICK, K. and CATTELL, R. B. (1965) The relationship between certain personality factors and measures of cortical arousal, *Neuropsychologia*, **3**, 129–51.

PEEKE, S. C. and GRINGS, W. W. (1968) Magnitude of UCR as a function of variability in the CS-UCS relation, *J. Exp. Psychol.* **77**, 64–9.

PERELZWEIG, I. (1907) *Materials on the study of conditioned reflexes.* Thesis. St. Petersburg: Military Medical Academy.

PERLS, F., HEFFERLINE, R. F. and GOODMAN, P. (1951) *Gestalt therapy*, New York: Julian Press.

PERRY, D., BUSSEY, K. and PERRY, L. (1975) Factors influencing the imitation of resistance to deviation, *Dev. Psychol.* **11**, 724–31.

PERVOMAISKY, B. YA., YALDYGINA, A. S. and PERVAMAISKY, E. B. (1975) Study of the type of higher nervous activity in twins, *Zh. Vyssh. Nerv. Deyat. im. I. P. Pavlova*, **25**, 700–5.

PETRIE, A. (1960) Some psychological aspects of pain and the relief of suffering. *Ann. N. Y. Acad. Sci.* **86**, 13–27.

PETRIE, A. (1967) *Individuality in pain and suffering,* Chicago: University Press.

PETRIE, A., COLLINS, W. and SOLOMON, P. (1960) The tolerance for pain and for sensory deprivation, *Am. J. Psychol.* **73**, 80–90.

PETROVA, M. K. (1914) Concerning the theory of irradiation of excitation and inhibitory processes. Dissertation, St. Petersburg.

PETROVA, M. K. (1929) Interrelation between excitatory and inhibitory processes in dogs of various types of nervous system. *Tr. Fiziol. Lab. im. I. P. Pavlova,* **3**, 2–3.

PETROVA, M. K. (1934) Further data on the determination of strength of nervous system in experimental animals, *Arch. Biol. Sci.* **34**, 1–3.

PEVZNER, M. S. (1959) *Oligophrenic children,* Moscow: Akad. Pedagog. Nauk RSFSR.

PHILLIPS, L. W. (1958) Mediated verbal similarity as a determinant of the generalisation of the conditioned GSR, *J. Exp. Psychol.* **55**, 56–62.

PIAGET, J. (1948) *The moral judgment of the child,* Glencoe, Ill.: Free Press.

PIAGET, J. (1951) *Play, dreams and imitation in childhood,* New York: Norton.

PIERS, E. V. and KIRCHNER, E. P. (1969) Eyelid conditioning and personality: positive results from nonpartisans, *J. Abnorm. Psychol.* **74**, 336–9.

PILLSBURY, W. B. (1908) *Attention,* New York: Macmillan.

PISHKIN, V. and HERSHIER, D. (1963) Respiration and G.S.R. as functions of white sound in schizophrenia, *J. Consult. Psychol.* **27**, 330–7.

PIVOVAROV, A. S. and GUSELNIKOV, V. I. (1979) Changes in input resistance of a cortical neurone and in threshold of stimulation of its electro-excitable membrane by depolarising current in the process of habituation, *Zh. Vyssh. Nerv. Deyat. im. I. P. Pavlova,* **29**, 619–30.

PLATONOV, K. I. (1959) *The word as a physiological and therapeutic factor,* Moscow: Foreign Languages Publishing House.

PLOMIN, R. and WILLERMAN, L. (1975) A criterion control study and a twin study of reflection-impulsivity in children, *J. Educ. Psychol.* **67**, 4, 537–48.

PLOTKIN, W. B. (1976) On the self-regulation of the occipital alpha rhythm: control strategies, state of consciousness and the role of physiological feedback, *J. Exp. Psychol., General,* **106**, 1, 66–99.

PLUM, A. (1969) Visual evoked responses: their relationship to intelligence. Ph.D. Thesis, University of Florida.

PLUTCHIK, R. (1954) The role of muscular tension in maladjustment. *J. Genet. Psychol.* **50**, 45–62.

PODKOPAEV, N. A. (1924) Movement of inhibitory processes, *Tr. Fiziol. Lab. im. I. P. Pavlova,* **1**, 1.

PODKOPAEV, N. A. (1952) *Method of Conditioned Reflex Study,* Izd. Akad. Nauk SSSR.

POLEY, W. and ROYCE, J. R. (1976) Factors of mouse emotionality at the second order, third order and fourth order, *Muilti. Behav. Res.* **11**, 63–76.

POLLACK, M., KATU, R. L., KARP, E. and FINK, M. (1960) Individual differences in the perception of the upright in hospitalized psychiatric patients. Paper read at Eastern Psychological Association, New York.

POLYAKOV, G. I. (1959) *The structural organisation of the cortical representation of the various analysers in man,* Vestnik Akad. Med. Nauk SSSR.

POLYAKOVA, I. V. (1963a) Transfer of attention and individual typological properties of higher nervous activity, Paper I, Comparison of data on typological differences in the after effect of the excitatory process with the "real-life indices" of the nervous processes. *Dokl. Akad. Pedagog. Nauk RSFSR,* **1**.

POLYAKOVA, I. V. (1963b) Features of transfer of attention with respect to certain individual typological properties of higher nervous activity, Paper II, Comparison of data on typological differences in the after-effect of the inhibitory process with the "real-life indices" of the mobility of the nervous processes, *Akad. Pedagog. Nauk RSFSR* (Moscow), **129**.

POMERLAU-MALCUIT, A. (1974) Cardiac activity and behaviour: measures of the first interaction processes between the new-born organism and his environment, *Can. Psychol.* **15**, 1, 43–60.

POMONAREV, M. F. (1955) The effects of caffeine and of bromide on the times of the latent and motor components in the motor reactions of man. *Fiziol. Zh. SSSR,* **44**, 90–7.

POSER, E. (1960) Figural after-effect as a personality correlate, Proc. XVIth Inter. Congr. Psych. Amsterdam: North-Holland.

POSER, E. G. (1962) A simple and reliable apparatus for the measurement of pain, *Am. J. Psychol.* **75**, 304–5.

POSHIVALOV, V. P. (1977) Inversion of inter-species relations: isolated mice attack rats, *Zh. Vyssh. Nerv. Deyat. im. I. P. Pavlova,* **27**, 1316–18.

POSNER, M. I. (1973) Coordination of internal codes, in, W. G. Chase (Ed.), *Visual information processing,* New York: Academic Press.

POWAZEK, M. and JOHNSON, J. T. (1973) Heart rate response to novel and signal stimuli in non-retarded and retarded subjects, *Am. J. Ment. Defic.* **78**, 3, 286–91.

POWAZEK, M. and JOHNSON, J. T. (1975) Heart rate and respiration to novel and signal stimuli in nonretarded and retarded subjects, *Am. J. Ment. Defic.* **78**, 3, 286–91.

POZNANSKAYA, I. B. (1930) Investigation of negative induction in the cerebral cortex of the child, in, *Basic mechanisms in the conditioned-reflex activity of the child,* Moscow-Leningrad.

PRESSEY, A. W. (1970) Sex differences on tests of VFAE, *Acta Psychol.* **34**, 78–88.

PRIBRAM, K. H. (1967) The new Neurology and the biology of the emotions: A structural approach. *Amer.* Psychol., **22 (10),** 830–8.

PROSSER, C. L. and HUNTER, W. S. (1936) The extinction of startle responses and spinal reflexes in the white rat, *Am. J. Physiol.* **117**, 609–18.

PURVES, D. (1980) Neuronal competition, *Nature, Lond.* **287**, 585–6.

PUSHKIN, V. N. (1972) Vigilance as a function of strength of the nervous system, in, V. D. Nebylitsyn and J. A. Gray (Eds.) *Biological bases of individual behaviour,* pp. 310–24, London: Academic Press.

PUTNAM, L. E., ROSS, L. E. and GRAHAM, F. K. (1974) Cardiac orienting during "good" and "poor" differential eyelid conditioning, *J. Exp. Psychol.* **102**, 4, 563–73.

QUAY, H. C. (1965) Psychopathic personality as pathological stimulation seeking, *Am. J. Psychiat.* **122**, 180–3.

QUAY, H. C. and HUNT, W. A. (1965) Psychopathy, neuroticism and verbal conditioning, *J. Consult. Psychol.* **29**, 283.

RABINOVICH, R. L. (1960) method of studying mobility of basic nervous functions, *Zh. Vyssh. Nerv. Deyat. im. I. P. Pavlova,* **11**, 5.

RACHMAN, S. (1960) Galvanic skin response in identical twins, *Psychol. Rep.* **6**, 298.

RACHMAN, S. (1967) Systematic desensitization, *Psychol. Bull.* **67**, 93–103.

RACHMAN, S. (1968a) The role of muscular relaxation in desensitization therapy, *Behav. Res. Ther.* **6**, 159–66.

RACHMAN, S. (1968b) *Phobias: their nature and control,* Springfield, Ill.: Charles C. Thomas.

RAEVSKII, A. M. (1972) On the mechanism of reaction time in man as a function of prior verbal instructions, *Vop. Psikhol.* **18**, 4, 118–21.

RAO, D. C., MORTON, N. E. and YEE, S. (1974) Analysis of family resemblance, II, A linear model for familial correlation, *Am. J. Hum. Genet.* **26**, 311–59.

RAPAPORT, D. (1942) *Emotions and memory,* Baltimore: Williams & Wilkins.

RASKIN, D. (1963) Some factors influencing semantic conditioning and generalisation of autonomic responses. Unpublished doctoral dissertation, University of California, Los Angeles. Cited by Morgensen and Martin (1969).

RASKIN, D. (1969) Semantic conditioning and generalisation of autonomic responses, *J. Exp. Psychol.* **79**, 69–76.

RASKIN, D. (1973) Attention and arousal, in, W. Prokasy and D. Raskin (Eds.), *Electrodermal activity in psychological research,* New York: Academic Press.

RASKIN, D. (1975) Decreased skin conductance response habituation in chronically anxious patients, *Biol. Psychol.* **2**, 309–19.

RAVICH-SHCHERBO, I. V. (1956) Study of typological differences in mobility of the nervous processes in the visual analyzer, in, B. M. Teplov (Ed.), *Typological features of higher nervous activity in man,* Vol. 1, Moscow: Akad. Pedagog. Nauk RSFSR.

RAVICH-SHCHERBO, I. V. (1959) Some features of the after-effect of the motor reaction in oligophrenic children, in, B. M. Teplov (Ed.), *Typological features of higher nervous activity in man*, Vol. 2, Moscow: Akad. Pedagog. Nauk RSFSR.

RAVICH-SHCHERBO, I. V. (1974) Genetic factors underlying nervous system characteristics and their stability. Symposium, Tallin.

RAVICH-SHCHERBO, I. V. and SHIBAROVSKAYA, G. A. (1972) The structure of dynamism of nervous processes in children of school age, in, V. D. Nebylitsyn (Ed.), *Problems of differential psychophysiology*, Vol. 7, Moscow: Pedagogika.

RAVICH-SHCHERBO, I. V. and SCHWARTZ, L. A. (1959) Correlations between the speed of arousal and termination of nervous processes as indices of mobility of the nervous system, *Vop. Psikhol.* 5.

RAVICH-SHCHERBO, I. V. and TRIFANOVA, M. K. (1967) Age features of some electroencephalographic reactions, in, B. M. Teplov (Ed.), *Typological features of higher nervous activity in man*, Vol. 2, Moscow: Akad. Pedagog. Nauk RSFSR.

RAWNSLEY, A. I. and HARRIS, J. D. (1952) Studies in short-duration auditory fatigue, II, Recovery time, *J. Exp. Psychol.* **43,** 138–42.

RAY, R. and BROWN, D. A. (1976) The behavioural specificity of stimulation: a systems approach to procedural distinctions of classical and instrumental conditioning. *Pavlov J. Biol. Sc.* **11,** 3–23.

RAZENKOV, I. P. (1924) Changes in the excitatory processes in the dog's cerebral cortex under difficult conditions, *Tr. Fiziol. Lab. im. I. P. Pavlova*, **1,** 1.

RAZRAN, G. (1934) Conditioned withdrawal responses in adult human subjects, *Psychol. Bull.* **31,** 111–43.

RAZRAN, G. (1935) Conditioned responses: an experimental study and a theoretical analysis, *Arch. Psychol.* **28** (Whole No. 190).

RAZRAN, G. (1938) Studies in configural conditioning, VII. Ratios and elements in salivary conditioning to various musical intervals, *Psychol. Rec.* **2,** 370–6.

RAZRAN, G. (1939) A quantitative study of meaning by a conditioned salivary technique (semantic conditioning), *Science, N. Y.* **90,** 89–91.

RAZRAN, G. (1949a) Sentential and propositional generalizations of salivary conditioning to verbal stimuli, *Science, N. Y.* **109,** 447–8.

RAZRAN, G. (1949b) Semantic and phonetographic generalization of salivary conditioning to verbal stimuli. *J. Exp. Psychol.* **39,** 642–52.

RAZRAN, G. (1949c) Some psychological factors in the generalization of salivary conditioning to verbal stimuli, *Am. J. Psychol.* **62,** 247–56.

RAZRAN, G. (1949d) Attitudinal determinants of conditioning and of generalization of conditioning, *J. Exp. Psychol.* **39,** 820–9.

RAZRAN, G. (1949e) Stimulus generalization of conditioned responses, *Psychol. Bull.* **46,** 337–65.

RAZRAN, G. (1952) Experimental semantics, *Trans. N. Y. Acad. Sci.* **14,** 171–7.

RAZRAN, G. (1955) Partial reinforcement of salivary CRs in adult human subjects: preliminary study, *Psychol. Rep.* **1,** 409–16.

RAZRAN, G. (1957) The dominance-contiguity theory of the acquisition of classical conditioning, *Psychol. Bull.* **54,** 1–46.

RAZRAN, G. (1961a) Raphael's "idealess" behaviour, *J. Comp. Physiol. Psychol.* **54,** 366–7.

RAZRAN, G. (1961b) The observable unconscious and the inferable conscious in current Soviet psychology: interoceptive conditioning, semantic conditioning and the orienting reflex, *Psychol. Bull.* **68,** 81–147.

RAZRAN, G. (1971) *Mind in Evolution*, Boston: Houghton Mifflin.

RECHTSCHAFFEN, A. (1958) Neural satiation reactions, inhibition and extraversion-introversion, *J. Abnorm. Soc. Psychol.* **61,** 495–6.

REESE, W. G. and DYKMAN, R. A. (1960) Conditional cardiovascular reflexes in dogs and men, *Psychol. Rev.* **40,** 4, 250–65.

REICH, W. (1942) *The function of the orgasm*, London: Panther.

REICH, W. (1949) *Character analysis*, New York: Orgone Institute Press.

RESCORLA, R. A. and LOLORDO, V. M. (1965) Inhibition of avoidance behaviour, *J. Comp. Physiol. Psychol.* **59**, 406–2.

RESCORLA, R. A. and WAGNER, A. R. (1972) A theory of Pavlovian conditioning: variations in the effectiveness of reinforcement and nonreinforcement, in, A. H. Black and W. F. Prokasy (Eds.) *Classical conditioning II: current research and theory,* New York: Appleton-Century-Crofts.

REYKOWSKI, J. (1976) Intrinsic motivation and intrinsic inhibition of aggressive behaviour. Paper presented at the conference on psychological issues in changing aggression. Warsaw.

REYKOWSKI, J. (1977) Spontaneous aggression and spontaneous factors which inhibit it, *Przeglad Psychologiczny,* **20**, 203–28.

REYNOLDS, B (1945) Extinction of trace conditioned responses as a function of the spacing of trials during acquisition and extinction series, *J. Exp. Psychol.* **35**, 81–95.

REYNOLDS, D. (1966) Time and event uncertainty in unisensory reaction time, *J. Exp. Psychol.* **71**, 286–93.

REZNIKOFF, M. and HONEYMAN, M. S. (1967) MMPI profiles of monozygotic and dizygotic twin pairs, *J. Consult. Psychol.* **31**, 100.

RHODES, L. E., DUSTMAN, R. E. and BECK, E. C. (1969) The visual evoked response: a comparison of bright and dull children, *Electroenceph. Clin. Neurophysiol.* **27**, 364–72.

RICE, M. E. and CHAPLIN, T. C. (1979) Social skills training for hospitalized male arsonists, *J. Behav. Ther. Psychiat.* **10**, 105–8.

RICHARDSON, A. (1969) *Mental Imagery*, New York: Springer.

RICHLIN, M., WEISINGER, M. and WEINSTEIN, S. (1971) Interhemispheric asymmetries of evoked cortical responses in retarded and normal children, *Cortex,* **7**, 98–105.

RIESS, B. F. (1940) Semantic conditioning involving the galvanic skin reflex. *J. Exp. Psychol.* **26**, 238–40.

RIESS, B. F. (1946) Genetic changes in semantic conditioning, *J. Exp. Psychol.* **36**, 143–52.

RIKMAN, V. V. (1932) Traces of defensive reflexes as an analogue of traumatic neuroses, *Tr. Fiziol. Lab. im. I. P. Pavlova,* **4**, 102–67.

RILEY, P. M. (1974) Habituation of the orienting response as a function of inter- and intra-transfer of concept information, *Diss. Abstr. Int.* **34**, 7-b, 3541–2.

RIMM, D. C. and BOTRELL, J. (1969) Four measures of visual imagination, *Behav. Res. Ther.* **7**, 63–9.

ROBERTS, A. H., SCHULER, J., BACON, J., ZIMMERMAN, R. L. and PATTERSON, R. (1975) Individual differences and autonomic control: absorption, hypnotic susceptibility, and the unilateral control of skin temperature, *J. Abnorm. Psychol.* **84**, 272–9.

ROBINSON, D. (1980) Relationships between human personality, human intelligence and properties of the diffuse thalamocortical system. Unpublished Dissertation, University of Oxford.

ROBINSON, E. and GANTT, W. H. (1947) The orienting reflex (questioning reaction): cardiac, respiratory, salivary and motor components, *Bull. Johns Hopkins Hosp.* **80**, 231–53.

RODIN, E. A., GRISELL, J. L., GUDOBBN, R. D. and ZACHAV, G. (1965) Relationship of EEG background rhythms to photic evoked responses, *Electroenceph. Clin. Neurophysiol.* **19**, 301–4.

ROESSLER, R., BURCH, N. R. and CHILDERS, H. E. (1966) Personality and arousal correlates of specific galvanic skin responses, *Psychophysiol.,* **3**, 115–30.

ROGER, A., VORONIN, L. G. and SOKOLOV, E. N. (1959) Electroencephalographic study of temporary connections in cases of extinction of the orienting reflex in man, *Zh. Vyssh. Nerv. Deyat. im. I. P. Pavlova,* **8**, 3–16.

ROITBAK, A. I. (1956) Dendrites and the process of inhibition, *Gargrskiye Besedy,* **2**, 165–87.

ROITBAK, A. I. (1958a) Concerning the mechanisms of extinction of orientation and conditioned reflexes, *Physiol. Bohemoslov.* **7**, 125–34.

ROITBAK, A. I. (1958b) Electrical manifestations in the neural center of the conditioned stimulus, *Trans. Inst. Fiziol. Tbilisi,* **11**, 120–54.

ROKOTOVA, N. A. (1952) Formation of temporary connections in dogs between traces of "indifferent" stimuli, *Tr. Inst. Fiziol. im. I. P. Pavlova,* **1**, 35–42.

ROKOTOVA, N. A. (1954) Physiological mechanisms of temporary connections among "indifferent" stimuli, *Zh. Vyssh. Nerv. Deyat. im. I. P. Pavlova,* **4**, 516–25.

RORER, L. G. (1972) The 16 PF test, in, O. K. Buros (Ed.), *VIIth mental measurement year book*, pp. 332–3. New Jersey: Gryphon Press.

ROSENHAN, D. and WHITE, G. M. (1967) Observation and rehearsal as determinants of pro-social behaviour, *J. Personality Soc. Psychol.* **5**, 424–31.

ROSENKOETTEN, L. I. (1973) Resistance to temptation: inhibitory and disinhibitory effects of models, *Dev. Psychol.* **8**, 1, 80–4.

ROSENTAL, D. L. and TROSHIN, A. S. (1963) New data on substantial changes during damage and excitation of cells, *Cytology*, **5**, 4.

ROSENTHAL, D., WENDER, P. H., KETY, S. S., SCHULSINGER, F., WEINER, J. and OSTERGAARD, L. (1968) Schizophrenics' offspring reared in adoptive homes, in, D. Rosenthal and S. S. Kety (Eds.), *The transmission of schizophrenia*, London: Pergamon Press.

ROSENTHAL, I. S. (1930) Towards a description of the orienting and defensive reflexes, *Arkh. Biol. Nauk*, **30**, 1.

ROSS, M. (1976) The self perception of intrinsic motivation, in, J. H. Hancy, W. J. Ickes and R. F. Kidd (Eds.), *New directions in attribution research*, Hillsdale, New Jersey: Erlbaum.

ROSS, S. A. (1971) A test of the generality of the effects of pre-school models, *Dev. Psychol.* **4**, 262–7.

ROTH, W. T. (1973) Auditory evoked responses to unpredictable stimuli, *Psychophysiol.* **10**, 125–38.

ROTTER, J. B. (1954) *Social learning and clinical psychology*, New York: Prentice-Hall.

ROTTER, J. B. (1966) Generalized expectancies for interval vs. external control of reinforcement, *Psychol. Monogr.* **80**, 1 (Whole No. 609).

ROUBERTOUX, P. and CARLIER, M. (1973) Genetic analysis of behaviour: (1958–1971): II, Results, *Année Psychologique*, **73**, 1, 151–223.

ROUTENBERG, A. (1968) The two-arousal hypothesis: reticular formation and limbic system, *Psychol. Rev.* **75**, 51–80.

ROWLAND, L. W. (1936) The somatic effects of stimuli graded in respect to their exciting character, *J. Exp. Psychol.* **19**, 547–60.

ROYCE, J. R. (1973) The conceptual framework for a multi-factor theory of individuality, in, J. R. Royce (Ed.), *Multivariate analysis and psychological theory*, pp. 305–407, New York: Academic Press.

ROYCE, J. R. (1977) On the construct validity of open-field measures, *Psychol. Bull.* **84**, 1098–106.

ROYCE, J. R., POLEY, W. and YEUDALL, L. R. (1973) Behaviour-genetic analysis of mouse emotionality: I. Factor analysis, *J. Comp. Physiol. Psychol.* **83**, 36–47.

ROZHANSKY, N. A. (1913) Materials on the physiology of sleep. Dissertation, St. Petersburg.

ROZHDESTVENSKAYA, V. I. (1955) An attempt to measure the strength of the excitatory process through aspects of its irradiation and concentration in the visual analyser, *Vop. Psikhol.* **3**.

ROZHDESTVENSKAYA, V. I. (1959a) Strength of the nervous system as shown in the ability of the nerve cells to withstand persistent concentrated excitation, in, B. M. Teplov (Ed.), *Typological features of higher nervous activity in man*, Vol. 2, Moscow: Akad. Pedagog. Nauk RSFSR.

ROZHDESTVENSKAYA, V. I. (1959b) Strength of the nerve cells as shown in the nature of the effect of additional stimulation on visual sensitivity, in, B. M. Teplov (Ed.), *Typological features of higher nervous activity in man*, Vol. 2, Moscow: Akad. Pedagog. Nauk RSFSR.

ROZHDESTVENSKAYA, V. I. (1963a) Determination of inhibitory strength in man through prolonging the action of the differential stimulus, in, B. M. Teplov (Ed.), *Typological features of higher nervous activity in man*, Vol. 3, Moscow: Akad. Pedagog. Nauk RSFSR.

ROZHDESTVENSKAYA, V. I. (1963b) Manifestation of typological features of the nervous system in man during elaboration of delayed photochemical reflexes, in, B. M. Teplov (Ed.) *Typological features of higher nervous activity in man*, Vol. 3, Moscow: Akad. Pedagog. Nauk RSFSR.

ROZHDESTVENSKAYA, V. I. (1973) The effect of the strength of the nervous system and of activation level on performance on a monotonous task, *Vop. Psikhol.* **19**, 5, 49–57.

ROZHDESTVENSKAYA, V. I. (1975) Title not given. In, *The Functional state of the brain*, p. 53 Moscow: MGV. Cited by Gorbunov, Sirotskii and Maravenko (1978).

ROZHDESTVENSKAYA, V. I. and LEVOCHKINA, M. A. (1972) Functional states when performing monotonous work and the strength of the nervous system, in, V. D. Nebylitsyn (Ed.), *Problems of differential psychophysiology*, Vol. 7, Moscow: Pedagogika.

ROZHDESTVENSKAYA, V. I., GOLUBEVA, E. A. and SHIBAROVSKAYA, G. A. (1965) An experimental study of mental fatigue, in, B. M. Teplov (Ed.), *Typological features of higher nervous activity in man*, Vol. 4, Moscow: Prosveshcheniye.

ROZHDESTVENSKAYA, V. I., GOLUBEVA, E. A. and YERMOLAYEVA-TOMINA, L. B. (1967) The relation between functional states and typological properties of the nervous system, in, B. M. Teplov (Ed.), *Typological features of higher nervous activity in man*, Vol. 5, Moscow: Prosveshcheniye.

ROZHDESTVENSKAYA, V. I.. GOLUBEVA, E. A. and YERMOLAYEVA-TOMINA, L. B. (1969a) On general and partial factors in considering strength of nervous system, in, V. D. Nebylitsyn (Ed.) *Problems of differential psychophysiology*, Vol. 6, pp. 15–37, Moscow: Prosveshcheniye.

ROZHDESTVENSKAYA, V. I., GOLUBEVA, E. A. and YERMOLAYEVA-TOMINA, L. B. (1969b) The role of strength of nervous system in the dynamics of working capacity in different forms of activity, in, V. D. Nebylitsyn (Ed.), *Problems of differential psychophysiology*, Vol. 6, pp. 138–48, Moscow: Prosveshcheniye.

ROZHDESTVENSKAYA, V. I., GOLUBEVA, E. A. and YERMOLAYEVA-TOMINA, L. B. (1972) Alterations in functional state as affected by different kinds of activity and strength of the nervous system, in, V. D. Nebylitsyn and J. A. Gray (Eds.), *Biological bases of individual behaviour*, London: Academic Press.

ROZHDESTVENSKAYA, V. I., NEBYLITSYN, V. D., BORISOVA, M. N. and YERMOLAYEVA-TOMINA, L. B. (1960) A comparative study of different indices of strength of the nervous system in man, *Vop. Psikhol.* **5**, 41–56.

ROZHDESTVENSKAYA, V. I., GOLUBEVA, E. A., YERMOLAYEVA-TOMINA, L. B., ALEKSANDROVA, N. I. and KLYAGIN, V. S. (1967) Title not given. In, B. M. Teplov (Ed.), *Typological features of higher nervous activity in man*, Vol. 5, p. 103, Moscow: Prosveshchenie. Cited by Gorbunov, Sirotskii and Maravenko (1978).

RUBINSTEYN, S. L. (1957) *Being and consciousness*. Moscow: Akad. Nauk SSSR.

RUBINSTEYN, S. L. (1959) *Principles and ways of development of psychology*, Moscow: Akad. Nauk SSSR.

RUBINSTEYN, S. L. (1960) *Thinking and principles of analysis, synthesis and generalization: experimental studies*, Moscow: Akad. Nauk SSSR.

RUNDQUIST, E. A. (1933) the interitance of spontaneous activity in rats, *J. Comp. Psychol.* **16**, 415–38.

RUPP, W., BADIAN, M., OSTERMANN, G. and SETTIG, W. (1980) Tourniquet pain and neuroticism score, *World Conference on Clinical Pharmacology and Therapeutics, London, 1980*. Contributions by teams of Clinical Pharmacology Hoechst Aktiengesellschaft. Hoechst Aktiengesellschaft.

RUSALOV, V. M. (1972a) Evoked bioelectrical activity of the frontal regions of the cortex and GSR to light and sound stimuli, in, V. D. Nebylitsyn (Ed.), *Problems of differential psychophysiology*, Vol. 7, Moscow: Pedagogika.

RUSALOV, V. M. (1972b) On the factors of variability of evoked potentials registered in the frontal regions of the brain in man, in, V. D. Nebylitsyn (Ed.), *Problems of differential psychophysiology*, Vol. 7, Moscow: Pedagogika.

RUSHMER, R. F. (1962) Effects of nerve stimulation and hormones on the heart: the role of the heart in general circulatory regulation, in, W. F. Hamilton (Ed.), *Handbook of physiology*, Section 2, Circulation, Vol. 1, pp. 533–50, Washington: American Physiology Society.

RUSHTON, J. P. (1976) Socialization and the altruistic behaviour of children, *Psychol. Bull.* **83**, 898–913.

RUSHTON, J. P. and TEACHMAN, G. (1978) The effects of positive reinforcement, attributions, and punishment on model induced altruism in children, *J. Personality Soc. Psychol.* **4**, 2, 322–5.

RUST, J. (1976) Generalisation and dishabituation of the orienting response to a stimulus of lower intensity, *Physiol. Psychol.* **4**, 1, 99–101.

RUST, T. (1975) Genetic effects in cortical auditory evoked potentials: a twin study, *Electroenceph. Clin. Neurophysiol.* **39**, 4, 321–7.

SADLER, T. G. (1970) The role of extraversion and neuroticism in human operant conditioning. Ph.D. Thesis, University of Houston.

SADLER, T. G. and MIFFORD (1971) The interaction of extraversion and neuroticism in human operant behaviour, *J. Exp. Res. Person.* **5,** 4, 278–85.

SALES, S. M. and THROOP, W. F. (1972) Relationship between kinaesthetic after effects and "strength of the nervous system", *Psychophysiol.* **9,** 492–7.

SALVI, R. J. (1976) Central components of the temporary threshold shift, in, H. Henderson (Ed.) *Effects of noise on hearing,* New York: Raven Press.

SALVI, R., HENDERSON, D. and HAMERNIK, R. (1975) Auditory fatigue: retrocochlear components, *Science, N. Y.* **190,** 486–7.

SAMEROFF, A. J. and KELLY, P. (1978) Socio-economic status, racial and mental health factors in infant temperament. Unpublished Manuscript. Cited by Thomas and Chess (1978).

SAMUELS, I. (1959) Reticular mechanisms and behaviour, *Psychol. Bull.* **56,** 1–25.

SANGIULIANO, I. A. (1951) An investigation of the relationship between the perception of the upright in space and several factors in personality organization. Unpublished doctoral dissertation, Fordham University. Cited by Witkin, Dyk, Faterson, Goodenough and Karp (1962).

SARASON, I. G. and GANZER, V. J. (1973) Modelling and group discussion in the rehabilitation of juvenile delinquents, *J. Counsel. Psychol.* **5,** 442–9.

SARASON, I. G., SMITH, R. and DIENER, E. (1975) Personality research: components of variance attributable to the person and the situation, *J. Personality Soc. Psychol.* **32,** 199–204.

SATALOFF, J., VASSALLO, L. and MENDUKE, H. (1972a) Long term study relating temporary and permanent hearing loss, in. K. Kay, M. Hipskind and M. Shafer (Eds.), *Adverse effects of common environmental pollutants,* pp. 206–9, New York: MSS Info. Corps.

SATALOFF, J., VASSALLO, L. and MENDUKE, H. (1972b) Temporary and permanent hearing loss, in, K. Kay, M. Hipskind and M. Shafer (Eds.), *Adverse effects of common environmental pollutants,* pp. 210–13, New York: MSS Info. Corps.

SATINDER, K. P. (1965) Effects of intermodal stimulation on figural after-effects, *Br. J. Psychol* **57,** 1–2, 1–5.

SAVAGE, R. D. (1964) Electro-cerebral activity, extraversion and neuroticism, *Br. J. Psychiat.* **110,** 98.

SCARR, S. (1966a) The origins of individual differences in adjective check list scores, *J. Consult. Psychol.* **30,** 354–7.

SCARR, S. (1966b) The Adjective Check List as a personality assessment technique with children: validity of the scales. *J. Consult. Psychol.* **30,** 122–8.

SCARR, S. (1966c) Genetic factors in activity motivation, *Child Dev.* **37,** 663–74.

SCARR, S. (1968) Environmental bias in twin studies, in, S. G. Vandenberg (Ed.), *Progress in human behaviour genetics,* pp. 205–13, Baltimore: Johns Hopkins Press.

SCARR, S. (1969) Social introversion-extraversion as a heritable response, *Child Dev.* **40,** 823–32.

SCHACHTER, M. (1952) Contribution à l'étude du psychodiagnostic de Rorschach chez les jumeux, *Encéphale,* **41,** 23–4.

SCHACHTER, S. (1957) Pain, fear and anger in hypertensives and normotensives, *Psychosom. Med.* **19,** 17–29.

SCHACHTER, S. (1971) *Emotion, obesity and crime,* New York: Academic Press.

SCHACHTER, S. and LUTANE, B. (1964) Crime, cognition and the autonomic nervous system, in, M. R. Jones (Ed.), *Nebraska symposium on motivation,* pp. 221–75, Lincoln: University of Nebraska Press.

SCHAEFER, E. S. and BAYLEY, N. (1963) Maternal behaviour, child behaviour and their inter-correlations from infancy through adolescence, *Monogr. Soc. Res. Child. Dev.* **28,** 3, 1–127.

SCHAFER, R. (1948) *Clinical application of psychological tests,* New York: International Universities Press.

SCHAFFER, H. R. (1965) Changes in developmental quotients under two conditons of maternal separation, *J. Soc. Clin. Psychol.* **4,** 39–46.

SCHAFFER, H. R. (1977) *Mothering: the developing child,* Glasgow: William Collins.

SCHAFFER, H. R. and EMERSON, P. E. (1964) Patterns of response to physical contact in early human development, *J. Child Psychol. Psychiat.* **5**, 1–13.

SCHALLING, D. (1970) Contributions to the validation of some personality concepts. Reports from the Psychological Laboratories, the University of Stockholm, Suppl. 1.

SCHALLING, D. (1971) Tolerance for experimentally induced pain as related to personality, *Scand. J. Psychol.* **12**, 271–81.

SCHALLING, D. and LEVANDER, S. (1964) Ratings of anxiety-proneness and responses to electrical pain stimulation, *Scand. J. Psychol.* **5**, 1–9.

SCHMAUK, F. J. (1970) Punishment, arousal and avoidance learning in sociopaths, *J. Abnorm. Psychol.* **76**, 325–35.

SCHNORE, M. M. (1959) Individual patterns of physiological activity as a function of task differences and degree of arousal, *J. Exp. Psychol.* **58**, 117–28.

SCHOENFELD, W. N. (1966) Editorial. Some old work for modern conditioning theory, *Condit. Reflex,* **1**, 219–23.

SCHOENFELD, W. N. (1971) Conditioning the whole organism, *Condit. Reflex,* **6**, 125–8.

SCHULTZ, J. H. (1932) *Das Autogene Training,* Stuttgart: Thieme Verlag.

SCHWARTZ, G. E. (1973) Biofeedback as therapy: some theoretical and practical issues, *Am. Psychol.* **28**, 666–73.

SCHWARTZ, G. E., FAIR, P. L., SALT, P., MANDEL, M. and KLERMAN, G. L. (1976) Facial muscle patterning to affective imagery in depressed and non-depressed subjects, *Science, N. Y.* **192**, 489–91.

SCHWARTZ, L. A. (1948) Knowledge of the world and its sound form as a conditioned stimulus, *Byull. Eksp. Biol. Med.* **25**, 292–4.

SCHWARTZ, L. A. (1949) Knowledge of the world and its sound form as a conditioned stimulus, *Byull. Eksp. Biol. Med.* **27**, 412–15.

SCHWARTZ, L. A. (1959) Ob individualnych razliczijach w kriticzeskoy czastotie mielkaniy i dlitielnosti otricatiel nogo posledowatielnogo obraza (W) *Tipologiczeskije osobennosti wysszej niervnoy deyatel'nosti czelowieka.* Moskwa: APN RSFSR.

SCHWARTZ, L. A. (1960) Conditioned reflexes to verbal stimuli, *Vop. Psikhol.* **6**, 86–98.

SCHWARTZ, L. A. (1963) Speed of recovery of absolute visual sensitivity after illumination as an index of nervous processes lability and other tests as to mobility, in, B. M. Teplov (Ed.) *Typological Features of Higher Nervous Activity in Man,* Vol. 3, Moscow: Akad. Pedagog. Nauk RSFSR.

SCHWARTZ, M. and SHAGASS, C. (1964) Recovery functions of human somatosensory and visual evoked potentials, *Ann. N. Y. Acad. Sc.* **112**, 510–25.

SCHWARTZ, V. B. (1970) Some genetic aspects of physical work capacity in children, in, *The organisation of public health, the history of medicine and social hygiene,* Conference Proceedings, Tallin.

SCOTT, F. D. and WILKINSON, D. (1962) Adaptation as related to the introversion-extraversion dimension. Technical Report. Grant MH 06956–01. National Institute of Mental Health. Cited by Coles, Gale and Kline (1971).

SCOTT, J. P. (1942) Genetic differences in the social behaviour of inbred strains of mice, *J. Hered.* **33**, 11–15.

SCOTT, J. P. (1957) Animal and human children, *Children,* **4**, 163–8.

SCOTT, J. P. (1962) *Animal Behaviour,* New York: American Museum of Natural History.

SCOTT, J. P. (1966) Agonistic behaviour of mice and rats: a review, *Am. Zoologist,* **6**, 683–701.

SCOTT, J. P. and FULLER, J. L. (1965) *Genetics and the social behaviour of the dog,* Chicago: University of Chicago Press.

SCULLY, H. E. and BASMAJIAN, J. V. (1969) Motor-unit training and influence of manual skill, *Psychophysiol.* **5**, 625–32.

SEARLE, L. V. (1949) The organization of hereditary maze-brightness and maze-dullness, *Genet. Psychol. Monogr.* **39**, 279–325.

SEARS, R. R. (1965) Development of the gender role, in, F. A. Beach (Ed.) *Sex and Behaviour,* New York: Wiley.

SEARS, R. R., RAU, L. and ALPERT, R. (1965) *Identification and child training,* Stanford, Calif.: Stanford University Press.

SEARS, R. S., MACCOBY, E. E. and LEWIN, H. (1957) *Patterns of childrearing,* Evanston, Ill.: Row, Peterson.

SECHENOV, I. M. (1863) Reflexes of the brain, *Meditsinsk vestnik,* **3**, 461–84, 493–512.

SECHENOV, I. M. (1878) Elements of thought, *Vestnik Yevropy,* **2**, 39–107, 457–533.

SECHENOV, I. M. (1892) Object, thought and reality, in, D. Anuchin (Ed.) *Pomoshch Golodayushchim,* Moscow: Russkiye Vedomsti.

SECHENOV, I. M. (1935) *Complete works,* Moscow.

SELIGMAN, M. E. P. (1970) On the generality of the laws of learning, *Psychol. Rev.* **77**, 406–18.

SELIVANOVA, A. T. (1979) Disturbances of situational reflexes and experimental neurosis elicited by changes in environmental factors, *Zh. Vyssh. Nerv. Deyat. im. I. P. Pavlova,* **29**, 72–9.

SELL, J. M. and DUCKWORTH, J. J. (1974) Field dependence, neuroticism and extraversion, *Percept. Mot. Skills,* **38**, 2, 589–90.

SELLS, S. B., DEMAREE, R. G. and WILL, D. P. (1970) Dimensions of personality, I, Conjoint factor structure of Guilford and Cattell trait markers, *Multiv. Behav. Res.* **5**, 391–422.

SELLS, S. B., DEMAREE, R. G. and WILL, D. P. (1971) Dimensions of personality, II, Separate factor structure in Guilford and Cattell trait markers, *Multiv. Behav. Res.* **6**, 135–85.

SEREDINA, M. I. (1956a) Age characteristics involved in the generalisation of conditioned word stimuli, in, A. G. Ivanov-Smolenskii (Ed.), *Works of the Institute of Higher Nervous Activity: pathophysiological series,* Vol. II, Moscow: Akad. Nauk SSSR.

SEREDINA, M. I. (1956b) Elective irradiation of the inhibitory process from the second signalling system into the first, in, A. G. Ivanov-Smolenskii (Ed.), *Works of the Institute of Higher Nervous Activity: pathophysiological series,* Vol. II, Moscow: Akad. Nauk SSSR.

SERGEYEV, B. F. (1956) Formation of inhibitory connections between so-called indifferent stimuli, *Dokl. Akad. Nauk SSSR,* **107**, 346–9.

SEUNATH, O. M. (1975) Personality, reinforcement and learning, *Percept. Mot. Skills,* **41**, 459–63.

SHAGASS, C. (1942) Conditioning the human occipital alpha rhythm to a voluntary stimulus, *J. Exp. Psychol.* **31**, 367–79.

SHAGASS, C. (1955) Anxiety, depression and the photically driven EEG, *A.M.A. Archs. Neurol. Psychiatry,* **74**, 3–10.

SHAGASS, C. (1972) *Evoked brain potentials in psychiatry,* New York: Plenum.

SHAGASS, C. (1976) An electrophysiological view of schizophrenia, *Biol. Psychiat.* **11**, 3–30.

SHAGASS, C. and LIPOWSKI, F. J. (1958) Effects of methedine on critical flicker fusion and its relation to personality and affect, *J. Nerv. Ment. Dis.* **127**, 407–16.

SHAGASS, C. and MALMO, R. B. (1954) Psychodynamic themes and localized muscular tension during psychotherapy, *Psychosom. Med.* **16**, 295–313.

SHAGASS, C. and SCHWARTZ, M. (1965) Age, personality and somatosensory cerebral evoked responses, *Science, N.Y.* **148**, 1359–61.

SHAGASS, C., OVERTON, D. A. and BARTOLUCCI, G. (1969) Evoked responses in schizophrenia, in, D. V. Siva Sankrat (Ed.), *Schizophrenia: current concepts and research,* pp. 220–35, Hicksville, N.Y.: PJD Publications.

SHAGASS, C., SCHWARTZ, M. and KRISHNAMOORTI, S. R. (1965) Some psychologic correlates of cerebral responses evoked by light flash, *J. Psychosom. Res.* **9**, 223–31.

SHAGASS, C., HASETH, K., CALLOWAY, E. and JONES, R. (1968) EEG-evoked relationships and perceptual performance, *Life Sci.* **7**, 19, 1083.

SHAKOW, D. (1950) Some psychological features of schizophrenia, in, M. L. Reymert (Ed.), *Feelings and emotions: the Moosehart symposium,* New York: McGraw-Hill.

SHANNON, I. L. (1974) Effects of visual and olfactory stimulation on parotid secretion rate in the human, *Proc Soc. Exp. Biol. Med.* **146**, 1128–31.

SHAPIRO, D. and CRIDER, A. (1966) Operant electrodermal conditioning: some effects of multiple schedules of reinforcement. *Technical Report No. 14, Office of Naval Research Contract Nonr-1866(43).* Harvard Medical School.

SHAPIRO, D. and CRIDER, A. (1967) Operant electrodermal conditioning under multiple schedules of reinforcement, *Psychophysiol.* **4**, 168–75.

SHAPIRO, D., CRIDER, A. and TURSKY, B. (1964) Differentiation of an autonomic response through operant reinforcement, *Psychonom. Sci.* **1**, 147–8.

SHAPIRO, A. P., NICOTERO, J., SAPIRA, J. and SCHEIB, E. T. (1968) Analysis of the variability of blood pressure, pulse rate and catecholamine responsivity in identical and fraternal twins, *Psychosom. Med.* **30**, 506–20.

SHARPLESS. C. and JASPER, H. (1956) Habituation of the arousal reaction, *Brain,* **79**, 655–80.

SHASTIN, N. R. (1925) Conditioned preparatory stimuli, *Acta Univ. Voroneg.* 146–51.

SHATAN, C. (1961) Unconscious motor behaviour and psychotherapy, *Proc. Third World Cong. Psychiatry* **1**, 1075–8.

SHATAN, C. (1963) Unconscious motor behaviour, kinesthetic awareness and psychotherapy, *Am. J. Psychother.* **17**, 17–30.

SHAW, W. A. (1938) The distribution of muscular action potentials during imaging, *Psychol. Rec.* **2**, 195–216.

SHCHUKIN, M. P. (1963) Some typologically conditioned differences in the course of the orienting and executive activity in learning elementary labour skills, *Vop. Psikhol.* **6**.

SHEALY, C. N., MORTIMER, J. T. and HAGFORS, N. R. (1970) Dorsal column electroanalgesia, *J. Neurosurg.* **32**, 560.

SHEARN, D. W. (1962) Operant conditioning of heart rate, *Science, N. Y.* **137**, 530–1.

SHEEHAN, P. W. (1967) A shortened form of the Bett's Questionnaire upon mental imagery, *J. Clin. Psychol.* **23**, 386–9.

SHEVRIN, H. (1973) Brain wave correlates of subliminal stimulation, unconscious attention, primary and secondary process thinking, and repressiveness, *Psychol. Issues,* **8**, 56–87.

SHEVRIN, H., SMITH, W. H. and FRITZLER, D. E. (1969) Repressiveness as a factor in the subliminal activation of brain and verbal responses, *J. nerv. Ment. Dis.* **149**, 261–9.

SHIBAROVSKAYA, G. A. (1978) Genotypical bases of the dynamism of nervous processes, in, B. M. Lomov and I. V. Ravich-Shcherbo (Eds.), *Problems in the genetics of psychophysiology,* pp. 137–44, Moscow: Instit. Psikhol. Akad. Nauk SSSR, Izd. Nauka.

SHIELDS, J. (1962) *Monozygotic twins: brought up apart and together,* London: Oxford University Press.

SHIELDS, J. (1971) Heredity and psychological abnormality, in, H. J. Eysenck (Ed.), *Handbook of abnormal psychology,* London: Pergamon.

SHIGEHISA, P. M., SHIGEHISA, T. and SYMONS, J. R. (1973) Effects of intensity of auditory stimulation on photopic visual sensitivity in relation to personality, *Jap. Psychol. Res.* **15**, 164–72.

SHINCHKO, G. A. (1959) Formation of temporary connections through association of several indifferent stimuli, *Zh. Vyssh. Nerv. Deyat. im. I. P. Pavlova,* **9**, 519–25.

SHINCHKO, G. A. (1969) *The second-signal system and its physiological mechanisms,* Leningrad: Meditsina.

SHIRLEY, M. M. (1931) *The first two years, a study of twenty-five babies, Vol. I, Postural and locomotor development,* Minneapolis: University of Minnesota Press.

SHITOV, F. M. and LAKOVLEVA, V. V. (1937) *Byull. Eksp. Biol. Med.* **4**, 296 (In Russian).

SHKOL'MIK-YARROS, E. S. (1958) Efferent pathways of the visual cortex, *Zh. Vyssh. Nerv. Deyat. im. I. P. Pavlova,* **4**, 289–304.

SHLYAKHTA, N. F. (1972) Study of twins in connection with the properties of the nervous system, in, V. D. Nebylitsyn (Ed.), *Current problems of differential psychophysiology,* Vol. 7, Moscow: Pedagogika.

SHLYAKHTA, N. F. (1975) Studies of genotypic components of the nervous system strength syndrome with respect to excitation (in adolescent twins), Candidate's Dissertation, University of Moscow.

SHLYAKHTA, N. F. and PANTELEYEVA, T. A. (1978) Study of genetic factors underlying excitatory strength of the nervous system, in, B. M. Lomov and I. V. Ravich-Shcherbo (Eds.), *Problems in the genetics of psychophysiology*, pp. 94–110, Moscow: Instit. Psikhol. Akad. Nauk SSSR Izd. Nauka.

SHNIDMAN, S. R. (1969) Avoidance conditioning of skin potential responses, *Psychophysiol.* **6**, 38–44.

SHUCARD, D. W. (1969) Relationships among measures of the cortical evoked potential and abilities comprising human intelligence. Ph.D. Thesis, Unviersity of Denver.

SHUMILINA, A. I. (1949) The functional significance of the frontal regions of the brain in the conditioned-reflex activity of the dog, in, P. K. Anokhin (Ed.), *Problems in higher nervous activity*, Moscow: Akad. Nauk Med. SSSR.

SHUMSKAYA, I. A. and KOROCHKIN, L. I. (1975) The rate of RNA synthesis in the rat hippocampus during learning, *Zh. Vyssh. Nerv. Deyat. im. I. P. Pavlova,* **25**, 778–83.

SIDDLE, D. A. T. (1970) Vigilance decrement and speed of habituation of the GSR component of the orienting response, *Br. J. Psychol.* **63**, 2, 191–4.

SIDDLE, D. A. T. (1974) overextinction of the evoked skin conductance response: an EEG study, *Psychophysiol.* **11**, 6, 630–8.

SIDDLE, D. A. T. and GLEN, S. M. (1974) habituation of the orienting response to simple and complex stimuli, *Am. J. Ment. Defic.* **78**, 6, 688–93.

SIDDLE, D. A. T. and HERON, P. A. (1976) Effects of length of training and amount of tone frequency change on amplitude of autonomic components of the orienting response, *Psychophysiol.* **13**, 4, 281–7.

SIDDLE, D. A. T. and MANGAN, G. L. (1971) Arousability and individual differences in resistance to distraction, *J. Exp. Res. Person.* **5**, 295–303.

SIDDLE, D. A. T., FOGGITT, R. H. and NICOL, A. R. (1973) Individual differences in over-extinction of the SCR component of the orienting response, *Biol. Psychol.* **1**, 53–61.

SIDDLE, D. A. T$_x$, MORRISH, R. B., WHITE, K. D. and MANGAN, G. L. (1969) A further study of the relation of strength-sensitivity of the nervous system to extraversion. *J. Exp. Res. Person.* **3**, 264–7.

SILVERMAN, J. (1967) Variations in cognitive control and psychophysiological defense in the schizophrenias, *Psychosom. Med.* **29**, 225–51.

SILVERMAN, J. (1972) Stimulus intensity modulation and psychological disease. *Psychopharmacologia,* **24**, 42–80.

SILVERMAN, J., BUCHSBAUM, M. and HENKIN, R. (1969) Stimulus sensitivity and stimulus intensity control, *Percept. Mot. Skills,* **28**, 71–8.

SIMON, B., HOLZBERG, J. D. and UNGER, J. F. (1951) A study of judgment in the psychopathic personality, *Psychiatric Q.* **25**, 132–50.

SIMONOV, P. V. (1979) Need-informational organisation of brain activity, *Zh. Vyssh. Nerv. Deyat. im. I. P. Pavlova,* **29**, 467–77.

SIMONSON, E. and BROZEK, J. (1952) Flicker fusion frequency: background and application, *Physiol. Rev.* **32**, 349–78.

SINGER, D. L. (1968) Aggression arousal, hostile humor, cartharsis, *J. Personality Soc. Psychol. Monogr. Suppl.* **8**, 1, 2.

SINKEVICH, Z. L. (1930) Study of combined external inhibition to food, defensive and orienting conditioned reflexes, in, *Basic mechanisms of conditioned reflex activity in the child.* Moscow.

SIQUELAND, E. R. and LIPSITT, L. P. (1966) Conditioned head-turning in human newborns, *J. Exp. Child Psychol.* **3**, 356–76.

SKINNER, B. F. (1938) *The behaviour of organisms: an experimental analysis,* New York: Appleton-Century-Crofts.

SKINNER, B. F. (1953) *Science and human behaviour,* New York: Macmillan.

SKIPIN, G. V. (1932) Irradiation and concentration of the inhibitory process. *Tr. Fiziol. lab. im. I. P. Pavlova,* **4**, 1–2.

SKZPEK, G. J. (1969) Effect of perceptual isolation and arousal on anxiety, complexity preference in psychopathic and neurotic delinquents, *J. Abnorm. Psychol.* **74**, 321–9.

SLATER, A. M. and FINDLAY, J. M. (1975) Binocular fixation in the newborn baby, *J. Exp. Child Psychol.* **20**, 2, 248–73.

SLATER, E. and SHIELDS, J. (1953) Psychotic and neurotic illnesses in twins, *Spec. Rep. Ser. Med. Res. Coun.* **278**. H.M.S.O.

SMALL, C. S. (1974) Extraversion and introversion: an arousal and habituation comparison, *Diss. Abstr.* **34**, 8-b, 4059.

SMIRNOV, A. A. (1966) *Problemy psikhologii pamyati,* Moscow: Prosveshcheniye.

SMITH, B. (1968) Habituation and spontaneous recovery of skin conductance and heart rate in schizophrenics and controls as a function of repeated tone presentaton, *Diss. Abstr.* **28**, 1668, 3068–9.

SMITH, H. C. (1949) Psychometric checks on hypotheses derived from Sheldon's work on physique and temperament, *J. Personality,* **17,** 310–20.

SMITH, M. I. (1966) Variables influencing the orienting reflex, reinforcement and verbalisation in verbal conditioning. Unpublished doctoral dissertation, University of California, Los Angeles. Cited by Maltzman and Mandel (1968).

SMITH, P. C. (1973) Temporal cluster and individual differences in the behaviour of pre-school children, in, R. P. Michael and J. H. Crook (Eds.) *Comparative ecology and behaviour of primates,* pp. 751–98, London: Academic Press.

SMITH, P. K. and CONNOLLY, K. (1972) Patterns of play and social interaction in pre-school children, in, N. G. Blurton-Jones (Ed.) *Ethological studies of child behaviour,* New York and London: Cambridge.

SMITH, R. T. (1965) A comparison of socio-environmental factors in monozygotic and dizygotic twins, testing an assumption, in, S. G. Vandenberg (Ed.), *Methods and goals in human behaviour genetics,* New York: Academic Press.

SMITH, S. L. (1966) The effect of personality and drugs on auditory threshold when risk-taking factors are controlled. Unpublished study. Cited by J. A. Gray (1967).

SNYDER, M. (1974) Self-monitoring of expressive behaviour, *J. Personality Soc. Psychol.* **30,** 526–37.

SNYDER, S. H. (1977) Opiate receptors and internal opiates, *Scient. Am.* March, 44–56.

SOKOLOV, E. N. (1958a) *Perception and the conditioned reflex,* Moscow: Izd. Mosk. Gos. Univ. English translation by R. Worters and A. D. B. Clarke (Eds.) (1963) Oxford: Pergamon Press.

SOKOLOV, E. N. (1958b) The orienting reflex, its structure and mechanism, in, *The orienting reflex and exploratory behaviour,* Moscow: Izd. Akad. Pedagog. Naúk RSFSR.

SOKOLOV, E. N. (1960) Neuronal models and the orienting reflex, in, M. A. Brazier (Ed.), *The central nervous system and behaviour,* Transactions, 3rd Conference Josiah Macey Jnr. Foundation, pp. 187–276.

SOKOLOV, E. N. (1963a) Modelling in the central nervous system of man and animals, *Gagrskiye Besedy,* **4,** 183–202.

SOKOLOV, E. N. (1963b) Higher nervous functions: the orienting reflex, *Ann. Rev. Physiol.* **25,** 545–80.

SOKOLOV, E. N. (1966) Orienting reflex: an information regulator, in, A. Leont'ev, A. Luria and A. Smirnov (Eds.), *Psychological research in the U.S.S.R,* Moscow: Progress.

SOKOLOV, E. N. (1969) The modelling properties in the nervous system, in, M. Cole and I. Maltzman (Eds.), *Handbook of contemporary Soviet psychology,* pp. 671–706, New York: Basic Books.

SOKOLOV, E. N. (1970) In, L. Chertok (Ed.), *Psychophysiological mechanisms of hypnosis,* Berlin, Heidelberg. New York: Springer Verlag, 80.

SOKOLOV, E. N. (1975) The neuronal mechanisms of the orienting reflex, in, E. N. Sokolov and O. S. Vinogradova (Eds.), *Neuronal mechanisms of the orienting reflex,* pp. 217–35, Hillsdale, New Jersey: Erlbaum.

SOKOLOV, E. N. (1976) Learning and memory: habituation as negative learning, in, M. R. Rosenzweig and E. L. Bennett (Eds.), *Neural mechanisms of learning and memory,* pp. 475–82, Cambridge, Mass. and London, England: MIT Press.

SOKOLOV, E. N. (1977) The detector, the commanding neurone and plastic convergence, *Zh. Vyssh. Nerv. Deyat. im. I. P. Pavlova,* **27,** 691–8.

REFERENCES                                                                           531

SOKOLOV, E. N. (1978) A neuronal model of the stimulus in a reflex arc, *Soviet Psychol.* **17,** 2.

SOKOLOV, E. N. and PAROMONOVA, M. P. (1961) Progressive changes in the orienting reflex in man during the development of sleep inhibition, *Zh. Vyssh. Nerv. Deyat. im. I. P. Pavlova,* **11,** 217.

SOLLEY, C. M. and MURPHY, G. (1960) *Development of the perceptual world,* New York: Basic Books.

SOLOMON, R. and COLES, R. (1954) A case of failure of generalization of imitation learning across drives and across situations, *J. Abnorm. Soc. Psychol.* **49,** 7–13.

SOLTYSIK, S. (1960) Studies on avoidance conditioning, II, Differentiation and extinction of avoidance reflexes, *Acta Biol. Exp. Vars.* **20,** 171.

SOROKIN, P. A. (1954) *The ways and power of love,* Boston: Cohen Beaken.

SOSKIS, D. A. and SHAGASS, C. (1974) Evoked potential tests of augmenting-reducing. *Psychophysiol.* **11,** 175–90.

SOSNOWSKI, T. (1978) Reactivity, level of stimulation, and some features of verbal behaviour in small task-oriented groups, *Pol. Psychol. Bull.* **9,** 3, 129–37.

SOUTHWICK, C. H. (1969) Aggressive behaviour of rhesus monkeys in natural and captive groups, in, S. Carattini and E. B. Sigg (Eds.), *Aggressive behaviour,* Amsterdam: Excerpta Medica.

SPAIN, D. (1966) Eyelid conditioning and arousal in schizophrenic and normal subjects, *J. Abnorm. Psychol.* **71,** 260–6.

SPEARMAN, C. (1927) *The abilities of man,* London: Macmillan.

SPENCE, K. W. (1954) The relation of response latency and speed to the intervening variables and N in S-R theory, *Psychol. Rev.* **61,** 209–16.

SPENCE, K. W. (1964) Anxiety (drive) level and performance in eyelid conditioning, *Psychol. Bull.* **61,** 129–39.

SPENCE, K. W. and TAYLOR, J. A. (1951) Anxiety and strength of UCS as determinants of amount of eyelid conditioning, *J. Exp. Psychol.* **42,** 183–8.

SPENCE, S. H. and MARZILLIER, J. S. (1979) Social skills training with adolescent male offenders, 1, Short term effects, *Behav. Res. Ther.* **17,** 7–16.

SPIELBERGER, C. D. (1962) The role of awareness in verbal conditioning, in, C. W. Eriksen (Ed.), *Behaviour and awareness,* pp. 73–101, Durham: Duke University Press. Also published in (1962) *J. Person.* **30,** Suppl.

SPIELBERGER, C. D. (1965) Theoretical and epistemological issues in verbal conditioning, in, S. Rosenberg (Ed.), *Directions in psycholinguistics,* pp. 149–200, New York: Macmillan.

SPIELBERGER, C. D. (1972) Anxiety as an emotional state, in, C. D. Spielberger (Ed.), *Anxiety and behaviour,* pp. 3–20, New York: Academic Press.

SPIELBERGER, C. D. and DE NIKE, L. D. (1966) Descriptive behaviourism versus cognitive theory in verbal operant conditioning, *Psychol. Rev.* **73,** 306–26.

SPIELBERGER, C. D., KLING, J. K. and O'HAGAN, E. J. (1978) Dimensions of psychopathic personality: antisocial behaviour and anxiety, in, R. D. Hare and D. Schalling (Eds.), *Psychopathic behaviour: approaches to research.*

SPILKER, B. and CALLOWAY, E. (1969) "Augmenting" and "reducing" in averaged visual evoked responses to sine wave light, *Psychophysiol.* **6,** 49–57.

SPINKS, J. A. and SIDDLE, D. A. T. (1976) Effect of stimulus information and stimulus duration on amplitude and habituation of the electrodermal orienting response, *Biol. Psychol.* **4,** 1, 29–39.

SPITZ, H. H. and LIPMAN, R. S. (1960) A comparison of mental retardates and normals on kinaesthetic figural aftereffects, *J. Abnorm. Soc. Psychol.* **62,** 686–7.

SPITZ, R. A. (1954a) Infantile depression and the general adaptation syndrome, in, H. Hock and J. Zubin (Eds.), *Depression,* pp. 93–108, New York: Grune.

SPITZ, R. A. (1954b) Unhappy and fatal outcomes of emotional deprivation and stress in infancy, in, I. Galston (Ed.), *Beyond the germ theory,* pp. 120–31, New York: Health Education Council.

STAATS, A. W. (1963) (with contributions by C. W. Staats) *Complex human behaviour,* New York: Holt, Rinehart & Winston.

STAATS, A. W. (1970) A learning-behaviour theory: a basis for unity in behavioural-social science, in, A. R. Gilgen (Ed.), *Contemporary scientific psychology,* New York: Academic Press.

STAATS, A. W. (1975) *Social behaviourism,* Homewood, Ill.: Dorsey.

STAATS, A. W. (1980) "Behavioural interaction" and "interactional psychology" theories of personality: similarities, differences, and the need for unification, *Br. J. Psychol.* **71**, 205–20.

STALIN, J. V. (1951) *Marxism and Linguistics,* New York.

STANLEY, W. L. and SCHLOSBERG, H. (1953) The psychophysiological effects of tea, *J. Psychol.* **36**, 435–48.

STEIN, A. H. and WRIGHT, J. C. (1964) Imitative learning under conditions of nuturance and nurturance withdrawal, *Child Dev.* **35**, 927–38.

STEIN, L. (1966) Habituation and stimulus novelty: a model phenomenon for the study of neuronal substrates of behaviour, *Psychol. Rev.* **73**, 16–43.

STEPHENS, J. H., HARRIS, A. H. and BRADY, J. V. (1972) Large magnitude heart rate changes in subjects instructed to change their heart rates and given exteroceptive feedback, *Psychophysiol.* **9**, 283–5.

STEPHENSON, D. and SIDDLE, D. A. T. (1976) Effects of "below-zero" habituation on the electrodermal orienting response to a test stimulus, *Psychophysiol.* **13**, 1, 10–15.

STEPHENSON, W. (1953) *The study of behaviour — Q technique and its methodology,* Chicago: University of Chicago Press.

STERN, J. A. (1966) Stability/lability of physiological response systems. *Ann. N. Y. Acad. Sci.* **134**, 1018–27.

STERN, J. A. and JANES, C. L. (1973) Personality and psychopathology, in, W. F. Prokasy, and D. C. Raskin (Eds.), *Electrodermal activity in psychological research,* pp. 284–346, London: Academic Press.

STERN, J. A. and PLAPP, J. (1969) Psychophysiology and clinical psychology, in, C. D. Spielberger (Ed.), *Current topics in clinical and community psychology,* New York: Academic Press.

STERN, J. A., STEWART, M. A. and WINOCUR, G. (1961) An investigation of some relationships between various measures of galvanic skin response. *J. Psychosom. Res.* **5**, 215–23.

STERN, R. M. and KAPLAN, B. E. (1967) Galvanic skin response: voluntary control and externalization, *J. Psychosom. Res.* **10**, 349–53.

STERN, R. M. and LEWIS, N. L. (1968) Ability of actors to control their GSRs and express emotions, *Psychophysiol.* **4**, 294–9.

STERNBACH, R. A. (1960) Some relationships among various "dimensions" of autonomic activity, *Psychosom. Med.* **22**, 430–4.

STEVENS, J. R. (1973) An anatomy of schizophrenia? *Arch. Gen. Psychiat.* **29**, 177–89.

STEVENS, S. S. (1951) *Handbook of experimental psychology,* New York: Wiley.

STEWART, D. J. and RENICK, J. M. (1970) Verbal conditioning and dependency behaviour in delinquents, *J. Abnorm. Psychol.* **76**, 357–77.

STEWART, M., WINOCUR, G., STERN, J., GUZE, S., PFEIFFER, E. and HORNUNG, F. (1959) Adaptation and conditioning of the GSR in psychiatric patients, *J. Ment. Sci.* **105**, 1102–11.

STOCKS, P. (1930) A biometric investigation of twins and their brothers and sisters, *Ann. Eugen.* **4**, 49–108.

STOUT, G. F. (1896) *Analytic Psychology,* 4th ed. (1918) London: Allen & Unwin.

STRELAU, J. (1969) *Temperament and type of nervous system,* Warsaw: PWN.

STRELAU, J. (1970a) Nervous system type and extraversion-introversion: a comparison of Eysenck's theory with Pavlov's typology, *Pol. Psychol. Bull.* **1**, 17–24.

STRELAU, J. (1970b) Individual work styles in pupils and temperament traits. *Kwartalnik. Pedagog.* **15**, 3.

STRELAU, J. (1972a) A diagnosis of temperament by non-experimental techniques, *Pol. Psychol. Bull.* **3**, 97–105.

STRELAU, J. (1972b) The general and partial nervous system types — data and theory, in, V. D. Nebylitsyn and J. A. Gray (Eds.), *Biological bases of individual differences.* London: Academic Press.

STRELAU, J. (1974a) Temperament as an expression of energy level and temporal features of behaviour, *Pol. Psychol. Bull.* **5**, 119–27.

STRELAU, J. (1974b) *Temperament and type of nervous system,* 2nd ed., Wrociaw: Panstwowe Wydawnictwo Naukowe.

STRELAU, J. (1975a) Reactivity and activity style in selected occupations, *Pol. Psychol. Bull.* **6**, 199–206.

STRELAU, J. (1975b) Pavlov's typology and current investigations in this area, *Ned. Tijdschr. Psychol.* **30**, 177–200.

STRELAU, J. (1977) Behavioural mobility versus flexibility and fluency of thinking: an empirical test of the relationship between temperament and abilities, *Pol. Psychol. Bull.* **8**, 75–82.

STRELAU, J. (1978) *The role of temperament in mental development,* Wroclaw: WSIP.

STRELAU, J. (1980) *Regulatory functions of temperament.* Wroclaw: Ossolineum.

STRELAU, J. and KRAJEWSKI, A. (1974) Individual work style and strength of nervous system, in, K. M. Gurevich (Ed.) *Psychophysiological issues in vocational training,* pp. 176–86, Moscow: Sovietskaya Rossiya.

STRELAU, J. and TERELAK, J. (1974) The alpha-index in relation to temperamental traits, *Studia Psychologica,* **16**, 40–50.

STRELAU, J., KLONOWICZ, T. and ELIASZ, A. (1972) Physiological mechanisms of temperament traits, *Przeglad Psychol.* **15**, 25–51.

STRELTSOVA, N. L. (1955) The characteristics of some unconditioned reflexes in schizophrenics, in, *Proceedings of the All Union theoretical — practical conference dedicated to the Centenary of S. S. Korsakov and to current psychological problems,* Moscow: Medgiz.

STRUCHKOV, I. M. (1976) Switchover between disparate conditioned reflexes, *Soviet Psychol.* **15**, 2–103.

STRZALKOWSKA, G. (1977) Relation between "real self" and "ideal self" and level of stimulation requirement. Unpublished M.A. Thesis, Warsaw University.

STUMPH, C. (1965) Drug action on the electrical activity of the hippocampus, *Int. Rev. Neurobiol.* **8**, 77–138.

SULLIVAN, H. S. (1945) *Conceptions of modern psychiatry,* Washington D.C.: W. A. White Psychiatric Foundation.

SUTKER, P. B. (1970) Vicarious conditioning and sociopathy, *J. Abnorm. Psychol.* **76**, 380–6.

SUVUROVA, V. V. (1975) Functional asymmetry of great hemispheres as a problem of differential psychophysiology, *Vop. Psikhol.* **5**, 26–33.

SUZDALEVA, V. A. and CHUPRIKOVA, N. I. (1974) Speed parameters of associative responses and the typological properties of the human nervous system, *Vop. Psikhol.* **3**, 137–44.

SWEENY, D. R. and FINE, B. J. (1965) Pain reactivity and field dependence, *Percept. Mot. Skills,* **21**, 757–8.

SWEETBAUM, H. A. (1963) Comparison of the effects of introversion-extraversion and anxiety on conditioning, *J. Abnorm. Soc. Psychol.* **66**, 249–54.

SYNDULKO, K., PARKER, D., MALTZMAN, I. and ZISKIND, E. (1975) Central and autonomic nervous system measures of conditioning in sociopaths and normals. Paper read at Meeting of Society for Psychophysiological Research, Toronto.

SZPILER, J. A. and EPSTEIN, S. (1976) Availability of an avoidance response as related to autonomic arousal, *J. Abnorm. Psychol.* **85**, 73–82.

TAYLOR, J. A. (1953) A personality scale of manifest anxiety, *J. Abnorm. Soc. Psychol.* **48**, 285–90.

TEECE, J. J. and COLE, J. O. (1972) Psychophysiologic responses of schizophrenics to drugs, *Psychopharmacologia,* **24**, 159–200.

TEICHNER, W. H. (1968) Interaction of behavioural and physiological stress reactions, *Psychol. Rev.* **75**, 271–91.

TELFORD, C. W. (1931) The refractory phase of voluntary responses, *J. Exp. Psychol.* **14**, 1–35.

TEPLOV, B. M. (1937) Induction changes in the absolute and differential sensitivity of the eye, *Ophthalmology,* **11**, 1.

TEPLOV, B. M. (1941) The problem of inductive changes in absolute visual sensitivity. *Probl. Psychol. Vision,* **1**.

TEPLOV, B. M. (1956) Problems in the study of general types of higher nervous activity in man and animals, in, B. M. Teplov (Ed.), *Typological features of higher nervous activity in man,* Vol. 1, Moscow: Akad. Pedagog. Nauk RSFSR.

TEPLOV, B. M. (1963) New data on investigation of human nervous system properties, in, B. M.

Teplov (Ed.), *Typological features of higher nervous activity in man*, Vol. 3, Moscow: Akad. Pedagog. Nauk RSFSR.

TEPLOV, B. M. (1964) Problems in the study of general types of higher nervous activity in man and animals, in, J. A. Gray (Ed.) (1964b, pp. 3–156).

TEPLOV, B. M. and NEBYLITSYN, V. D. (1963) An experimental study of the properties of man's nervous system, *Zh. Vyssh. Nerv. Deyat. im. I. P. Pavlova*, **13**, 5.

TEPLOV, B. M. and NEBYLITSYN, V. D. (1966) Results of experimental studies on properties of the nervous system in man, in, A. Leont'ev, A. Luria and A. Smirnov (Eds.), *Psychological research in the USSR*, Vol. 1, pp. 181–98, Moscow: Progress Publications.

TERWILLIGER, R. F. (1963) Evidence for a relationship between figural after-effects and after-images. *Amer. J. Psychol.*, **76**, 306–10. .

THELEN, M. H., FREY, R. A., DOLLINGER, S. I. and PAUL, S. C. (1976) Use of videotaped models to improve the interpersonal adjustment of delinquents, *J. Consult. Clin. Psychol.* **44**, 492.

THOMAS, A. (1979) The significance of temperament for early behavioural development. Paper given at International Conference on Temperament, Need for Stimulation and Activity. Warsaw.

THOMAS, A. and CHESS, S. (1978) *Temperament and Development*, New York: Brunner/Mazel.

THOMAS, A., CHESS, S. and BIRCH, H. G. (1968) *Temperament and behaviour disorders in children*, London: University of London.

THOMAS, A., BIRCH, H. G., CHESS, S., HERTZIG, M. E. and KORN, S. (1963) *Behavioural individuality in early childhood*, New York: University Press.

THOMPSON, R. F. and KRAMER, R. F. (1965) Role of association cortex in sensory preconditioning, *J. Comp. Physiol. Psychol.* **60**, 186–91.

THOMPSON, R. F. and SPENCER, W. A. (1966) Habituation: a model phenomenon for the study of neuronal substrates of behaviour, *Psychol. Rev.* **73**, 16–43.

THOMPSON, T. and STURM, T. (1965) Classical conditioning of aggressive display in Siamese Fighting Fish, *J. Exp. Analysis Behav.* **8**, 397–403.

THOMPSON, W. R. (1954) Inheritance and development of intelligence, *Res. Publ. Ass. Res*, in, *Ner. Ment. Dis.* **33**, 209–31.

THOMPSON, W. R. (1957) Traits, factors and genes, *Eugen. Q.* **4**, 8–16.

THOMPSON, W. R. (1968) Development and the biophysical bases of personality, in, E. F. Borgatta and W. W. Lambert (Eds.), *Handbook of personality theory and research*, pp. 149–214, Chicago: Rand McNally.

THORNDIKE, E. L. (1935) *The psychology of wants, interest and attitudes*, New York: Appleton-Century-Crofts.

THURSTONE, L. L. (1951) *The concealed figures test*, The Psychometric Laboratory, University of North Carolina.

THURSTONE, T. G., THURSTONE, L. L. and STRANDSKOV, H. H. (1955) A psychological study of twins. Report No. 4. Psychometric Laboratory: University of North Carolina.

TIMOFEEVA, T. A. (1947) Investigation of higher nervous activity in a dog of the strong, equilibrated type with a marked passive-defensive reflex, *Trans. Inst. Evol. Fiziol. Patol. Vyssh. Nerv. Deyat.* **1**.

TIMSIT-BERTHIER, M., DELAUNOY, N. and ROUSSEAU, J. C. (1973) Slow potential changes in psychiatry, 1, Contingent negative variation, *Electroenceph. Clin. Neurophysiol.* **35**, 335–61.

TIZARD, B. (1966) Evoked change in EEG and electrodermal activity during the waking and sleeping states, *Electroenceph. Clin. Neurophysiol.* **20**, 122.

TOMAN, I. (1941) Flicker potentials and the alpha rhythm in man, *J. Neurophysiol.* **4**, 1.

TOMASZEWSKI, T. (1963) *Introduction to psychology*, Wroclaw: PWN.

TORGERSON, A. M. (1973) Temperamental differences in infants: their cause as shown through twin studies. Unpublished Doctoral Dissertation, University of oslo. Cited by Thomas and Chass (op. cit.).

TOGERSON, A. M. (1979) Temperamental differences in 6-year old twins. Paper given at International Conference on Temperament, Need for Stimulation and Activity. Warsaw.

TORGERSON, S. and KRINGLEN, E. (1971) Blood pressure and personality: a study of the relationship between intrapair differences in systolic blood pressure and personality in monozygotic twins, *J. Psychosom. Res.* **15**, 2, 183–91.

TRANEL, N. (1962) Effect of perceptual isolation on introverts and extraverts. *J. Psychiat. Res.* **1**, 185–92.

TRASLER, G. (1978) Relations between psychopathy and persistent criminality: methodological and theoretical issues, in, R. D. Hare and D. Schalling (Eds.), *Psychopathic behaviour: approaches to research,* Chichester, N.Y.: Wiley.

TRAUGOTT, N. M. (1934) The inter-relations of immediate and symbolic projections in the process of the formation of conditioned inhibition, *Trans. Lab. Fiziol. Vyssh. Nervn. Deyat. Reb.* **4**, 273–303.

TROSHIKHIN, V. A. and NOSAR, B. I. (1976) Reactions to acute hypoxia of albino rats of different higher nervous activity types, *Zh. Vyssh. Nerv. Deyat. im. I. P. Pavlova,* **26**, 1238–43.

TROWILL, J. A. (1967) Instrumental conditioning of the heart rate in the curanized rat, *J. Comp. Physiol. Psychol.* **63**, 7–11.

TRUBNIKOVA, R. S. (1971a) K voprosu o sootnpshenii zapominaniya materiala raznogo ob'ema i soderzhaniya s siloy nervnoy sistemy, *Materialy IV Vsesoyuz, S'ezda Obshchestva psikhologov SSSR,* Tbilisi: Mesniereba.

TRUBNIKOVA, R. S. (1971b) K voprosu o sootnoshenii mekhanicheskoy i logicheskoy pamyati, in, *Novy issledovaniya v psikhologii i vozrastnoy fiziologii,* Tbilisi.

TRYON, R. C. (1942) Individual differences, in, F. A. Moss (Ed.), *Comparative psychology,* Ch. 12, New York: Prentice-Hall.

TRZEBINSKI, J. (1973) Personal involvement, an authority's approval, and originality of thinking. Unpublished M.A. Thesis, Institute of Psychology, University of Warsaw.

TUKE, D. H. (1884) *The influence of the mind upon the body,* 2nd ed., London: Churchill.

TUPES, E. C. and CHRISTAL, R. E. (1961) Recurrent personality factors based on trait ratings. USAF Lackland Air Force Base, Personnel Laboratory, Technical Report. ASD-TR-61-97.

TURNER, L. H. and SOLOMON, R. L. (1962) Human traumatic avoidance conditioning. *Psychol. Monogr.* **76**, 40 (Whole no. 559).

TUROVSKAYA, Z. G. (1963a) The nature of typological differences in the expression of after-effects of nervous processes, *Vop. Psikhol.* **3**.

TUROVSKAYA, Z. G. (1963b) The relation between some indices of strength and mobility of the nervous system in man, in, B. M. Teplov (Ed.), *Typological features of higher nervous activity in man,* Vol. 3, Moscow: Akad. Pedagog. Nauk RSFSR.

TURSKY, B. and HIGGINS, J. D. (1971) Manipulation of shock-elicited pain by concurrent tactile stimulation: an extension of prior findings. Paper presented at the Annual Meeting of the Society for Psychophysiological Research, St. Louis.

UKHTOMSKII, A. A. (1927) Dominance as a factor of behaviour, *Vestnik kommunisticheskoy Akademii,* **22**, 215–41.

UKHTOMSKII, A. A. (1937) Fiziologicheskoy pokoy i labil'nost Kak biologicheskie faktory, *Uchenyne zapiski LGU,* 17.

ULETT, G. A., GLESSER, G., WINOCUR, G. and LAWLER, A. (1953) The EEG and reaction to photic stimulation as an index of anxiety-proneness, *Electroenceph. Clin. Neurophysiol.* **5**, 23–32.

ULRICH, R. E. and AZRIN, N. H. (1962) Reflexive fighting in response to aversive stimulation. *J. Exp. Analysis Behav.* **5**, 511–20.

URICH, R. E., STACHNIK, T. J., BRIERTON, G. R. and MABRY, J. H. (1964) Unpublished study.

UMANSKII, L. I. (1961) K voprosu o parcialnych tripach vyssej niervnoy dieyatel'nosti czelovieka, *Vop. Psikhol.* **6**.

UNGAR, D. (1959) The importance of protein structure in the absorption of ions in the mechanism of cell excitation. *Cytology,* **1**, 5.

UNGER, S. M. (1964) Habituation of the vasoconstrictive orienting reaction, *J. Exp. Psychol.* **67**, 11–18.

UTKINA, N. S. (1964) Typological differences affecting the school assessment of certain attentional phenomena, in, *Typological research on the psychology of personality and work,* Perm: UOOP and PGPI.

VAGG, P. R. and HAMMOND, S. B. (1976) The number and kind of invariant personality (Q) factors: a partial replication of Eysenck and Eysenck, *Br. J. Soc. Clin. Psychol.* **15,** 121–9.

VALE, J. R. and VALE, C. A. (1969) Individual differences and general laws in psychology: a reconciliation, *Am. Psychol.* **24,** 1093–108.

VANDENBERG, S. G. (1960) Hereditary factors in normal personality traits (as measured by inventories), in, J. Wortis (Ed.) *Recent advances in biological psychiatry,* New York: Grune. Also, *Research Report No. 19* (1966) Louisville Twin Study, University of Louisville, School of Medicine.

VANDENBERG, S. G. (1962) The hereditary abilities study: hereditary components in a psychological test battery, *Amer. J. Hum. Genet.* **14,** 220–37.

VANDENBERG, S. G. (Ed.) (1965) *Multivariate analysis of twin differences,* in, S. G. Vandenberg (Ed.), *Methods and goals in human behaviour genetics,* New York: Academic Press.

VANDENBERG, S. G. (1966) Contributions of twin research to psychology, *Psychol. Bull.* **66,** 327–52.

VANDENBERG, S. G. (1967) Hereditary factors in normal personality traits (as measured by inventories), in, J. Wortis (Ed.), *Recent advances in biological psychiatry,* Vol. 9, pp. 65–104, New York: Plenum Press.

VANDENBERG, S. G. and FALKNER, F. (1965) Heriditary factors in human growth. *Hum. Biol.* **37,** 357–65.

VANDENBERG, S. G., STAFFORD, R. E., BROWN, A. and GRESHAM, J. (1966) *The Louisville Twin Study,* University of Louisville School of Medicine, Louisville, Kentucky.

VAN DER MAELEN, A. L., STRAUSS, M. F. and STARR, R. H. (1974) Influence of obstetric medication on auditory habituation in the newborn, *Dev. Psychol.* **11,** 6, 711–14.

VANDO, A. (1969) A personality dimension related to pain tolerance. Unpublished Doctoral Dissertation, Columbia University.

VAN DYKE, J. L., ROSENTHAL, D. and RASMUSSEN, P. V. (1974) Electrodermal functioning in adopted-away offspring of schizophrenics, *J. Psychiat. Res.* **10,** 199–215.

VAN EGEREN, L. F., HEATHER, B. W. and HEIN, P. L. (1971) Desensitization of phobias: some psychophysiological propositions, *Psychophysiol.* **8,** 213–28.

VARDEPETYAN, G. A. (1967) *Zh. Vÿssh. Nervn. Deyat. im. I. P. Pavlova. 17,* **1,** 95. English translation in *Neuroscience translations,* 1967–1968, No. 1, pp. 1–11.

VASILETZ, T. V. (1974) Genetic basis on the mobility of nervous process in motor reactions, *Vop. Psikhol.* **5,** 126–40.

VASILETZ, T. V. (1978) Mobility as a nervous system characteristic: Genetic aspects, in, B. M. Lomov and I. V. Ravich-Shcherbo (Eds.), *Problems in the genetics of psychophysiology,* pp. 111–26, Moscow: Inst. Psikhol. Akad. Nauk SSSR. Izd. Nauka.

VASIL'EV, A. N. (1960) The relation between reaction times to the onset and termination of a signal as an index of stength of the nervous system, *Vop. Psikhol.* **6.**

VATSURO, E. G. (1945) The investigation of the comparative lability of the processes of higher nervous activity as applied to the functioning of the separate analysers, *Tr. Inst. Fiziol. im. I. P. Pavlova,* 12(2).

VATSURO, E. G. (1949) The principle of leading afferentiation in the theory of higher nervous activity, *J. Physiol. Lond.* **35,** 5.

VATSURO, E. G. and KOLESNIKOV, M. S. (1948) On the difference between functional properties of separate analysers. *13th Conference on Physiological Problems.* Abstracts of papers. Moscow: Akad. Nauk SSSR.

VATSURO, E. G. and SHTODIN, M. P. (1947) Mechanism underlying the behaviour of the anthropoid ape (chimpanzee). Second communication. *Tr. Inst. Fiziol. im. I. P. Pavlova,* **1.**

VAUGHAN, G. and MANGAN, G. L. (1963) Conformity to group pressure in relation to the value of the task material, *J. Abnorm. Soc. Psychol.* **66,** 2, 179–83.

VAUGHAN, H. G. and HULL, R. C. (1965) Functional relation between stimulus intensity and photically evoked cerebral responses in man, *Nature, Lond.* **206,** 720–2.

VENABLES, P. H. (1960) The affect of auditory and visual stimulation on the skin potential response of schizophrenics, *Brain,* **83,** 77–92.

VENABLES, P. H. (1963) The relationship between level of skin potential and fusion of paired light flashes in schizophrenic and normal subjects, *J. Psychiat. Res.* **1,** 279.

VENABLES, P. H. (1966) Psychophysiological aspects of schizophrenia, *Br. J. Med. Psychol.* **39,** 289–97.

VENABLES, P. H. (1968) Signals, noise, refractoriness and storage: some concepts of value to psychopathology? Biometrics Research Workshop, Session 3.

VENABLES, P. H. (1969) Sensory aspects of psychopathology, in, J. Zubin and C. Shagass (Eds.), *Neurobiological aspects of psychopathology,* Ch. 7, New York: Grune & Stratton.

VENABLES, P. H. (1971) Perception, attention and arousal in schizophrenia. Paper presented at the meeting of the Finnish Psychiatric Association, Tampere, Finland.

VENABLES, P. H. (1973) Input regulation and psychopathology, in, M. Hammer, K. Salzinger and S. Sutton (Eds.), *Psychopathology: contributions from the social, behavioural and biological sciences,* pp. 261–84, New York: Wiley.

VENABLES, P. H. (1974) The recovery limb of the skin conductance response. In: S. A. Mednick, F. Schulsinger, J. Higgins and B. Bell (Eds.), *Genetics, environment and psychopathology.*

VENABLES, P. H. (1975) A psychophysiological approach to research in schizophrenia, in, D. C. Fowles (Ed.), *Clinical applications of psychophysiology,* pp. 106–37, New York: Columbia University Press.

VENABLES, P. H. (1977) The electrodermal psychophysiology of schizophrenics and children as risk for schizophrenias: controversies and developments. *Schiz. Bull.* **3,** 1, 28–48.

VENABLES, P. H. and CHRISTY, M. J. (1973) Mechanisms, recording techniques and quantification of responses, in, W. F. Prokasy and D. C. Raskin (Eds.), *Electrodermal activity in psychological research,* pp. 1–124, New York: Academic Press.

VENABLES, P. H. and TIZARD, J. (1956) Paradoxical effects in the reaction time of schizophrenics, *J. Abnorm. Soc. Psychol.* **53,** 220–4.

VENABLES, P. H. and TIZARD, J. (1958) The effects of auditory stimulus intensity on the reaction time of schizophrenics, *J. Ment. Sci.* **104,** 1160–4.

VENABLES, P. H. and WARWICK-EVANS, L. A. (1968) The effect of stimulus amplitude on the threshold of fusion of two flashes, *Q. J. Exp. Psychol.* **20,** 30–7.

VERBATEN, M. N. (1972) The influence of subject variables on rate of habituation of the orientating reflex. Utrecht, Netherlands: University of Utrecht Psychological Laboratory, No. 4.

VERNON, P. E. (1950) *The Structure of Human Abilities,* London: Methuen.

VINCE, M. A. (1948) The intermittency of control movements and the psychological refractory period, *Br. J. Psychol.* **38,** 149–57.

VINOGRADOVA, O. S. (1957) *Proceedings of conference on the orienting reflex,* Moscow.

VINOGRADOVA, O. S. (1961) *The orienting reflex and its neurophysiological mechanisms,* Moscow: Akad. Pedagog. Nauk RSFSR.

VINOGRADOVA, O. S. (1966) Investigation of habituation in single neurons of different brain structures with special reference to the hippocampus, in, Proceedings of the International Congress of Psychology, Moscow, Vol. 1, Biological and physiological problems in psychology, 173–4.

VINOGRADOVA, O. S. (1975) The hippocampus and the orienting reflex, in, E. N. Sokolov and O. S. Vinogradova (Eds.), *Neuronal mechanisms of the orienting reflex,* pp. 128–54, Hillsdale, New Jersey: Erlbaum.

VOGEL, F. (1970) The genetic basis of the normal human electrocephalogram (EEG), *Hum. Genet.* **10,** 91–114.

VOGEL, F. and FUJIYA, E. (1969) The incidence of some inherited EEG variants in normal Japanese and German males. *Hum. Genet.* **7,** 38–42.

VOGEL, F. and SCHALT, E. (1979) The electroencephalogram (EEG) as a research tool in human behaviour genetics: psychological examinations in health males with various inherited EEG variants. III: Interpretation of the results, *Hum. Genet.* **47,** 81–111.

VOGEL, F., SCHALT, E. and KRUGER, J. (1979) The electroencephalogram (EEG) as a research tool in human behaviour genetics: psychological examinations in healthy males with various inherited EEG variants. II: Results, *Hum. Genet.* **47**, 47–80.

VOGEL, F., BROVERMAN, D. M., KLAIBER, E. L. and KUN, K. H. (1969) EEG response to photic stimulation as a function of cognitive style, *Electroenceph. Clin. Neurophysiol.* **27**, 186–90.

VOGEL, F., SCHALT, E., KRUGER, J., PROPPING, P. and LEHNERT, R. F. (1979) The electrocephalogram (EEG) as a research tool in human behaviour genetics: psychological examinations in healthy males with various inherited EEG variants. I: Rationale of the study, materials, methods, heritability of test parameters. *Hum. Genet.* **47**, 1–45.

VOGEL, W. (1961) The relationship of age and intelligence to autonomic functioning. *J. Comp. Physiol. Psychol.* **54**, 133–8.

VOIGT, W. H. (1968) Conditioning the human pupillary response, *Percept. Mot. Skills*, **26**, 975–82.

VOIKU, K. (1964) Electroencephalographic indices of dynamism of excitation with 10 yr old children. Dissertation, Moscow University.

VOLOKOV, A. A. and SHILYAGINA, N. N. (1968) Concerning the participation of the reticular formation in forming the reaction of rhythm assimilation in the visual cortex in ontogeny, in, *Problems of dynamic localisation of cerebral functions,* Moscow: Medgiz.

VORONIN, L. G. and SOKOLOV, E. N. (1960) Cortical mechanisms of the orienting reflex and its relation to the conditioned reflex, in, H. H. Jasper and G. D. Smirnov (Eds.), Moscow colloquium on electroencephalography of higher nervous activity, Montreal, *Electroenceph. Clin. Neurophysiol.* Suppl. 13, 335–46.

VORONIN, L. G., SOKOLOV, E. N. and BAO-KHUA, U. (1959) Type features of the orientation reflex in man, *Vop. Psikhol.* **5**, 73–88.

VOWLES, D. and HARWOOD, D. (1966) The effect of exogenous hormones on aggressiveness and defensive behaviour in the ring dove *(Streptopetia risoria), J. Endocr.* **36**, 35–51.

VYGOTSKY, L. S. (1956) *Selected psychological works,* Moscow: Akad. Pedagog. Nauk RSFSR.

VYGOTSKY, L. S. (1960) *Development of the higher mental functions,* Moscow: Akad. Pedagog. Nauk RSFSR.

VYGOTSKY, L. S. (1972) Problems of age periods in child development, *Vop. Psikhol.* **2**.

VYGOTSKY, L. S. (1979) Consciousness as a problem in the psychology of behaviour, *Soviet Psychol.* **17**, No. 4, 3–35.

VYRZHIKOVSKI, S. N. and MAYOROV, F. P. (1933) Material on the influence of upbringing on the habitual form or higher nervous activity in the dog, *Tr. Fiziol. Lab. im. I. P. Pavlova,* **5**.

WACHTEL, P. L. (1967) Conceptions of broad and narrow attention, *Psychol. Bull.* **68**, 417–29.

WAGGONER, R. A. (1960) Differences in response latency and response variability between high and low anxiety subjects in a flicker fusion task, *J. Abnorm. Soc. Psychol.* **61**, 355–9.

WAGMAN, I. H., PIERCE, D. S. and BURGER, R. E. (1965) Proprioceptive influence in volitional control of individual motor units, *Nature, Lond.* **207**, 5000, 957–8.

WAGNER, A. R. (1963) Conditioned frustration as a learned drive. *J. Exp. Psychol.,* **66**, 142–148.

WALL, P. D. and SWEET, W. H. (1967) Temporary abolition of pain in man, *Science, N. Y.* **155**, 108–9.

WALTER, W. G. (1964) The convergence and interaction of visual, auditory and tactile responses in human non-specific cortex, in, H. Whipple and R. Katzmann (Eds.), Sensory evoked responses in man. *Ann. N.Y. Acad. Sc.* **112**, 1, 320–61.

WALTER, W. G. (1966) *The living brain,* Moscow: Mir Publishers.

WALTER, W. G. (1969) The development of electrocerebral activity in children, *Mod. Perspect. Psychiat.* **3**, 391–417.

WALTERS, G. C. and GRUSEC, J. C. (1977) *Punishment,* San Francisco: W. H. Freeman.

WALTERS, R. H. and ANDRES, D. (1967) Punishment procedures and self-control. Unpublished paper. A.P.A., Washington D.C. Quoted in Parke (1972).

WALTERS, R. H. and PARKE, R. D. (1964) Influence of response consequences to a social model on resistance to deviation, *J. Exp. Child Psychol.* **1**, 269–80.

WALTERS, R. H., LEAT, M. and MEZEI, L. (1963) Inhibition and disinhibition of responses through empathetic learning, *Can. J. Psychol.* **17**, 235–43.

WALTERS, R. H., PARKE, R. D. and CANE, V. (1965) Timing of punishment and the observation of consequences to others as determinants of response inhibition, *J. Exp. Child Psychol.* **2**, 10–30.

WANG, G. H. (1964) *The neural control of sweating,* Madison: University of Wisconsin Press.

WARD, W. D. (1975) Studies of asymptotic TTS. Aerospace medical specialists meeting: Advisory Group for Aerospace Research and Development (AGARD), North Atlantic Treaty Organisation, Toronto, Canada.

WARD, W. D., GLORIG, A. and SKLAR, D. L. (1955) Relation between recovery from temporary threshold shift and duration of exposure, *J. Acoust. Soc. Amer.* **31**, 600–2.

WARDELL, D. (1974) Stimulus intensity and introversion-extraversion, *Br. J. Soc. Clin. Psychol.* **13**, 4, 425–6.

WARDEN, C. and JACKSON, T. (1935) Imitative behaviour in the rhesus monkey, *J. Genet. Psychol.* **46**, 103–25.

WASHBURN, M. F., HUGHES, G., STEWARD, C. and SLIGH, G. (1930) Reaction time, flicker and affective sensitiveness as tests of extraversion and introversion, *Am. J. Psychol.* **42**, 412–13.

WATERS, W. F. and McDONALD, D. G. (1974) Effects of "below zero" habituation on spontaneous recovery and dishabituation of the orienting response, *Psychophysiol.* **11**, 5, 548–58.

WATERS, W. F. and McDONALD, D. G. (1975) Stimulus and temporal variables in the "below-zero" habituation of the orienting response, *Psychophysiol.* **12**, 4, 461–4.

WEDENSKII, N. (1903) Die Erregung, Hemmung und Narkose, *Pfügers Arch. Ges. Physiol.* **100**, 1–144.

WEDENSKII, N. (1920) Accessory electrotonic alterations of excitability, *Petersburg Bull. Acad. Imper.* Sc. 14, Ser. VI, 332–59.

WEERTZ, T. C. and ROBERTS, R. (1976) The physiological effects of imagining anger-provoking and fear-provoking scenes, *Psychophysiol.* **13**, 174.

WEINSTEIN, A. L. and ZHIV, V. P. (1973) Tenning-test as an indicator of typological differences. Proceedings VI All-Union Scientific Conference on Physiology of Labour, Moscow.

WELDON, E. (1967) An analogue of extraversion as a determinant of individual differences in behaviour in the rat, *Br. J. Psychol.* **58**, 253–9.

WENGER, M. A. (1948) Studies of autonomic balance in Army Air Force personnel, *Comp. Psychol. Monogr.* **19**, 4. University of California Press, Berkeley.

WENGER, M. A. and BAGCHI, B. K. (1961) Studies of autonomic functions in practitioners of yoga in India, *Behavl Sci.* **6**, 312–23.

WENGER, M. A. and WELLINGTON, M. (1943) The measurement of autonomic balance in children: method and normative data.

WENGER, M. A., BAGCHI, B. K. and ANAND, B. K. (1961) Experiments in India on "voluntary" control of the heart and pulse, *Circulation,* **24**, 1319–25.

WENGER, M. A., CLEMENS, T. L., COLEMAN, D. R., CULLEN, T. D. and ENGEL, B. T. (1961) Autonomic response specificity, *Psychosom. Med.* **23**, 185–93.

WERTHEIMER, M. (1955) The variability of auditory and visual absolute thresholds in time, *J. Genet. Psychol.* **52**, 111–48.

WERTHEIMER, M. (1962) Psychomotor co-ordination of auditory and visual space at birth, *Science, N. Y.* **140**.

WERTHEIMER, M. and ARONSON, E. (1958) Personality rigidity as measured by aniseikonic lenses and by perceptual tests of metabolic efficiency. *J. Genet. Psychol.* **58**, 41–49.

WHIMBEY, A. E. and DENENBERG, V. H. (1967) Two independent behavioural dimensions in open-field performance, *J. Comp. Physiol. Psychol.* **63**, 500–4.

WHITE, B. L. (1963) Development of perception during the first six months. Paper read at the American Association for the Advancement of Science, December.

WHITE, B. L., CASTLE, P. and HELD, R. (1964) Observations on the development of visually directed reaching. *Child. Dev.* **35**, 349–64.

WHITE, K. D. (1968) The relationship of visual after-images to extraversion and neuroticism. Unpublished thesis, University of Queensland.

WHITE, K. D. (1975) The significance of individual differences in the control of salivation. Unpublished doctoral dissertation, University of Queensland.

WHITE, K. D. (1977a) Salivation and the law of initial value, *Psychophysiol.* **14,** 6, 560–2.

WHITE, K. D. (1977b) Salivation: a review and experimental investigation of major techniques, *Psychophysiol.* **14,** 2, 203–12.

WHITE, K. D. (1978) Salivation: the significance of imagery in its voluntary control, *Psychophysiol.* **15,** 3, 196–203.

WHITE, K. D. and MANGAN, G. L. (1972) Strength of the nervous system as a function of personality type and level of arousal, *Behav. Res. Ther.* **10,** 139–46.

WHITE, K. D., MANGAN, G. L., MORRISH, R. B. and SIDDLE, D. A. T. (1969) The relation of visual after-images to extraversion and neuroticism, *J. Exp. Res. Pers.* **3,** 268–74.

WHITE, R. W. (1959) Motivation reconsidered: the concept of competence, *Psychol. Rev.* **66,** 297–333.

WHITING, J. W. M. (1960) Resource mediation and learning by identification, in, I. Iscoe and H. W. Stevenson (Eds.), *Personality development in children,* Houston: University of Texas Press.

WHITING, J. W. M. and CHILD, I. L. (1953) *Child training and personality,* New Haven: Yale University Press.

WIGGINS, J. S. (1973) *Personality and prediction: principles of personality assessment,* Reading, Mass.: Addison-Wesley.

WILCOX, J. and BUSH, M. A. (1972) Heterosis for punishment induced inhibition of drinking in laboratory rats, *Life. Sci.* **11,** 1, 403–12.

WILDE, G. J. S. (1964) Inheritance of personality traits: an investigation into the hereditary determination of neurotic instability, extraversion, and other personality traits by means of a questionnaire administered to twins, *Acta Psychol.* **22,** 37–51.

WILDER, J. (1958) Modern psychophysiology and the law of initial value, *Am. J. Psychother.* **12,** 199–221.

WILLERMAN, L. (1973) Activity level and hyperactivity in twins, *Child Dev.* **44,** 288–93.

WILLIAMS, S. A. (1963) Novelty, GSR and stimulus generalisation, *Can. J. Psychol.* **17,** 52–61.

WILSON, J. W. D. and DYKMAN, R. A. (1960) Background autonomic activity in medical students, *J. Comp. Physiol. Psychol.* **53,** 405–11.

WINOCUR, G., STEWART, M. STERN, J. and PFEIFFER, E. (1962) A dynamic equilibrium in GSR habituation: The effects of inter-stimulus interval, *J. Psychosom. Res.* **6,** 117–22.

WINTER, K., BROADHURST, A. and GLASS, A. (1972) Neuroticism, extraversion and EEG amplitude. *J. Exp. Res. Person.* **6,** 1, 44–57.

WISH, M. and KAPLAN, S. (1977) Towards an implicit theory of inter-personal communication, *Sociometry,* **40,** 234–46.

WITKIN, H. A., DYK, R. B., FATERSON, H. F., GOODENOUGH, D. R. and KARP, S. A. (1962) *Psychological differentiation,* New York: John Wiley & Sons.

WITT, G. M. and HALL, C. S. (1949) The genetics of audiogenic seizures in the house mouse, *J Comp. Physiol. Psychol.* **42,** 58–63.

WOLF, T. M. (1973) Effects of televised modelled verbalisations and behaviour on resistance to deviation, *Dev. Psychol.* **8,** 51–6.

WOLFF, S. and WOLFF, H. G. (1947) *Human Gastric Function,* New York: Oxford University Press.

WOLFENSBERGER, W. and O'CONNOR, N. (1965) Stimulus intensity and duration effects on EEG and GSR responses of normals and retardates, *Am. J. Ment. Defic.* **70,** 21–37.

WOLPE, J. (1958) *Psychotherapy by reciprocal inhibition,* Stanford: Stanford University Press.

WOLPE, J. (1961a) The systematic desensitization treatment of neuroses, *J. Nerv. Ment. Dis.* **132,** 189–203.

WOLPE, J. (1961b) The systematic desensitization treatment of neuroses, Proceedings of the Third World Congress of Psychiatry, Vol. 1, 1052–56.

WOODROW, H. (1914) The measurement of attention, *Psychol. Monogr.* **17,** (Whole No. 76).

WOODWORTH, R. S. (1915) A revision of imageless thought, *Psychol. Rev.* **22,** 1–27.

WOODWORTH, R. S. (1938) *Experimental Psychology,* New York: Holt.

WOODWORTH, R. S. and SCHLOSBERG, H. (1955) *Experimental psychology*, New York: Holt.

WUNDT, W. (1911) *Grundzüge der physiologischen Psychologie*. Leipziga; Englemann (1874).

WYLER, A. R. (1977) Operant conditioning of epileptic neurons in monkeys and its theoretical application to EEG operant conditioning in humans, *Pavlov J. Biol. Sci.* **12**, 3, 130–46.

WYRWICKA, W. (1952) On the mechanism of the motor conditioned reaction, *Acta Biol. Exp. Vars.* **16**, 131–7.

WYRWICKA, W. (1973) The organization of classical and instrumental conditional reactions, *Condit. Reflex,* **8**, 28–40.

YAKOVLEVA, V. V. (1938) Determination of mobility of the nervous process on the dog by means of double transformation of the conditioned stimulus, *Tr. Fiziol. Lab. im. I. P. Pavlova,* **8**.

YAREMKO, R. M. and BUTLER, M. C. (1975) Imaginal experience and attenuation of the galvanic skin response to shock, *Bull. Psychonom. Soc.* **5**, 317–18.

YAREMKO, R. M. and WERNER, M. (1974) Cognitive conditioning: imagined stimulus contiguity and the third interval conditional GSR, *Pavlov J. Biol. Sci.* **9**, 215–21.

YAREMKO, R. M., BLAIR, M. W. and LECKHART, B. T. (1970) The orienting reflex to changes in a conceptual stimulus dimension, *Psychonom. Sci.* **21**, 115–16.

YAREMKO, R. M., GLANVILLE, B. B. and LECKHART, B. T. (1972) Imagery-mediated habituation of the orienting reflex, *Psychonom. Sci.* **27**, 204–6.

YERKES, R. M. and DODSON, J. D. (1908) The relation of strength of stimulus to rapidity of habit-formation, *J. Comp. Neurol. Psychol.* **18**, 459–582.

YERMOLAYEVA-TOMINA, L. B. (1959) Concentration of excitation and the strength of nervous system, in, B. M. Teplov (Ed.), *Typological features of higher nervous activity in man*, Vol. 2, Moscow: Izd. Akad. Pedagog. Nauk RSFSR.

YERMOLAYEVA-TOMINA, L. B. (1960) Individual differences in the ability to concentrate attention and strength of nervous system, *Vop. Psikhol.* **2**.

YERMOLAYEVA-TOMINA, L. B. (1963) On the question of the use of psychogalvanic response index determining nervous system type in man, in, B. M. Teplov (Ed.), *Typological features of higher nervous activity in man*, Vol. 3, Moscow: Akad. Pedagog. Nauk RSFSR.

YERMOLAYEVA-TOMINA, L. B. (1965) Individual differences in G.S.R., in, B. M. Teplov (Ed.), *Typological features of higher nervous activity in man*, Vol. 4, Moscow: Prosveshcheniye.

YERMOLAYEVA-TOMINA, L. B. (1977) An experimental study of creative abilities, *Vop. Psikhol.* **4**, 74–84.

YOSHII, N., PRUVOT, P. and GASTAUT, H. (1957) Electrographic activity of the mesencephalic reticular formation during conditioning in the cat, *Electroenceph. Clin. Neurophysiol.* **9**, 4.

YOUNG, J. P. R. and FENTON, G. W. (1971) An investigation of the genetic aspects of the alpha attenuation response, *Psychol. Med.* **1**, 365–71.

YOUNG, J. P. R., LADER, M. H. and FENTON, G. W. (1972) A twin study of the genetic influences on the electroencephalogram, *J. Med. Genet.* **9**, 13–16.

YOUNG, P. A., EAVES, L. J. and EYSENCK, H. J. (1980) Intergenerational stability and changes in the causes of variation in personality, *J. Pers. Ind. Diff.* **1** 1, 57–72.

YUMATOV, E. A. and SOTSELYAS, A. S. (1979) Comparative analysis of stability of cardio-vascular system function during immobilisation of rats of different lines, *Zh. Vyssh. Nerv. Deyat. im. I. P. Pavlova,* **29**, 345–52.

ZAGORUL'KO, T. M. (1958) Nekotory dannye elektrofiziologicheskogo analiza oboronitel'nogo uslovnogo refleksa u glolubey, in, *Problemy sravnitel'noy fiziologii i patologii vysshey nervnoy deyatel'nosti*. Leningrad: In-ta eksperimental'noy meditsiny AMN SSSR.

ZAHN, T. P. (1964) Autonomic reactivity and behaviour in schizophrenia, *Psychiat. Res. Rep.* **19**, 156–73.

ZAHN, T. P. (1975) Psychophysiological concomitants of task performance in schizophrenia, in, M. L. Kietzman, S. Sutton and J. Zubin (Eds.), *Experimental approaches to psychopathology*, pp. 109–31, New York: Academic Press.

ZAHN, T. P. (1977) Autonomic nervous system characteristics possibly related to a genetic predisposition to schizophrenia, *Schiz. Bull.* **3**, 1, 49–60.

ZAHN, T. P., CARPENTER, W. T. (Jr.) and McGLASHAN, T. H. (1975) Autonomic variables related to short-term outcome in acute schizophrenic patients. Paper presented at the Annual Meeting of the Society for Psychophysiological Research, Toronto.

ZAHN, T. P., ROSENTHAL, T. and LAWLOR, W. A. (1968) Electrodermal and heart rate orienting reactions in chronic schizophrenics, *J. Psychiat. Res.* **6**, 117–34.

ZAHN, T. P., ROSENTHAL, D. and SHAKOW, P. (1963) Reaction times in schizophrenic and normal subjects in relation to the sequence of series of regular preparatory intervals, *J. Abnorm. Soc. Psychol.* **62**, 44-52.

ZAITSEVA, L. M. (1975) Neurophysiological mechanisms of formation of signal significance of words in children of early age, *Zh. Vyssh. Nerv. Deyat. im. I. P. Pavlova,* **25**, 681–9.

ZAKLYAKOVA, V. N. (1965) Comparative role of direct and verbal reinforcement in formation of stereotypes, in, M. N. Kol'tsova (Ed.), *Materials for symposium on man's system of signals,* pp. 49–52 Leningrad.

ZAMBRZHITSKY, I. A. (1959) Cytoarchitectonics and the Neuronal Structure of the Limbic Region in Primates, in, *Development of the central nervous system,* Moscow.

ZAMENHOF, S., VAN MARTHENS, E. and MARGOLIS, F. L. (1968) DNA (cell number) and protein in neonatal brain: alteration by material dietary protein restriction, *Science, N.Y.* **160**, 322-3.

ZAV'YALOV, A. V. and KONISSAROV, V. I. (1968) Correlation between the sensitivity of the kinesthetic and visual analyzers in man, *Zh. Vyssh. Nerv. Deyat. im. I. P. Pavlova,* **18**, 1, 38–44.

ZEIGLER, H. P. (1964) Displacement activity and motivational theory: a case study in the history of ethology, *Psychol. Bull.* **61**, 362–76.

ZELENYI, G. P. (1906) Data contributing to the problem of the response to acoustic stimuli in dogs. Dissertation, St. Petersburg.

ZEVAL'D, L. O. (1964) The limits of differential inhibition under different functional states, *Zh. Vyssh. Nerv. Deyat. im. I. P. Pavlova,* **14**, 2.

ZHINKIN, N. I. (1966) The encoding paths in inner speech, *Vop. Yazykoznaniya,* **6**.

ZHINKIN, N. I. (1967) The internal codes of language and the external codes of speech, in, *To honor Roman Jakobson,* The Hague.

ZHOROV, P. A. and YERMOLAYEVA-TOMINA, L. B. (1972) Concerning the relation between extraversion and strength of the nervous system, in, V. D. Nebylitsyn and J. A. Gray (Eds.), *Biological bases of individual differences,* pp. 262–8, London: Academic Press.

ZIMNY, G. H. (1965) Body image and physiological responses, *J. Psychosom. Res.* **9**, 185–8.

ZIMNY, G. H. and SCHWABE, L. W. (1966) Stimulus change in habituation of the orienting response, *Psychophysiol.* **2**, 103–15.

ZIMNY, G. H., PAWLICK, G. F. and SAUR, D. P. (1969) Effects of stimulus order and novelty on orienting responses, *Psychophysiol.* **6**, 166–73.

ZIZLINA, N. N. (1957) An electrophysiological study of the functional state of the brain of normal children and oligophrenics by the method of rhythmic photic stimuli. Dissertation, Moscow University.

ZUCKERMAN, M. (1964) Perceptual isolation as a stress situation, *Archs Gen. Psychiat.* **11**, 228–76.

ZUCKERMAN, M. (1971) Dimensions of sensation-seeking, *J. Consult. Clin. Psychol.* **36**, 45–52.

ZUCKERMAN, M. (1974) The sensation-seeking motive, in, B. Maher (Ed.), *Progress in experimental personality research,* Vol. 7, New York: Academic Press.

ZUCKERMAN, M. (1975) *Manual and research report for the sensation seeking scale (SSS),* Newark: University of Delaware.

ZUCKERMAN, M., MURTAUGH, T. and SIEGAL, J. (1974) Sensation seeking and cortical augmenting-reducing, *Psychophysiol.* **2**, 535–42.

ZUCKERMAN, M., PERKSY, H. and CURTIS, G. (1968) Relationship among anxiety, depression, hostility and autonomic variables, *J. Nerv. Ment. Dis.* **146**, 481–7.

ZUCKERMAN, M., BONE, R. N., NEARY, R., MANGELSDORFF, D. and BRUSTMAN, B. (1972) What is the sensation seeker? Personality trait and experience correlates of the sensation seeking scales, *J. Cons. Clin. Psychol.* **39**, 308–21.

# AUTHOR INDEX

543

562

# SUBJECT INDEX